ANNUAL REVIEW OF MICROBIOLOGY

ANNUAL REVIEW OF MICROBIOLOGY

CHARLES E. CLIFTON, *Editor*
Stanford University

SIDNEY RAFFEL, *Associate Editor*
Stanford University

MORTIMER P. STARR, *Associate Editor*
University of California

VOLUME 20

1966

ANNUAL REVIEWS, INC.
PALO ALTO, CALIFORNIA, U.S.A.

ANNUAL REVIEWS, INC.
PALO ALTO, CALIFORNIA, U.S.A.

Library of Congress Catalog Card Number: 49-432

———————

FOREIGN AGENCY

Maruzen Company, Limited
6, Tori-Nichome Nihonbashi
Tokyo

PRINTED AND BOUND IN THE UNITED STATES OF AMERICA BY
GEORGE BANTA COMPANY, INC.

PREFACE

With great pleasure we express once again our gratitude to those authors who have contributed to the *Annual Review of Microbiology*. Microbiology is an ever-expanding field of endeavor and only with the aid of timely and informative reviews can we hope to maintain some touch with the advances in fields other than those of our immediate interest. Growth has been so rapid in some fields, or of more immediate interest to particular groups, that other *Reviews*, e.g., the *Annual Review of Genetics* or the *Annual Review of Phytopathology*, now include various subjects of microbiological interest or nature. These reviews are listed on page 423 as a convenience for our readers.

We regret that factors beyond the control of the authors have made it impossible to present chapters on Blue-Green Algae, Microbiological Patents, Regulation of Enzyme Synthesis, Heterogeneity of Virus Populations, Bacterial Cytology, Zoonoses, Murine Virus Leukemia, and Mechanism of Synthesis of Protein and Nucleic Acids. The three last-named chapters will appear in Volume 21.

At this time, we wish to express our thanks to Dr. Boris Magasanik for his valuable contribution as a member of the Editorial Committee during the past five years, and to welcome Dr. Gunther Stent as Dr. Magasanik's successor on the Committee.

We also express our appreciation for the valuable assistance rendered by the Staff of Annual Reviews, Incorporated, by our printers, the Banta Company, and acknowledging in particular the invaluable aid given us by Miss Beryl V. Daniel as Assistant Editor.

THE EDITORIAL COMMITTEE

CONTENTS

PREFATORY CHAPTER: MICROBIOLOGY—PAST, PRESENT, AND FUTURE, *C. E. Clifton* 1

BIOSYNTHESIS OF LIPIDS IN MICROORGANISMS, *M. Kates* 13

THE CLASSIFICATION OF VIRUSES, *A. Lwoff and P. Tournier* . . . 45

BIOLOGY OF THE MYXOBACTERIA, *M. Dworkin* 75

THE RELATION OF THE PSITTACOSIS GROUP (CHLAMYDIAE) TO BACTERIA AND VIRUSES, *J. W. Moulder* 107

STRUCTURE AND FUNCTION IN PROTOZOA, *A. V. Grimstone* 131

YEAST GENETICS, *R. K. Mortimer and D. C. Hawthorne* 151

DEVELOPMENTAL CHANGES DURING THE FORMATION AND BREAKING OF THE DORMANT STATE IN BACTERIA, *H. O. Halvorson, J. C. Vary, and W. Steinberg* 169

BIOSYNTHETIC MODIFICATIONS INDUCED BY DNA ANIMAL VIRUSES, *M. Green* 189

TUMOR ANTIGENS, *G. Klein* 223

THE BIOSYNTHESIS OF BACTERIAL POLYSACCHARIDES, *B. L. Horecker* . 253

INTERFERON, *S. Baron and H. B. Levy* 291

MICROBIOLOGY OF WASTE WATERS, *A. F. Gaudy, Jr. and E. T. Gaudy* 319

RESISTANCE OF PLANTS TO INFECTIOUS AGENTS, *J. Kuć* 337

MICROBIAL TRANSFORMATION AND TRANSFECTION, *J. Spizizen, B. E. Reilly, and A. H. Evans* 371

SUPPRESSION, *L. Gorini and J. R. Beckwith* 401

OTHER REVIEWS OF MICROBIOLOGICAL INTEREST 423

AUTHOR INDEX 425

SUBJECT INDEX 441

CUMULATIVE INDEX OF CONTRIBUTING AUTHORS, VOLUMES 16 TO 20 453

CUMULATIVE INDEX OF CHAPTER TITLES, VOLUMES 16 TO 20 . . . 454

C. E. Clifton

PREFATORY CHAPTER
MICROBIOLOGY—PAST, PRESENT, AND FUTURE

By Charles E. Clifton

*Department of Medical Microbiology, Stanford University
School of Medicine, Stanford, California*

Twenty some years ago, the results of a canvass of representative microbiologists indicated the need for an *Annual Review of Microbiology*, patterned along the lines established by the *Annual Review of Biochemistry* and the *Annual Review of Physiology*. I was appointed Editor, with Sidney Raffel and H. Albert Barker as Associate Editors. An Editorial Committee comprised of M. D. Eaton, W. E. Herrell, J. M. Sherman, E. C. Stakman, W. H. Taliaferro, and C. B. van Niel was entrusted with the selection of topics and authors for the initial volume. These men served on the Committee for at least five years, a policy of replacing one member each year and reducing the Committee to five members, being adopted in 1951. We are in debt to the original committeemen and to their successors for the time and effort devoted by them in the selection of topics and authors.

During the lifetime of this *Review*, knowledge regarding various groups of microorganisms has increased by leaps and bounds. The advances have been unequal for different groups and in different fields, but advances have been made in our understanding of forms ranging from the near-molecular, near-living filtrable viruses to those forms on the borderline between the micro- and macro-forms of life.

Studies on the structure of microorganisms and on the nature and function of their component parts continue to be of major interest and, in many instances today, these studies are at the macromolecular level, hence, the present field of fashion, molecular biology. This reflects growth of knowledge and subsequent change in major emphasis from general studies on growth, metabolism, and death to detailed studies at the molecular level in fields such as enzymology and genetics. This trend is apparent if one peruses the list of topics for each volume of this *Review*. At times, the microbe has been the center of interest in these studies, at times, a tool in studies of higher forms of life, but, in either case, use of the microorganism or of its parts has led to a better understanding of life in general.

During the first nineteen meetings of the Editorial Committee, its members selected topics for review in an attempt to cover the more pertinent and timely literature. At the twentieth meeting, the pattern was broken, albeit temporarily, and the Editor was coerced into agreeing to write on the general topic of Microbiology—Past, Present, and Future, in commemoration of Volume 20 of this *Review*. Of the past, I know a little, of the present, less, and as for the future—many clues regarding the nature of life in general are yet to be discovered in the world of the microbe. We can hope that the bits of information that have been collected over the years will be fitted together, as in a jigsaw puzzle, with those yet to be obtained to provide for future generations a more complete picture of Nature's marvel, the living cell. At the same time, one must hope that such a picture serves only as a base for other explorations into the mysteries of life and will not deprive future generations of the joy of the quest for new knowledge.

Of one thing we can be certain—future volumes of this *Review* will contain more accurate accounts of our knowledge at any particular time than can come from any phantasy derived from the hallucinations of an editor gazing into a crystal ball. All that can be done now, the editor having been voted down, is to proceed with a tale of sorts and to shift any shortcomings onto the shoulders of those who forced the task upon an unwilling author.

We are in a state of extreme specialization scientifically, and to review one's own field of special interest tends to limit its appeal; to make it too general may destroy any potential value it might have for a wider group of readers. Many of the microbe's contributions have been reviewed in these and in other volumes, hence, a review of reviews seemed not to be desirable. The above possibilities were discarded and a personal approach was selected in the hope that it might provide some bits of interest, particularly to the newcomer in microbiology, regarding some aspects of the growth of an individual as well as of a science. This account is, therefore, a backward glance at the progress of microbiology during the thirty-seven years in which the author has been actively engaged in teaching and research in some aspects of this branch of science.

Chance often plays an important role in the development of an individual or of a science. While pursuing graduate work in physical chemistry at Ohio State University, chance led to an offer of a fellowship in biophysics at the Mayo Foundation, a branch of the Graduate Division of the University of Minnesota. Facilities and support for basic research at the Foundation were excellent and in general far surpassed those available in most universities. In addition to the personal instruction and help offered by C. Sheard, J. M. Ort, and E. J. Baldes in biophysics, contact with men such as E. C. Kendall in biochemistry, W. Boothby in metabolism, F. Mann, J. Bollman, and J. Markowitz in physiology, and of E. C. Rosenow in bacteriology, served to develop a broader interest in problems of biological nature. Rochester was a favorite spot for visitors from all over the world, and in seminars and conversation they introduced us to other phases of research in biology and medicine. It mattered little if no one knew what biophysics was, except to me when Ph.D. examinations rolled around, for we were free to pursue research of interest to us. In December of 1928, I was awarded the first Ph.D. degree in biophysics granted in the United States.

After graduation, I worked for a few months in the research laboratories of the Eastman Kodak Company, but, again, chance enters the story. E. W. Schultz, Chairman of the Department of Bacteriology and Experimental Pathology at Stanford, mentioned to Dr. Sheard of the Biophysics Section of the Mayo Foundation that he was looking for a man trained in physics and chemistry to aid in ultrafiltration and electrophoresis studies on filtrable viruses. As a result of this conversation, an offer of an instructorship at Stanford was made by Dr. Schultz and was accepted by me in the fall of 1929.

At that time the Department of Bacteriology and Experimental Pathology (now Medical Microbiology) at Stanford consisted of E. W. Schultz, W. H. Manwaring, who devoted his time to writing and research, P. J. Beard, who held a joint appointment with Sanitary Engineering, and two new instructors, E. W. Dewey in immunology, and myself. A considerable portion of my first year at Stanford was devoted to becoming better acquainted with bacteria and other forms of microbic life. Teaching activities of the Department consisted of a thorough course in medical bacteriology, a general course for students in the School of Biological Sciences, a course in immunology, and some special work for sanitary engineering students.

Bacterial physiology was added to the curriculum in 1930 and I was entrusted with a course that has changed year by year, both in subject matter and in emphasis. At about the same time, attention was devoted to the development of the graduate program. My teaching load was heavy for many years and included general bacteriology, bacterial physiology, immunology for a couple of years, and considerable sharing in the laboratory portion of the course in medical bacteriology. Formal courses were offered in the summer quarter for several years and this reduced the time free for research.

In the early 1930's, the course in bacterial physiology was concerned primarily with the application of the concepts of physical and colloidal chemistry to the problems of bacteriology and immunology, with particular attention being given to growth and death of bacteria. Rahn's *Physiology of Bacteria* was of great help regarding factors influencing growth and death, and the three volumes of *Physiology and Biochemistry of Bacteria* by Buchanan and Fulmer were of marked value as reference material. The appearance of Stephenson's *Bacterial Metabolism* and of Kluyver's *Chemical Activities of Micro-organisms* served to shift emphasis from the kinetic aspects of growth and death to more biochemical ones. These books also sparked a desire to spend some time in the laboratories of the latter two authors, a desire that was fulfilled in the academic year of 1936–1937.

During the 1930's, it was becoming apparent that Nature was more sparing in her ways than was once thought to be the case, and that she had developed rather uniform patterns of metabolism in all forms of life, a unity of biochemistry so ably propounded by Kluyver. The studies of Kluyver of the metabolism of bacteria, and of his former pupil, van Niel, on photosynthetic bacteria, were outstanding in the early phase of rapid growth of bacterial physiology as we know it today. The appearance of Knight's *Bacterial Nutrition* in the middle 1930's also served to stimulate interest in the study of bacteria as such rather than as agents of positive or negative economic value. Bacterial physiology developed rapidly in the decade 1940–1950, and during that time formal courses in this field were initiated in many universities. At about the same time, virology advanced to the status of a separate discipline in the general field of microbiology.

My first research at Stanford was on the preparation and calibration of collodion membranes and on their use in ultrafiltration studies with various viruses. At the December, 1930, meeting of the Society of American Bacteriologists I reported that the virus of poliomyelitis is less than 50 mμ in diameter. It was a thrill for a newcomer to be congratulated by C.-E. A. Winslow who insisted on the preparation of an article for the *Journal of Bacteriology* (1), and to have the work reported in *Time* magazine. Subsequent studies indicated a diameter of about 25 mμ, a value in close agreement with those determined in later studies by other workers, using the electron microscope. At about the same time, Mendelsohn, Clifton & Lewis (2) reported that the chicken tumor Number 1 virus was less than 50 mμ and possibly less than 15 mμ in diameter. Ultrafiltration studies with other viruses were never completed, owing in part to the high cost of animals, and also to a shift in personal interest to problems more biochemical in nature.

In the early 1930's at Stanford, E. W. Schultz was studying the value of bacteriophages as therapeutic agents. These viruses were the subject of various other studies in Stanford laboratories. It had been reported that they could be concentrated to a very marked extent by electrophoresis in agar. Considerable time was spent without success in attempting to confirm this report. This project was dropped when the original investigator was unable to repeat the work and it became apparent that the use of the same pipette throughout the phage titrations was responsible for the high titers apparently observed. I learned at an early date the need for attention to detail in carrying out the dilutions so frequently required in quantitative microbiological work.

Schultz & Krueger (3) had reported that a staphylococcus phage was inactivated by methylene blue. I studied dye inactivation of phage in more detail and reported (4) that inactivation is the result of a photodynamic effect in the presence of oxygen. Later, other workers used this photodynamic action of methylene blue for the inactivation of various animal viruses in the hope of producing vaccines less altered in their antigenic characteristics than ones prepared with the use of more active reagents. Other studies with phage dealt with purification by adsorption on alumina gel and subsequent elution (5), electric charge and isoelectric points of various phages as determined by the extent of migration in paper strips [Clifton & Madison (6)], and preservatives for bacteriophage suspensions (7). During this same period of time, movies on experimental poliomyelitis and on laboratory techniques were prepared for teaching purposes.

My research for the Doctorate had been on oxidation-reduction potentials in glucose solutions. It was an attempt to determine the concentration of a minute but apparently definite amount of a powerful reductant or "active glucose" responsible for the high reduction intensities developed in sugar solutions. A potentiometer was available in the Bacteriology Department at Stanford, a constant-temperature water bath was constructed from odds and ends (Woolworth's was a good source of various supplies when working on a very limited budget), and once again I was measuring oxidation-reduction potentials.

A paper on oxidation-reduction potentials in cultures of *Staphylococcus aureus* (8) was followed by a second (9) on the rate of reduction of ferricyanide by resting *Escherichia coli*. Warburg respirometers were a rarity at that time, the rate of reduction of methylene blue was hard to follow quantitatively, and it was shown that the rate of reduction of ferricyanide could be used as an accurate measure of metabolic activity. It was concluded that the concentrations of substrate, organisms, and oxidant play important and closely connected roles in controlling the rate of metabolism in cultures and suspensions of bacteria. This conclusion was supported by the results of studies on oxidation-reduction potentials and ferricyanide-reducing activities in peptone [Clifton, Cleary & Beard (10)], and glucose-peptone [Clifton & Cleary (11)] cultures and suspensions of *E. coli*. It was reported in these papers that the rate of reduction of ferricyanide per cell tended to decrease with increasing age of the cells in stationary cultures, but remained constant in continuous flow cultures once a maximum population had been established. It became apparent that continuous flow cultures were good sources of cells for studies on the kinetics of metabolism or for other purposes where cells of uniform age would be of value. However, the use of cells from continuous flow cultures for various studies did not become popular until quite a few years later.

The studies on continuous flow cultures were extended [Cleary, Clifton & Beard (12)] to include factors influencing bacterial populations. It was concluded that the population would not mount above a certain maximum even with the effects of inhibitory substances reduced to a low level since the major population-limiting factor appeared to be the amount of energy and building material available per cell per unit time. A small Sigma Xi grant at this time made it possible to purchase Warburg equipment with which one could make more "physiologically correct" measurements of metabolism than could be accomplished with ferricyanide or dye reduction tests.

The results of a study of oxygen consumption in lactate cultures of *E. coli* [Clifton, Cahen & Morrow (13)], and of a comparative study (14) with *Aerobacter aerogenes*, *Salmonella typhosa*, and *E. coli* lent additional support to the concept that the concentration gradient of foodstuffs between the cell and its environment is a major factor in controlling growth. These studies lent additional support to the concept that the maximum population that can develop in an otherwise favorable environment is controlled primarily by the availability of sufficient building material and energy per cell per unit time to provide for the requirements of the cells for growth. Hence, the rate of division would decrease and approach zero as the rate of uptake of one or more essential substances became the limiting factor(s).

We realized that the solubility of nutrients and osmotic pressure effects in concentrated solutions would limit the amount of foodstuffs that could be supplied per unit volume of culture per unit time, and that it would be difficult or impossible to meet the enormous oxygen demand of high populations owing to the limited solubility of oxygen. We often tend to forget that each new generation of cells in a culture represents the formation of about as many cells as were formed in the culture up to the initiation of the particular generation under consideration. Hence, with each new generation there is a demand for approximately as much energy and building materials as utilized during the previous history of the culture if a minimum generation time is to be maintained.

The fall and winter months of the 1936–1937 academic year were spent in Marjory Stephenson's laboratory at Cambridge, and the spring and summer months with A. J. Kluyver at Delft. This proved to be a most instructive and, at the same time, enjoyable year. D. D. Woods was just finishing his work for his doctorate with Marjorie Stephenson, and Ernest Gale and Sydney Elsden were just beginning graduate work. The four of us shared a large laboratory. Lifetime friendships began there.

Woods and I collaborated [Woods & Clifton (15, 16)] in studies on the metabolism of *Clostridium tetanomorphum*. While working with this organism we were not too popular in the laboratory since some of its end products could be recognized very readily by olfactory responses. Studies on the metabolism of *Clostridium botulinum* and *Clostridium tetani* were reported in subsequent years [Clifton (17–19)]. After World War II, attention was again devoted to the anaerobes, and results of nitritional and metabolic studies with *Clostridium feseri* were reported by Jones & Clifton (20), and with *C. tetanomorphum* by Nakano & Clifton (21).

The studies of Barker (22) and of Geisberger (23) on oxidative assimilation were extended during the months spent in Kluyver's laboratory at Delft. It was reported [Clifton (24)] that sodium azide or 2,4-dinitrophenol in suitable concentrations inhibited oxidative assimilation and induced complete oxidation of a substrate. These results suggested an inhibition of energy transfer to the energy-requiring assimilatory reactions. The role of oxidative phosphorylation and of the energy-rich phosphate bond in energy transfer, however, was not known in 1937.

The studies on oxidative assimilation were continued at Stanford, Clifton & Logan (25, 26) reporting that about the same amount of assimilation was noted in actively proliferating cultures as in washed suspensions of *E. coli*. Pickett & Clifton (27) reported that dinitrophenol blocked assimilation by yeast but oxidation did not go to completion, the glucose normally assimilated being fermented in the presence of the poison.

Pickett & Clifton (28) studied the assimilation of glucose by yeast and demonstrated an actual increase in both the carbon and carbohydrate content of the cells. The results, however, were not in agreement with those predicted from Warburg data, about one third rather than the predicted two thirds of the glucose being assimilated, while one third was converted to soluble end products. The remainder was oxidized to carbon dioxide. M. J. Pickett [Pickett & Clifton (29)] also studied the effect of selective poisons on the utilization of glucose by microorganisms. He was the first student to obtain the doctorate under my guidance.

An accelerated teaching program followed our entrance into World War II and left less time for research. In addition, I taught courses in general bacteriology at San Jose State College to help relieve the manpower shortage. Studies on the anaerobes and on assimilation were halted, and attention was directed toward penicillin production. I reported (30) that penicillin could be produced in good yield (for that time) in continuous flow cultures, and that such a method might be feasible on a commercial scale. The submerged culture method was developed at about the same time and proved to be more satisfactory for the production of penicillin. The early phase of studies on penicillin was an exciting one but, at the same time, not devoid of heartaches when one could not provide this antibiotic for use in the treatment of cases brought to our attention.

After peace was declared, larger classes were the rule and for a couple of years veterans set the pace for student work. More students entered into graduate work and teaching duties remained heavy. The *Annual Review of Microbiology* was founded in 1945, and shortly therafter the first steps were taken in the writing of *Introduction to the Bacteria* (31). Two reviews [Clifton (32, 33)] on microbial assimilation were prepared and somehow I found time to serve on a local school board during a period of extremely rapid population growth, and later, on civic committees.

Shortly after going to Yale, E. L. Tatum wrote, asking me to send him a number of strains of *E. coli* from our collection. Among these was K-12, the strain used in most of my studies. K-12 gave rise to mutants with which Tatum & Lederberg (34) were able to demonstrate sexual recombination in bacteria. Here is another example of the effect of chance—K-12, by chance, having certain characteristics which facilitated the demonstration of sexual recombination by competent workers in microbial genetics.

Following World War II, my time was devoted again to studies on assimilation, and also on the metabolism of anaerobes. In addition, a number of studies on other aspects of bacterial physiology were carried on, particularly in minor problems in genetics, colicine production, nutritional factors influencing phage production, heat production in washed suspensions of bacteria, and in bacterial cytology, primarily by students working for the Master of Science degree. One of the better studies of this type was on nuclear changes observed in multiplying cells of a variant of *Bacillus anthracis* [Clifton & Ehrhard (35)]. Activities as a consultant at various times, and as acting head of the Department served to prevent life from becoming monotonous.

I strove always to spend as much time as possible with the students who were working with me for advanced degrees. During the spring quarter of the school year, we held weekly seminars in our home, finding that the students communicated more freely in a home atmosphere, and that they enjoyed the touch of home life and delicacies provided by Mrs. Clifton. Barbecues long remembered brought each spring quarter to an end.

No attempt has been made to cite all papers, and only a few more will be mentioned. An often neglected study, but to me an interesting one, dealt with growth and assimilation in cultures of *Saccharomyces cerevisiae* [Swanson & Clifton (36)]. We reported that actively proliferating cultures under fully aerobic conditions utilized the carbohydrate substrate primarily by the process of fermentative assimilation. This type of metabolism predominated until the carbohydrate source was depleted, oxidative assimilation then occurring from intermediate products of saccharide dissimilation. The energetics of oxidative assimilation were considered in other studies [e.g., Siegel & Clifton (37)], it being noted that the same extent of assimilation occurred from pairs such as pyruvate and lactate although more energy would be available from the oxidation of the more reduced member of the pair.

I have been interested in the autotrophs, both chemo- and photosynthetic species, but have never had much time to devote to them. I was pleased when one of our graduate students displayed some interest and this led to a study on oxidative assimilation by *Hydrogenomonas facilis* [Marino & Clifton (38)]. Although we are primarily a department of medical microbiology, our students have always had freedom of choice of their research problems within the limits of available equipment and capabilities of the faculty members for directing the proposed research. For many years, I was the only department member interested in physiology but, in more recent years, association with Ram Navalkar and Emmett Johnson as postdoctoral fellows, and with Hal Ramsey as a research associate has been of benefit in developing students who are interested in the field of bacterial physiology.

Another problem of many facets that has been of theoretical interest to me is why some bacteria are virulent, i.e., capable of inducing an infection when introduced through a specific route into a susceptible host. We carried out a comparative study on respiration [Heplar, Clifton, Raffel & Futrelle (39)], and growth [Guy, Raffel & Clifton (40)], of virulent and avirulent strains of *Mycobacterium tuberculosis*. There was some evidence that respiration and growth of avirulent strains were inhibited to a greater extent than were those of virulent ones at low oxygen tensions. The differences, however, were too small to account entirely for the failure of avirulent strains to become established under the low oxygen tension prevailing in tissue cells. Numerous studies have been carried out on factors influencing, or concerned with, the virulence of pathogenic species [e.g., see review by Panos & Ajl (41)], but our knowledge in this field is very inadequate, and the field is ripe for, and deserving of, much work. The right idea is needed—what chance will bring it forth and who will take advantage of the chance?

Two major operations in the 1950's were inhibiting factors for a time, but bed was as good a place as any in which to read proof of my *Introduction to*

Bacterial Physiology (42) and the *Annual Review of Microbiology*. While con-valescing from the second surgery I turned to painting, somewhat by chance, and there are indications that I am improving as an artist. Anyhow, it is fun!

During the past ten years, most of my research activities have been de-voted to oxidative assimilation, with particular emphasis on preferential utilization of the individual carbon atoms in a molecule, the distribution of labeled carbon in the cells, and the influence of an exogenous substrate on the endogenous respiration of the cells. During the course of glucose-carbon distribution studies, it became apparent that none of the equations advanced for use in calculating the relative contribution of the glycolytic and the pen-tose pathways of oxidation were accurate. None of the authors had considered the extent to which different carbons in the molecule of glucose were as-similated or were found in end products of metabolism other than carbon dioxide. Neither did they consider the influence of glucose degradation prod-ucts or of assimilation of portions of the molecule on cyclic processes. A paper on this subject was turned down by two editors, both concluding that everyone knew that the equations were not accurate. They did not explain how they reached that particular conclusion. Students may learn the various pathways of oxidation, but they should also learn that substrates provide building material as well as energy and that there is no Maxwell demon within the cell selecting which glucose molecule, or portion thereof, will be oxidized over a particular pathway, be assimilated, or be discarded as waste material.

The more recent studies on oxidative assimilation and endogenous meta-bolism were summarized [Clifton (43)] in a conference—Endogenous Metab-olism with Special Reference to Bacteria—arranged by the New York Academy of Sciences. Work is continuing on endogenous metabolism and on a closely related problem, energy of maintenance. If an external source of energy is supplied to a washed suspension of bacteria, will those cells be maintained in a more or less steady-state? Our results indicate that the aging process can be inhibited but that energy alone does not suffice to maintain life. Everywhere we look we find that Nature has developed marvelous machines for the conversion of inert matter into organized cells but these are limited with respect to their life span, the maintenance of a species being de-pendent upon multiplication of cells rather than upon maintenance of the status quo.

Chance, inclination, student interest, availability of equipment, and de-velopments in a particular field of research all play a part in the development of one's research program. It is difficult at times to keep up with the progress being made in a particular field; it becomes almost impossible for a teacher to do so in the many fields comprising bacterial physiology. Progress, in the decades covered in this review, has been truly phenomenal and its end is not in sight. An attempt to summarize some of the major advances made during this time will be evident in the following paragraphs.

The major pathways of fermentation have been worked out in detail and many of the individual reactions have been demonstrated with enzyme preparations. But we must not lose sight of the fact that Pasteur, Harden and Young, Neuberg, Buchner, Wildier, and many others, bit by bit and with incredibly "inadequate" means, laid the foundation upon which this phase of microbiology was erected. During the decades covered in this review, the Embden-Meyerhof pathway of oxidation was found to feed into the newly discovered Krebs or tricarboxylic acid cycle and that a second major pathway of glucose oxidation, the pentose pathway, exists in the cell. It became apparent that the carbons of various substrates were fed into the Krebs cycle and that this cycle, in conjunction with the electron transport chain, serves as the major generator of high-energy bonds. In the more "advanced" cells, the mitochondrion, with its array of enzymes and coenzymes, serves as the powerhouse; in the bacteria, the powerhouse is simpler—or is more complex— depending upon one's point of view.

Generations of physiologists have known that the energy trapped in various chemical bonds during the course of photosynthesis could be utilized by chemosynthetic forms of life. But, how? The nature of energy transfer did not become apparent until the discovery, in quite recent years, of the high-energy, or energy-rich, phosphate bond and similar energy-rich bonds such as found in acetyl-coenzyme A. Dissimilation, energy transfer, and assimilation began to fit into a coherent picture, depicting the major chemical events taking place within the cell. These reactions, and reactants, were found to be similar in all forms of life, a remarkable unity of biochemical events being noted in widely different cells and organisms.

Microbiology has contributed to our general knowledge of the nature and function of vitamins, the studies of Lwoff and of Knight in the 1930's in particular, serving as important stepping stones in our understanding of the nutritional requirements of man and of bug, as well. It became apparent that cells and organisms differed among themselves in their powers of synthesis, and that certain preformed chemical structures may be essential for growth and maintenance. Mutants, or strains, of a species were found to differ in their nutritional requirements, i.e., in their synthetic abilities. But, we must remember that in the 1930's, "mutant" was a four-letter word for many microbiologists.

Variations, either temporary or permanent in character, were noted by Pasteur and subsequent workers. Yet, bacteria did or did not mutate, they did or did not possess a nucleus. Personal prejudices and one's scientific environment tended to be deciding factors in a somewhat confused field of study. The studies of Robinow and of Piekarski were particularly valuable in establishing the existence of visible nuclear (chromatinic) structures within bacteria. The demonstration of transformation of a particular character by means of deoxyribonucleic acid, of transduction, and of sexual recombination have cleared up many of the early misunderstandings regarding bacterial variation.

The studies of Beadle and Tatum with *Neurospora crassa* were extended to various bacteria. Biochemical mutants, that is, those devoid of particular synthetic abilities possessed by their wild ancestor, became available and were employed in the mating experiments of Tatum and Lederberg mentioned earlier in this review. The whole field of bacterial genetics has evolved as if by magic in a relatively few years. Today, one can pinpoint the location of a particular gene on the chromosome of a particular species of bacteria. Repressor, suppressor, and other genes as well as episomes and other factors have entered the story and one cannot be certain as yet that the climax has been reached. Studies on heredity in bacteria have illuminated the heredity of man. The things we marvel at today will be taken for granted tomorrow. What does the future hold?

Studies on, or with the help of, microorganisms have contributed greatly to our understanding of the nature of the macromolecules, in particular the proteins and nucleic acids, which so closely control our activities. Progress has been made in our knowledge regarding the arrangement of the bases in the nucleic acids, and today it is believed that the information essential for directing the synthesis of protein molecules is held in triplet arrangements of the bases which serve as codes for particular amino acids. Also, the controlled synthesis of macromolecules has been accomplished in the laboratory. Is this, eventually, a major step in the creation of a form of life?

As for the future, no one can predict with a high degree of accuracy the nature of the progress that will be made in microbiology within the next decade or two. It is held to be true by some that the moon is made of blue cheese. This concept may be substantiated or refuted within the next few years. No doubt, other problems will be posed and solved but their answers may not be as obvious as the one for the problem advanced above.

Micro- as well as macro-biology is in ferment and is expanding. No one can predict the biology of the future with any certainty, but it will be the product of a multiplicity of approaches. The physicist, the chemist, the biologist as such, the physician, the mathematician, the engineer, the statesman, and many others may contribute in one manner or another to its progress, but—progress it will, not only as pure science but as applied science as well. Our burgeoning populations will require expanded sources of food and the population crisis may be only a few short years away. Applied microbiology will have to aid in the conservation of the free energy garnered from light and stored in chemical bonds by photosynthetic cells. Will that complex biological entity, man, be able to make the adjustment to a world even more dependent upon the microbe than it is today? There are problems for the future that remain to be solved, and chance, properly taken advantage of, will play a role in helping today's students to carry on from where we leave off.

Progress in microbiology will lead to a better understanding of all of the phenomena associated with life in general and to a world in which the activities of microorganisms will be directed more and more toward more economical use of our natural resources. It will be a world in which microorganisms are our partners rather than, in many instances, at least from our viewpoint, enemies. In the long-range plan of Nature, however, the prophecy "Some little bug will get you someday" from a song popular some years ago, still holds true and illustrates the important role of microbes in the various cycles of nature, the scheme of things as they are.

LITERATURE CITED

1. Clifton, C. E., Schultz, E. W., and Gebhardt, L. P., *J. Bacteriol.*, **22**, 7 (1931)
2. Mendelsohn, W., Lewis, M. R., and Clifton, C. E., *Am. J. Hyg.*, **14**, 421 (1931)
3. Schultz, E. W., and Krueger, A. P., *Proc. Soc. Exptl. Biol. Med.*, **26**, 101 (1928)
4. Clifton, C. E., *Proc. Soc. Exptl. Biol. Med.*, **28**, 734 (1931)
5. Clifton, C. E., *Proc. Soc. Exptl. Biol. Med.*, **28**, 32 (1930)
6. Clifton, C. E., and Madison, R. W., *J. Bacteriol.*, **22**, 255 (1931)
7. Clifton, C. E., *Proc. Soc. Exptl. Biol. Med.*, **24**, 370 (1932)
8. Clifton, C. E., *J. Bacteriol.*, **35**, 495 (1933)
9. Clifton, C. E., *Proc. Soc. Exptl. Biol. Med.*, **31**, 109 (1933)
10. Clifton, C. E., Cleary, J. P., and Beard, P. J., *J. Bacteriol.*, **28**, 541 (1934)
11. Clifton, C. E., and Cleary, J. P., *J. Bacteriol.*, **28**, 561 (1934)
12. Cleary, J. P., Beard, P. J., and Clifton, C. E., *J. Bacteriol.*, **29**, 205 (1935)
13. Clifton, C. E., Cahen, S. F., and Morrow, G., *Proc. Soc. Exptl. Biol. Med.*, **35**, 40 (1936)
14. Clifton, C. E., *J. Bacteriol.*, **33**, 145 (1937)
15. Woods, D. D., and Clifton, C. E., *Biochem. J.*, **31**, 1774 (1937)
16. Woods, D. D., and Clifton, C. E., *Biochem. J.*, **32**, 345 (1938)
17. Clifton, C. E., *Proc. Soc. Exptl. Biol. Med.*, **40**, 338 (1939)
18. Clifton, C. E., *J. Bacteriol.*, **39**, 485 (1940)
19. Clifton, C. E., *J. Bacteriol.*, **44**, 179 (1942)
20. Jones, L. W., and Clifton, C. E., *J. Bacteriol.*, **65**, 560 (1953)
21. Nakano, J. H., and Clifton, C. E., *Proc. Soc. Exptl. Biol. Med.*, **84**, 394 (1953)
22. Barker, H. A., *J. Cellular Comp. Physiol.*, **8**, 231 (1936)
23. Geisberger, G., *Beiträge zur Kenntnis der Gattung Spirillum Ehbg.* (Doctoral dissertation, University of Utrecht, 1936)
24. Clifton, C. E., *Enzymologia*, **4**, 246 (1937)
25. Clifton, C. E., and Logan, W. A., *Proc. Soc. Exptl. Biol. Med.*, **38**, 619 (1938)
26. Clifton, C. E., and Logan, W. A., *J. Bacteriol.*, **37**, 523 (1939)
27. Pickett, M. J., and Clifton, C. E., *Proc. Soc. Exptl. Biol. Med.*, **46**, 443 (1941)
28. Pickett, M. J., and Clifton, C. E., *J. Cellular Comp. Physiol.*, **21**, 77 (1943)
29. Pickett, M. J., and Clifton, C. E., *J. Cellular Comp. Physiol.*, **22**, 147 (1943)
30. Clifton, C. E., *Science*, **98**, 69 (1943)
31. Clifton, C. E., *Introduction to the Bacteria*. (McGraw-Hill, New York, 1950)
32. Clifton, C. E., *Advan. Enzymol.*, **6**, 269 (1946)
33. Clifton, C. E., *Antonie van Leeuwenhoek J. Microbiol. Serol.*, **12**, 186 (1947)
34. Tatum, E. L., and Lederberg, J., *J. Bacteriol.*, **53**, 673 (1947)
35. Clifton, C. E., and Ehrhard, H.-B., *J. Bacteriol.*, **63**, 537 (1952)
36. Swanson, W. H., and Clifton, C. E., *J. Bacteriol.*, **56**, 115 (1948)
37. Siegel, B., and Clifton, C. E., *J. Bacteriol.*, **60**, 585 (1950)
38. Marino, R. J., and Clifton, C. E., *J. Bacteriol.*, **69**, 188 (1955)
39. Heplar, J. Q., Clifton, C. E., Raffel, S., Futrelle, C., *J. Infect. Diseases*, **94**, 90 (1954)
40. Guy, L. R., Raffel, S., and Clifton, C. E., *J. Infect. Diseases*, **94**, 99 (1954)
41. Panos, C., and Ajl, S. J., *Ann. Rev. Microbiol.*, **17**, 297 (1963)
42. Clifton, C. E., *Introduction to Bacterial Physiology*. (McGraw-Hill, New York, 1957)
43. Clifton, C. E., *Ann. N.Y. Acad. Sci.*, **102**, 655 (1963)

BIOSYNTHESIS OF LIPIDS IN MICROORGANISMS[1,2,3]

By Morris Kates

Division of Biosciences, National Research Council, Ottawa, Canada

Contents

BIOSYNTHESIS OF FATTY ACIDS........................ 14
Saturated Fatty Acids.................................. 14
  Malonyl-coenzyme A pathway.............................. 14
  Products of synthesis..................................... 17
Unsaturated Fatty Acids............................... 18
  Aerobic pathway... 18
  Polyunsaturated fatty acids................................ 22
  Anaerobic pathway....................................... 24
Cyclopropane and Branched-Chain Fatty Acids............. 26
  Cyclopropane acids....................................... 26
  Methyl-branched acids.................................... 28
  Multimethyl-branched chains............................... 30
Polar Fatty Acids..................................... 31
  n-Hydroxy acids... 31
  Mycolic acids... 32
BIOSYNTHESIS OF COMPLEX LIPIDS..................... 34
Glycolipids... 34
  Glycosyl diglycerides..................................... 34
  Glycosides of hydroxy fatty acids........................... 36
  Lipopolysaccharides...................................... 36
Phosphatides... 36
  Phosphatidic acid....................................... 36
  Phosphatidyl serine and phosphatidyl ethanolamine.............. 37
  N-Methylation of phosphatidyl ethanolamine to lecithin.......... 38
  Plasmalogens... 39
  Phosphatidyl glycerol and its amino acid esters................. 39
  Phosphatidyl inositol and its glycoside derivatives.............. 39

During the last five years, knowledge concerning the chemical nature of lipids in microorganisms has increased at an enormous rate. Concurrently,

[1] The survey of the literature pertaining to this review was concluded in December 1965.

[2] The following abbreviations will be used: ACP (acyl carrier protein); CMP, CDP, CTP (cytidine mono-, di-, and triphosphate, respectively); FAD (flavin adenine dinucleotide); FMN (flavin mononucleotide); GDP (guanidine diphosphate); NAD$^+$ and NADH (nicotinamide adenine dinucleotide and its reduced form); NADP$^+$ and NADPH (nicotinamide adenine dinucleotide phosphate and its reduced form); TDP (thymidine diphosphate); UDP (uridine diphosphate).

[3] Issued as National Research Council No. 9022.

studies of lipid biosynthesis have begun to reveal the pathways and mechanisms by which many of the simple and complex lipid molecules are assembled from simple metabolites. It is the purpose of this review to attempt to systematize this knowledge and to point the way for investigation of areas requiring further study. Previous reviews by Asselineau & Lederer (1), Wakil (2), Mead (3), and Kates (4) have covered some of the earlier developments in this field. The present review will be limited to coverage of recent developments in the biosynthesis of fatty acids, glycolipids, and phospholipids, and will not deal with carotenoids or hydrocarbons, as these fields have been covered recently by Jensen (5) and McKenna & Kallio (6), respectively. Other topics such as glycerides, coenzyme Q, sterols, etc., have been omitted for lack of space.

BIOSYNTHESIS OF FATTY ACIDS
SATURATED FATTY ACIDS

Malonyl-coenzyme A pathway.—Biosynthesis of normal, long-chain, even-numbered, saturated fatty acids in bacteria is now known to occur by the same pathway, i.e., the malonyl-CoA pathway, as in mammalian tissues [see the detailed reviews by Vagelos (7); Lynen (8); Wakil (2, 9); and Green & Wakil (10)]. The first and rate-limiting step (7) in the *de novo* synthesis of long-chain fatty acids is the ATP and Mn^{++}-dependent carboxylation of acetyl-CoA to form malonyl-CoA, catalyzed by the biotin-containing enzyme acetyl-CoA carboxylase (Reactions 1–3):

$$HCO_3^- + ATP + biotin\ enzyme \overset{Mn^{++}}{\rightleftharpoons} CO_2^{--}\ biotin\ enzyme + ADP + P_i \qquad 1.$$

$$CO_2^{--}\ biotin\ enzyme + CH_3CO\text{-}SCoA \rightleftharpoons biotin\ enzyme + {}^-OOCCH_2CO\text{-}SCoA \qquad 2.$$

$$Sum: HCO_3^- + ATP + CH_3CO\text{-}SCoA \overset{Mn^{++}}{\rightleftharpoons} {}^-OOCCH_2CO\text{-}SCoA + ADP + P_i \qquad 3.$$

Acetyl-CoA carboxylase was first discovered by Wakil (11) in pigeon liver and then independently by Kusunose et al. (12) in *Mycobacterium avium*. Elucidation of the Reactions 1–3 in which it is involved (2, 3, 7, 9) opened the way for all subsequent investigations of fatty acid biosynthesis. In microorganisms, Reaction 3 has been demonstrated in cell-free extracts of *M. avium* (12), *M. tuberculosis* (13), *M. smegmatis* (12, 13), *Nocardia asteroides* (12), and yeast (*Saccharomyces cerevisiae*) (14).

The fatty acid synthesizing systems ("fatty acid synthetase") in animal tissues (2, 7, 9, 15), plants (16, 17), bacteria (7, 12, 13, 18–21) and yeast (8) are soluble cytoplasmic enzyme complexes which catalyze the following over-all reaction (for palmitic acid synthesis):

$$CH_3CO\text{-}SCoA + 7\ HOOCCH_2CO\text{-}SCoA + 14\ NADPH + 14H^+$$
$$\rightarrow CH_3(CH_2)_{14}COOH + 7\ CO_2 + 8\ CoA\text{-}SH + 14\ NADP^+ + 6H_2O \qquad 4.$$

According to Lynen (8); [see Vagelos (7)], the synthesis is achieved through the repetition of a cycle of the following reactions, the intermediate products remaining covalently bound to the enzyme protein:

$$\text{enzyme-SH} + \text{acetyl-S-CoA} \rightleftharpoons \overset{\overset{\displaystyle \text{SH}}{|}}{\text{enzyme-S-acetyl}} + \text{CoA-SH} \qquad 5.$$

$$\overset{\overset{\displaystyle \text{SH}}{|}}{\text{enzyme-S-acetyl}} + \text{malonyl-S-CoA} \rightleftharpoons \overset{\overset{\displaystyle \text{S-malonyl}}{|}}{\text{enzyme-S-acetyl}} + \text{CoA-SH} \qquad 6.$$

$$\overset{\overset{\displaystyle \text{S-malonyl}}{|}}{\text{enzyme-S-acetyl}} \rightleftharpoons \overset{\overset{\displaystyle \text{S-acetoacetyl}}{|}}{\text{enzyme-SH}} + CO_2 \qquad 7.$$

$$\overset{\overset{\displaystyle \text{S-acetoacetyl}}{|}}{\text{enzyme-SH}} + \text{NADPH} + H^+ \rightleftharpoons \overset{\overset{\displaystyle \text{S-hydroxybutyryl}}{|}}{\text{enzyme-SH}} + \text{NADP}^+ \qquad 8.$$

$$\overset{\overset{\displaystyle \text{S-hydroxybutyryl}}{|}}{\text{enzyme-SH}} \rightleftharpoons \overset{\overset{\displaystyle \text{S-crotonyl}}{|}}{\text{enzyme-SH}} + H_2O \qquad 9.$$

$$\overset{\overset{\displaystyle \text{S-crotonyl}}{|}}{\text{enzyme-SH}} + \text{NADPH} + H^+ \rightleftharpoons \overset{\overset{\displaystyle \text{S-butyryl}}{|}}{\text{enzyme-SH}} + \text{NADP}^+ \qquad 10.$$

$$\overset{\overset{\displaystyle \text{S-butyryl}}{|}}{\text{enzyme-SH}} \rightleftharpoons \overset{\overset{\displaystyle \text{SH}}{|}}{\text{enzyme-S-butyryl}} \qquad 10a.$$

After transfer of the butyryl group back to the fatty acyl site (Reaction 10a), the butyryl-S-enzyme then condenses with another malonyl-CoA and the cycle is repeated as many times as is required to give the appropriate long-chain acid. Thus, the two carbons at the methyl end of the fatty acid are derived from acetyl-CoA, and the remaining C_2 units from malonyl-CoA [see (7) and (8)].

In contrast to the fatty acid synthetase from yeast (8) and pigeon liver (15) which have resisted fractionation, the synthetase from *Clostridium kluyveri* (18, 19) or *Escherichia coli* (20–23) has been resolved into two or more proteins. One of these, first described as a heat-stable protein cofactor for the *C. kluyveri* (18) and *E. coli* (20–23) synthetase, has subsequently been isolated as a pure protein from the latter organism (23–26). It was found to contain a prosthetic group, 4'-phosphopantetheine, which binds acyl groups as thioesters (23–26), and was designated as an 'acyl carrier protein' (ACP) (24). The 4'-phosphopantetheine prosthetic group is now known to be linked by a phosphodiester linkage to the hydroxyl group of one of the three serine residues in ACP, the sequence of amino acids around this serine being Gly-Ala-Asp-Ser-Leu (27, 28). The acyl carrier protein has been shown to be involved in fatty acid synthesis in systems from bacteria (18–26) and plants (16, 17).

Vagelos and co-workers, in a series of brilliant investigations (29–33), have succeeded in isolating from *E. coli* five of the six enzymes catalyzing the conversion of acetyl-CoA and malonyl-CoA to fatty acid (Reactions 5–10). Each of the enzymes requires ACP or the appropriate acyl-ACP, and the reactions catalyzed are as follows:

$$\text{acetyl-S-CoA} + \text{ACP-SH} \xrightleftharpoons[\text{transacylase (29)}]{\text{acetyl}} \text{acetyl-S-ACP} + \text{CoA-SH} \qquad \textbf{11.}$$

$$\text{malonyl-S-CoA} + \text{ACP-SH} \xrightleftharpoons[\text{transacylase (29)}]{\text{malonyl}} \text{malonyl-S-ACP} + \text{CoA-SH} \qquad \textbf{12.}$$

$$\text{acetyl-S-ACP} + \text{malonyl-S-ACP} \xrightleftharpoons[\text{synthetase (30)}]{\beta\text{-ketoacyl-ACP}} \text{acetoacetyl-S-ACP}$$

$$+ \ CO_2 + \text{ACP-SH} \qquad \textbf{13.}$$

$$\text{acetoacetyl-S-ACP} + \text{NADPH} + \text{H}^+ \xrightleftharpoons[\text{reductase (29)}]{\beta\text{-ketoacyl-ACP}} \text{D-}\beta\text{-hydroxybutyryl-S-ACP}$$

$$+ \ \text{NADP}^+ \qquad \textbf{14.}$$

$$\text{D-}\beta\text{-hydroxybutyryl-S-ACP} \xrightleftharpoons[\text{hydrase (31)}]{\text{enoyl-ACP}} \text{crotonyl-S-ACP} + H_2O \qquad \textbf{15.}$$

$$\text{crotonyl-S-ACP} + \text{NADPH} + \text{H}^+ \xrightleftharpoons[\text{reductase (32)}]{\text{enoyl-ACP}} \text{butyryl-S-ACP} + \text{NADP}^+ \qquad \textbf{16.}$$

Studies of the transacylation Reactions 11 and 12, at first suggested (29) that two types of ACP molecules were involved, one specific for acetyl and the other for malonyl. Later direct experiments (30), in which chemically synthesized acetyl-ACP, malonyl-ACP and acetoacetyl-ACP were used, showed that neither the β-ketoacyl-ACP synthetase nor the β-ketoacyl-ACP reductase (Reactions 13 and 14, respectively) could distinguish between the chemically synthesized and the enzymatically synthetized acyl-ACP's. The present evidence (30) thus favors the theory that there is only one type of ACP which accepts either acetyl or malonyl groups indiscriminantly.

The β-ketoacyl-ACP synthetase which catalyzes the condensation of acetyl-ACP and malonyl-ACP (Reaction 13) was found to contain a functional SH-group which could be protected against iodoacetamide inhibition by prior incubation of the enzyme with acetyl-ACP but not with acetyl-CoA or malonyl-ACP (30). These results suggest (30) that the acetyl group of acetyl-ACP is transferred to the SH group of the β-ketoacyl-ACP synthetase, prior to condensation with malonyl-ACP. Reaction 13 would then consist of two steps:

acetyl-S-ACP + HS-enzyme (β-ketoacyl-ACP synthetase)

$$\rightleftharpoons \text{acetyl-S-enzyme} + \text{ACP-SH} \quad \textbf{17.}$$

acetyl-S-enzyme + malonyl-S-ACP

$$\rightleftharpoons \text{acetoacetyl-S-ACP} + CO_2 + \text{HS-enzyme} \quad \textbf{18.}$$

Experiments to substantiate this mechanism are in progress (30).

The β-ketoacyl-ACP synthetase, while absolutely specific for acyl-ACP thioesters (30), shows a broad specificity with respect to chain length of the acyl group; thus, for example, hexanoyl-ACP was found to replace acetyl-ACP in the synthetase reaction (30). This is in accord with the concept that reaction 13 is the chain-elongating step in fatty acid synthesis [see references (7) and (8)]. The question whether fatty acid synthesis in mammalian systems also occurs via acyl-ACP intermediates has been partially settled by the recent demonstration that acyl-ACP derivatives from *E. coli* are utilized in several of the reactions catalyzed by a fatty acid synthetase preparation from rat epididymal adipose tissue, including the condensing Reaction 13 (29, 30, 33). Experiments designed to identify the mammalian ACP are in progress (33).

The β-ketoacyl-ACP reductase, which catalyzes the reduction of β-keto-acyl-S-ACP to D-β-hydroxyacyl-S-ACP (Reaction 14), while not strictly specific for acyl-ACP derivatives [acetoacetyl-CoA and acetoacetyl-S-pantetheine are slowly reduced (29, 33)], is strictly dependent on NADPH, being inactive with NADH (29). The dependence of this reductive step on NADPH and the formation of only the D-β-hydroxy isomer are characteristic of all the fatty acid synthetase systems studied so far (7, 8, 16, 17, 20, 29), and clearly distinguish this system from the system involving reversal of the β-oxidation cycle in which this reduction requires NADH and produces the L-β-hydroxy isomer [see (8)].

The enoyl-ACP hydrase, which catalyzes the reversible dehydration only of the D-β-hydroxyacyl isomer (Reaction 15) is absolutely specific for ACP derivatives and does not react at all with either the CoA or the pantetheine derivatives (31). The final step, the reduction of the *trans* double bond in crotonyl-ACP to butyryl-ACP by enoyl-ACP reductase (Reaction 16) has been demonstrated so far only with a partially purified preparation from *E. coli* (32); this reductive step is also dependent on NADPH (7, 8, 32). In the yeast (8) and *C. kluyveri* (18, 21) synthetases, reduction of the crotonyl thioester is further dependent on the presence of flavin mononucleotide in the complex; FMN was shown to function in the transfer of hydrogen from NADPH to the double bond (8).

Lynen (8) has visualized the yeast synthetase as a complex of "six different enzymes arranged around a functional sulfhydryl group which firmly binds the intermediates of fatty acid synthesis in close proximity to the active sites of the component enzymes." Whether a similar arrangement might also apply to the *E. coli* synthetase, with ACP acting as the central core, must await further experimentation.

Products of synthesis.—The major product of the fatty acid synthetase of avian liver (2, 34) and yeast (8) is palmitic acid, with minor amounts of myristic and stearic acids. In the bacterial systems studied, a wider range of fatty acids is synthesized. Thus, the soluble system from *M. avium* Takeo synthesized C_{20}, C_{22}, and C_{24} normal saturated acids in addition to palmitic and stearic acids (35); myristic and octanoic acids have also been reported to be formed in the same system (36). Even longer-chain acids, C_{26} to C_{32}, in addition to the C_{16} to C_{24} acids, were synthesized from acetate by cell-free extracts of *M. tuberculosis* H37Ra (37). Similar results were reported by Winder et al. (13) for cell-free extracts of *M. smegmatis* and *M. tuberculosis* BCG, which incorporated acetate into the following normal saturated acids: an acid of chain length $<C_6$, octanoic, palmitic, stearic, C_{20}, and at least

two longer-chain acids; it should be noted that these acids were esterified to material insoluble in lipid solvents and were liberated only after vigorous saponification. The fatty acid synthetase from *E. coli* (20, 38) was found to incorporate C^{14} from 2-C^{14}-malonyl CoA largely into *cis*-11-octadecenoic acid (*cis*-vaccenic acid). Only a few per cent of the total C^{14} incorporated was found in palmitic and stearic acids; in addition, a considerable proportion of the C^{14} (20 per cent) appeared in fatty acids with a chain length greater than C_{18}, which were not found in whole cells (20). These results were obtained with partially purified fatty acid synthetase (20, 38) which still contained enzymes involved in synthesis of unsaturated acids (see section on unsaturated fatty acids, anaerobic pathway). Since palmitic acid is a major acid in whole cells of *E. coli* (20), it would be of interest to know which fatty acids are synthesized in a reconstructed synthetase system consisting of the purified enzymes obtained by Vagelos et al. (33).

Factors controlling the termination of the fatty acid synthesizing cycle, and thus determining the chain length of the final fatty acid, have not yet been elucidated. Lynen (8) demonstrated the presence in yeast synthetase of an enzyme catalyzing the transfer of a long-chain acyl group from the SH group of the enzyme complex to CoA, and showing maximal activity with palmitic and stearic acid. He considered this to be the chain-terminating reaction accounting for the prevalence of palmitic and stearic acids in yeast lipids. However, it is doubtful whether this explanation holds for fatty acid synthetases in other organisms, since it has been shown that the end products of the fatty acid synthetase in avian liver (15, 34), *E. coli* (38), and *Bacillus megaterium* (39) are free fatty acids and not the acyl-CoA derivatives.

Saturated, straight-chain, odd-numbered fatty acids (particularly C_{13}, C_{15}, and C_{17} acids) are known to occur in several bacteria (4, 40–42, 137). Synthesis of odd-numbered fatty acids occurs in rat adipose tissue via the malonyl-CoA pathway with propionyl CoA as primer instead of acetyl-CoA (43); a similar mechanism using valerate as primer may also operate in bacteria (137).

Unsaturated Fatty Acids

The biosynthetic reactions involved in formation of unsaturated fatty acids have been elucidated largely through the investigations of Bloch and his associates; the subject has been reviewed by Wakil (2), Kates (4), Vagelos (7), Mead (3, 44, 45), Bloch et al. (46), O'Leary (47), and Hofmann (48). Two separate mechanisms are known for the synthesis of monounsaturated acids, one a direct desaturation of corresponding saturated acids requiring both oxygen and NADPH, the other an anaerobic system involving chain elongation of a short-chain unsaturated fatty acid precursor.

Aerobic pathway.—Early studies had indicated that monounsaturated acids could be formed by desaturation of corresponding saturated acids [see reviews of Mead (3, 44, 45); and Bloch et al. (46)]. Direct demonstration of this process was achieved by Bloomfield & Bloch (49), who showed that cell-free extracts of yeast (*S. cerevisiae*) converted palmitate to palmitoleate and stearate to oleate via their CoA derivatives:

$$CH_3(CH_2)_{14}CO\text{-}SCoA \xrightarrow{O_2, \ NADPH} CH_3(CH_2)_5CH=CH(CH_2)_7CO\text{-}SCoA \qquad 19.$$
$$\text{(Palmitic)} \hspace{5cm} \text{(Palmitoleic)}$$

$$CH_3(CH_2)_{16}CO\text{-}SCoA \xrightarrow{O_2, \ NADPH} CH_3(CH_2)_7CH=CH(CH_2)_7CO\text{-}SCoA \qquad 20.$$
$$\text{(Stearic)} \hspace{5cm} \text{(Oleic)}$$

The cell-free yeast system was found to be particulate, to require both molecular oxygen and NADPH (partially replaceable by NADH), and to act only on the CoA derivatives of the fatty acids. The fact that the system was insensitive to cyanide and that methylene blue could not replace molecular oxygen suggested the participation of an oxygenase reaction. The desaturation was visualized as proceeding by way of a hydroxy acid (either the 9- or 10-hydroxy derivative), the dehydration of which would yield the desired unsaturated acid (46, 49). Although 9- or 10-hydroxystearic acids could substitute fully for oleic acid as a growth factor for yeast grown anaerobically, and seemed to be converted partially to oleic acid (50), neither compound was later found to be an intermediate in the biosynthesis of oleic acid (46, 51). The hydroxystearic acids are apparently converted to ethyl esters of the acetylated acids by the anaerobically growing cells; the acetylation reaction could also be demonstrated in the cell-free particulate system with acetyl-CoA as acetyl donor (51).

James et al. (52) showed that 10-hydroxystearate is formed, probably from stearate, by fecal microorganisms, and suggested that it might be converted further to oleate. Marsh & James (53) subsequently demonstrated the formation of hydroxystearates from stearate by liver homogenates, yeast cells, and cell-free yeast extracts, but conversion of the hydroxy acids to oleate occurred in only low yields (less than 5 per cent). Keto acids have also been suggested as possible intermediates in the biosynthesis of unsaturated acids (54), but 9-ketostearate proved not to be converted to oleate in liver (53) or in the yeast system (55). Other potential intermediates, such as the phosphate ester of 10-hydroxystearate (46), 9,10-dihydroxystearate (55), 9,10-*cis*-epoxystearate (55), and stearolic acid (56) were equally ineffective.

An alternative mechanism suggested by Light et al. (51) is the direct abstraction of a hydrogen from each of carbon atoms 9 and 10 in palmitic or stearic acid, with oxygen serving as the electron acceptor without entering into covalent linkage with a carbon atom of the acid. Schroepfer & Bloch (57) recently showed that the desaturating enzyme system from *Corynebacterium diphtheriae* stereospecifically removes one particular hydrogen atom, having the D-configuration, from each pair of hydrogens at carbon atoms 9 and 10 during conversion of stearate to oleate, and also that hydrogen removal at carbon atom 9 probably precedes that at carbon atom 10. These results could be interpreted as favoring the alternative mechanism described above, but further clarification of the intermediate reactions in the aerobic mechanism and the roles played by oxygen and NADPH must await fractionation of the particulate system into individual enzymes; attempts to achieve this have so far been unsuccessful (51).

Recently, Klein (58) investigated the cellular localization of lipid-synthesizing systems in *S. cerevisiae*. He found that the desaturating system was associated with ribosomal-like particles sedimented at 100,000 $\times g$, which could be further fractionated by treatment with desoxycholate into RNA-free particles with lipogenic activity. The particulate fraction alone carried out the synthesis of unsaturated fatty acids of shorter chain lengths (C_{12} to C_{16}) and also of nonsaponifiable lipids; when added to the supernatant fraction, which alone formed mostly saturated acids, overall fatty acid synthesis was stimulated with a pronounced increase in unsaturated acids; synthesis of nonsaponifiable lipids (chiefly sterols) was also greatly increased.

The aerobic mechanism has also been demonstrated in whole cells of *Mycobacterium phlei* (59, 60), and this has been confirmed by studies with cell-free extracts (61, 62). The *M. phlei* system was shown to require NADPH and oxygen, but, in contrast to the yeast system (49), a flavin (FAD or FMN) and Fe^{++} were also specifically required; in addition, NADH could not replace NADPH as it did in the yeast system. In the cell-free system of *M. phlei*, stearoyl- and palmitoyl-CoA were desaturated to the corresponding *cis*-9-unsaturated acids (62) but in whole cells grown on palmitic-1-C^{14}, the major C_{16}-unsaturated acid formed was the *cis*-10 isomer (60). The explanation for the difference between the *in vitro* and *in vivo* systems is as yet unknown.

Biosynthesis of unsaturated fatty acids has also been shown to occur by the aerobic mechanism in *C. diphtheria*, *Micrococcus lysodeikticus*, and *B. megaterium* (63). In the first two bacteria, stearic and palmitic acids were found to undergo oxygen-dependent desaturation to the corresponding *cis*-9-unsaturated acids, whereas in *B. megaterium* stearic and palmitic were converted to the previously unknown *cis*-5-octadecenoic and *cis*-5-hexadecenoic acids, respectively. Myristic and lauric acids were not desaturated by *B. megaterium* but instead were chain-elongated to palmitic acid which was then desaturated to the Δ^5-derivative. Also, desaturation of palmitic acid by growing cultures of *B. megaterium* was found to be temperature-dependent, increasing from negligible values at 30° C to almost complete desaturation at 23° C.

Apart from these three bacteria, no other member of the order Eubacteriales or of the order Pseudomonadales has so far been found to form monounsaturated fatty acids by direct oxygen-dependent desaturation of saturated fatty acids (46, 63, 64). On the other hand, the aerobic mechanism appears to be the only (or predominant) route to unsaturated acids in members of the orders Actinomycetales (59, 62, 64), Beggiatoales (64), and Myxobacterales (63, 64), as well as in yeasts (49, 53) and other fungi (60, 64), protozoa (64–71), and higher animals (53, 72–74).

Among photosynthetic organisms, the primitive photosynthetic bacteria employ exclusively the anaerobic pathway (see below) for synthesis of mono-unsaturated fatty acids, polyunsaturated acids being absent (75–77); on the other hand, blue-green algae (60, 64, 78, 79) and red algae (64, 80) employ the oxidative desaturation mechanism. Green algae, although at first reported to be unable to desaturate stearate directly to oleate (55, 64, 80), are now also known to utilize the aerobic mechanism. James et al. (75, 76, 81) have shown that cells of *Chlorella vulgaris* desaturate stearate directly to oleate in a phosphate buffer (0.2 M, pH 7.4) medium but not in a tryptone-glucose medium. Oxidative desaturation of palmitate to palmitoleate and *trans*-3-hexadecenoate was also demonstrated (82), and formation of the latter isomer was shown to require light. Higher plants and certain phyto-flagellates, however, synthesize unsaturated fatty acids by a pathway which is not yet clearly understood but is distinct from either the aerobic or anaerobic mechanisms (55, 64, 83, 86). Although oxygen was shown to be required for synthesis of oleic from acetate or C_8 to C_{14} saturated precursors by various higher plant preparations (83–86), neither palmitic nor stearic acids were directly desaturated to the corresponding monoenoic acids. These findings were recently confirmed by Fulco (87) with slices of the ice-plant, *Carpobrotus chilense;* it was also found that 1-C^{14}-myristic acid, in addition to being incorporated intact into oleic and palmitoleic acids, was directly desaturated to 9-tetradecenoic acid in the presence of oxygen and light.

Intact cells of the phytoflagellate *Euglena gracilis* have also been found not to desaturate stearate or palmitate (55, 64, 80), but recent studies by Nagai & Bloch (88) with cell-free extracts have thrown new light on the problem of unsaturated fatty acid synthesis in plants. The enzyme system from photoauxotrophic cells was found to desaturate specifically the stearoyl-ACP derivative, and not stearoyl-CoA, in the presence of oxygen and NADPH. Extracts from heterotrophic cells, however, readily desaturated the CoA esters of stearic and palmitic acids, but not the ACP derivatives, apparently by the same mechanism as in yeast (46). With both enzyme systems the unsaturated acid formed was the *cis*-9 isomer (oleic or palmitoleic). In addition, the enzyme system from photoauxotrophic cells was able to elongate the ACP derivatives of octanoate, decanoate, and dodecanoate to long-chain saturated and unsaturated acids, but only in the presence of oxygen. The following pathways were postulated for synthesis of unsaturated acids in photoauxotrophic *Euglena* (88):

$$C_{10} \longrightarrow C_{12} \longrightarrow C_{14} \longrightarrow C_{16} \longrightarrow C_{18}$$

with O_2 branches:

$$cis\text{-}3\text{-}C_{12} \rightarrow cis\text{-}5\text{-}C_{14} \rightarrow cis\text{-}7\text{-}C_{16} \rightarrow cis\text{-}9\text{-}C_{18}$$

$$cis\text{-}3\text{-}C_{10} \rightarrow cis\text{-}5\text{-}C_{12} \rightarrow cis\text{-}7\text{-}C_{14} \rightarrow cis\text{-}9\text{-}C_{16} \rightarrow cis\text{-}11\text{-}C_{18}$$

The mechanism would explain the presence of cis-9- and cis-11-octadecenoic, and cis-7- and cis-9-hexadecenoic acids (89, 90), as well as the cis-5- and cis-7-tetradecenoic acids (89), in photoauxotrophic *Euglena* cells. Other phytoflagellates, such as the predominantly heterotrophic members of the chrysomonads (e.g., *Ochromonas malhamensis*), and the nonphotosynthetic euglenid, *Astasia longa*, form oleic acid only by direct desaturation of stearic acid (80). Correlation between patterns of fatty acid biosynthesis and phylogenetic classification of microorganisms has been discussed in detail by Bloch and co-workers (55, 64, 80).

Polyunsaturated fatty acids.—With the exception of bacteria (Pseudomonadales, Eubacteriales, Actinomycetales), the ability to form polyunsaturated fatty acids appears to be universal among microorganisms, plants, and animals [see Mead (3, 44, 45); Wakil (2, 92); Bloch et al. (55, 64, 91, 93); and Korn et al. (71)]. Higher animals are unable to desaturate oleic to linoleic or α-linolenic acids, but are able to synthesize C_{20} and C_{22} polyunsaturated acids from dietary linoleic acid, by chain elongation and desaturation in a divinylmethane pattern toward the carboxyl end of the chain (45, 55, 64, 71). On the other hand, higher plants, green algae, and yeasts (55, 76, 85) are able to desaturate oleic acid to linoleic and linolenic acids, but only toward the methyl end of the chain, and are unable to convert the C_{18}-unsaturated acids to longer chain acids; diatoms (94–96), brown and red algae (80, 97), and phytoflagellates (64, 80, 89, 90, 93), however, are able to synthesize C_{20} and C_{22} polyunsaturated acids.

Desaturation of oleic acid to linoleic acid and possibly further to α-linolenic acid by growing or resting cells of the yeast, *Torulopsis utilis*, was first demonstrated by Yuan & Bloch (98). This conversion was shown to require oxygen, but requirement for NADPH could not be demonstrated with the whole cells. Attempts to demonstrate the participation of the most probable hydroxy acid intermediate, ricinoleic acid (12-hydroxy-cis-9-octadecenoic acid), showed that this substrate was not converted to linoleic acid. Subsequent studies by Meyer & Bloch (99) with a cell-free microsomal system verified the oxygen dependence, and demonstrated the requirement for NADPH and the CoA derivative of oleic acid as substrate, showing that the mechanism of desaturation of oleic acid is probably quite analogous to that for desaturation of stearic acid in yeast (49).

A similar system is present in plant leaves and *C. vulgaris* (75, 76, 83, 100), which were found to desaturate oleic acid aerobically to linoleic and α-linolenic acids; in the absence of light the conversion was decreased presumably because of a decrease in NADPH. Using cell-free homogenates of *Chlorella* (100), the desaturating enzyme system was shown to be localized in the chloroplasts, to be active only with oleoyl-CoA, and to require oxygen and NADH or NADPH; the oleate activating system which converts oleate to oleoyl-CoA resided in the chloroplast-free supernatant. The reactions catalyzed by this system are as follows:

$$cis\text{-}9\text{-}C_{18} \to cis\text{-}9\text{-}C_{18}\text{-}CoA \xrightarrow[\text{NADPH, NADH}]{O_2} cis, cis\text{-}9,12\text{-}C_{18}\text{-}CoA$$

$$\xrightarrow[\text{NADPH, NADH}]{O_2} cis, cis, cis\text{-}9,12,15\text{-}C_{18} \qquad 21.$$

Conversion of oleate to linoleate has also been demonstrated in *Tetrahymena* species (65), and in other protists (55, 64, 71, 80, 90), with the exception of the cellular slime mold, *Dictyostelium discoideum* (68, 69). This organism produces diunsaturated acids of unusual structure: 5,9-hexadecadienoic, 5,9-heptadecadienoic, 5,9-octadecadienoic, and 5,11-octadecadienoic acids, and in addition, the unusual 9-heptadecenoic acid. The results of labeling experiments with growing cells suggested the following pathways for their synthesis:

$$C_{16} \xrightarrow{-2H} \Delta^9\text{-}C_{16} \xrightarrow{-2H} \Delta^{5,9}\text{-}C_{16} \qquad 22.$$

$$C_{17} \xrightarrow{-2H} \Delta^9\text{-}C_{17} \xrightarrow{-2H} \Delta^{5,9}\text{-}C_{17} \qquad 23.$$

$$C_{18} \xrightarrow{-2H} \Delta^9\text{-}C_{18} \xrightarrow{-2H} \Delta^{5,9}\text{-}C_{18} \qquad 24.$$

$$C_{16} \xrightarrow{-2H} \Delta^9\text{-}C_{16} \xrightarrow{+C_2} \Delta^{11}\text{-}C_{18} \xrightarrow{-2H} \Delta^{5,11}\text{-}C_{18} \qquad 25.$$

Conversion of linoleic to octadecatrienoic acids in protists may follow either the "plant" or "animal" pathway, or both (71). Thus, euglenids (80, 89, 90), algae (97, 100), and certain zooflagellates (71) synthesize only α-linolenic (*cis, cis, cis*-9,12,15-C_{18}-trienoic) acid; ciliates (64, 65, 80), and other zooflagellates (71) synthesize only γ-linolenic (*cis, cis, cis*-6,9,12-C_{18}-trienoic) acid; and phytomonads and chrysomonads (64, 80, 101) and still other zooflagellates (71) synthesize both isomers. Amoebae, however, do not synthesize any C_{18}-trienoic acids (66, 80).

Conversion of linoleic acid to arachidonic acid in protists may proceed by two separate pathways. Heterotrophic *Euglena* (89, 90) and amoebae (66, 80) chain-elongate linoleic to 11,14-C_{20}-dienoic acid, which is then progressively desaturated towards the carboxyl end to 5,8,11,14-C_{20}-tetraenoic (arachidonic) acid:

$$\Delta^{9,12}\text{-}C_{18} \xrightarrow{+C_2} \Delta^{11,14}\text{-}C_{20} \to \Delta^{8,11,14}\text{-}C_{20} \to \Delta^{5,8,11,14}\text{-}C_{20} \qquad 26.$$

Certain zooflagellates (71) however, utilize the pathway found in higher animals (45):

$$\Delta^{9,12}\text{-}C_{18} \to \Delta^{6,9,12}\text{-}C_{18} \xrightarrow{+C_2} \Delta^{8,11,14}\text{-}C_{20} \to \Delta^{5,8,11,14}\text{-}C_{20} \qquad 27.$$

In photoauxotrophic *Euglena*, formation of C_{20}-polyunsaturated acids probably follows the "plant" pathway (65, 71, 89, 90):

$$\Delta^{9,12}\text{-}C_{18} \to \Delta^{9,12,15}\text{-}C_{18} \xrightarrow{C_2} \Delta^{11,14,17}\text{-}C_{20} \to \Delta^{8,11,14,17}\text{-}C_{20} \to \Delta^{5,8,11,14,17}\text{-}C_{20} \qquad 28.$$

Further chain elongation and desaturation to C_{22}-tetra, -penta, and -hexaenoic acids also occurs in *Euglena* (89, 90) and green algae (97), but the exact pathways are not known, although desaturation both towards the carboxyl and methyl ends undoubtedly takes place (71, 89, 90). Green algae (97) and photoauxotrophic *Euglena* (89, 90) also contain a characteristic series of polyunsaturated-C_{16} acids, which appear to arise by the following sequence:

$$\Delta^7\text{-}C_{16} \rightarrow \Delta^{7,10}\text{-}C_{16} \rightarrow \Delta^{7,10,13}\text{-}C_{16} \quad \text{and} \quad \Delta^{4,7,10}\text{-}C_{16} \rightarrow \Delta^{4,7,10,13}\text{-}C_{16} \qquad 29.$$

The phylogenetic relations and implications of the various pathways of biosynthesis of polyunsaturated fatty acids are discussed in detail by Bloch and co-workers (55, 64, 80, 91) and by Korn (71, 89).

In regard to the mechanism of desaturation involved in the formation of polyunsaturated acids (apart from the C_{18}-di and -trienes) little is known on the enzyme level, although Bloch (55) considers the desaturation reactions to be oxidative, as in the formation of oleic, linoleic, and linolenic acids by yeast and green algae (99, 100). The mechanism for chain elongation is also not known with certainty, but Wakil (92) considers chain elongation of C_{16}- and C_{18}-unsaturated acids to occur by condensation of their CoA esters with acetyl-CoA and not malonyl-CoA in the presence of NADH and NADPH, as was shown for the formation of *cis*-vaccenic acid from palmitoleyl-CoA by rat liver mitochondria (73, 74). In this connection, Cheniae (102) has found that cell-free preparations of *Euglena* synthesize C_{16}-C_{20} fatty acids from acetyl-CoA with ATP, NADH, and NADPH as cofactors, the system being avidin-insensitive and not requiring bicarbonate; the degree of unsaturation of the products was not determined. On the other hand, Nugteren (103) has shown that chain elongation of γ-linolenic acid to homo-γ-linolenic acid ($\Delta^{8,11,14}\text{-}C_{20}$) occurs in rat liver microsomes by reaction of the CoA ester with malonyl-CoA and NADPH. Further study will be necessary to determine which of these chain-elongating mechanisms is utilized by protists.

Anaerobic pathway.—This pathway appears to be restricted to bacteria of the orders Eubacteriales and Pseudomonadales, and has been the subject of several extensive reviews (4, 46–48). Hofmann and associates first suggested [see (1, 47, 48)], on the basis of studies of fatty acid requirements and metabolism in lactobacilli and other bacteria, that the biosynthesis of monounsaturated fatty acids in these organisms occurred by chain elongation of existing short-chain unsaturated fatty acid precursors. Subsequently, Bloch and associates showed that in certain bacteria (*C. butyricum* and *C. kluyveri*) C_{12} or C_{14} saturated fatty acids were converted only to longer chain saturated fatty acids, whereas octanoic acid was converted to 9-hexadecenoic and 11-octadecenoic acids, and decanoic acid was converted to 7-hexadecenoic and 9-octadecenoic acids, under anaerobic conditions (46, 104, 105). To account for the formation of these isomers and of others found in various bacteria (4, 46), the following sequence of reactions was proposed (60):

$$\text{hexanoic acid} \xrightarrow{C_2} \text{3-ketooctanoic} \rightarrow \text{3-hydroxyoctanoic} \xrightarrow{-H_2O} cis\text{-3-octenoic}$$

$$\xrightarrow{3C_2} cis\text{-9-tetradecenoic} \xrightarrow{C_2} cis\text{-11-hexadecenoic} \xrightarrow{C_2} cis\text{-13-octadecenoic} \qquad 30.$$

octanoic acid $\xrightarrow{C_2}$ 3-ketodecanoic $\rightarrow$ 3-hydroxydecanoic $\xrightarrow{-H_2O}$ cis-3-decenoic

$\xrightarrow{2C_2}$ cis-7-tetradecenoic $\xrightarrow{C_2}$ cis-9-hexadecenoic $\xrightarrow{C_2}$ cis-11-octadecenoic   31.

decanoic acid $\xrightarrow{C_2}$ 3-ketododecanoic $\rightarrow$ 3-hydroxydodecanoic $\xrightarrow{-H_2O}$ cis-3-dodecenoic

$\xrightarrow{C_2}$ cis-5-tetradecenoic $\xrightarrow{C_2}$ cis-7-hexadecenoic $\xrightarrow{C_2}$ cis-9-octadecenoic   32.

The novel and distinguishing features of this proposed scheme are: (a) the pathway for synthesis of saturated fatty acids may separate off into synthesis of unsaturated fatty acids at the hydroxy-C_8 to -C_{12} levels but no higher; (b) the separation occurs at the dehydration step of the 3-hydroxy acid with the formation of the cis-3-enoic acid rather than the trans-2-isomer known to be the intermediate in chain elongation; and (c) chain elongation of the cis-3-enoic acid occurs by the addition of C_2 units to the carboxyl end without reduction or shifting of the existing cis-double bond.

Consistent with the proposed participation of short-chain monoenoic acids in the above scheme (Reaction 31), is the recent finding by O'Leary (106) of cis-3-decenoic, cis-5-dodecenoic, and cis-7-tetradecenoic acids (in amounts of about 1 per cent or less) in several lactobacilli and streptococci; in addition, small amounts of cis-3-dodecenoic and cis-5-tetradecenoic acids were found in the streptococci, consistent with Reaction 32. Experimental evidence in support of the chain lengthening of short-chain monoenoic acids was obtained by Baronowsky et al. (107) who found that growing cells of C. butyricum incorporated C^{14}-3-decenoic acid into cis-9-hexadecenoic and cis-11-octadecenoic acid, according to Reaction 31, but not into saturated fatty acids.

Direct evidence for the key reaction in the scheme, namely, the β, γ-dehydration of the 3-hydroxy acid to form the cis-3-enoic acid has also been obtained. Lennarz et al. (20) found that the partially purified fatty acid synthetase of E. coli (vide supra), which produces high proportions of cis-11-octadecenoic acid, also catalyzes the dehydration of 3-hydroxydecanoyl-CoA to a mixture of trans-2- and cis-3-decenoic acids, the latter isomer being the intermediate in the formation of cis-11-octadecenoic acid postulated in Reaction 31; the trans-2 isomer is known to be an intermediate in the synthesis of saturated fatty acids. Norris et al. (108) have subsequently purified the E. coli synthetase system 10- to 15-fold, and were able to separate the β-hydroxy decanoate dehydrase from the synthetase complex by mild heat treatment; the dehydrase was then purified 104-fold. Using the highly purified dehydrase, it was possible to demonstrate that the enzyme was specific for the D-β-hydroxydecanoyl thiolester (both the CoA and the N-acetylcysteamine derivatives were active) and for a chain length of C_{10}; the β-hydroxy-C_8 and -C_{12} derivatives were dehydrated at rates less than 1 per cent of the dehydration rate of the C_{10}-derivative and the only products were the 2-monoenoic acids. The purified dehydrase activity was also shown to be dependent on phosphate concentration, both the rate and the proportion of cis-3-isomer increasing with increasing phosphate concentration; the V_{max} of the reaction was, however, unaffected. Addition of the purified dehydrase to a purified synthetase preparation which produced mostly saturated acids, resulted in a greatly increased synthesis of unsaturated acids. The *E. coli* dehydrase was thus postulated by Norris et al. (108) to act as a regulator for the formation of the unsaturated C_{10}-precursor, and, hence, as a regulator for synthesis of unsaturated fatty acids.

Bishop & Still (109) have found small amounts of 8-hexadecenoic, 8-octadenoic, and 10-octadecenoic acids in *Serratia marcescens*. To account for the formation of these isomers, they suggested that the β-hydroxydecanoic intermediate might be dehydrated to the *cis*-2-decenoic acid as well as to the *cis*-3-isomer; chain elongation of the 2-isomer would give the 8-hexadecenoic and 10-octadecenoic acids, and similar dehydration of 3-hydroxydodecanoic acid followed by chain elongation would give the 8-octadecenoic acid. However, while it is possible that dehydration of a 3-hydroxy acid to the *cis*-2-enoic acid occurs in *S. marcescens*, the dehydrases known so far (8, 20, 31, 108) produce either the *trans*-2- or the *cis*-3-, or both, isomers.

Wood et al. (77) have studied the biosynthesis of unsaturated fatty acids in five species of photosynthetic bacteria. The major unsaturated acids in these bacteria were the *cis*-9-C_{16} and *cis*-11-C_{18} monoenoic acids, with traces of the *cis*-9-C_{18} monoenoic acid in two of the species. Anaerobic growth in the light in the presence of 2-C^{14}-acetate led to rapid labeling of the unsaturated acids, and no direct desaturation of labeled myristic, palmitic, or stearic acids under aerobic or anaerobic conditions was observed. Instead, these acids were broken down and the monoenoic acids produced were randomly labeled. It was concluded that the unsaturated fatty acids in photosynthetic bacteria are synthesized by the anaerobic pathway, the 9-hexadecenoic and 11-octadecenoic acids being formed by Reaction sequence 31, and the 9-octadecenoic by Reaction sequence 32.

In regard to the mechanism of chain elongation used in the anaerobic pathway, it is of interest that Alberts et al. (29) mentioned, in their recent paper, the identification of a fatty acyl transacylase, distinct from acetyl and malonyl transacylase, which catalyzes the transfer of longer chain acyl groups from CoA to ACP. They suggested that this enzyme might be involved in "elongation, desaturation, oxidation, or esterification reactions." Further studies of this enzyme will be of great interest in regard to the mechanism of chain elongation of the *cis*-3-monoenoic acid intermediates in the anaerobic pathway.

CYCLOPROPANE AND BRANCHED-CHAIN FATTY ACIDS

This subject has been reviewed previously by Asselineau & Lederer (1), Hofmann (48), Kates (4), Lederer (110–112, 219), O'Leary (47, 113), Asselineau (114), and Asselineau & Bennet (220).

Cyclopropane acids.—The C_{17} and C_{19} cyclopropane acids are fairly widespread among bacteria (4, 47, 48, 114), being present in the lipids of Gram-negative bacteria, such as *E. coli* (115), *S. marcescens* (109), and *Agrobacterium tumefaciens* (116), and of Gram-positive bacteria, such as lactobacilli and streptococci (48). Hofmann and co-workers, who first isolated and established the structure of a cyclopropane acid, "lactobacillic acid," as *cis*-11,12-methylene octadecanoic acid, proposed that this acid was synthesized by the addition of a C_1 unit across the double bond of *cis*-11-octadecenoic (*cis*-vaccenic) acid (48); the C_{17} cyclopropane acid, *cis*-9, 10-methylene hexadecanoic acid, would presumably be synthesized by analogous reactions starting with *cis*-9-hexadecenoic (palmitoleic) acid. This proposal was later verified experimentally when it was shown by tracer techniques that actively growing cells of *Lactobacillus arabinosus* incorporated *cis*-vaccenic acid intact into lactobacillic acid (117), and that the carbon atom added to form the cyclopropane ring was derived from the methyl group of methionine (118–120). Biosynthesis of the C_{17} and C_{19} cyclopropane acids was also shown to occur by the same mechanism in *E. coli* (118, 120, 121), *Aerobacter aerogenes* (122), and *S. marcescens*, *A. tumefaciens* and *C. butyricum* (121, 123). The overall reactions are as follows:

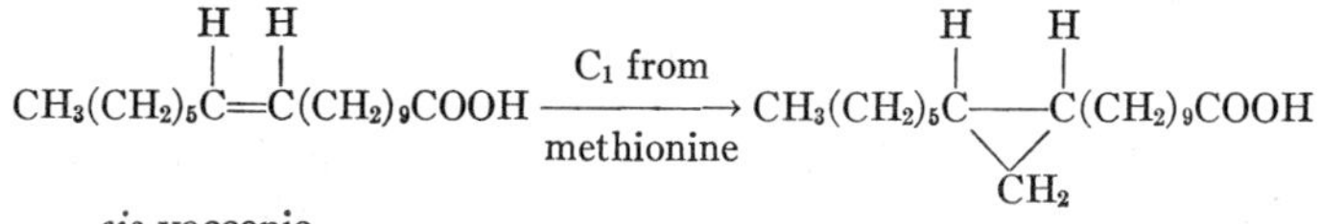

$$
\underset{\textit{cis}\text{-vaccenic}}{CH_3(CH_2)_5\overset{H}{\underset{|}{C}}=\overset{H}{\underset{|}{C}}(CH_2)_9COOH} \xrightarrow[\text{methionine}]{C_1 \text{ from}} CH_3(CH_2)_5\overset{H}{\underset{|}{C}}\underset{\underset{CH_2}{\diagdown\diagup}}{\qquad}\overset{H}{\underset{|}{C}}(CH_2)_9COOH \qquad 33.
$$

$$
\underset{\text{palmitoleic}}{CH_3(CH_2)_5\overset{H}{\underset{|}{C}}=\overset{H}{\underset{|}{C}}(CH_2)_7COOH} \xrightarrow[\text{methionine}]{C_1 \text{ from}} CH_3(CH_2)_5\overset{H}{\underset{|}{C}}\underset{\underset{CH_2}{\diagdown\diagup}}{\qquad}\overset{H}{\underset{|}{C}}(CH_2)_7COOH \qquad 34.
$$

The active donor of the C_1 unit used to form the ring was later shown by O'Leary (122) to be S-adenosylmethionine, and this has been confirmed by other investigators (123). Furthermore, studies with tritium- and deuterium-labeled methionine have now shown that only two of the three hydrogen atoms of the methyl group in S-adenosylmethionine are involved in the transfer of the C_1 unit, most likely by the following reactions (124):

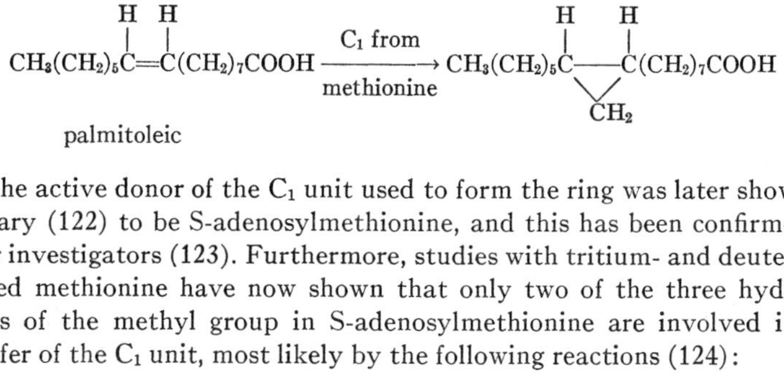

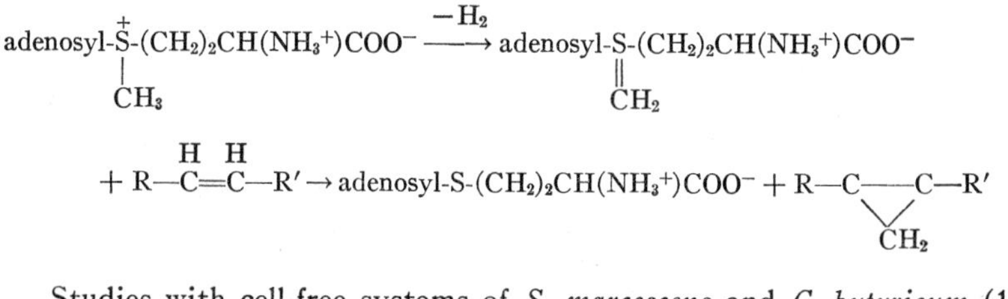

$$
\underset{\underset{CH_3}{|}}{\text{adenosyl-}\overset{+}{S}\text{-}(CH_2)_2CH(NH_3{}^+)COO^-} \xrightarrow{-H_2} \underset{\underset{CH_2}{\|}}{\text{adenosyl-S-}(CH_2)_2CH(NH_3{}^+)COO^-}
$$

$$
+\ R\text{---}\overset{H}{\underset{|}{C}}=\overset{H}{\underset{|}{C}}\text{---}R' \rightarrow \text{adenosyl-S-}(CH_2)_2CH(NH_3{}^+)COO^- + R\text{---}\underset{\underset{CH_2}{\diagdown\diagup}}{C}\text{---}C\text{---}R' \qquad 35.
$$

Studies with cell-free systems of *S. marcescens* and *C. butyricum* (123) have shown that the actual olefin acceptor in Reactions 33 to 35 is an unsaturated phosphatidyl ethanolamine, which is a major phosphatide in these bacteria. The cyclopropane fatty acid synthetase from *C. butyricum* was purified 50-fold by Chung & Law (125) and was shown to catalyze the transfer of a methyl group of S-adenosylmethionine specifically to a monounsaturated acid moiety in purified phosphatidyl ethanolamine, provided the substrate was dispersed in micellar suspension with the aid of anionic surfactants (cationic surfactants were inhibitory):

$$
\begin{array}{l}
\overset{\displaystyle O^-}{\underset{\displaystyle |}{}} \\
CH_2OP(O)OCH_2CH_2NH_3{}^+ \\
| \\
\overset{H\;\;H}{\underset{|\;\;|}{}} \\
CHOOC(CH_2)_7C{=}C(CH_2)_5CH_3 \\
| \\
CH_2OOCR
\end{array}
\xrightarrow[\text{methionine}]{\text{S-adenosyl-}}
\begin{array}{l}
\overset{\displaystyle O^-}{\underset{\displaystyle |}{}} \\
CH_2OP(O)OCH_2CH_2NH_3{}^+ \\
| \\
\overset{H\;\;H}{\underset{|\;\;|}{}} \\
CHOOC(CH_2)_7C{-}C(CH_2)_5CH_3 \\
\diagdown\diagup \\
CH_2 \\
CH_2OOCR + \text{S-adenosylhomocysteine}
\end{array}
\qquad 36.
$$

The synthetase was also found (126) to act on the unsaturated acids in both the β- and the α-positions of phosphatidyl ethanolamine although preference was shown towards the α-position. The products of the reaction were phosphatidyl ethanolamine containing ester-bound cyclopropane fatty acids, and S-adenosylhomocysteine. The latter was found to be inhibitory toward the purified enzyme, but this could be prevented by the addition of a protein fraction present in crude extracts which effects the degradation of S-adenosyl-homocysteine (127). The purified cyclopropane fatty acid synthetase showed no requirement for cofactors and appeared to act as a single protein fraction (125).

Cyclopropane fatty aldehyde moieties have recently been found in ethanolamine- and N-methylethanolamine-plasmalogens of *C. butyricum* (128). These cyclopropane aldehydes have been shown by Chung & Goldfine (129) to be synthesized by a mechanism analogous to that for cyclopropane fatty acids (Reaction 36), in an *in vitro* system consisting of the crude or purified *C. butyricum* cyclopropane fatty acid synthetase (125) and a micellar dispersion of the purified ethanolamine plasmalogen from the same organism. These results indicate either that the synthetase does not distinguish between ester linkages and vinyl ether linkages in the phosphatidyl ethanolamine substrate, or that a separate enzyme specific for plasmalogens is present in the preparation.

Methyl-branched acids.—Iso- and anteiso-branched fatty acids (chiefly C_{12} to C_{17}) are the principal fatty acids in many Gram-positive bacteria (4, 40, 114, 130–133), in *Ruminococci* (134), and also in *Streptomyces* species (135). Lennarz (136) has shown that the synthesis of the anteiso-C_{15} and -C_{17} acids in cells of *M. lysodeikticus* occurs by chain elongation of 2-methylbutyrate (derived from isoleucine), probably in the form of its CoA derivative, as follows:

$$CH_3CH_2\overset{\overset{\displaystyle CH_3}{|}}{C}HCO\text{-}SCoA \xrightarrow{+5C_2} CH_3CH_2\overset{\overset{\displaystyle CH_3}{|}}{C}H(CH_2)_{10}CO\text{-}SCoA$$

$$\xrightarrow{+C_2} CH_3CH_2\overset{\overset{\displaystyle CH_3}{|}}{C}H(CH_2)_{12}CO\text{-}SCoA \qquad 37.$$

Studies with *Ruminococci* (134) have also shown that the anteiso-C_{15} acid arises from 2-methylbutyrate by Reaction 37. The iso-C_{15} and -C_{17}-branched acids were found to be formed by chain elongation of isovalerate (derived from leucine):

$$CH_3\overset{\overset{\displaystyle CH_3}{|}}{C}HCH_2CO\text{-}SCoA \xrightarrow{+5C_2} CH_3\overset{\overset{\displaystyle CH_3}{|}}{C}H(CH_2)_{11}CO\text{-}SCoA$$

$$\xrightarrow{+C_2} CH_3\overset{\overset{\displaystyle CH_3}{|}}{C}H(CH_2)_{13}CO\text{-}SCoA \qquad 38.$$

Synthesis of iso-C_{14} and -C_{16}-branched acids in these organisms occurred by chain elongation of isobutyrate:

$$CH_3\overset{\overset{\displaystyle CH_3}{|}}{C}HCO\text{-}SCoA \xrightarrow{+5C_2} CH_3\overset{\overset{\displaystyle CH_3}{|}}{C}H(CH_2)_{10}CO\text{-}SCoA \xrightarrow{+C_2} CH_3\overset{\overset{\displaystyle CH_3}{|}}{C}H(CH_2)_{12}CO\text{-}SCoA \quad 39.$$

Evidence for the formation of small amounts of the corresponding aldehydes from the same precursors was also obtained (134). The rumen bacterium *Bacteroides succinogenes* was found (137) to incorporate C^{14} from isobutyrate-1-C^{14} and valerate-1-C^{14} into the fatty acid and aldehyde moieties of the phosphatides (largely ethanolamine plasmalogen).

Kaneda (138) has shown that iso-C_{15} and -C_{17} branched acids are synthesized in *B. subtilis* by Reaction 38, either from isovalerate or leucine, and that iso-C_{14} and -C_{16} acids were synthesized by Reaction 39 from isobutyrate or valine. The latter substrates, however, also gave rise to small but appreciable amounts of iso-C_{15} and iso-C_{17} acids. Similar findings were reported also by Allison et al. (134).

The chain-elongating mechanism involved in the biosynthesis of these branched-chain acids (Reactions 37 to 39) is presumed to be the malonyl-CoA pathway, since this system has been shown to be operative in the synthesis of branched-chain acids by rat adipose tissue (43). However, this has yet to be verified in bacteria by studies with cell-free systems.

A distinctly different mechanism has been found for the biosynthesis of the branched-chain acid, tuberculostearic (10-methylstearic) acid in *M. phlei* (59), whereby a C_1 unit derived from methionine is added to carbon 10 of oleic acid:

Stearic → $CH_3(CH_2)_7CH=CH(CH_2)_7COOH$
                      oleic

$$\xrightarrow[\text{methionine}]{+C_1 \text{ from}} CH_3(CH_2)_7\overset{\overset{\displaystyle CH_3}{|}}{C}HCH_2(CH_2)_7COOH \quad 40.$$
                                          10-methylstearic

A similar sequence of reactions, starting with palmitic and giving rise to a methylpalmitic acid, was also shown to occur in *M. phlei* (59, 60), but the structure of this C_{17}-branched acid was not determined. Lederer and co-workers (see 110, 111) have confirmed the finding that methionine is the source of the C-methyl group in tuberculostearic acid, using a human avirulent strain (H37Ra) of *M. tuberculosis*. It is evident from Reaction sequence 40 that tuberculostearic acid is on the same oxidation level as stearate, and therefore must have been formed from oleate by a process that includes a reductive step (59). Jauréguiberry et al. (139) have shown that the formation of 10-methyl stearic acid by cells of *M. smegmatis* involves the transfer of the methyl carbon from methionine with only two of its hydrogen atoms. The possibility that a 9,10-methylene-C_{18} (dihydrosterculic) acid might be the precursor of 10-methyl-C_{18} acid was ruled out by Lederer and co-workers (110, 111) when they found that C^{14}-labeled dihydrosterculic acid was not converted to tuberculostearic acid by cells of *M. phlei*. Other possible intermediates in the transalkylation process leading to formation of tuberculostearic acid have been discussed by Lederer (111, 112). Further studies of the intermediate steps of this transmethylation reaction, using cell-free systems will be of great interest.

   Multimethyl-branched chains.—The tubercle bacillus contains a series of methyl-branched acids, mycocerosic acids, the main component of which is a C_{32} acid, 2,4,6,8-tetramethyloctacosanoic (1, 114). Lederer and co-workers (140) have proposed that this acid is biosynthesized by condensation of a normal C_{20} acid with four moles of propionic acid:

$$CH_3(CH_2)_{18}COOH + 4 \overset{\overset{\displaystyle *}{}}{C}H_2COOH$$
$$| $$
$$CH_3$$

$$\rightarrow CH_3(CH_2)_{19}—\overset{}{C}H\overset{\overset{\displaystyle *}{}}{C}H_2—\overset{}{C}H\overset{\overset{\displaystyle *}{}}{C}H_2—\overset{}{C}H\overset{\overset{\displaystyle *}{}}{C}H_2—\overset{}{C}H\overset{\overset{\displaystyle *}{}}{C}OOH \quad 41.$$
$$\qquad\qquad | \qquad\quad | \qquad\quad | \qquad\quad |$$
$$\qquad\qquad CH_3 \quad\;\; CH_3 \quad\;\; CH_3 \quad\;\; CH_3$$

                              mycocerosic acid

   Experimental evidence in favor of Reaction 41 was obtained (140) by incubation of *M. tuberculosis* (strain H37Ra) with 1-C^{14}-propionate; degradation of the isolated labeled C_{32} acid showed that close to 25 per cent of the C^{14} was in the carboxyl group, most of the remainder was in carbons 3, 5, 7, and 9, and none was in the methyl branches. Evidence that propionic acid is also the precursor of a homologous C_{26} acid (probably a 2,4,6,-trimethyl branched acid) was also obtained (140).

The analogous α,β-unsaturated phthienoic acids, present in virulent strains of *M. tuberculosis* (1, 114), are considered to arise by a pathway similar to Reaction 41 (111, 140):

$$CH_3(CH_2)_{16}\text{—}COOH + 3\ CH_2COOH \rightarrow CH_3(CH_2)_{17}\overset{|}{\text{—}}CHCH_2\overset{|}{C}HCH=\overset{|}{C}\text{—}COOH \quad 42.$$

with methyl (CH_3) branches as shown.

Phthienoic acid

Studies with cell-free systems would be of great value in establishing the intermediates and cofactors involved in the biosynthesis of the mycocerosic and phthienoic acids.

Isoprenoid-branched chains occur rarely in bacteria, but a recent example is the finding that the lipids of *Halobacterium cutirubrum* contain 3,7,11,15-tetramethylhexadecyl groups ether-linked to glycerol (141). Preliminary experiments have shown that $2\text{-}C^{14}$-mevalonate and $1\text{-}C^{14}$-acetate, but not $2\text{-}C^{14}$-malonate, are incorporated into these chains by whole cells (142).

POLAR FATTY ACIDS

n-Hydroxy acids.—2-Hydroxy fatty acids, although relatively rare in microorganisms, are known to occur as amides of phytosphingosine (cerebrins) in yeasts and other fungi (see 143). However, nothing is known about the biosynthesis of these acids.

In contrast, the 3-hydroxy acids (as their D-(−)-isomers) are fairly widespread in bacteria and yeasts, usually occurring as ester-bound or glycoside-bound extracellular lipids [see (1, 4, 114)]. For example, D-3-hydroxy-C_{16} and -C_{18} acids are present as mannitol or pentitol esters in *Rhodotorula* spp. (144); D-3-hydroxy-C_{10}, -C_{12}, and -C_{14} acids occur in lipopolysaccharides of Gram-negative bacteria (109, 145–147); and the D-3-hydroxy-C_{10} acid occurs in the rhamnolipid of *Pseudomonas aeruginosa* (148). D-3-Hydroxy acids are synthesized as intermediates in the biosynthesis of saturated fatty acids by the malonyl-CoA pathway (Reaction 8 or 14) but apparently remain enzyme-bound and do not accumulate. A separate system for their synthesis and transformation into glycolipids thus probably exists, although no experimental evidence is available on this point. However, Davidoff & Korn (70) have obtained a cell-free enzyme system from the slime mold, *D. discoideum*, which effects the conversion of C_{14}, C_{16}, and C_{18} fatty acyl-CoA to the corresponding 3-hydroxy acids by hydration of the intermediate *trans*-2-enoic acids, as follows:

$$R\text{—}CH_2CH_2CO\text{—}SCoA \rightarrow R\text{—}\overset{\overset{\displaystyle H}{|}}{C}=\underset{\underset{\displaystyle H}{|}}{C}\text{—}CO\text{—}SCoA \rightleftharpoons R\text{—}\underset{\underset{\displaystyle OH}{|}}{C}HCH_2CO\text{—}SCoA \quad 43.$$

Although the 3-hydroxy acids accumulate in this *in vitro* system, other enzymes present in the cells dehydrate them back to the *trans*-2-enoic acids and convert the latter to *cis*- and *trans*-3-enoic acids which are then further metabolized (70). Formation of 10-hydroxystearic acid by hydration of oleic acid has been demonstrated in a pseudomonad (149).

An entirely different enzyme system for the formation of hydroxy acids has been demonstrated in a soil-growing pseudomonad by Coon and co-workers (150–153). Cell-free enzyme preparations of this organism were shown to carry out ω-oxidation of octane to octanol and octanoic acid (150, 151), and of C_8 to C_{18} fatty acids to the ω-hydroxy acids and ultimately to the dicarboxylic acids (152, 153):

$$CH_3(CH_2)_nCH_3 \xrightarrow[NADH]{O_2} CH_3(CH_2)_nCH_2OH \xrightarrow{NAD^+} CH_3(CH_2)_nCOOH$$

$$\xrightarrow[NADH]{O_2} HOCH_2(CH_2)_nCOOH \xrightarrow{NAD^+} HOOC(CH_2)_nCOOH \qquad 44.$$

The initial oxidative attack at the terminal methyl group was shown to be aerobic and to require NADH and Fe^{2+}, and at least two enzymes; oxidation of the ω-hydroxyl required NAD^+ and may involve separate hydroxy- and aldehyde-dehydrogenases (150). The enzyme system shows a much higher affinity for C_8 to C_{14} acids than for C_{16} or C_{18} acids (153). Similar ω-oxidation systems have been demonstrated in rat liver (154), in a species of *Coryne-bacterium* (155), and in the yeast *Torulopsis magnoliae* (156, 157). In the latter organism, oxidation of palmitic, stearic, oleic, and linoleic acids and normal hydrocarbons gave rise to the corresponding $(\omega$-1)-hydroxy acids in addition to the ω-hydroxy acids; furthermore, the hydroxy acids formed accumulated as extracellular glycolipids, consisting of hydroxy acid glycosides of partially acetylated sophorose (156). An ω-oxidizing system in *Micrococcus cerificans* (158) converts *n*-alkanes to the corresponding primary alcohols which then accumulate as palmitate esters.

Mycolic acids.—Lederer and co-workers have recently established the overall biosynthetic pathways for several of the mycolic acids (see 110, 112). Incubation of *C. diphtheriae* with 1-C^{14}-palmitic acid yielded corynomycolic acid labeled exclusively in carbons 1 and 3, demonstrating a direct condensation of two molecules of palmitic acid, as follows (159):

$$CH_3(CH_2)_{14}COOH + \underset{\underset{\underset{CH_3}{|}}{\overset{|}{(CH_2)_{13}}}}{CH_2\!-\!COOH} \rightarrow CH_3(CH_2)_{14}CH(OH)\!-\!\underset{\underset{\underset{CH_3}{|}}{\overset{|}{(CH_2)_{13}}}}{CH\!-\!COOH} \qquad 45.$$

corynomycolic acid

Analogous condensation of one mole of palmitoleic acid with one mole of palmitic acid could presumably yield the unsaturated corynomycolenic acid (112):

$$CH_3(CH_2)_5CH\!=\!CH(CH_2)_9COOH + \underset{\overset{|}{C_{14}H_{29}}}{CH_2\!-\!COOH}$$

$$\rightarrow CH_3(CH_2)_5CH{=}CH(CH_2)_9CH(OH){-}\underset{\underset{\textstyle C_{14}H_{29}}{|}}{CH}{-}COOH \quad 46.$$

corynomycolenic acid

Nocardia species contain a homologous series of β-hydroxy α-branched acids (C_{46} to C_{58}) with two and three double bonds, known as nocardic acids having the following general structures (160):

$$CH_3(CH_2)_7CH{=}CH(CH_2)_xCH{=}CH(CH_2)_yCH{=}CH(CH_2)_z{-}\underset{\underset{\textstyle CH_3}{\overset{\textstyle |}{(CH_2)_n}}}{CH}{-}COOH$$

$$x + y + z = 15, 17, \text{ or } 21$$
$$n = 11 \text{ or } 13$$

$$CH_3(CH_2)_7CH{=}CH(CH_2)_xCH{=}CH(CH_2)_y{-}\underset{\underset{\textstyle CH_3}{\overset{\textstyle |}{(CH_2)_n}}}{CH}{-}COOH$$

$$x + y = 25, 27, \text{ or } 29$$
$$n = 11 \text{ or } 13$$

Biosynthetic studies of nocardic acids in *N. asteroides* by Etémadi & Lederer (161), using $1\text{-}C^{14}$-palmitate as precursor, showed that carbons 1 and 2 and the α-chain are derived from one molecule of palmitic, another molecule of palmitic being incorporated into the remaining long chain. It was therefore proposed (161) that nocardic acids are biosynthesized by chain elongation and desaturation of palmitic and, finally, condensation with a second molecule of palmitic:

$$CH_3(CH_2)_{14}COOH + n(CH_3COOH)$$

$$\rightarrow CH_3(CH_2)_7CH{=}CH(CH_2)_xCH{=}CH(CH_2)_y{-}COOH + \underset{\underset{\textstyle C_{14}H_{29}}{|}}{CH_2}COOH$$

$$\rightarrow CH_3(CH_2)_7CH{=}CH(CH_2)_xCH{=}CH(CH_2)_y{-}CH(OH){-}\underset{\underset{\textstyle C_{14}H_{29}}{|}}{CH}{-}COOH \quad 47.$$

An analogous series of acids, α-smegmamycolic acids (C_{76} to C_{79}) occur in *M. smegmatis* (162), and one of these has recently been shown to have the following structure (162):

$$CH_3(CH_2)_{17}CH{=}CH(CH_2)_{13}{-}\underset{\underset{\textstyle CH_3}{|}}{CH}{-}CH{=}CH{-}CH(CH_2)_{17}{-}CH(OH){-}\underset{\underset{\textstyle C_{22}H_{45}}{|}}{CH}{-}COOH$$

Biosynthetic studies by Etémadi & Lederer (163) have shown that tetracosanoic acid is incorporated intact into the carboxyl-terminal 24 carbons, and that the C-methyl group is derived from methionine. It is of interest that tetracosanoic acid is a major product of the fatty acid synthetase from *M. tuberculosis* (37).

More complex mycolic acids, containing two hydroxyls and three long-chain branches, are present in *M. tuberculosis* (110, 112), and mycolic acids containing cyclopropane rings have also been found in this and other mycobacteria (112, 164). A more detailed discussion of the biosynthesis of fatty acids of mycobacteria has been presented in recent reviews by Lederer (110–112), and Asselineau (114).

It might also be mentioned that the biosynthetic pathway to phthiocerol, a C_{33}- or C_{35}-methoxy diol present in *M. tuberculosis* has recently been established as follows (165):

$$CH_3(CH_2)_{22}\text{—}COOH + 3\ CH_3COOH$$

$$\rightarrow CH_3(CH_2)_{22}\text{—}\overset{\overset{\displaystyle OH}{|}}{CH}\text{—}CH_2\overset{\overset{\displaystyle OH}{|}}{CH}(CH_2)_3COOH + 2\ \underset{\underset{\displaystyle CH_3}{|}}{CH_2}COOH$$

$$\rightarrow CH_3(CH_2)_{22}\text{—}\overset{\overset{\displaystyle OH}{|}}{CH}\text{—}CH_2\text{—}\overset{\overset{\displaystyle OH}{|}}{CH}(CH_2)_4\text{—}CH\text{—}CO\text{—}CH\text{—}COOH$$
$$\underset{\underset{\displaystyle CH_3}{|}\quad\underset{\displaystyle CH_3}{|}}{}$$

$$\xrightarrow{-CO_2} CH_3(CH_2)_{22}\text{—}\overset{\overset{\displaystyle OH}{|}}{CH}CH_2\overset{\overset{\displaystyle OH}{|}}{CH}(CH_2)_4CH\text{—}CO\text{—}CH_2CH_3$$
$$\underset{\underset{\displaystyle CH_3}{|}}{}$$

$$\xrightarrow[\text{methionine}]{C_1} CH_3(CH_2)_{22}\text{—}\overset{\overset{\displaystyle OH}{|}}{CH}\text{—}CH_2\text{—}\overset{\overset{\displaystyle OH}{|}}{CH}(CH_2)_4\text{—}CH\text{—}\overset{\overset{\displaystyle OCH_3}{|}}{CH}\text{—}CH_2CH_3 \qquad 48.$$
$$\underset{\underset{\displaystyle CH_3}{|}}{}$$

phthiocerol

BIOSYNTHESIS OF COMPLEX LIPIDS
GLYCOLIPIDS

Glycosyl diglycerides.—This class of lipids is quite widespread among microorganisms, such as Gram-positive bacteria (166–170), Gram-negative bacteria (171), pneumococci (166, 181), green algae (172, 173), blue-green algae (78, 79, 174), *Euglena* (90, 175), and diatoms (95). In bacteria, these glycolipids are relatively minor components of the total lipids [except for pneumococci (166) in which they occur in considerable amounts] and their glycosyl moieties contain a range of sugars [e.g., glucosyl, diglucosyl, galactosyl-glucosyl, mannosyl, etc. (166)]. Photosynthetic organisms [except photosynthetic bacteria which apparently lack these glycolipids (77)] contain exclusively mono- and digalactosyl diglycerides, which are the major lipid components in these organisms, and are concentrated in the chloroplasts or chromatophores [see reviews (173, 176, 177)].

Relatively few studies have been made on the biosynthesis of glycosyl-diglycerides (173, 176). Ferrari & Benson (178) observed a rapid incorporation of C^{14} into monogalactosyl diglyceride, followed by digalactosyl diglyceride during photosynthesis in $C^{14}O_2$ by *Chlorella pyrenoidosa*, and concluded that the digalactosyl diglyceride was synthesized by galactosidation of the monogalactosyl diglyceride. These authors proposed the following mechanism for biosynthesis of the galactolipids:

D-2, 3-diglyceride + UDP-galactose

$$\rightarrow \text{galactosyl diglyceride} \xrightarrow{\text{UDP-Gal}} \text{digalactosyl diglyceride} \quad 49.$$

Neufeld & Hall (179) have demonstrated that spinach chloroplasts catalyze the transfer of galactose from UDP-galactose to an endogenous acceptor, with the formation of mono-, di-, tri-, and possibly tetra-galactosyl diglycerides; the nature of the lipid acceptor was not further investigated.

Lennarz (169, 180) showed that an enzyme preparation from *M. lysodeikticus* catalyzed the formation of the two major glycolipids present in this bacterium, monomannosyl diglyceride and dimannosyl diglyceride, when incubated with GDP-D-mannose and crude 2,3-diglyceride. A third, unidentified mannosyl-containing acidic lipid was also formed by a separate enzyme system requiring GDP-mannose, Mg^{++}, and an uncharacterized acidic compound isolated from total lipid extracts.

Kaufman et al. (181) have demonstrated the biosynthesis of the galactosyl glucosyl diglyceride in type XIV pneumococcus as occurring by transfer of galactose from UDP-galactose to glucosyl diglyceride; the latter is probably synthesized by transfer of glucose from UDP-glucose to a diglyceride.

A unique sulfoglycolipid, 6-sulfoquinovosyl $(1\rightarrow1')$-$2',3'$-diglyceride, has been found in photosynthetic organisms (77, 95, 182), and appears to be concentrated in the lamellar membranes of chloroplasts (182). This sulfolipid is rapidly labeled by *Chlorella* during photosynthesis in the presence of S^{35}-sulfate or $C^{14}O_2$, and at a much slower rate in the dark (178, 182). By analogy with the biosynthesis of galactosyl diglyceride from UDP-galactose (179), it was suggested by Benson (182) that the sulfolipid might be synthesized by transfer of the sulfoquinovosyl group from a nucleoside diphosphosulfoquinovose, identified in extracts of *Chlorella* (183), to a diglyceride:

nucleoside diphosphosulfoquinovose + diglyceride

$$\rightarrow \text{sulfoquinivosyl diglyceride} + \text{nucleoside diphosphate} \quad 50.$$

Available evidence does not favor formation of the sulfonic acid group by oxidation of sulfhydryl or disulfide precursors (182, 211, 212). The sulfonic acid group has been suggested (184) to arise by transfer of a sulfonyl group directly from phosphoadenosine phosphosulfate to C_6 of a suitable hexose precursor, which may be nucleotide bound. Biosynthesis of the sulfoquinovose by a glycolytic sequence from sulfopyruvate, which may arise from cysteic acid (212), is also conceivable (182, 183).

It might also be mentioned that several extremely halophilic bacteria have been found to contain a dihydrophytyl diether analogue of a glycosylsulfate diglyceride (185). The glycosyl moiety consists of a trisaccharide of glucose, mannose, and galactose, the latter sugar being esterified with sulfate at C-3. Cells of *Halobacterium cutirubrum* grown in the presence of C^{14}-labeled acetate or mevalonate, incorporated C^{14} mostly into the dihydrophytyl groups; with C^{14}-glycerol, label appeared in the glycerol and sugar moieties as well as in the long chains; S^{35}-sulfate was incorporated as such into the glycolipid sulfate (142).

Glycosides of hydroxy fatty acids.—Several examples of this type of glycolipid are known to exist in microorganisms: the rhamnolipid, 2-*O*-α-L-rhamnopyranosyl-α-L-rhamnopyranosyl-D-3-hydroxydecanoyl-D-3-hydroxydecanoate of *Pseudomonas aeruginosa* (148, 186), the sophorosides of hydroxypalmitic and hydroxystearic acids produced by the yeast, *T. magnoliae* (156, 157), and the mycosides of mycobacteria (110).

Burger et al. (187) have recently established the biosynthetic pathway for the rhamnolipid of *P. aeruginosa*. Using partially purified enzymes, they showed that this glycolipid was synthesized by stepwise transfer of L-rhamnose from TDP-L-rhamnose to 3-hydroxydecanoyl-3-hydroxydecanoate, as follows:

2 D-3-hydroxydecanoyl-CoA → D-3-hydroxydecanoyl-D-3-hydroxydecanoate   51.

$$\xrightarrow{\text{TDP-L-rhamnose}} \text{L-rhamnosyl-D-3-hydroxydecanoyl-D-3-hydroxydecanoate} \qquad 52.$$

$$\xrightarrow{\text{TDP-L-rhamnose}} \text{L-rhamnosyl-L-rhamnosyl-D-3-hydroxydecanoyl-D-3-hydroxydecanoate} \ 53.$$

The rhamnosyl transferring enzymes (Reactions 52 and 53) have been obtained free of the enzyme catalyzing Reaction 51.

Lipopolysaccharides.—The walls of most Gram-negative bacteria contain a complex lipopolysaccharide, which consists of a polysaccharide linked to a glycolipid ("lipid A") through 3-deoxyoctulosonate residues; lipid A appears to consist of two glycosidically linked glucosamine residues fully acylated with acetyl and β-hydroxyacyl groups [see review by Carter et al. (176)]. Incorporation of galactose followed by glucose (from UDP-galactose and UDP-glucose, respectively) into the lipopolysaccharide has been demonstrated with a particulate enzyme fraction of *E. coli* (188). A soluble enzyme fraction was found to catalyze the transfer of 3-deoxyoctulosonate from CMP-deoxyoctulosonate to a lipid acceptor (composed of glucosamine, 3-hydroxymyristate, and phosphate) derived from the lipopolysaccharide by combined alkaline and acid hydrolysis (188, 213). Enzymatic transfer of glycosyl residues from UDP-galactose into the lipopolysaccharide of *Salmonella typhimurium* has been shown to require phosphatidyl ethanolamine containing unsaturated fatty acids (214).

PHOSPHATIDES

Phosphatidic acid.—Phosphatidic acid has been shown to play a central role in the biosynthesis of phosphatides in animal tissues (189). Three major pathways are known for the biosynthesis of phosphatidic acid: (*a*) stepwise acylation of α-glycerophosphate with acyl-CoA catalyzed by the enzyme acyl-CoA L-α-glycerophosphate acyltransferase, as demonstrated by Kornberg & Pricer with a liver preparation (190):

$$\text{L-}\alpha\text{-glycerophosphate} \xrightarrow{\text{acyl-CoA}} \text{lysophosphatidic acid} \xrightarrow{\text{acyl-CoA}} \text{phosphatidic acid} \quad 54.$$

(b) phosphorylation of a diglyceride with ATP, catalyzed by diglyceride phosphokinase, as demonstrated with brain extracts (191):

$$\text{D-2, 3-diglyceride} \xrightarrow{\text{ATP}} \text{phosphatidic acid} \quad 55.$$

(c) phosphorylation of a monoglyceride with ATP to a lysophosphatidic acid, catalyzed by monoglyceride phosphokinase from brain (215), followed by acylation of lysophosphatidic acid with fatty acyl-CoA, catalyzed lysophosphatidate acyl-CoA transferase from brain or liver (216):

$$\text{monoglyceride} \xrightarrow{\text{ATP}} \text{lysophosphatidic acid} \xrightarrow{\text{acyl-CoA}} \text{phosphatidic acid} \quad 56.$$

Biosynthesis of phosphatidic acid by the transacylase pathway (Reaction 54) has been demonstrated recently in yeast (192) and spinach leaves (193, 194); it probably also operates in *Chlorella* (195). Indications that this pathway is utilized by *E. coli* have been reported by Pieringer (196). This author has shown that *E. coli* also contains diglyceride and monoglyceride phosphokinase, and has demonstrated the formation of phosphatidic and lysophosphatidic acid by Reactions 55 and 56, respectively, using a cell-free particulate preparation from this organism (197). However, it is not yet known which of the three pathways is utilized by *E. coli* cells for the *de novo* synthesis of phosphatidic acid.

Kennedy and co-workers (189) have shown that phosphatidic acid functions as a precursor of many phosphatides in the form of cytidine diphosphate diglyceride. In animal systems, CDP-diglyceride is synthesized by the reaction of phosphatidic acid with CTP, catalyzed by the enzyme phosphatidic acid cytidyltransferase. This enzyme has not yet been demonstrated in microorganisms.

Phosphatidyl serine and phosphatidyl ethanolamine.—Kanfer & Kennedy (198) have shown that cell-free extracts of *E. coli* catalyze the net synthesis of phosphatidyl serine from serine and CDP-diglyceride as follows:

$$\text{CDP-diglyceride} + \text{L-serine} \rightarrow \text{phosphatidyl serine} + \text{CMP} \quad 57.$$

The enzyme, L-serine-CMP phosphatidyl transferase, was purified sevenfold and was found to be specific for L-serine and to require CDP-diglyceride; the enzyme activity was stimulated by the nonionic detergent Cutscum and by higher alcohols (optimally, octanol), and was dependent on a high ionic strength; sulfhydryl inhibitors, KF, or divalent cations had no effect (198).

In whole cells of *E. coli*, phosphatidyl serine is barely detectable, phosphatidyl ethanolamine being the major lipid (199). This fact is accounted for by the presence of a highly active phosphatidyl serine decarboxylase in *E. coli* (198). This enzyme has been isolated and partially purified and was shown to be highly specific for the decarboxylation of phosphatidyl serine, L-serine itself being unaffected:

$$\text{Phosphatidyl serine} \rightarrow \text{phosphatidylethanolamine} + CO_2 \quad 58.$$

Biosynthesis of phosphatidyl ethanolamine in *E. coli* thus most likely occurs exclusively by the sequence of Reactions 57 and 58, and not via the CDP-ethanolamine pathway utilized in animal tissues (198).

N-Methylation of phosphatidyl ethanolamine to lecithin.—Goldfine & Ellis (200), in a survey of 21 species of bacteria, found only two species, *Agrobacterium radiobacter* and *A. rhizogenes*, both in the Rhizobiaceae family, which incorporated C^{14} from methyl-labeled methionine into N-methylethanolamine, N,N-dimethylethanolamine and choline of the corresponding phosphatides; two other species, *C. butyricum* (201) and *Proteus vulgaris*, incorporated C^{14} into N-methylethanolamine of the corresponding phosphatide but could not carry out further transmethylation to the dimethyl derivative or to choline; the remaining species appeared to be incapable of effecting the methylation of the ethanolamine base moiety (200). Another *Agrobacterium*, *A. tumefaciens*, previously known to contain lecithin (116), has also been shown to incorporate the methyl group of methionine into the choline and other N-methylated base moieties of the phosphatides (121). Subsequently, Kaneshiro & Law (202) showed that cell-free extracts of this bacterium catalyzed the stepwise methylation of phosphatidyl ethanolamine to lecithin with S-adenosylmethionine as methyl donor:

$$\text{phosphatidyl ethanolamine} \xrightarrow{+C_1} \text{phosphatidyl-N-methylethanolamine} \qquad 59.$$

$$\xrightarrow{+C_1} \text{phosphatidyl N,N-dimethylethanolamine} \qquad 60.$$

$$\xrightarrow{+C_1} \text{phosphatidyl choline} \qquad 61.$$

The enzyme system has been fractionated into a soluble enzyme which catalyzes Reaction 59, and a particulate fraction which catalyzes all three steps (Reactions 59–61). The soluble enzyme has been purified 40-fold and shown to act only on phosphatidyl ethanolamine suitably dispersed in micellar form, no cofactors being required; sulfhydryl inhibitors had no effect but S-adenosylhomocysteine, one of the products of the transmethylations, was inhibitory (202). *A. tumefaciens* was also shown to synthesize phosphatidyl serine and phosphatidyl ethanolamine by Reactions 57 and 58 (203). Furthermore, synthesis of phosphatidyl choline by the CDP-choline pathway could not be demonstrated, and direct incorporation of exogenous choline into lecithin was not observed (203). It therefore may be concluded that the reaction sequence 57 to 61 is the only pathway for lecithin synthesis in *A. tumefaciens*. Lecithin has recently also been found in some photosynthetic bacteria (77, 217), and in *Nitrocystis oceanus* and several strains of Hyphomicrobium (218). Biosynthesis of lecithin in the latter organisms most likely occurs by reaction sequence 59 to 61 (218).

The accumulation of phosphatidyl N-methyl and N,N-dimethylethanolamine in *Neurospora crassa* mutants which require choline and are unable to synthesize lecithin, suggests that, here, too, these methylated lipids are precursors of lecithin (204). Formation of lecithin by the methylation pathway (Reactions 59 to 61) has also been suggested to occur in *Chlorella vulgaris* (195) and in the diatom, *Navicula peliculosa* (95).

Plasmalogens.—This class of phosphatide has so far been found only in *C. butyricum* (128) and in ruminal bacteria (134, 137). One of the latter bacteria, *Bacteroides succinogenes*, was shown to incorporate labeled isobutyrate and valerate into the aldehyde and acyl moieties of ethanolamine plasmalogen (137). *C. butyricum* was found to contain phosphatidyl N-methyl ethanolamine mainly in plasmalogen form, phosphatidyl ethanolamine equally divided between diacyl and plasmalogen forms, and phosphatidyl glycerol predominantly in the diacyl form (205). Time course studies with P^{32}-phosphate showed that diacyl forms were probably the precursors of the corresponding plasmalogen forms, and this was consistent with the fact that carboxy-labeled fatty acids were converted to lipid-bound aldehydes of the same chain length and structure (205). However, the pathway for formation of the vinyl ether linkage in plasmalogens has yet to be elucidated.

Phosphatidyl glycerol and its amino acid esters.—Phosphatidyl glycerol and, in many cases, its amino acid esters, are major phosphatide components in many bacteria (4, 206). Kanfer & Kennedy (199) have shown that phosphatidyl glycerol has a metabolically dynamic function in cells of *E. coli*. These authors (198) have also established the biosynthetic pathway for phosphatidyl glycerol in *E. coli*, which is identical to the pathway previously demonstrated in animal tissues (189):

$$\text{CDP-diglyceride} + \text{L-}\alpha\text{-glycerophosphate} \rightarrow \text{Phosphatidylglycerolphosphate}$$
$$\rightarrow \text{Phosphatidyl glycerol} + P_i \qquad 62.$$

The enzyme system isolated from *E. coli* had similar properties to the system in rat liver, except that the bacterial enzyme showed an absolute requirement for Mn^{++} (198).

With regard to the biosynthesis of amino acid esters of phosphatidyl glycerol (206), no information is available on an enzyme level. However, labeled amino acids are incorporated into phospholipid by *B. megaterium* protoplasts (207); cells of *S. aureus* incorporate labeled glycerol and lysine into phosphatidyl glycerol-*O*-lysine (208); and isolated membrane fractions from *B. megaterium* and *E. coli* incorporate P^{32}-phosphate into amino acid-containing phosphatides (209). The *O*-amino acid esters of phosphatidyl glycerol accumulate in the stationary growth phase (206), but low pH also favors their formation (210). Lennarz et al. (221) have recently reported the incorporation of C^{14}-L-lysine into phosphatidyl glycerol *O*-lysyl ester by crude cell-free extracts of *Staphylococcus aureus*, in the presence of ATP, Mg^{++}, and an unidentified heat-stable factor.

Phosphatidyl inositol and its glycoside derivatives.—Generally, phosphatidyl inositol rarely occurs in the lipids of bacteria (1, 4, 114, 133, 167). Mycobacteria, however, contain considerable amounts of phosphatidyl inositol, mostly in the form of glycoside derivatives (1, 4, 114). *Mycobacterium phlei* and *Mycobacterium tuberculosis* contain a family of phosphatidyl inositol mono- to hexa-mannosides, in which one mannose group is attached to position 2 of myoinositol and position 6 may contain zero to five mannose residues (222–224). Biosynthesis of phosphatidyl inositol is known to occur in animal tissues by the following reaction (189):

CDP—diglyceride + inositol → phosphatidyl inositol + inositol + CMP 63.

The biosynthetic pathway for this phosphatide in bacteria has not yet been determined but recently Hill & Ballou (225) have shown that growing cultures of *M. phlei* incorporated myoinositol-2-^{3}H into phosphatidyl inositol, and its di- and penta-mannosides, in decreasing order of specific activities. A particulate enzyme preparation was obtained which was shown to catalyze the incorporation of mannose-C^{14} from GDP-mannose-C^{14} into the phosphatidyl inositol monomannoside, probably by the following reaction (225):

GDP—Mannose + phosphatidyl inositol → GDP + phosphatidyl inositol
monomannoside 64.

LITERATURE CITED

1. Asselineau, J., and Lederer, E., in *Lipide Metabolism*, 337–406. (Bloch, K., Ed., John Wiley & Sons, New York, 1960)
2. Wakil, S. J., *Ann. Rev. Biochem.*, **31**, 369–406 (1962)
3. Mead, J. F., *Ann. Rev. Biochem.*, **32**, 241–68 (1963)
4. Kates, M., *Advan. Lipid Res.*, **2**, 17–20 (1964)
5. Jensen, S. L., *Ann. Rev. Microbiol.*, **19**, 163–82 (1965)
6. McKenna, E. J., and Kallio, R. E., *Ann. Rev. Microbiol.*, **19**, 183–208 (1965)
7. Vagelos, P. R., *Ann. Rev. Biochem.*, **33**, 139–72 (1964)
8. Lynen, F., *Federation Proc.*, **20**, 941–51 (1961)
9. Wakil, S. J., *J. Lipid Res.*, **2**, 1–20 (1961)
10. Green, D. E., and Wakil, S. J., in *Lipide Metabolism*, 1–40. (Bloch, K., Ed., John Wiley & Sons, New York, 1960)
11. Wakil, S. J., *J. Am. Chem. Soc.*, **80**, 6465 (1958)
12. Kusunose, M., Kusunose, E., Kowa, Y., and Yamamura, Y., *J. Biochem.* (*Japan*), **46**, 525–27 (1959)
13. Winder, F. G., Brennan, P., and Ratledge, C., *Biochem. J.*, **93**, 635–40 (1964)
14. Den, H., and Klein, H. P., *Biochim. Biophys, Acta*, **49**, 429–30 (1961)
15. Hsu, R. Y., Wasson, G., and Porter, J. W., *J. Biol. Chem.*, **240**, 3736–46 (1965)
16. Overath, P., and Stumpf, P. K., *G. Biol. Chem.*, **239**, 4103–10 (1964)
17. Brooks, J. L., and Stumpf, P. K., *Bio-chim. Biophys. Acta*, **98**, 213–16 (1965)
18. Goldman, P., Alberts, A. W., and Vagelos, P. R., *Biochem. Biophys. Res. Commun.*, **5**, 280–85 (1961)
19. Alberts, A. W., Goldman, P., and Vagelos, P. R., *J. Biol. Chem.*, **238**, 557–65 (1963)
20. Lennarz, W. J., Light, R. J., and Bloch, K., *Proc. Natl. Acad. Sci. U.S.*, **48**, 840–46 (1962)
21. Goldman, P., Alberts, A. W., and Vagelos, P. R., *J. Biol. Chem.*, **238**, 1255–61 (1963)
22. Alberts, A. W., *Federation Proc.*, **22**, 362 (1963)
23. Wakil, S. J., Pugh, E. S., and Sauer, F., *Proc. Natl. Acad. Sci. U.S.*, **52**, 106–14 (1964)
24. Majerus, P. W., Alberts, A. W., and Vagelos, P. R., *Proc. Natl. Acad. Sci. U.S.*, **51**, 1231–38 (1964)
25. Majerus, P. W., Alberts, A. W., and Vagelos, P. R., *ibid.*, **53**, 410–17 (1965)
26. Sauer, F., Pugh, E. L., Wakil, S. J., Delaney, R., and Hill, R. L., *Proc. Natl. Acad. Sci. U.S.*, **52**, 1360–66 (1964)
27. Majerus, P. W., Alberts, A. W., and Vagelos, P. R., *J. Biol. Chem.*, **240**, 4723–26 (1965)
28. Pugh, E. L., and Wakil, S. J., *J. Biol. Chem.*, **240**, 4727–33 (1965)
29. Alberts, A. W., Majerus, P. W., B., and Vagelos, P. R., *Biochemistry*, **3**, 1563–71 (1964)
30. Alberts, A. W., Majerus, P. W., and Vagelos, P. R., *Biochemistry*, **4**, 2265–74 (1965)
31. Majerus, P. W., Alberts, A. W., and

Vagelos, P. R., *J. Biol. Chem.*, **240**, 618–21 (1965)

32. Goldman, P., *J. Biol. Chem.*, **239**, 3663–67, (1964)

33. Vagelos, P. R., Alberts, A. W., and Majerus, P. W., *Ann. N. Y. Acad. Sci.*, **131**, 177–88 (1965)

34. Bressler, R., and Wakil, S. J., *J. Biol. Chem.*, **237**, 1441–48 (1962)

35. Kusunose, E., Kusunose, M., Kowa, Y., and Yamamura, Y., *J. Biochem. (Japan)*, **47**, 689–93 (1960)

36. Ebina, T., Munakata, M., Munakata, T., and Kobuya, G., *Compt. Rend. Soc. Biol.*, **155**, 1190–92 (1960)

37. Pierard, A., and Goldman, D. S., *Arch. Biochem. Biophys.*, **100**, 56–65 (1963)

38. Goldman, P., Alberts, A. W., and Vagelos, P. R., *J. Biol. Chem.*, **238**, 3579–83 (1963)

39. Massaro, E. J., and Lennarz, W. J., *Biochemistry*, **4**, 85–90 (1965)

40. Kates, M., Kushner, D. J., and James, A. T., *Can. J. Biochem. Physiol.*, **40**, 83–94 (1962)

41. Bordet, C., and Michel, G., *Biochim. Biophys. Acta*, **70**, 613–26 (1963)

42. Knivett, V. A., Cullen, J., and Jackson, M. J., *Biochem. J.*, **96**, 2C–3C (1965)

43. Horning, M. G., Martin, D. B., Karmen, A., and Vagelos, P. R., *J. Biol. Chem.*, **236**, 669–72 (1961)

44. Mead, J. F., in *Lipide Metabolism*, 41–68. (Bloch, K., Ed., John Wiley & Sons, New York, 1960)

45. Mead, J. F., *Federation Proc.*, **20**, 952–55 (1961)

46. Bloch, K., Baronowsky, P. E., Goldfine, H., Lennarz, W. J., Light, R., Norris, A. T., and Scheuerbrandt, G., *Federation Proc.*, **20**, 921–27 (1961)

47. O'Leary, W. M., *Bacteriol Rev.*, **26**, 421–47 (1962)

48. Hofmann, K., *Fatty Acid Metabolism in Microorganisms*. (John Wiley & Sons, New York, 78 pp., 1963)

49. Bloomfield, D. K., and Bloch, K., *J. Biol. Chem.*, **235**, 337–45 (1960)

50. Lennarz, W. J., and Bloch, K., *J. Biol. Chem.*, **235**, PC26 (1960)

51. Light, R., Lennarz, W. J., and Bloch, K., *J. Biol. Chem.*, **237**, 1793–1800 (1962)

52. James, A. T., Webb, J. P. W., and Kellock, T. D., *Biochem. J.*, **78**, 333–39 (1961)

53. Marsh, J. B., and James, A. T., *Biochim. Biophys. Acta*, **60**, 320–28 (1962)

54. Keeney, M., Katz, I., and Schwartz,

D. P., *Biochim. Biophys. Acta*, **62**, 615–16 (1962)

55. Bloch, K., in *The Control of Lipid Metabolism*, 1–16. (J. K. Grant, Ed., Academic Press, London & New York, 1963)

56. Meyer, F., and Bloch, K., *J. Biol. Chem.*, **238**, 2654–59 (1963)

57. Schroepfer, G. J., Jr., and Bloch, K., *J. Biol. Chem.*, **240**, 54–63 (1964)

58. Klein, H. P., *J. Bacteriol.*, **90**, 227–34 (1965)

59. Lennarz, W. J., Scheuerbrandt, G., and Bloch, K., *J. Biol. Chem.*, **237**, 664–71 (1962)

60. Scheuerbrandt, G., and Bloch, K., *J. Biol. Chem.*, **237**, 2064–68 (1962)

61. Fulco, A. J., and Bloch, K., *Biochim. Biophys. Acta*, **63**, 545–46 (1962)

62. Fulco, A. J., and Bloch, K., *J. Biol. Chem.*, **239**, 993–97 (1964)

63. Fulco, A. J., Levy, R., and Bloch, K., *J. Biol. Chem.*, **239**, 998–1003 (1964)

64. Erwin, J., and Bloch, K., *Science*, **143**, 1006–12 (1964)

65. Erwin, J., and Bloch, K., *J. Biol. Chem.*, **238**, 1618–27 (1963)

66. Korn, E. D., *J. Biol. Chem.*, **238**, 3584–87 (1963)

67. Korn, E. D., *ibid.*, **239**, 396–400 (1964)

68. Davidoff, F., and Korn, E. D., *J. Biol. Chem.*, **238**, 3199–3209 (1963)

69. Davidoff, F., and Korn, E. D., *ibid.*, **238**, 3210–15 (1963)

70. Davidoff, F., and Korn, E. D., *ibid.*, **239**, 2496–2506 (1964)

71. Korn, E. D., Greenblatt, C. I., and Lees, A. M., *J. Lipid Res.*, **6**, 43–50 (1965)

72. Stoffel, W., *Biochem. Biophys. Res. Commun.*, **6**, 270–73 (1961)

73. Holloway, P. W., and Wakil, S. J., *J. Biol. Chem.*, **239**, 2489–95 (1964)

74. Elovson, J., *Biochim. Biophys. Acta*, **106**, 291–303 (1965)

75. Harris, R. V., Wood, B. J. B., and James, A. T., *Biochem. J.*, **94**, 22P–23P (1965)

76. James, A. T., Harris, R. V., Hitchcock, C., Wood, B. J. B., and Nichols, B. W., *Fette, Seifen, Anstrichmittel*, **67**, 393–96 (1965)

77. Wood, B. J. B., Nichols, B. W., and James, A. T., *Biochim. Biophys. Acta*, **106**, 261–73 (1965)

78. Levin, E., Lennarz, W. J., and Bloch, K., *Biochim. Biophys. Acta*, **84**, 471–74 (1964)

79. Nichols, B. W., Harris, R. V., and James, A. T., *Biochem. Biophys. Res. Commun.*, **20**, 256–62 (1965)

80. Erwin, J., Hulanicka, D., and Bloch,

K., *Comp. Biochem. Physiol.*, **12**, 191–207 (1964)

81. Harris, R. V., Harris, P., and James, A. T., *Biochim. Biophys. Acta*, **106**, 465–73 (1965)

82. Nichols, B. W., Harris, P., and James, A. T., *Biochem. Biophys. Res. Commun.*, **21**, 473–79 (1965)

83. James, A. T., *Biochim. Biophys. Acta*, **70**, 9–19 (1963)

84. Stumpf, P. K., and James, A. T., *Biochim. Biophys. Acta*, **70**, 20–32 (1963)

85. James, A. T., in *The Control of Lipid Metabolism*, 17–28. (Grant, J. K., Ed., Academic Press, London & New York, 1963)

86. Stumpf, P. K., (See Ref. 85, 29–36)

87. Fulco, A. J., *Biochim. Biophys. Acta*, **106**, 211–12 (1965)

88. Nagai, J., and Bloch, K., *J. Biol. Chem.*, **240**, PC3702–3 (1965)

89. Korn, E. D., *J. Lipid Res.*, **5**, 352–62 (1964)

90. Hulanicka, D., Erwin, J., and Bloch, K., *J. Biol. Chem.*, **239**, 2778–87 (1964)

91. Erwin, J., and Bloch, K., in *Metabolism & Physiological Significance of Lipids*, 29–31. (Dawson, R. M. C., and Rhodes, D. N., Eds., John Wiley, London, N.Y., 1964)

92. Wakil, S. J. (See Ref. 91, 3–27)

93. Erwin, J., and Bloch, K., *Biochem. Z.*, **338**, 496–511 (1963)

94. Klenk, E., and Eberhagen, D., *Z. Physiol. Chem.*, **328**, 189–97 (1962)

95. Kates, M., and Volcani, B. E., *Biochim. Biophys. Acta*, **116**, 264–78 (1966)

96. Ackman, R. G., Jangaard, P. M., Hoyle, R. J., and Brockerhoff, H., *J. Fish Res. Bd. Canada*, **21**, 747–56 (1964)

97. Klenk, E., Knipprath, W., Eberhagen, D., and Koof, H. P., *Z. Physiol. Chem.*, **334**, 44–59 (1963)

98. Yuan, C., and Bloch, K., *J. Biol. Chem.*, **236**, 1277–79 (1961)

99. Meyer, F., and Bloch, K., *Biochim. Biophys. Acta*, **77**, 671–73 (1963)

100. Harris, R. V., and James, A. T., *Biochim. Biophys. Acta*, **106**, 456–64 (1965)

101. Haines, T. H., Aaronson, S., Gellerman, J., and Schlenk, H., *Nature*, **194**, 1282–83 (1962)

102. Cheniae, G. M., *Biochim. Biophys. Acta*, **70**, 504–16 (1963)

103. Nugteren, D. H., *Biochim. Biophys. Acta*, **106**, 280–90 (1965)

104. Goldfine, H., and Bloch, K., *J. Biol. Chem.*, **236**, 2596–2601 (1961)

105. Scheuerbrandt, G., Goldfine, H., Baronowsky, P. E., and Bloch, K., *J. Biol. Chem.*, **236**, PC71 (1961)

106. O'Leary, W. M., *Biochemistry*, **4**, 1621–27 (1965)

107. Baronowsky, P. E., Lennarz, W. J., and Bloch, K., *Federation Proc.*, **21**, 288 (1962)

108. Norris, A. T., Matsumura, S., and Bloch, K., *J. Biol. Chem.*, **239**, 3653–62 (1964)

109. Bishop, D. G., and Still, J. L., *J. Lipid Res.*, **4**, 81–86 (1963)

110. Lederer, E., *Angew. Chem. Intern. Ed., Engl.*, **3**, 393–400 (1964)

111. Lederer, E., *Biochem. J.*, **93**, 449–68 (1964)

112. Lederer, E., Proceedings of the Plenary Sessions. *Proc. Intern. Congr. Biochem., New York, 1964.*

113. O'Leary, W. M., in *Transmethylation and Methionine Biosynthesis*, 94–105. (Shapiro, B., and Schlenk, H., Eds., Univ. of Chicago Press, Chicago, 1965)

114. Asselineau, J., *Les Lipides Bactériens.* (Herman, Paris, 350 pp., 1962)

115. Kaneshiro, T., and Marr, A. G., *J. Biol. Chem.*, **236**, 2615–19 (1961)

116. Kaneshiro, T., and Marr, A. G., *J. Lipid Res.*, **3**, 184–89 (1962)

117. O'Leary, W. M., *J. Bacteriol.*, **77**, 367–73 (1959)

118. O'Leary, W. M., *ibid.*, **78**, 709–13 (1959)

119. Liu, T.-Y., and Hofmann, K., *Biochemistry*, **1**, 189–91 (1962)

120. Chalk, K. J. I., and Kodicek, E., *Biochim. Biophys. Acta*, **50**, 579–81 (1961)

121. Law, J. H., Zalkin, H., and Kaneshiro, T., *Biochim. Biophys. Acta*, **70**, 143–51 (1963)

122. O'Leary, W. M., *J. Bacteriol.*, **84**, 967–72 (1962)

123. Zalkin, H., Law, J. H., and Goldfine, H., *J. Biol. Chem.*, **238** 1242–48 (1963)

124. Pohl, S., Law, J. H., and Ryhage, R., *Biochim. Biophys. Acta*, **70**, 583–85 (1963)

125. Chung, A. E., and Law, J. H., *Biochemistry*, **3**, 967–74 (1964)

126. Hildebrand, J. G., and Law, J. H., *Biochemistry*, **3**, 1304–8 (1964)

127. Chung, A. E., and Law, J. H., *Biochemistry*, **3**, 1989–93 (1964)

128. Goldfine, H., *J. Biol. Chem.*, **239**, 2130–34 (1964)

129. Chung, A. E., and Goldfine, H., *Nature*, **206**, 1253–54 (1965)

130. Bergh, A. K., Webb, S. J., and

McArthur, C. S., *Can. J. Biochem.*, **42**, 1141–51 (1964)

131. Saito, K., *J. Biochem.* (*Japan*), **47**, 699–709; 710–19 (1960)

132. Huston, C. K., and Albro, P. W., *J. Bacteriol.*, **88**, 425–32 (1964)

133. Macfarlane, M. G., *Biochem. J.*, **79**, 4P (1961)

134. Allison, M. J., Bryant, M. P., Katz, I., and Keeney, M., *J. Bacteriol.*, **83**, 1084–93 (1962)

135. Ballio, A., Barcellona, S., and Boniforti, L., *Biochem. J.*, **94**, 11C–13C (1965)

136. Lennarz, W. J., *Biochem. Biophys. Res. Commun.*, **6**, 112–16 (1961)

137. Wegner, G. H., and Foster, E. M., *J. Bacteriol.*, **85**, 53–61 (1963)

138. Kaneda, T., *J. Biol. Chem.*, **238**, 1229–35 (1963)

139. Jauréguiberry, G., Law, J. H., McCloskey, J. A., and Lederer, E., *Biochemistry*, **4**, 347–53 (1965)

140. Gastambide-Odier, M., Delaumeny, J. M., and Lederer, E., *Biochim. Biophys. Acta*, **70**, 670–78 (1963)

141. Kates, M., Yengoyan, L. S., and Sastry, P. S., *Biochim. Biophys. Acta*, **98**, 252–68 (1965)

142. Kates, M., Wassef, M., and Kushner, D. J. (Unpublished results)

143. Stanacev, N. Z., and Kates, M., *Can. J. Biochem. Physiol.*, **41**, 1330–34 (1963)

144. Tulloch, A. P., and Spencer, J. F. T., *Can. J. Chem.*, **42**, 830–35 (1964)

145. Ikawa, M., Koepfli, J. B., Mudd, S. G., and Nieman, C., *J. Am. Chem. Soc.*, **75**, 1035–38 (1953)

146. Law, J. H., *Bacteriol. Proc.*, 129 (1961)

147. Kaneshiro, T., and Marr, A. G., *Biochim. Biophys. Acta*, **70**, 271–77 (1963)

148. Jarvis, F. G., and Johnson, M. J., *J. Am. Chem. Soc.*, **71**, 4124–26 (1949)

149. Wallen, L. L., Benedict, R. G., and Jackson, R. W., *Arch. Biochem. Biophys.*, **99**, 249–53 (1962)

150. Baptist, J. N., Gholson, R. K., and Coon, M. J., *Biochim. Biophys. Acta*, **69**, 40–47 (1963)

151. Gholson, R. K., Baptist, J. N., and Coon, M. J., *Biochemistry*, **2**, 1155–59 (1963)

152. Kusunose, M., Kusunose, E., and Coon, M. J., *J. Biol. Chem.*, **239**, 1374–80 (1964)

153. Kusunose, M., Kusunose, E., and Coon, M. J., *ibid.*, **239**, 2135–39 (1964)

154. Preiss, B., and Bloch, K., *J. Biol. Chem.*, **239**, 85–88 (1964)

155. Kester, A. S., and Foster, J. W., *J. Bacteriol.*, **85**, 859–69 (1963)

156. Gorin, P. A. J., Spencer, J. F. T., and Tulloch, A. P., *Can. J. Chem.*, **39**, 846–55 (1961)

157. Tulloch, A. P., Spencer, J. F. T., and Gorin, P. A. J., *ibid.*, **40**, 1326–38 (1962)

158. Finnerty, W. R., and Kallio, R. E., *J. Bacteriol.*, **87**, 1261–65 (1964)

159. Gastambide-Odier, M., and Lederer, E., *Biochem. Z.*, **333**, 285–95 (1960)

160. Bordet, C., Etémadi, A. H., Michel, G., and Lederer, E., *Bull. Soc. Chim. France*, 234–35 (1965)

161. Etémadi, A. H., and Lederer, E., *Bull. Soc. Chim. Biol.*, **46**, 107–13 (1964)

162. Etémadi, A. H., Okuda, R., and Lederer, E., *Bull. Soc. Chim. France*, 868–70 (1964)

163. Etémadi, A. H., and Lederer, E., *Biochim. Biophys. Acta*, **98**, 160–67 (1965)

164. Gastambide-Odier, M., Delaumeny, J. M., and Lederer, E., *Compt. Rend.*, **259**, 3404–7 (1964)

165. Gastambide-Odier, M., Delaumeny, J. M., and Lederer, E., *Chem. Ind., London*, 1285–86 (1963)

166. Brundish, D. E., Shaw, N., and Baddiley, J., *Biochem. J.*, **97**, 158–65 (1965)

167. Macfarlane, M. G., *Biochem. J.*, **80**, 45P (1961)

168. Macfarlane, M. G., *ibid.*, **82**, 40P (1962)

169. Lennarz, W. J., *J. Biol. Chem.*, **239**, PC3110–12 (1964)

170. Vorbeck, M. L., and Marinetti, G. V., *Biochemistry*, **4**, 296–305 (1965)

171. Reeves, R. E., Latour, N. E., and Lousteau, R. J., *Biochemistry*, **3**, 1248–49 (1964)

172. Nichols, B. W., *Biochim. Biophys. Acta*, **106**, 274–79 (1965)

173. Benson, A. A., *Ann. Rev. Plant Physiol.*, **15**, 1–16 (1964)

174. Holton, R. W., Blecker, H. H., and Onore, M., *Phytochemistry*, **3**, 595–602 (1964)

175. Rosenberg, A., and Pecker, M., *Biochemistry*, **2**, 254–58 (1964)

176. Carter, H. E., Johnson, P., and Weber, E. J., *Ann. Rev. Biochem.*, **34**, 109–42 (1965)

177. Allen, C. F., and Good, P., *J. Am. Oil Chem. Soc.*, **42**, 610–14 (1965)

178. Ferrari, R. A., and Benson, A. A., *Arch. Biochem. Biophys.*, **93**, 185–92 (1961)

179. Neufeld, E. H., and Hall, E. W., *Biochem. Biophys. Res. Commun.*, **14**, 503–5 (1964)

180. Lennarz, W. J., *Federation Proc.*, **24,** 479 (1965)
181. Kaufman, B., Kundig, F. D., Distler, J., and Roseman, S., *Biochem. Biophys. Res. Commun.*, **18,** 312–18 (1965)
182. Benson, A. A., *Advan. Lipid Res.*, **1,** 387–94 (1963)
183. Shibuya, I., Yagi, T., and Benson, A. A., in *Studies on Microalgae and Photosynthetic Bacteria*, 627–36. (Japanese Soc. Plant Physiologists, Ed., Univ. Tokyo press, Tokyo, 1963)
184. Zill, L. P., and Cheniae, G. M., *Ann. Rev. Plant Physiol.*, **13,** 225–64 (1962)
185. Kates, M., Palameta, B., Kushner, D. J., and Gibbons, N. E., *Federation Proc.*, **25,** 405 (1966)
186. Edwards, J. R., and Hayashi, J. A., *Arch. Biochem. Biophys.*, **111,** 415–21 (1965)
187. Burger, M. M., Glaser, L., and Burton, R. M., *J. Biol. Chem.*, **238,** 2595–2602 (1963)
188. Edstrom, R. D., and Heath, E. C., *Federation Proc.*, **23,** 380 (1964)
189. Kennedy, E. P., *Federation Proc.*, **20,** 934–40 (1961)
190. Kornberg, A., and Pricer, W. E., Jr., *J. Biol. Chem.*, **204,** 345–57 (1953)
191. Hokin, M. R., and Hokin, L. E., *J. Biol. Chem.*, **234,** 1381–86 (1959)
192. Kuhn, N. J., and Lynen, F., *Biochem. J.*, **94,** 240–46 (1965)
193. Cheniae, G. M., *Plant Physiol.*, **40,** 235–43 (1965)
194. Sastry, P. S., and Kates, M., *Can. J. Biochem.*, **44,** 459–67 (1966)
195. Sastry, P. S., and Kates, M., *ibid.*, **43,** 1445–53 (1965)
196. Pieringer, R. A., *Federation Proc.*, **24,** 476 (1965)
197. Pieringer, R. A., and Kunnes, R. S., *J. Biol. Chem.*, **240,** 2833–38 (1965)
198. Kanfer, J., and Kennedy, E. P., *J. Biol. Chem.*, **239,** 1720–26 (1964)
199. Kanfer, J., and Kennedy, E. P., *ibid.*, **238,** 2919–22 (1963)
200. Goldfine, H., and Ellis, M. E., *J. Bacteriol.*, **87,** 8–15 (1964)
201. Goldfine, H., *Biochim. Biophys. Acta*, **59,** 504–6 (1962)
202. Kaneshiro, T., and Law, J. H., *J. Biol. Chem.*, **239,** 1705–13 (1964)

203. Sherr, S. I., and Law, J. H., *J. Biol. Chem.*, **240,** 3760–65 (1965)
204. Hall, M. O., and Nyc, J. F., *J. Lipid Res.*, **2,** 321–27 (1961)
205. Baumann, N. A., Hagen, P.-O., and Goldfine, H., *J. Biol. Chem.*, **240,** 1559–67 (1965)
206. Macfarlane, M. G., *Advan. Lipid Res.*, **2,** 91–125 (1964)
207. Hunter, G. D., and Goodsall, R. A., *Biochem. J.*, **78,** 564–70 (1961)
208. Gale, E. F., and Folkes, J. P., *Biochem. J.*, **94,** 390–400 (1965)
209. Hill, P. B., *Biochim. Biophys. Acta*, **57,** 386–89 (1962)
210. Houtsmuller, U. M. T., and van Deenen, L. L. M., *Biochim. Biophys. Acta*, **106,** 564–76 (1965)
211. Nissen, P., and Benson, A. A., *Biochim. Biophys. Acta*, **82,** 400–3 (1964)
212. Davies, W. H., Mercer, E. I., and Goodwin, T. W., *Biochem. J.*, **98,** 369–73 (1966)
213. Mayer, R. M., Edstrom, R. D., and Heath, E. C., *Federation Proc.*, **24,** 479 (1965)
214. Rothfield, L., and Takeshita, M., *Federation Proc.*, **24,** 479 (1965)
215. Pieringer, R. A., and Hokin, L. E., *J. Biol. Chem.*, **237,** 653–58 (1962)
216. Pieringer, R. A., and Hokin, L. E., *ibid.*, **237,** 659–63 (1962)
217. Lascelles, J., and Szilagyi, J. F., *J. Gen. Microbiol.*, **38,** 55–64 (1965)
218. Hagen, P.-O., Goldfine, H., and Williams, P. J., LeB., *Science* (In press, 1966)
219. Lederer, E., in Biosynthesis of lipids. *Proc. Intern. Congr. Biochem.*, *5th, Moscow, 1961,* 96—. (Popjak, G., Ed., Pergamon Press, London, 1963)
220. Asselineau, J., and Bennet, P. (See Ref. 91, 111–23)
221. Lennarz, W. J., *Federation Proc.*, **25,** 521 (1966)
222. Lee, Y. C., and Ballou, C. E., *J. Biol. Chem.*, **239,** 1316–27 (1964)
223. Ballou, C. E., and Lee, Y. C., *Biochemistry*, **3,** 682–85 (1964)
224. Lee, Y. C., and Ballou, C. E., *ibid.*, **4,** 1395–1404 (1965)
225. Hill, D. L., and Ballou, C. E., *J. Biol. Chem.*, **241,** 895–902 (1966)

THE CLASSIFICATION OF VIRUSES[1]

By André Lwoff and Paul Tournier

Institut Pasteur, Paris, and Institut de Recherches Scientifiques sur le Cancer, Villejuif, France

Contents

Introduction	46
Viruses	46
Terminology	47
Evolution of the Principles of Classification	48
The Lwoff-Horne-Tournier System	51
The Taxonomic Value of Groups	55
Stability of the Family	55
Subdivision of Families	57
The genus	57
The genetic material	57
The structural units and the capsomers	57
The capsid	57
The peplomers	57
The peplos	58
The enzymes	58
The features of viral development	58
Cell-virus interaction	58
The specificity	58
The virulence	58
The symptomatology	58
Discussion	58
Antigenicity and classification	58
The structure of the RNA	59
Critiques Directed Against the L.H.T. System	59
Variants of the L.H.T. System	61
Nomenclature and Systematics	62
The Defunct Subcommittee and the International Status of the Nomenclature of Viruses	63
Picorna	63
Papova	63
Varia	63
Anomalies	63
More anomalies	64
Classification of Viruses	66
Nomina conservanda	71

[1] The survey of the literature pertaining to this review was concluded in December 1965.

Introduction

We have been asked to discuss the classification of viruses. To classify is to arrange or distribute in classes according to a method or a system. As classifications end with the definition of categories, and as categories have to be named, it is impossible to discuss classification without discussing nomenclature. Alas!

We shall try to apply the rules of grammar. The word "virus" being a noun will be used as such and not as an adjective. When an adjective is needed, we shall make use of the adjective "viral." Some readers will accuse us of affectation. We hope to be forgiven for, our mother language being French, we do not feel entitled to violate English grammar.

Viruses

Words must have a meaning. It was proposed in 1953 [Lwoff (1)] that viruses should be separated from nonviruses by the use of a few discriminative characters: (a) Virions possess only one type of nucleic acid, either DNA or RNA. Other agents possess both types. (b) Virions are reproduced from their sole nucleic acid, whereas other agents are reproduced from the integrated sum of their constituents. (c) Virions are unable to grow and to undergo binary fission.

These three features were considered to be correlated and subordinated. The differential definition of viruses and of higher protists was further discussed in 1957 and today a few more discriminative criteria have been added [Lwoff (2)]: (d) Absence in the viruses of the genetic information for the synthesis of the Lipman system, the system responsible for the production of energy with high potential. (e) Viruses make use of the ribosomes of their host cells. This is defined as absolute parasitism.

These features, being absent in other agents, are characteristic of viruses: they are present in all viruses but absent in all nonviruses such as bacteria, including the agents of psittacosis, protozoa, etc.; that is, in all protists, whether procaryotic or eucaryotic. In order to know what a bacterium is, the reader is referred to Stanier & van Niel's (3) masterly review.

It is clear that an infectious agent either does or does not possess the attributes of a virus; it cannot be intermediate between viruses and nonviruses. This may seem to be a truism. Nevertheless, *Virology*, in 1963, published a paper on the ornithosis agent which is called a virus and is described as intermediate between rickettsia and "true" viruses.[2]

In the same year, a great virologist[2] considered the agent of psittacosis to be a virus for following reasons: the agent is closely related to viruses, it is known as a virus, there is a resemblance between the "psittacosis virus" and poxvirus. Another great virologist,[2] in 1964, expressed a similar opinion: the agents of psittacosis, lymphogranuloma, and trachoma lie between "true viruses" and bacteria.

[2] For obvious reasons, we have decided that we should not quote these papers.

Two other virologists, following these illustrious examples, state that the position of the rickettsia and of the psittacosis lymphogranuloma-trachoma group is still controversial for, unlike the "true" viruses, they possess DNA and RNA.

Thus, a few virologists recognize three categories of infectious agents: true viruses, pseudoviruses, and bacteria. None of these groups is defined by our colleagues. It is clear that, according to our criteria, true viruses are viruses and that pseudoviruses are bacteria. If one likes the perpetuation of confusion and disorder one can, of course, well decide that the bacterium which causes psittacosis is a virus and that the poxvirus is a bacterium. Why not? If the categories are not defined and if the terms are devoid of meaning, any sequence of words can be produced. Why, after all, separate viruses from bacteria? Since the time of Aristotle, it has been conceded that categories exist by virtue of a definition. Of course, to select the valid discriminatory character of a category is a tiring intellectual effort. Yet, from time to time we have to justify our appurtenance to the species *Homo sapiens*.

Before classifying viruses, it was necessary to state what they are. This is now done. Infectious agents which possess the characters of viruses are viruses, whether they are parasites of mammals, reptiles, insects, bacteria, mushrooms, or of higher plants. Viruses are viruses [Lwoff (4)].

It is remarkable that so many classifications of viruses begin by separating plant viruses on the one hand from animal viruses on the other. Sometimes plant virologists simply ignore "animal" viruses and vice versa. Yet, some plant viruses are able to multiply in insects which are animals. Some animal viruses are able to multiply in bacteria which are considered as plants. Some bacteriophages multiply in plants. The word, virus, obviously has the same meaning for a plant pathologist, for a bacteriologist, and for an animal virologist. A classification of viruses based on the taxonomic position of the host is therefore blunted or stunted, or perhaps runted. A general virologist is interested in viruses in general, and not in particular diseases of plants or animals. For a general virologist, the virus transcends the host and the disease.

TERMINOLOGY

A few terms introduced after 1959 will be defined. The virion is the ultimate phase of viral development. The virion is composed of the viral genetic material surrounded by one or two coats or shells. The capsid (from the Greek *capsa* meaning box) is the proteinic shell which is in contact with the nucleic acid and encloses it. The capsomeres (from the Greek *meron* meaning part) are the parts of the box [Lwoff, Anderson & Jacob (5)]. Originally, the word capsomere designated the visible pieces of which the capsid is built. But it was noticed that the visible parts of a capsid with helical symmetry represent one molecule, that is, they are monomers, whereas the visible parts of a capsid with cubic symmetry are probably composed of five or six molecules, that is, they are oligomers.

An international gathering, of which we were members, decided at Cold Spring Harbor that a capsomere is the result of the assemblage of a few molecules or structural units [Caspar et al. (6)]. Therefore, the visible structures which constitute the capsid of a virion with helical symmetry and which are monomers are not "capsomeres" but "structural units."

It would have been much simplier to decide (a) that the capsid is, as originally proposed, composed of capsomeres, and (b) that the capsomeres of virions with cubic symmetry are oligomers while those of virions with helical symmetry are monomers. This solution will probably prevail sooner or later.

The number of structural units and of capsomeres in the capsid of a given virus is constant. The structure composed of the nucleic acid surrounded by the capsid is the nucleocapsid [Caspar et al. (6)]. Some nucleocapsids are naked, others are enveloped by a second shell; this is the peplos or the mantle. Just as a capsid is made of capsomeres, a peplos is made of peplomers. The number of peplomers of a given virion seems to be constant. This constancy accounts for the constancy of size. The genetic determinant of the peplomer is viral. When the peplos is composed only of viral proteins, it is an homopeplos. When cellular material, such as lipids, is mixed in it, it is a heteropeplos. Sometimes each peplomer provides attachment for another viral molecule, the hemagglutinin. The peplos is then said to be diplopeplos because two viral molecules take part in its structure. When no hemagglutinin molecules are attached, the chlamyd is called haplopeplos.

Thus, a virion is either a naked or an enveloped nucleocapsid. The virion as a whole is infectious and the genetic material is also infectious. At the cellular level, an infection is the introduction into the cell of an entity able to reproduce itself. "Infectious" means possessing the capacity to infect. It is really strange to see the expression "noninfectious protein" appearing in so many papers: a protein, because it cannot fail to reproduce, cannot be described as infectious, even if it penetrates into a cell. In addition, it seems preferable not to make use of the terms, "incomplete virus" or "noninfectious antigen," to designate the capsid or the hemagglutinin. A capsid is a capsid and an hemagglutinin is an hemagglutinin. Considering our knowledge of the virion, the expression "incomplete virus" could be abandoned without damage. The various constitutive parts of the virion, because they have names, should be referred to by their name. Perhaps this is too simple.

Evolution of the Principles of Classification

Infectious diseases were known before the agents which caused them, and the individuality of diseases was assigned to the specificity of the etiological agents. It is therefore natural that the agents were nominated according to the disease. This is true for plants as well as for animals and applies to viruses as well as to other infectious agents.

Bennett (7), in 1939, on behalf of the Committee for Virus Nomenclature of the Council of the American Phytopathological Society, proposed the following criteria for classification:

1. Type of symptoms produced on different species and varieties of susceptible plants.

2. Morphological and cytological disturbances produced.

3. Relation of insect vectors to virus transmission.

4. Antigenic reactions in animals and plants.

5. Chemical and physical properties of the viruses themselves.

In 1941, Bawden (8) suggested that viral nomenclature should be based on morphological, chemical, and serological information, that is, on the properties of the virion. Brandes and his co-workers (1957–1964), and especially Brandes & Wetter in 1959 (9), classified plant viruses with helical symmetry according to the diameter and length of the virion, and utilized serology in order to recognize natural affinities.[3]

TABLE I

COOPER'S SYSTEM OF ANIMAL VIRUSES

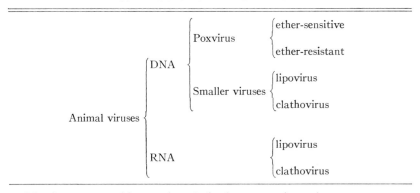

Lipoviruses are sensitive to ether; clathoviruses are ether-resistant.

As far as urophages are concerned (bacteriophages possessing a tail), Bradley (10) proposed a classification in which the anatomy and physiology of the tail plays an important role.

The system proposed by Cooper concerns only viruses of animals [Cooper (11)]. Yet it represents considerable progress. For the first time, the criteria of systematics are on a hierarchical basis. The first subdivision is based on the nature of the genetic material, whether RNA or DNA, a subdivision which has been widely—we should say universely—accepted. But from here on, the system is somehow wobbly. DNA viruses are subdivided into poxviruses and smaller deoxy viruses, and each group is subdivided according to ether sensitivity. The same criteria are applied directly to riboviruses. Ether

[3] It should be noted that preparations of virions are sometimes contaminated with antigens from the host plants. This, of course, is a serious drawback for certain types of serological investigations.

sensitivity was proposed by Andrewes & Hortsmann (12) as a criterion in 1949 and is related to the presence in the virion of essential lipids. The peplos (the envelope) of some viruses does contain lipids. Yet, ether sensitivity and the presence of an envelope are sometimes correlated, but not always. Among the poxviruses, for example, some representatives are ether-sensitive, others ether-insensitive, and a number of intermediary situations are known. Yet, whether ether-sensitive or resistant, all of the poxviruses possess a common complement-fixing antigen and exhibit the property of derepressing a cellular decapsidase responsible for the "reactivation"; they obviously belong to the same "family." It is therefore impossible to regard ether sensitivity as a criterion for the definition of groups of high hierarchical order. Ether sensitivity could at best be utilized for the separation of species.

The next criterion retained by Cooper is the diameter of the virion. But to adopt size without paying attention to the type of symmetry, leads to illogical categories. Moreover, within virions possessing a helical symmetry, it is the diameter of the nucleocapsid and not its length which has to be taken into account.

Despite these imperfections, one should give credit to Cooper for having established, for the first time, a hierarchy of structural character for the delimitation of groups.

The system proposed in 1963 by Hamparian, Hilleman & Ketler (13) is derived from Cooper's classification. It concerns only animal viruses and makes use, as first parameters, of the nature of the nucleic acid and sensitivity to ether. Its originality is to take as a third criterion the sensitivity of the virion to acidity (pH 3). A look at the system shows that within the four groups defined by the two first parameters, sensitivity to acid does not lead to subdivisions. Sensitivity to pH permits only the separation of rhinoviruses from enteroviruses. Thus, sensitivity to acid can be utilized within a family, but not as a criterion for the definition of groups of high hierarchical rank, i.e., those above the genus.

In 1961, Horne & Wildy (14) pointed out that the nature of symmetry be used for classification. Wildy (15) has insisted on the importance of the shape of the virion for this purpose. Again in 1962, Lwoff, Horne and Tournier (who, from now on, will be referred to as L.H.T.) made a practical use of all of these suggestions, and proposed a system which will be examined in detail below [Lwoff, Horne & Tournier (16, 17)].

MacLeod & Markham (18), discussing the relations between turnip yellow mosaïc and wild cucumber mosaïc virus, concluded that the gross anatomy of the particles, their weight and the composition of their nucleic acids, would be the most important criteria for establishing relationships among viruses. MacLeod & Markham noted also that serological relationships are more correlated with anatomy, that is, the way in which the capsidal proteins are organized, than to the actual composition of proteins. This is a pertinent and important observation.

This survey of classification of viruses is far from exhaustive. We have

TABLE II

HAMPARIAN, HILLEMAN AND KETLER'S SYSTEM OF ANIMAL VIRUSES

Nucleic acid type	Ether and/or chloroform sensitivity	pH3 lability	Miscellaneous characters	Families or groups
DNA	Stable	Stable		Adenovirus Papovavirus
		Labile		
	Labile	Stable		
		Labile		Poxvirus Herpesvirus
RNA	Stable	Stable		Reovirus Enterovirus
		Labile		Rhino-coryzavirus
	Labile	Stable		
		Labile		Arbovirus Myxovirus

not mentioned those systems which are a mere collection of diseases or a mere list of names, for we are interested in classifying and not in cataloguing.

THE LWOFF-HORNE-TOURNIER SYSTEM

The L.H.T. system was proposed in 1962 [Lwoff, Horne & Tournier (16, 17)] (see Table III). Its aim was to embrace the viral world as a whole. A number of criteria had therefore to be eliminated. First, the disease, because symptoms vary with the host species, with its genetic constitution and its

TABLE III

THE LWOFF-HORNE-TOURNIER SYSTEM

PHYLUM	SUBPHYLA	CLASSES	ORDERS	SUBORDERS	FAMILIES: For helical viruses: diameter of the nucleocapsid / For cubical viruses: number of triangulation and number of capsomer	
	Type of genetic material	Symmetry of the nucleocapsid H: helical C: cubical B: binal	Nucleocapsid Naked (N) or Enveloped (E)	Nucleocapsid Rigid (R) or Flexuous (F)		
Vira	DNA Deoxyvira	H Deoxyhelica	N —			
			E Chitovirales		100 Å	Poxviridae.
		C Deoxycubica	N Haplovirales		1–12	Microviridae.
					3–32	Parvoviridae.
					7–72	Papilloviridae.
					25–252	Adenoviridae.
					81–812	Iridoviridae.
					?	Inoviridae.
			E Peplovirales		16–162	Herpesviridae.
		B Deoxybinala	N Urovirales			Phagoviridae.
			E			—
	RNA Ribovira	H Ribohelica	N Rhabdovirales	R: Rigidovirales	120–130 Å	Dolichoviridae.
					150	Protoviridae.
					200	Pachyviridae.
				F: Flexivirales	100–110	Leptoviridae.
					120–130	Mesoviridae.
					150	Adroviridae.
			E Sagovirales		90 Å	Myxoviridae.
					180	Paramyxoviridae.
						Stomatoviridae.
		C Ribocubica	N Gymnovirales		3–32	Napoviridae.
					9–92	Reoviridae.
			E Togavirales		?	Arboviridae.

The names of the groups are those proposed by the P.C.N.V.

age, and with the environment. Symptoms vary also with the genetic constitution of the virus. Second, the vegetative phase was excluded because, for obvious reasons, a system founded on the vegetative virus is not possible, at least for the time being.

Thus, only one basis remained: the virion. The viral cycle culminates in the virion, except in defective viruses. All virions share a certain number of discriminative features on which the definition of viruses is founded. But, within the framework of structural likeness, numerous types of organization have been recognized. The structure of the virion was therefore selected for the L. H. T. system. It turned out that the use of four features permit the classification of viruses. These four features, called "essential integrants," are the following:

1. Genetic material, DNA or RNA, as in Cooper's system.

2. Symmetry of the virus: helical, cubical, or binal (binal applies to urophages which possess two different symmetrical structures—the head and the tail).

3. Nucleocapsid: naked or enveloped.

4. Quantitative data: diameter of the nucleocapsid for virion with helical symmetry; number of capsomers for the virion with cubical symmetry.

When these four essential integrants are put to work, one ends up with groups of viruses; some had been previously recognized as natural groups, such as myxoviruses, herpesviruses, etc. (see Table III). The members of these groups had been united because they share a number of biological properties and also because their virions have the same pattern of organization. Placing them into categories is as simple as could be wished.

Our ignorance of the origin of viruses has often been stated. It seems possible that viruses have evolved by mutation from some normal cellular nucleic acid. If so, the viral nucleic acid has necessarily preceded the appearance of viral proteins. The mutations should have allowed first the production of enzymes necessary for the autonomous multiplication of the viral genetic material, and second, the production of capsidal proteins.

If this picture corresponds to reality, Cooper's choice of the nucleic acid of the virion as first character for the subdivision of viruses is entirely justified and this is why it was adopted by L.H.T.

The second most important character is, according to L.H.T., the architecture of the virion—its symmetry—which reflects the structure and architecture of capsidal proteins. The primitive virions, whatever their symmetry, could have been naked nucleocapsid from which the enveloped virions have evolved; the subdivision into naked and enveloped is accordingly subordinated to the subdivision according to symmetry. Finally comes the number of capsomeres for the "cubical" (C) virions and the diameter of the nucleocapsid for the "helical" (H) virions. In the absence of any paleontological data it is clear, as already pointed out, that this hierarchy is, from a phylogenetic point of view, arbitrary. Let us now consider a few hypotheses concerning the evolution of viruses.

I–Either the viral world has originated from one single ancestor possessing either DNA (D) or RNA (R) or it has not, that is, some ancestors were D and others R.

II–C and H viruses have either derived from one single parent whether H or C or have evolved independently from ancestors which, at the start of viral life, were already H or C.

As we assume that the primitive virions were naked nucleocapsids, we shall therefore neglect the character N and E. A few schemes of the possible evolution of viruses is given.

(*a*) Monophyletic origin (origin unknown)

$$DNA\text{-}C \rightleftharpoons RNA\text{-}C$$
$$\updownarrow \qquad\qquad \updownarrow$$
$$DNA\text{-}H \rightleftharpoons RNA\text{-}H$$

(*b*) Diphyletic origin. The nucleic acid remains constant, the symmetry varies:

$$DNA\text{-}C \rightleftharpoons DNA\text{-}H$$
$$RNA\text{-}C \rightleftharpoons RNA\text{-}H$$

(*c*) Diphyletic origin. The symmetry remains constant, the nucleic acid varies:

$$DNA\text{-}C \rightleftharpoons RNA\text{-}C$$
$$DNA\text{-}H \rightleftharpoons RNA\text{-}H$$

(*d*) Tetraphyletic origin

$$DNA\text{-}C \;-\;-\;-\;-\;-\; \rightarrow$$
$$DNA\text{-}H \;-\;-\;-\;-\;-\; \rightarrow$$
$$DNA\text{-}C \;-\;-\;-\;-\;-\; \rightarrow$$
$$RNA\text{-}H \;-\;-\;-\;-\;-\; \rightarrow$$

Whatever our views concerning viral evolution may be, that is, whatever evolutionary scheme we adopt (*a*, *b*, *c*, or *d*), only two classifications are possible:

$$DNA \begin{cases} H \\ C \end{cases} \qquad\qquad H \begin{cases} DNA \\ RNA \end{cases}$$

$$RNA \begin{cases} H \\ C \end{cases} \qquad\qquad C \begin{cases} DNA \\ RNA \end{cases}$$

A phylogenetic system, the dream of so many systematicians, must, of course, take evolution into account. For a monophyletic group, the hierarchy of subdivisions should correspond to the chronology of evolution: the earlier a given character has appeared, the higher is its hierarchy. For a polyphyletic group, hierarchy is arbitrary. The L.H.T. system is arbitrary, necessarily. Needless to say, comprehension of the groups is completely independent of the hierarchical order of the essential integrants.

The Taxonomic Value of Groups

Making use of the four essential integrants, the viral world has been sub-divided into categories. What is the taxonomic value of the various groups? The lowest one could be either a genus or a family. It appears that within a group defined by the four essential integrants, it could be convenient to distinguish different subgroups which can be considered as genera. Therefore we decide, arbitrarily, that the lowest group of the L.H.T. system, as defined by the four essential integrants, is a family. Accordingly, the higher groups are, respectively, orders, classes, and divisions.

The number of molecular species which enter a virion varies between two and perhaps ten. The systematics of viruses is thus based on the structure and interrelations of a small number of molecules. Is it therefore justifiable to equate the subdivisions of the L.H.T. system with orders, classes, and divisions?

The differences between two classes of viruses are clearly less important than those between two classes of bacteria. But these differences are also less important in procaryotic protists than in eucaryotic ones, less important in protists than in higher plants, less important in plants than in animals. In the living world, the differences between taxonomically or hierarchically homologous groups have not the same importance everywhere.

As it is convenient to designate the hierarchy of a group by a name, why not adopt for viruses the hierarchy utilized for animals, plants, and bacteria? Of course, the virologist has to be conscious of the fact that taxonomic groups have no reality except as concepts.

It would seem that this discussion is irrelevant. Yet, the decision taken has a consequence. According to all the codes of nomenclature, a family is named from its type genus. It is therefore important to know to which hierarchical category this rule must be applied.

Stability of the Family

The value of the L.H.T. system depends to a large extent on the stability of the family. The stability of the family depends, in turn, upon the stability of the four essential integrants. If current mutations should alter one of them, the species involved would *ipso facto* enter a new family, order, or class. If this were so, one would expect to find antigenically related viruses in different families. This is not the case. However, this negative finding does not mean much, for viruses belonging to the same family, and which are obviously close parents, are often antigenically unrelated. For the time being, we can only speculate and we would like to quote here the discussion of L.H.T.:

> The essential features and properties of a virus are, in the last analysis, the expression of the primary structure of the genetic material which controls the structure and properties of the proteins. Mutations which alter the primary structure of the structural genes alter the primary structure of proteins. The antigenicity of the virion might be modified by mutations and also the developmental charac-

teristics. Their biological characteristics may also be modified such as, for example, host range, virulence for the cell or for the organism, interactions of the cell/virus system, etc. Two viruses are considered related if they share a certain number of properties and, especially, if they share antigens.

During the course of viral evolution, a certain number of features have been modified. It is remarkable that those viruses generally recognized as related share the same four "essential integrants," namely: the nature of the nucleic acid, the type of architecture, the presence or absence of an envelope and, for viruses with cubic symmetry, the number of capsomeres. Whether or not the diameter of nucleo-capsids with helical symmetry will be among the "essential integrants" is not clear for the time being.

If the viral world is monophyletic, an unlikely hypothesis, this would indicate that "essential integrants" have been modified early in the course of evolution. If the viral world is polyphyletic, this indicates either that the essential integrants have not been modified during evolution or that they have been modified early in the course of evolution.

An explanation is thus offered for the fact that all viruses possessing common biological characteristics show the same "essential integrants," for example: adenoviruses, poxviruses, herpesviruses, myxoviruses, etc.

It does not follow that all viruses showing the same essential integrants are necessarily related. If essential integrants have not been modified by evolutionary processes, or if they have been modified very early, or if entities sharing the same essential integrants have originated independently, then it is clear that viruses belonging to the same group of our system might differ markedly from a biological point of view. This is precisely the case. For example, in the group of RCN viruses with 92 capsomeres are REO viruses and wound tumor viruses, which will probably have to be separated. The simplest idea is to subdivide the viruses according to the nature of their host, plant or animal. This leads to difficulties for those viruses which multiply both in plants and in insects. Moreover the criteria of our system are structural. The functional aspects of the virus such as host range or virulence have to intervene at the very end of the subdivisions in order, for example, to separate closely related viruses or mutants of a given virus. For the time being, the structural features which could permit separation of the REO viruses from the wound tumor viruses are unknown. In the meantime it seems worthwhile to look for possible relationships between REO viruses and wound tumor viruses such as, for example, antigenic similarities.

Thus, whatever hypothesis concerning the origin of viruses is accepted, the conclusion is reached that either the essential integrants of the virion have evolved early and have not undergone further evolution or that they have not evolved at all; that is, the actual essential integrants are the same as they were at the origin. It could be that an alteration of an essential integrant would imply numerous simultaneous mutations. This would mean that the probability of a mutation altering any one of the essential integrants is low. If viruses have originated from cellular organelles, it is possible that essential viral integrants correspond to structure having evolved in the cellular organelles before they have given rise to viruses. Whatever the hypotheses are, the real question is the stability of essential integrants. As the essential integrants are really stable they constitute valid characters for a system of viruses. It is hardly necessary to state that the criteria of this system are molecular and structural.

In other terms, we feel that the various viruses, when their "essential integrants" are established, will find their natural place in the system. By natural place, we mean they will fall in the same group as biologically related entities.

SUBDIVISION OF FAMILIES

The genus.

Thus, in making use of the four essential integrants of the virion, the kingdom of viruses has been subdivided into divisions, classes, orders, and families.

It might be convenient to subdivide a family into many genera, and we must discuss the characters which would be utilized for this purpose. Many of these characters have been mentioned by Lwoff, Horne and Tournier. The list of features is being completed here. The four essential determinants which define the family are, of course, excluded.

The genetic material.

1–The number of strands of nucleic acids, whether one or two.
2–The number of nucleotides.
3–The relative number of the four bases.
4–The sequence of bases.
5–The presence of abnormal nucleotides; whether, for example, the base is methylated or the pentose glycosylated.
6–The architecture of the genetic material within the capsid.

The structural units and the capsomers.

1–The molecular weight of the structural units.
2–The primary, secondary, and tertiary structure of the structural units.
3–The structure of the capsomers.
4–The antigenicity of the structural units of the isolated capsomers.

The capsid.

1–The dimension and architecture of the capsid.
2–The number of structural units or of capsomers.
3–The antigenicity of the capsid.
4–The nature of the protein, or material other than the structural units, associated with the capsid.
5–The properties of the capsid and of the nucleocapsid, its stability, resistance to various chemical and physical agents, etc.

The peplomers.

1–The molecular weight of the peplomers.
2–The primary, secondary, tertiary, and quaternary structure of the peplomers.
3–The antigenicity of the peplomers.

The peplos.

1–The number of peplomers.
2–The size and organization of the peplos.
3–The presence of hemagglutinin.
4–The antigenicity of the peplos.
5–The presence of cell material (especially the incorporation of cellular lipids which are responsible for ether sensitivity).
6–The hemolytic power.
7–The presence within the peplos of material other than the nucleocapsid.

The enzymes.

The nature, structure, and properties of the enzymes determined by the genetic material of the virus: neuramidinase, hemolysins?

The features of viral development.

The site of the synthesis of the viral material: nucleic acid, enzymes, capsidal proteins, etc.
The site of assembly of the virion.
The sensitivity to chemical and physical factors of the various phases of viral development.
The sensitivity to interferon.

Cell-virus interaction.

1–The alteration of cellular metabolism.
2–The alteration of cellular structures, especially of membranes.
3–The ability to destroy the mitotic apparatus.
4–The ability to elicit interferon synthesis.

The specificity.

1–The specificity for the host.
2–The specificity for the cell.

The virulence.

The symptomatology.

DISCUSSION

Antigenicity and classification.—Different viruses sometimes share antigenic properties. When this happens the viruses have so far proven to belong to the same family as defined by the four criteria of the L.H.T. system.

This is true for viruses of animals such as poxviruses, paramyxoviruses, and adenoviruses. It is true also for viruses of plants. Antigenic relations have been found only within the families as defined by the diameter of the nucleocapsid. Yet, all of the members of a given family do not necessarily share antigens. For example, *Adenovirus galli* is devoid of the complement-fixing group antigen common to the other genera of Adenoviridae.

It should be mentioned here that two members of the Reovirideae, a parasite of vertebrates, *Reovirus mammalis*, and a parasite of plants and insects, *Neovirus neoformans*, the wound tumour virus, belong to the same family. Streissle & Maramorosch (19) have recognized antigenic similarities between the two viruses, whereas these similarities have been denied by Gomatos & Tamm (20). The question remains open.

More data are needed concerning the antigenic properties of capsids and peplos and the sequences of amino acids of various viral proteins. For the time being, considering the few available data, one might conclude tentatively (*a*) that two viruses possessing a common antigen probably belong to the same family, and (*b*) that two viruses which do not possess a common antigen do not necessarily belong to different families.

The structure of the RNA.—Within the *Gymnovirales*, the Reoviridae are defined by the presence of 92 capsomers. It is interesting to note that the two Reoviridae which have been studied, *Reovirus mammalis* and *Neovirus neoformans*, possess a double-stranded RNA. All other viruses studied so far possess a single-stranded RNA. If it turns out that double-stranded RNA is a feature of all Reoviridae and is absent in all other families, this fact will have great significance and point toward the monophyletic origin of the family and to the validity of the L.H.T. system.

This list of viral features is, of course, not exhaustive. For the time being, the division of family into genera can be only tentative. It would, however, be surprising if all viruses have undergone a parallel evolution. Thus, one can foresee that the subdivision of families into genera will be based on criteria which will be different in different families.

A systematic and orderly survey of the different characters of various viral groups would be useful and fruitful. This would be the mere continuation of the work already done by so many virologists. What is needed is a little more systematization.

Critiques Directed Against the L.H.T. System

The L.H.T. system has received some attention and has been of course criticized. A critical examination of the critics is, at this point, necessary.

In the introduction to *Plant Virology*, Corbett & Sisler (21) wrote: "Such a system, although based on natural characteristics of the virus, would require that every laboratory have X-ray equipment and a crystallographer to classify viruses. Eventually, such a system may be useful, but at present I believe it is long before its time in the field of plant virology." Of course, this is not a criticism. It happens that many plant viruses, obviously ahead of their time, have already found their place in the L.H.T. system. Should we kick them out?

Plant pathologists, physicians, or veterinarians generally diagnose a disease by the symptoms. This is all right. A clinical diagnosis has been and is still useful. However, a scientific diagnosis of a virus must make use of non-clinical characters, namely, of the properties of the virion. Crystallography is not an absolute necessity in order to identify a virus. Serology or electron microscopy is sometimes sufficient and an electron microscope is sometimes available in the vicinity of a virological laboratory.

Biological classifications are dangerous, as will be shown by the example of arboviruses. This group was defined as viruses of vertebrates able to multiply in their arthropod vectors. It is already obvious that among viruses classified as arboviruses by virtue of the above definition, two structural types have been recognized: (a) typical myxovirus, the virus of vesicular stomatitis, (b) viruses possessing RNA, cubical symmetry, and an enveloped nucleocapsid. These true criteria permit the definition of an original group, which is an order, the Togavirales. The biological criteria are useless here. A virus possessing the structural characteristics of the order would be classified within the Togavirales even if not transmitted by arthropods.

Let us now consider other critics of the L.H.T. system. Andrewes, in 1964 (22), stated that the L.H.T. system brings together into one category certain plant and certain animal viruses. And what about those viruses which multiply in plants and in insects? Are they plant or animal viruses? Andrewes avoids this difficulty by considering, in his classification, only viruses of vertebrates.

Moreover, what is a "category"? A division, a class, an order, a family, a genus? At what level should the viruses of plants and animals be separated?

The critical discriminatory attitude of Andrewes towards plant viruses is the more remarkable in that he does not hesitate to include a few typical bacteria in his system of mammalian viruses.

Lanni (23) has classified taxonomies into three groups:

1. Classical taxonomy "which leans on ordinary phenotypic traits, host range, epidemiology, pathology, viral architecture, serology, more or less removed[4] from the genome."

2. Molecular taxonomy which utilizes the source of the ordinary phenotypic traits in the fine structure, mainly the nucleotid sequence of the genetic material.

3. Neoclassical taxonomy which stresses "hard" characters of the virion to the exclusion of "soft" characters and various biological properties. This is meant to describe the L.H.T. system.

Lanni objects that the L.H.T. system is not molecular in its own sense because it makes no "immediate use" of base composition or sequence of nucleic acid, the amino acid composition or sequence of polypeptide, serology, molecular test of homology (e.g., hybridization), or genetic recombination.

The decision that only the primary structure of a protein is "molecular" would seem to be arbitrary. The structures of higher order, that is, the

---

[4] Probably means remote.

architecture, being essential features of a molecule, would seem to be entitled to be called molecular.

Let us now examine Lanni's "molecular" system. Since viruses are reproduced from their genetic material, it follows that the whole virus, including the virion, is determined by the base sequence of its nucleic acid. Provided the code is entirely deciphered, knowing the base sequence of the structural genes means knowing the amino acid sequence of the proteins. Yet, for the time being, it is impossible to deduce the tertiary and quaternary structures of a protein from its amino acid sequence. Moreover, the architecture of a protein may be modified by various ligands. Of course, we all hope that in a not-too-distant future, the knowledge of the primary structure of the viral proteins will permit the deduction of the symmetry, size, and organization of the virion. This is not yet the case.

Finally, let us assume that we are able to reconstruct the phylogeny of a given virus. Mutations have lead to substitution of amino acids and to antigenic alterations. The question is immediately raised: how many amino acid substitutions will be needed in order to consider that we are dealing with a new species or a new genus? Not only the number of substitutions will have to be taken into account, but also their nature. If a few hundred amino acids belonging to twenty species are involved, one can foresee great battles.

In Lanni's system, the base sequence of the nucleic acid is selected because it determines the properties of the virus and of the virion itself. Yet, if it is admitted that the most convenient classification of viruses is based on the virion, is it not simpler to consider the virion than the base sequence? We are afraid that, at least for a few years, it will be easier to state that a virion possesses DNA, a cubical symmetry, that its capsid is naked and consists of 72 capsomeres, than to consider a list of 10,000 nucleotides. Lanni's system is a statement of inapplicable principles, and what virologists need is a real system.

In the summary of his paper, Lanni emphasizes the confused state of classical viral taxonomy and suggests that molecular taxonomy *sensu* Lanni is particularly suited to viruses. The "neoclassical" L.H.T. system has been completely forgotten. It possesses, however, two non-negligible advantages: it exists and it allows the classification of viruses.

Variants of the L.H.T. System

Two different aspects of virus classification must be considered—the criteria employed and the hierarchy.

In October 1962, the Subcommittee on Taxonomy of Viruses proposed that the major groups would be defined in terms of (*a*) nucleic acid composition, (*b*) sensitivity to ether, (*c*) presence of a limiting membrane, (*d*) symmetry, whether cubical or helical, and (*e*) number of capsomers.

When discussing Cooper's system, it was stated that among antigenically related poxviruses, some are ether-resistant, others, ether-sensitive. Therefore, ether sensitivity cannot be utilized as a criterion for systematics. The

four other criteria retained are those of the L.H.T. system. The diameter of
the nucleocapsid, which is an essential character for virions with helical symmetry, has not been mentioned.

In *Advances in Virus Research*, Andrewes (24) proposed in 1962 the use
of the following criteria: nucleic acid, size (without further specification),
number of capsomers, presence or absence of an envelope, multiplication in
the cytoplasm or in the nucleus, or in both, maturation at cell surface, ether
sensitivity.

In "The Viruses of Vertebrates" Andrewes (22) has proposed a classification restricted to viruses of vertebrates. It makes use of three criteria, hierarchically organized: the nature of the nucleic acid, the symmetry of the
virion, and the presence or absence of an envelope. His classifications would
seem, therefore, to be close to the L.H.T. system.

Another system was proposed by Andrewes (25) in *Bacteriological Reviews*
in 1965. The classification is based on four characters. First, the nucleic
acid, next, the symmetry, then the presence or absence of an envelope, and
finally, the number of capsomers for viruses with cubical symmetry. Thus,
Andrewes has finally eliminated all of the useless criteria he proposed in the
past and has kept only the four characters of the L.H.T. system, as well as
their hierarchy. Finally, he states that there is general agreement concerning
the characters which are used in defining the main families of viruses.

Huck has proposed what he describes as a compounded viral classification [Huck, (26)]. The backbone of this system, namely, the four first
columns, is a mere transcript of the L.H.T. system. The other columns mention only properties which are useless for the definition of groups of high
hierarchical order.

NOMENCLATURE AND SYSTEMATICS

The codes of nomenclature (botanical, zoological, bacteriological, and
viral) consider the problem of nomenclature and not those of systematics. If
one selects the discriminatory traits for the definition of taxa, if one sub-
divides taxa into subtaxa, or, more generally, if one organizes taxa into
categories, this is a matter of systematics. The word taxonomy is generally
utilized as synonymous with systematics. However, the naming of taxa,
taxonomy *sensu stricto*, is only the last step of systematics. The naming of
taxa is a matter of nomenclature and must accord with a code of nomenclature. The object of such a code is to bring about stability and universality of
scientific names in such a way that each name be unique, distinct, and—if
possible—comprehensible. The code is designed to achieve this goal and none
of its rules limits the freedom of thought or action in the field of systematics.
Virologists have to be bound by a code of nomenclature.

An international committee on nomenclature must deal with nomenclature and not with systematics. If must be alert to the correctness of names,
to see that they are in agreement with the code. It must, among other things,

verify that each genus has a type species, each family a type genus, and that each family is named from its type genus.

The Defunct Subcommittee and the International Status of the Nomenclature of Viruses

A few years ago, the judicial committee of the International Committee on Bacterial Nomenclature appointed a subcommittee on nomenclature of the viruses (SCNV). As this subcommittee no longer exists it will, for the sake of simplicity, be called the defunct subcommittee.

The International Code of Nomenclature of Bacteria and Viruses was, of course, supposed to be applied to viruses and, in theory, virologists should have conformed to its rules.

Let us recall that each family must have a type genus and that the name of the family is the name of the type genus followed by the suffix, aceae, for plants and bacteria, and ideae for animals. The name of the type genus and of the family are thus coordinated. This is a very wise rule indeed. A few examples of the "decisions" of the subcommittee will be analyzed.

Picorna.—The term, picorna, was proposed by the defunct subcommittee as the name of a "group" (27). Pico is a prefix in the metric system meant to indicate a submultiple of a unit, namely 10^{-12}, and rna stands for RNA. Thus, picorna means 10^{-12} ribonucleic acid.

Moreover, it is stated in the minutes of the subcommittee that the initial letters of picorna may be taken to refer to poliomyelitis, insensitivity to ether, Coxsackie, orphan, and rhinovirus. A disease, a chemical property, a virus, a state, and again a virus. This is ridiculous.

Papova.—The term, papova, was proposed by Melnick in 1962 (28) and endorsed by the defunct subcommittee in order to embrace the papilloma virus, the polyoma virus, and the vacuolating agent, hence pa-po-va. Let us suppose that later it is found that one of the three viruses must be excluded from the group. As a consequence, the name papova would become a nonsense name and would have to be changed. It is to avoid such a contingency that the rule was established, stating that a family must be named from its type genus. Papova, which does not correspond to a genus, cannot be the name of a family. *Delenda papova!*

Varia.—

ECHO stands for Enteric, Cytopathogenic, Human, Orphan.
ECBO stands for Enteric, Cytopathogenic, Bovine, Orphan.
NITA stands for Nuclear Inclusion Type A (!).
REO stands for Respiratory, Enteric, Orphan.
No comment.

Anomalies.—According to one of the decisions of the subcommittee, "size" is one of the important characteristics of viruses. Size, however, has a different meaning if one considers the nucleocapsid or the peplos. Moreover, in a rodlike helical virus, what is size? Is it the diameter of the nucleocapsid or its length?

More anomalies.—According to a decision of the defunct subcommittee, no plant virus should be in the same "group" with a mammalian virus. What is the meaning of the word group? Is it a phylum, a class, an order, a family, or a genus? The subcommittee did not take account of the fact that the word, group, applies to any category, whatever its hierarchical position, and that consequently, its decision was completely meaningless.

The defunct subcommittee had to apply the rules of the International Code of Nomenclature of Bacteria and Viruses, and decided that binominal nomenclature could not be applied to viruses. Moreover, all of its decisions, in order to be valid, had to be submitted to the Judicial Committee of Nomenclature. They were not so submitted and are therefore devoid of any legal, international value.

The subcommittee should have tried to devise a code, or at least to propose a few principles of nomenclature. This was not done. It christened groups without stating what these groups were. Moreover, the nomenclature it adopted is in disagreement with the spirit and rules of nomenclature, whether zoological, botanical, or bacterial. Rules are necessary in order to prevent nonsense. Nomenclature is not a game but a tool, and the key to an international language.

The situation was dramatic. It was obviously necessary and urgent that viruses should not be left in a taxonomic vacuum. The Executive Committee of I.A.M.S. (International Association of Microbiological Societies) discussed the matter with the President of the S.C.N.V. (Subcommittee for the Nomenclature of Viruses). The S.C.N.V. was dissolved. The Executive Committee of I.A.M.S. (E.C.I.A.M.S.) took following action at its Paris Meeting in July 1963. E.C.I.A.M.S.:

a) took notice of the willingness of most of the members of the subcommittee on viruses to dissolve this subcommittee,

b) decided that a new international committee, the International Committee on Nomenclature of Viruses (I.C.N.V.) be created, the counterpart of the International Committee on Bacteriological Nomenclature (I.C.B.N.).

c) decided that the members of the I.C.N.V. (like those of the I.C.B.N.) would be nominated by the National Societies. The first official meeting would be held during the IXth Congress in 1966 in Moscow.

Moreover, E.C.I.A.M.S. decided to create a provisional Committee, the P.C.N.V., whose task was to prepare the work of the future I.C.N.V. and of its Judicial Commission. E.C.I.A.M.S. nominated the members of the P.C.N.V. after consultation with the President of the I.C.B.N., the chairman of the S.C.N.V. and the President of the Advisory Council of I.A.M.S.

The members of the P.C.N.V. are: C. H. Andrewes (Coombe Bissett, Salisbury), P. D. Cooper (Canberra), S. Fazekas de St Groth (Canberra), H. S. Ginsberg (Philadelphia), D. Goldfarb (Moscow), L. Hirth (Strasbourg), G. Ivanovics

(Szeged), M. Kaplan (Genève), A. Lwoff (Paris), K. Maramorosch (Yonkers, New York), H. Pereira (Mill Hill, London), P. Tournier (Paris) and V. Zhdanov (Moscow).

The committee elected a President, Sir Christopher Andrewes, and a Secretary, Paul Tournier Villejuif (Seine).

The Committee discussed the problem extensively by correspondence and held its first—and last—meeting in Paris on June 25 and 26, 1965 (Dr. Fazekas de St Groth and Dr. Goldfarb were unable to attend the meeting).

The main task of the P.C.N.V. was, as already said, to prepare the work of the future Judicial Commission. It should be clear that only the I.C.N.V. will have the legal power to enforce a code of nomenclature and to take decisions concerning nomenclature of viruses. The P.C.N.V. has no right to take decisions, and can only make proposals or recommendations.

The members of the P.C.N.V. were provided with a typescript of this review which served as a working document. The proposals and recommendations of the P.C.N.V. have been published in a few journals (29). It seems useful to publish them again within the framework of this review.

PROPOSALS OF THE P.C.N.V.

PRINCIPLES

1. An International Nomenclature of Viruses is necessary. Viruses cannot be left in a taxonomic vacuum.

2. The only way to achieve an International Nomenclature of viruses is by a binominal system.

3. The code of nomenclature of bacteria cannot be applied to viruses.

4. Virologists will therefore have to build their own code.

COMMENTS

The Bacteriological code, as well as the Zoological and Botanical codes, includes the law of priority. To apply the law of priority to viruses would be almost impossible and would certainly be the cause of endless polemics. The decision as to which names should be maintained will be in the hands of the Judicial Commission (J.C.) of the International Committee of the Nomenclature of Viruses (I.C.N.V.).

NAMING OF TAXA

The names already in use should be maintained whenever it is possible. For the information of new names of taxa, the P.C.N.V. recommends:

1. No taxon should be named from a person,

2. Anagrams, siglas, hybrids of names, non-sense names should be prohibited.

3. Names should preferentially be latin or latinized greek names (see Zoological, Botanical and Bacteriological codes).

4. A species shall be selected to typify each genus. This type species shall be selected as being the most fully defined by published work (e.g. by serotype and other criteria), and should desirably be represented in a Type Culture Collection and held and maintained in replicate in 4 or 5 different countries. The task of describing genera and type species and of making detailed proposals for classification

shall be left to individual authors or to subcommittees of the future Judicial Commission.

5. A subgeneric name is formed by an epithet in brackets following the name of the genus. Example: *genus: Coxsackievirus, Subgenus: Coxsackievirus (A)*.

6. Different species belonging to different *subgenera* of the same *genus* can have the same name.

Example: *Coxsackievirus (A) primus, Coxsackievirus (B) primus*.

COMMENTS

This rule was adopted in order to be able to keep systems already in use. It implies that whenever a *genus* be subdivided into *subgenera*, the name of the *subgenera* must be mentioned.

7. Specific names can be names, as in Zoology, Botany or Bacteriology, but can also be letters or numerals. Yet the type species must have a latinized name. Example: Cocksackievirus (A) primus would be the type species. The other species could be 5, 18, α, β, etc. . . . This again will make it possible to maintain as valid, systems already in existence.

8. The names of all viral genera end in "virus," example: *Poliovirus, Napovirus*.

9. No viral genus names should be identical with the genus of a bacterium, a protozoon, an alga, that is with the names of procaryotic or eucaryotic protists. The genera of viruses, having to end with the suffix virus, this rule is therefore necessary only if, for example, the name of protist ends with the same suffix virus. If a bacterium is called Chlamydovirus, no viral genus can bear this name.

10. A genus shall be selected to typify each family.

11. A family is named from its type genus. Example: *Poxvirus, Poxviridae*.

12. The suffix for the family is *idae*, as in the zoological code. This ending was preferred to *aceae*, in use for plants and bacteria because:

a) It is more euphonious,

b) It allows discrimination between viral and bacterial families.

13. All viral genera ending in *virus* and all families being named from their type genus, it follows that all the viral families end with *viridae*.

14. It is proposed that the terms, phylum, division, class, order, family, genus and species are applied to viral taxa. This does not imply any homology between viral taxa and taxa belonging to other phyla.

15. Depersonalisation. The name of a taxon, whatever its rank, is not followed by the name of the author who proposed it. Example: If Smith-Dupont proposed the genus *Poxvirus*, the genus is *Poxvirus* and not *Poxvirus Smith-Dupont*.

16. In order to be valid a name has to be endorsed by the Judicial Commission. However the Judicial Commission can only decide that a name is correctly formed, that is in agreement with the rules, but as no right to reject a name on the ground, for example, that it is unnecessary. In other terms, the Judicial Commission deals with nomenclature and not with systematics. The necessity of a name, its justification can be studied by a specialized Committee or by an individual. It is clear that unnecessary names will on the long run die out.

CLASSIFICATION OF VIRUSES

The principles were applied and a list of names was proposed. Before giving this list, it is better to discuss classification.

As stated already the P.C.N.V. has to deal with nomenclature and not with systematics. As for any virologist, the P.C.N.V. has, however, the right to propose or to adopt a system. Moreover, it has also the right to propose names for the various taxa. Taking advantage of these rights, the P.C.N.V. has discussed the principles of classification and reached the following conclusions:

a) a system of viruses should embrace the viral world as a whole,

b) the criteria for the definition of divisions, classes, orders and families should be clearly defined.

The L.H.T. (Lwoff, Horne, Tournier) system was found to be the most suitable for the time being and is recommended as a provisional system.

1° PRINCIPLES

a) The virion shall be the basis of the taxonomy.

b) The following 4 characters of the virion shall be used for the definition of families without specifying any hierarchical significance at this stage.

I—The chemical nature of the nucleic acid (i.e. RNA or DNA)

II—The symmetry of the nucleocapsid (i.e. helical, cubical, or binal)

III—The presence or absence of an envelope for which the name *peplos* is proposed. A peplos is formed of *peplomers* just as a capsid is formed of capsomers

IV—For helical viruses: the diameter of the nucleocapsid
For cubical viruses: the number of triangulation and the number of capsomers.

The sum of these four criteria will define the family.

The hierarchy and taxa proposed by L.H.T. were discussed. The first criterion, which was proposed by P. D. Cooper, is the nature of the nucleic acid, hence two *divisions: deoxyvira* and *ribovira*. The second criterion is the type of symmetry, whether cubical or helical. Hence four *classes: deoxyhelica, deoxycubica ribohelica, ribocubica.* A group of viruses, bacteriophages possessing a tail, exhibit a double type of symmetry, that of the head and of the tail, that is a binal symmetry. As they are deoxyvira, a fifth class is proposed *deoxybinala.* If it is later found that some *ribovira* have a tail they would be called *ribobinala.* Then, each class is divided into orders according to whether the nucleocapsid is naked or enveloped.

The names of the orders will be found in the tables. All the viruses possessing an envelope or peplos have been given a name which includes a prefix corresponding to a greek or latin name meaning something like mantle.

The orders are subdivided into families according to the number of capsomers and the triangulation number (viruses with cubical symmetry) or according to the diameter of the nucleocapsid (viruses with helical symmetry). As the families are named from their type genus, no problem of nomenclature is posed by the naming of the family.

An alteration of the L.H.T. system proposed by Hirth was adopted by the P.C.N.V. The viruses possessing RNA, helical symmetry and a naked nucleocapsid, the order of *Rhabdovirales* is subdivided into two suborders according to the rigidity or flexibility of the virion. Each suborder is then subdivided into families

TABLE IV

NOMINA CONSERVANDA
Subphylum: Ribovira
Class:　　　Ribocubica
Order:　　　Gymnovirales

FAMILY (-viridae)	SUBFAMILIES (-virinae)	GENUS	TYPE SPECIES (*)	COMMON NAME
Napoviridae............	A. Napovirinae (nominative subfamily)........	Napovirus (type genus).	flavicans.	Turnip yellow mosaic.
	B. Picornavirinae........	1. *Picornavirus* (type genus).	aphthae.	Foot and mouth disease.
		2. *Poliovirus*.	primus.	Polio 1.
		3. *Coxsackievirus*.	(A) primus.	Coxsackie A1.
		4. *Echovirus*.	(hominis) primus.	ECHO 1.
		5. *Rhinovirus*.	(hominis) primus.	Rhinovirus 1.
		6. *Cardiovirus*.	ratii.	EMC.
	C. Androphagovirinae....	*Androphagovirus* (type genus).	bacterii.	RNA phage.
Reoviridae............		1. *Reovirus* (type genus).	(mammalis) primus (type genus).	Reovirus I.
		2. *Neovirus*.	neoformans.	Wound tumor virus.

Class:　Ribocubica.
Order:　Togavirales.

FAMILY (-viridae)	GENUS	TYPE SPECIES (*)	COMMON NAME
Arboviridae............	*Arbovirus* (type genus).	occidentalis (type genus).	WEE.

(*) Words in parentheses correspond to subgenera.

TABLE V

NOMINA CONSERVANDA
Subphylum: Ribovira
Class: Ribohelica

FAMILY (-viridae)	GENUS (-virus)	TYPE SPECIES (*)	COMMON NAME
Dolichoviridae..........	*Dolichovirus* (type genus).	brassicae.	Cabbage mosaic.
Protoviridae............	*Protovirus* (type genus).	tabaci.	Tobacco mosaic.
Pachyviridae...........	*Pachyvirus* (type genus).	crotalum.	Rattle mosaic.
Leptoviridae...........	*Leptovirus* (type genus).	solanum.	Potato X.
Mesoviridae............	*Mesovirus* (type genus).	pisum.	Pea mosaic.
Adroviridae............	*Adrovirus* (type genus).	trifolii.	White clover mosaic.
Myxoviridae............	1. *Myxovirus* (type genus).	(influenzae) A.	Influenzae A.
	2. *Rabiesvirus*.	canis.	Rabies.
	3. *Sigmavirus*.	drosophilae.	Virus of L'Héritier.
Paramyxoviridae........	1. *Paramyxovirus* (type genus).	(parainfluenzae) primus.	Myxovirus parainfluenzae 1.
	2. *Bronchovirus*.	syncytialis.	Respiratory syncytial.
Stomatoviridae.........	*Stomatovirus* (type genus).	bovis.	Vesicular stomatitis.

(*) Words in parentheses correspond to subgenera.

TABLE VI

NOMINA CONSERVANDA

Subphylum: Deoxyvira
Classes: Deoxyhelica, Deoxycubica, Deoxybinala

FAMILY (-viridae)	GENUS (-virus)	TYPE SPECIES (*)	COMMON NAME
Poxviridae...........	1. *Poxvirus* (type genus).	variolae.	Variola.
	2. *Dermovirus*.	orfi.	Contagious pustular dermatitis.
	3. *Pustulovirus*.	ovis.	Sheep pox.
	4. *Avipoxvirus*.	galli.	Fowl pox.
	5. *Fibromavirus*.	myxomatosis.	Rabbit myxoma.
	6. *Molluscovirus*.	hominis.	Molluscum contagiosum.
Microviridae........	1. *Microvirus* (type genus).	monocatena.	Phage φX 174.
Parvoviridae........	1. *Parvovirus* (type genus).	ratti.	Kilham rat virus.
Papillomaviridae....	1. *Papillomavirus* (type genus).	sylvilagi.	Shope papilloma virus.
	2. *Polyomavirus*.	neoformans.	Polyoma virus.
Adenoviridae.......	1. *Adenovirus* (type genus).	(hominis) quintus.	Adenovirus 5.
Iridoviridae........	1. *Iridovirus* (type genus).	tipulae.	Tipula iridescens.
Inophagoviridae.....	1. *Inophagovirus* (type genus).	bacterii.	fd phage (Hoffmann–Berling).
Herpesviridae.......	1. *Herpesvirus* (type genus).	hominis.	Herpes simplex virus.
	2. *Cytomegaliavirus*.	hominis.	Human cytomegalovirus.
Phagoviridae........	1. *Phagovirus* (type genus).	(coli)T secundus.	Phage T2.

(*) Words in parentheses correspond to subgenera.

according to the diameter of the nucleocapsid. The reasons for this procedure have been discussed by Hirth (30).

NOMINA CONSERVANDA

The P.C.N.V. considered that it would be useful if virologists could already agree on names which should be maintained. The P.C.N.V. therefore proposes a list of *nomina conservanda* and a list of new genera. A type species was selected for each genus.

APPENDIX I

1. A few binominal systems of nomenclature have been proposed in the past. One of the reasons for which they were not adopted is that they involved a radical change of universally accepted names. The P.C.N.V. has taken great care not to suppress names which are in common use.

2. A number of names such as, for example, *Echo, Reo,* are not in agreement with the rules proposed by the P.C.N.V.: they are sigla. Nevertheless the P.C.N.V. proposes them as *nomina conservanda* because they are in common use.

3. *Picorna* is now commonly used in order to designate a "group" of viruses. In order to be able to maintain this name for a taxon above the rank of genus and lower than an order, that is a family or a sub-family, it was necessary that a genus be named *Picorna*. This was done.

4. *Papova,* which is a hybrid of *Papilloma, Polyoma* and *Vacuolating agent* and does not correspond to a genus, could not be maintained.

APPENDIX II

DEFINITION OF THE TRIANGULATION NUMBER.

A polyhedron whose faces are all equilateral triangles is called a deltahedron. Deltahedra models can be constructed from folded cardboard nets of equilateral triangles. We have enumerated all possible deltahedra which have icosahedral symmetry ("icosa-deltahedra") [Caspar and Klug, 1963]. The icosahedron itself has 20 equilateral triangular faces, and any icosadeltahedron has 20 T facets, where T is the *triangulation number* given by the rule:

$T = Pf^2$ where P can be any number of the series 1, 3, 7, 13, 19, 21, 31, 37 . . . $(= h^2 + hk + k^2$, for all pairs of integers h and k having no common factor) and f is any integer. For a fixed value of P, increases in f from 1 upward correspond to successive subtriangulations of the primitive deltahedron.

THE CLASSES OF ICOSAHEDRAL DELHEDRA
TABULATION OF THE TRIANGULATION NUMBER: T.

Class:

P=1	 1	4	9	16	25	. . . .
P=3	. . . .	3	12		27	. . . .
Skew classes	. . . .		7	13	19 21	. . . .

Triangulation N° $T = Pf^2$ where $P = h^2 + hk + k^2$, h and k any pair of integers with no common factor and $f = 1, 2, 3, 4 \cdots$

No. of structure units $S = 60\ T$

No. of morphological units $M = 10T + 2$.
$$= 10(T-1) \text{ hexamers} + 12 \text{ pentamers}.$$

Some established virus examples.

Phage ϕX, $T = 1$; Turnip yellow mosaic virus $T = 3$; Herpes, Varicella $T = 16$; Adenovirus, Infectious canine hepatitis $T = 25$.

From Caspar and Klug. *Cold Spring Harbor Symposia on Quantitative Biology*, 1962, vol. XXVII, 13.

APPENDIX III

GLOSSARY-GLOSSAIRE.

Adros (gr.).................	Thick.	Epais.
Andreios (gr.)..............	Male.	Mâle.
Aphtai (gr.)................	Ulcerating vesicles in the mouth.	Aphtes.
Avis, avis (lat.).............	Bird.	Oiseau.
Beta, bêtae (lat.)...........	Beet.	Betterave.
Bos, bovis (lat.).............	Cow.	Vache.
Brassica, brassicae (lat.)......	Cabbage.	Chou.
Cavia, caviae (lat.)..........	Guinea pig.	Cobaye.
Chiton (gr.)................	Tunic.	Tunique.
Cricetus, criceti (lat.)........	Hamster.	Hamster.
Crotalon (gr.)..............	Rattle.	Grelot.
Dolichos (gr.)..............	Long.	Long.
Equus, equi (lat.)...........	Horse.	Cheval.
Flavus (lat.)................	Yellow.	Jaune.
Flecto, ere (lat.)............	To bend.	Courber.
Gallus, galli (lat.)...........	Cock.	Coq.
Gymno (gr.)................	Naked.	Nu.
Haploos (gr.)..............	Simple.	Simple.
Iris, iridos (gr.).............	Iris, Rainbow.	Iris, arc-en-ciel.
Is, inos (gr.)................	Fiber, filament.	Fibre, filament.
Leptos (gr.)................	Narrow.	Etroit.
Mesos (gr.).................	Middle.	Moyen.
Napus, napus (lat.)..........	Turnip.	Navet.
Ornis, ornithos (gr.).........	Bird.	Oiseau.
Oura, ouras (gr.)............	Tail.	Queue.

Ovis, ovis (lat.).............	Sheep.	Brebis.
Pachus (gr.).................	Thick.	Epais.
Parvus, parvi (lat.)..........	Small.	Petit.
Peplos (gr.).................	Woman mantle.	Manteau de femme.
Pisum, pisi (lat.)............	Pea.	Pois.
Protos (gr.).................	First	Premier.
Rana, ranae (lat.)...........	Frog.	Grenouille.
Rhabdos, Dou (gr.)..........	Rod.	Baguette.
Rigidus (lat.)...............	Rigid.	Rigide.
Sagum, sagi (lat.)...........	Mantle.	Saie.
Simia, simiae (lat.)..........	Monkey.	Singe.
Solanum, solani (lat.)........	Night shade.	Solanée.
Stoma, stomatos (gr.)........	Mouth.	Bouche.
Sus, suis (lat.)..............	Pig.	Porc.
Sylvilagus (lat.)............. Zoological name of the cottontail...................	Cottontail (wild rabbit).	Lapin sauvage du continent américain.
Toga, togae (lat.)...........	Toga (Roman mantle).	Toge.
Trifolium, ii (lat.)...........	Clover.	Trèfle.

LITERATURE CITED

1. Lwoff, A., *Bacteriol. Rev.*, **17**, 269–337 (1953)
2. Lwoff, A., *J. Gen. Microbiol.*, **17**, 239–53 (1957)
3. Stanier, R. Y., and van Niel, C. B., *Arch. Mikrobiol.*, **42**, 17–35 (1962)
4. Lwoff, A., in *The Viruses*, **2**, 187–201. (Burnet, F. M., and Stanley, W. M., Eds, Academic Press, New York, London, 408 pp., 1959)
5. Lwoff, A., Anderson, T. F., and Jacob, F., *Ann. Inst. Pasteur*, **97**, 281–89 (1959)
6. Caspar, D. L. D., Dulbecco, R., Klug, A., Lwoff, A., Stoker, M. G. P., Tournier, P., and Wildy, P., *Cold Spring Harbor Symp. Quant. Biol.*, **27**, 49–50 (1962)
7. Bennett, C. W., *Phytopathology*, **29**, 422– (1939)
8. Bawden, F. C., *Chronica Botan.*, **6**, 385– (1941)
9. Brandes, J., and Wetter, C., *Virology*, **8**, 99–115 (1959)
10. Bradley, D. E., *J. Roy. Microscop. Soc.*, **84**, 257–316 (1965)
11. Cooper, P. D., *Nature*, **190**, 302–5 (1961)
12. Andrewes, C. H., and Hortsmann, D. M., *J. Gen. Microbiol.*, **3**, 290–97 (1949)
13. Hamparian, V. V., Hilleman, M. R., and Ketler, A., *Proc. Soc. Exptl. Biol. Med.*, **112**, 1040–50 (1963)
14. Horne, R. W., and Wildy, P., *Virology*, **15**, 348–73 (1961)
15. Wildy, P., *Symp. Soc. Gen. Microbiol.*, **12**, 145–63 (1962)
16. Lwoff, A., Horne, R. W., and Tournier, P., *Compt. Rend.*, **254**, 4225–27 (1962)
17. Lwoff, A., Horne, R. W., and Tournier, P., *Cold Spring Harbor Symp. Quant. Biol.*, **27**, 51–55 (1962)
18. MacLeod, R., and Markham, R., *Virology*, **19**, 190–97 (1963)
19. Streissle, G., and Maramorosch, K., *Science*, **140**, 996–97 (1963)
20. Gomatos, P. J., and Tamm, I., *Proc. Natl. Acad. Sci. U.S.*, **50**, 878–85 (1963)
21. Corbett, M. K., and Sisler, H. D., *Plant Virology*. (Univ. of Florida Press, Gainesville, Fla., 527 pp., 1964)
22. Andrewes, C., *Viruses of Vertebrates*. (Baillère, Tindall and Cox, 401 pp., London, 1964)
23. Lanni, F., in *Plant Virology*, 386–426. (See Ref. 21)
24. Andrewes, C., *Advan. Virus Res.*, **9**, 271–96 (1962)
25. Andrewes, C., *Bacteriol. Rev.*, **29**, 1–8 (1965)
26. Huck, R. A., *Vet. Bull.* (*Commonwealth Bur. Animal Health*), **34**, 239–53 (1964)
27. International Enterovirus Study Group, *Virology*, **19**, 114–16 (1963)
28. Melnick, J. L., *Science*, **135**, 1128–30 (1962)
29. Proposals and recommendations of the Provisional Committee for Nomenclature of Viruses. *Ann. Inst. Pasteur*, **109**, 625–37 (1965)
30. Hirth, L., *Compt. Rend.*, **261**, 4556–58 (1965)

BIOLOGY OF THE MYXOBACTERIA[1,2]

By Martin Dworkin[3]

Department of Microbiology, University of Minnesota, Minneapolis, Minnesota

Contents

INTRODUCTION.. 75
DEFINITION OF THE GROUP...................................... 76
METHODS OF ISOLATION.. 76
ECOLOGY... 77
MORPHOLOGY.. 78
  Vegetative Cells.. 78
  Microcysts.. 79
NUTRITION.. 80
  Nitrogen Requirements... 81
  Effect of Mono- and Disaccharides....................... 83
  Vitamin Requirements.. 84
  Utilization of Macromolecules.............................. 85
  Utilization of Subcellular Fractions...................... 86
METABOLISM... 86
LIFE CYCLE AND MORPHOGENESIS.......................... 87
  The Fruiting Body.. 87
  Effect of the Nutritional Milieu on Fruiting Body Formation...... 88
  Chemotaxis... 89
  Microcyst Formation... 90
  Microcyst Germination... 91
  Morphogenetic Mutants... 92
RESISTANCE OF THE MICROCYST............................. 92
BACTERIOPHAGE... 93
PIGMENTS... 94
PATHOGENICITY.. 94
MOTILITY.. 95
LYTIC FACTORS AND ANTIBIOTIC ACTIVITY............. 95
  Lytic Activity... 96
  Production of Antibiotics....................................... 99
TAXONOMY... 99
EPILOGUE AND CONCLUSIONS................................. 102

INTRODUCTION

"A few years since, while collecting fungi at Kittery and in several other localities in New England and the southern states, the writer's attention was attracted by a bright orange colored growth occurring on decaying wood, fungi, and similar substances . . . " (1).

[1] The survey of the literature pertaining to this review was concluded in December 1965.

[2] Investigations originating from this laboratory were supported by grants from the Developmental Biology Program of the National Science Foundation.

[3] Career Development Awardee of the Public Health Service (1-K3-GM-5869-10).

Since Thaxter's description of the myxobacteria was reported in 1892, microbiology has progressed dramatically; in part, as a consequence of a rigorous analytical approach. Unfortunately, the myxobacteria have not shared in this bounty.

"Since their first recognition as an independent group by Thaxter (1) the higher myxobacteria have been studied far more extensively by cryptogamic botanists than by bacteriologists, a fact of no little consequence from the standpoint of our knowledge about them. Pure culture methods have been little used, and in general these organisms have been treated more as objects of morphological interest than as biological entities. We know hardly more of some species than the final structure of their fruiting bodies." (2)

Part of the difficulty in applying modern microbiological techniques to the fruiting myxobacteria can be attributed to the fact that, as a rule, they will not grow in a dispersed state in liquid media. The discovery by Woods (3) of a dispersed-growing variant of *Myxococcus xanthus* and the subsequent use of similar variants (4–6) has demonstrated that the fruiting myxobacteria are indeed amenable to analytical description.

It is the purpose of this review to summarize and evaluate the information about the fruiting myxobacteria that has accumulated over the past 73 years. Since Stanier's excellent review of the nonfruiting myxobacteria (2), little has been said about this group which needs repeating. Accordingly, except for an occasional allusion, the present review will be concerned with fruiting myxobacteria. For further perspective, the reader is referred to Stanier's revision of the classification of the myxobacteria in the 7th edition of *Bergey's Manual* (7), and to Starr & Skerman's recent vignette of the myxobacteria (8).

DEFINITION OF THE GROUP

The fruiting myxobacteria are procaryotic, nonphotosynthetic, Gram-negative protista. The group is characterized by three principal features: (a) Cells are nonflagellated, but vegetative rods move by gliding over the surface of a solid substrate. (b) The organisms go through a life cycle involving cellular aggregation of the vegetative rods followed by the formation of a fruiting body. Within the fruiting body, vegetative rods enter a resting state either by conversion to microcysts or by inclusion within a macrocyst. (c) Myxobacteria are invariably able to hydrolyze insoluble macromolecules.

METHODS OF ISOLATION

The successful isolation of fruiting myxobacteria depends on the utilization of three facts: (a) The myxobacteria are able to hydrolyze insoluble macromolecules in general, and in particular to lyse and grow on intact microbial cells. (b) The myxobacteria are overgrown by the more rapidly growing eubacteria when both are placed on rich media. (c) The myxobacteria form characteristic fruiting bodies when placed under the proper nutritional conditions.

Thaxter's original description of the myxobacteria (1) was based on observations made with fruiting bodies that occurred naturally on decayed wood, and plant material in general. In 1926 the Krzemieniewski's (9) developed an enrichment technique for the isolation of myxobacteria. It was based on the recognition of myxobacteria as indigenous inhabitants of the soil and on the fact that their frequent appearance on dung pellets reflects their tendency to grow on intact bacterial cells. In this technique, soil was placed on blotting paper in a petri dish, sterilized rabbit dung pellets laid on top of the soil, and water added to keep the system moist and inhibit the growth of fungi. Within 5 to 10 days, a variety of myxobacterial fruiting bodies appeared on the dung pellets. This technique enabled the Krzemieniewskis to compile their monumental catalogue of the myxobacteria (9–11).

Singh, in 1947 (12), made further use of the knowledge of the bacteriotrophic nature of the myxobacteria. He placed patches of living *Aerobacter* cells on the surface of a salts-agar base and sprinkled them with small particles of soil. The myxobacteria lysed the living *Aerobacter* cells and formed fruiting bodies within the lysed area. Cells were picked from the advancing front of the myxobacterial swarm and were then streaked on agar containing killed *Aerobacter* cells. With this technique, Singh was able to isolate a variety of fruiting myxobacteria in pure culture. McCurdy has recently described a method for the isolation of fruiting myxobacteria (13) with which he has been able to isolate 150 different species of myxobacteria, including members of *Myxococcus, Chondrococcus, Podangium,* and *Chondromyces.* Bark or soil was used as a source of inoculum and was placed on either sterilized dung[4] plates as described by the Krzemieniewski's (9) or on patches of washed *Aerobacter* cells as described by Singh (12). When the fruiting bodies appeared, they were picked and placed on an agar medium containing autoclaved *Escherichia coli* cells and salts. Fruiting bodies which appeared on this medium were removed and ground with glass beads in an Omnimixer. This apparently resulted in a physical separation of the myxobacterial cells from the contaminating eubacteria which are frequently quite difficult to remove. The mixture was once again streaked out on *E. coli* agar and the isolated fruiting bodies collected. This appears to be the method of choice at the present time.

ECOLOGY

Fruiting myxobacteria have been reported to occur in the soils of Poland (9), Great Britain (12), Vienna (14), Sweden (15), India (16), the Arctic (17), and Iowa (18). While the reports are not yet all in, it begins to appear as if the myxobacteria are ubiquitous inhabitants of normal soil, bark, and decaying plant material. Myxobacteria were considered at one time to be indigenous to dung pellets, and while Kühlwein has demonstrated the presence

---

[4] Ordal (personal communication) has pointed out the unsuitability of dung pellets collected from rabbits fed on laboratory diets. Either the nature of the diet or the presence of considerable amounts of antibiotics in the feed renders the pellets unsuitable for the isolation and cultivation of myxobacteria.

of myxobacteria in the dung of herbivores (19), the frequent appearance of fruiting bodies on dung pellets simply reflects the bacteriotrophic inclinations of the myxobacteria.

The absence of adequate techniques for quantitative determinations of the number of myxobacteria in soil has resulted in the lack of any critical information on their distribution in nature. Singh (12) attempted to determine the number of myxobacteria in soil and compost by counting the fruiting bodies which appeared when an appropriate dilution of soil was placed on a disk of *Aerobacter* cells on non-nutrient agar. The method is severely limited as to the types of myxobacteria that can be detected (Singh detected *Myxococcus fulvus*, *Myxococcus virescens*, and *Chondromyces exiguus*), and the counts were undoubtedly low. There were 5×10^5 fruiting bodies per gram of actively decomposing compost, and between 2×10^3 and 7.6×10^4 fruiting bodies per gram of farmyard manured soil. Attempts have been made to investigate the vertical distribution of the myxobacteria in the soil (9, 12), the relationship between the pH of the soil and the number and types of myxobacteria present (12, 15, 20), and the effect of the degree of cultivation on the nature of the myxobacterial flora (21–23). In all cases, the difficulty in determining accurately the numbers of fruiting myxobacteria present in the sample precludes any meaningful generalizations.

It is quite probable that two of the fundamental properties of the fruiting myxobacteria, gliding motility and the nutritional dependence of the organism on its ability to hydrolyze insoluble macromolecules, are related to each other in a more than casual fashion. An organism whose ecological niche is an aquatic one may depend on its flagellar motility and random collisions to bring it into contact with soluble substrate molecules. A terrestrial organism dependent on insoluble macromolecules for its sustenance is obliged to creep or crawl to its food.

MORPHOLOGY

Vegetative Cells

The vegetative cells of the myxobacteria are Gram-negative rods which fall into three categories. They are either thick rods with blunt ends (e.g., $1.2 \times 2.5 \mu$) exemplified by *Sorangium;* thin, delicate rods (e.g., 0.5×5–10μ) such as found in the *Cytophaga* and *Sporocytophaga* groups, and an intermediate group (e.g., $0.75 \times 5.0 \mu$) exemplified by *Myxococcus*.

The stereotype frequently applied to the myxobacteria is that they lack a rigid cell wall (7), or that they lack a cell wall completely (24–27). Electron micrographs of sufficient resolution to permit an examination of this question (28) reveal clearly that *M. xanthus* possesses a cell wall essentially indistinguishable from that which surrounds Gram-negative eubacteria in general. Mason & Powelson (29) have examined the walls of *M. xanthus* and have shown them to contain 4 to 5 per cent carbohydrate (including hexosamines), about 50 per cent ethanol-ether soluble material, and 5 per cent Kjeldahl nitrogen containing most of the amino acids (including diaminopimelic acid).

In other words, the chemical composition of the walls is grossly similar to that of other Gram-negative bacteria. Furthermore, the presence of diaminopimelic acid suggests a murein component. In view of the contribution of the murein to the rigidity of the cell walls of other bacteria, it would be most interesting if a quantitative determination of murein in myxobacterial walls revealed a chemical basis for their flexibility.

Imshenetsky & Alferov (26) claim to have demonstrated the presence of a "true" nucleus in various members of the fruiting myxobacteria. Their interpretation has been challenged by Kühlwein & Rossner (30), who stated that the "inclusion bodies" identified by Imshenetsky & Alferov as nuclei "can in no case be identified with nuclei." Furthermore, electron micrographs of thin sections of *M. xanthus* indicate that, when the specimens are prepared by a method designed to preserve the nuclear structure, a typical bacterial nucleoid is present (28).

Voelz (31) has recently demonstrated the presence in *M. xanthus* of two types of mesosomes morphologically similar to those found among the Gram-negative eubacteria. These two types of mesosomes not only differed morphologically, but their formation was induced by different environmental conditions. One of Voelz's micrographs [Fig. 2 of (31)] shows a distinct connection between a mesosome and the nuclear fibrils.

Correll & Lewin (32) have described a class of subcellular rod-shaped particles composed of RNA and protein, isolated from the gliding bacterium *Saprospira*. Similar particles, termed rhapidosomes, have been subsequently detected in *Archangium* (33), *Chondrococcus columnaris* (34), *Sporocytophaga myxococcoides* (35), *M. xanthus*, and *Cytophaga* (36). With the exception of the presence of rhapidosomes, there is no evidence at the moment to indicate that those myxobacteria which have been examined are not typical Gram-negative, procaryotic cells morphologically identical with the eubacteria.

MICROCYSTS

The microcysts of myxobacteria are optically refractile, Gram-negative, resting cells formed by all members of the myxobacteria except the genus *Cytophaga*. The microcysts vary from the refractile, spherical cells of the Myxococcaceae (about 1 to 2 μ diameter) to the refractile rods of the Sorangiaceae, Polyangiaceae, and Archangiaceae ($0.3-1.0 \times 1.5-5.0\,\mu$).

Dworkin & Voelz (37) have pointed out the necessity for distinguishing between true microcysts and spheroplasts which are frequently encountered in myxobacterial cultures. It is necessary that bodies referred to as microcysts fulfill the following criteria: (*a*) They must be capable of germination; (*b*) they must be resistant to physical or sonic disruption; (*c*) they must be refractile under the phase contrast microscope; (*d*) the sequence of morphological events leading to their formation must be clearly distinguishable from those characteristic of spheroplast formation. The failure to recognize this distinction between microcysts and spheroplasts has led to some regrettable confusion. Gräf (38, 39) and Bauer (40) have described a number of so-called new species and genera of myxobacteria (e.g., *Sphaerocytophaga fili-formis, Sphaeromyxa xanthochlora, Sporocytophaga cauliformis*) whose essential distinction in all cases is that they form spheroplasts in old culture. (These will be discussed in more detail in the sections on PATHOGENICITY and TAXONOMY.)

It has been suggested that in *Myxococcus* ". . . the myxobacterial microcyst is essentially a round vegetative cell surrounded by a dense capsule" (41). Electron micrographs of thin sections of microcysts of *M. xanthus* reveal that, from a morphological point of view, the cell wall is similar to that found surrounding the vegetative rods.

Adye & Powelson (42) have determined the chemical composition of the cell wall of microcysts of *M. xanthus* and have compared it to the walls of vegetative cells of the same organism. Since the walls from the two types of cells were isolated by considerably different methods, unqualified comparisons are not possible. However, the composition of the microcyst wall was grossly similar to that of the vegetative cell. Hydrolysis of the microcyst wall released a material which, on the basis of paper chromatography was tentatively identified as muramic acid. An earlier report (29) of the components of walls of vegetative cells made no mention of muramic acid. The microcyst is surrounded by a dense capsular material whose composition has not yet been determined. Holt & Powelson (43) analyzed the water-soluble slime produced by *M. xanthus*. Cells were grown on cellophane sheets laid on the surface of agar plates and were extracted before and after fruiting body formation. The slime in both cases contained protein, polysaccharide, lipid, and nucleic acids. The composition of the water-soluble extract changed after the formation of fruiting bodies but no determination was made of the extent of cell lysis at either time. Since the capsule of the microcyst is not removable with cold water (Dworkin, unpublished observations), it is possible that in both cases the slime originated from the vegetative cells and was contaminated to a lesser or greater extent by the products of the cell lysis.

NUTRITION

The myxobacteria grow characteristically on solid surfaces, and, rather than existing in a bath of nutrients, obtain their nutrients by solubilizing particulate insoluble substrates (e.g., bacterial carcasses, cellulose, chitin, agar, starch). This raises the question of what parameter to use for determining the nutritional requirements of the organism. If one decides that the most common parameter of growth, i.e., rate of exponential increase of cell material in liquid culture, does meaningfully describe the requirements of an organism which solubilizes particulate macromolecules while crawling across a piece of debris, one is still faced with an additional difficulty. Most fruiting myxobacteria simply will not grow dispersedly in liquid media, but grow rather as rings around the container or as clumps. While some myxobacteria can be cultured in a dispersed fashion (e.g., various members of *Myxococcus* and *C. columnaris*) the majority of them cannot. A common procedure for measuring the growth of myxobacteria consists of measuring the diameter of the myxobacterial swarm on agar or the diameter of the zone of lysis of a food bacterium. These approaches often yield data which are difficult to interpret, since neither the swarm diameter nor the diameter of the zone of lysis may accurately reflect the number of cells present. Even if one does obtain meaningful measurements of the extent or rate of vegetative growth, one must still be concerned with the nutritional effects on the number and size of fruiting bodies produced, the efficiency of microcyst formation, the rate of swarming of the colony, and possibly other parameters. It is clear, therefore, that there are a number of different types of nutritional problems which one must consider when examining the nutrition of myxobacteria. With these qualifications in mind, the following generalizations can be made: 1. The fruiting myxobacteria are bacteriotrophic, that is, they are capable of lysing intact bacterial cells and utilizing the solubilized products to satisfy all of their growth requirements; 2. they seem to grow better on living than autoclaved cells (44–46); 3. they can grow on a wide variety of Gram-positive and Gram-negative organisms (44, 48), as well as on various members of the higher protists, e.g., filamentous fungi, yeasts, and algae (44, 47). The generalization that they prefer Gram-negative nonpigmented bacteria (12, 49) has not been clearly confirmed by subsequent investigations (44, 48, 50); 4. while the fruiting myxobacteria can be easily grown in bacteria-free media, their requirements (except for the cellulose-decomposers) cannot be satisfied by a simple, salts-carbon source medium, but rather by media containing either complex nitrogenous materials (24, 51, 52) or mixtures of amino acids (6, 53).

NITROGEN REQUIREMENTS

Baur (51) first reported that members of the fruiting myxobacteria could be cultivated on media containing peptone. This report was followed by a number of others which showed that various species of *Myxococcus* (24, 55), *Polyangium fuscum* (24), *Melittangium*, and *Chondromyces* (56) among others, developed well on media with organic nitrogen present. These were not quantitative observations but served perfectly well to suggest the direction for a more precise evaluation of the nitrogen nutrition of myxobacteria. Subsequent attempts to accomplish this often ignored the considerable contamination of agar with organic nitrogen. For example, the diameter of the swarm colony of myxobacteria developing on agar plates with no nutrients added, was shown to be as high as 20 mm (57).

In a paper which appears to be the first attempt to define the nutritional requirements of fruiting myxobacteria in a liquid medium, Oxford (58) described a medium containing an acid hydrolysate of casein, asparagine, and salts. This medium ". . . would allow a just perceptible development of a film of growth of *M. virescens*." Loebeck (59), using a dispersed-growing variant of *M. virescens*, showed the organism to be capable of deaminating 16 of 18 amino acids tested. She reports a ". . . faint but perceptible turbidity. . ."

on a defined medium containing amino acids and salts. On the basis of the considerable enhancement of growth obtained on enzymatically hydrolyzed casein as compared to the acid hydrolysate, Loebeck concluded that ". . . peptides and possibly protein may serve as better substrates for growth than free amino acids."

Norén (60) used a variation of Oxford's asparagine-casein hydrolysate-salts, liquid medium as a basal medium to which he added individual amino acids in an attempt to detect stimulatory or inhibitory effects. He also devised an amino acid medium which attempted to duplicate the composition of casein hydrolysate. The effect on growth of deleting single amino acids was then investigated. Norén concluded from these studies that amino acids would satisfy the carbon and nitrogen requirements of *M. virescens* and further, he was able to divide the amino acids into three groups: those which were required, those which were stimulatory, and those which were inhibitory to growth.

Dworkin (6) devised a synthetic medium for a dispersed-growing strain of *M. xanthus* which would support exponential growth with a generation time of about eight hours. The essential nutritional requirements were supplied by amino acids, supporting Norén's findings with *M. virescens*. The amino acid requirements and stimulations did not, however, correspond to those described by Norén for *M. virescens*. This is not surprising as significant differences in responses to amino acids have been encountered among strains of the same species (Dworkin, unpublished results). It was also shown (6) that media containing enzymatically hydrolyzed protein resulted in optimal growth with a generation time of 3.5 hours. This is consistent with Loebeck's conclusions as to the comparative value of peptides and amino acids.

Chase (53) has devised a defined amino acid medium which supports the exponential growth of *C. columnaris*. The medium contained 12 amino acids, 9 of which were essential singly or in groups. The Krzemieniewski's, using a cellulose-salts medium with potassium nitrate as the sole source of nitrogen, isolated a number of species of *Sorangium* and two species of *Archangium* (61). A more detailed investigation of the nutrition of *Sorangium compositum* and *Sorangium nigrescens* (62) showed that while they could utilize cellulose as a carbon source with nitrate or ammonium salts as the sole source of nitrogen, they were unable to decompose cellulose with peptone as the source of nitrogen. The peptone may possibly have been serving as both a carbon and a nitrogen source and, as such, may have repressed cellulose utilization. Nutritionally, these cellulose-decomposing fruiting myxobacteria resemble *Cytophaga* and *Sporocytophaga* and fall in a distinct group from the noncellulose-decomposing myxobacteria. (There is no evidence that any of the latter group can utilize inorganic nitrogen for growth.) Stanier (63) has pointed out that the existence of these cellulose-decomposing myxobacteria ". . . is also relevant to the question of ecology, since it suggests that some of the fruiting myxobacteria share with the cytophagas a common ecological niche."

Effect of Mono- and Disaccharides

The data on the effect of carbohydrates constitute a morass of contradictory reports. The usual type of experiment consisted either of adding a sugar to a complex and essentially complete medium, e.g., 1 per cent peptone (64), to plain agar in the absence of added salts or nitrogen, or both (19, 57), or to dung decoction media (64). Growth would then be evaluated either visually and subjectively, or by measuring the colony diameter. Such data are extremely equivocal and difficult to evaluate and will not be considered here.

Stanier (2) reported that autoclaved glucose (and presumably reducing sugars in general) inhibited the growth of *Cytophaga* and *Sporocytophaga*, whereas filter-sterilized glucose did not. A similar effect has been reported for a number of species of *Myxococcus* (57) although the data are not as clear-cut as with the nonfruiting myxobacteria. In any event, it is necessary to view with suspicion all reports on the effect of sugars on the growth of myxobacteria made prior to 1942 [e.g. (65)] as well as all those afterward which did not take account of the possible inhibitory effect of autoclaved reducing sugars [e.g. (64)].

The work of Solnetzewa represented the first attempt to assess quantitatively the utilization of glucose by *Myxococcus* (55) and by *Melittangium* and *Chondromyces* (56). Glucose determinations on growing cultures of *M. virescens* and *M. rubescens* showed no disappearance of glucose, while similar determination on cultures of *Melittangium* and *Chondromyces* showed that, respectively, 18.5 per cent and 20.5 per cent of the glucose had disappeared after 20 days incubation. Growth was in a complex medium and was unaffected by the presence of the glucose.

Loebeck (59) and Loebeck & Klein (4), using a dispersed-growing culture of *M. virescens*, demonstrated that glucose, while unable to stimulate the rate of endogenous O_2 uptake, could be oxidized. Loebeck exposed a growing culture to ^{14}C-labeled glucose and collected metabolic $^{14}CO_2$. The specific activity of the glucose was not indicated, making it impossible to judge how much glucose was utilized. But over the period tested, 10 per cent of the added counts were recovered as CO_2. The glucose in this experiment was autoclaved separately from the medium and caused a slight inhibition of growth. Unautoclaved glucose was not tested.

Norén (67) quantitated the growth response of *M. virescens* by measuring photometrically the adhering "pseudoplasmodial"[5] swarm on the inside of glass tubes containing liquid media and incubated with shaking. Norén stated in a later publication (60) that the photometric values correlated with dry weight determinations but no data were given. Sugars were added to a

[5] The use of the term, "pseudoplasmodium" in connection with the myxobacteria should be discouraged, implying as it does an analogy with the motile slug of the Acrasiales. Not even a superficial relationship between the swarm of the myxobacteria and the myxomycetal pseudoplasmodium exists.

basal medium containing Casamino acids and salts, and the growth response then determined. Norén interpreted his data (60) as indicating that *M. virescens* is able to attack a large number of carbohydrates. In all cases, however, the growth rate was linear and the differences between the control and experimental rates were small. In the case of maltose and arabinose, however, the stimulation appears significant. It should be pointed out that ordinary Difco Casamino acids (acid-hydrolyzed casein) contains 14 per cent sodium chloride. A medium with 1 per cent Casamino acids will therefore contain over 0.02 M NaCl. In addition, approximately 0.02 M NaCl was added to the medium. Mason & Powelson (5) have shown that *M. xanthus* will lyse when as little as 0.01 M NaCl is present in the medium. Norén's interpretation, therefore, must be qualified by the fact that his organism may have been laboring under a sodium chloride inhibition. The organisms did not grow exponentially, and there is no indication of the accuracy of his method of measuring growth.

McDonald & Peterson have recently grown two species of *Archangium* in liquid culture (52). While the organism did not grow in a dispersed fashion and no data were presented on the quantitation of the growth response, the authors stated that "glucose was distinctly the carbon source of choice for *A. primigenum*, and the deletion of it from the medium in favor of any other carbon source resulted in marked inhibition of growth."

Using a chemically defined medium which would support the exponential growth of *M. xanthus*, Dworkin (6) reported that a small number of sugars, including fructose, glucose, and arabinose, resulted in a barely detectable stimulation of the growth rate. On the other hand, work in our laboratory indicated that no uptake of uniformly ^{14}C-labeled, high specific activity glucose could be demonstrated by growing cells of *M. xanthus* (Sadler, unpublished data). Furthermore, a diligent search for hexokinase activity in cell-free extracts of the same organism has been unsuccessful (Watson, unpublished data).

Chase (53) was unable to demonstrate any effect of carbohydrates on the growth of *C. columnaris* in a defined medium.

At the moment, the conflicting data regarding carbohydrate utilization by *Myxococcus* cannot be reconciled. It does appear, however, that if nonpolymeric carbohydrates do play a role in the nutrition of *Myxococcus*, it is a minor one.

VITAMIN REQUIREMENTS

Finck (64) and Oetker (44) examined various myxobacteria for vitamin requirements. In both cases no attempt was made to ensure the absence of growth factors from the basal agar medium. In addition, evaluation of the growth response was either subjective (64) or consisted of measuring the swarm diameter (44).

Norén found that the additions of riboflavin, calcium pantothenate, folic acid, biotin, and choline to a basal medium containing Difco vitamin-free Casamino acids, asparagine, and salts caused stimulation of the growth of *M. virescens* (60). In no case was the requirement an absolute one, and the maximum effects were small (e.g., readings of 50 versus 75 after seven days growth in control and complete vitamin medium, respectively).

Dworkin (6) measured the effect of vitamins on the rate and extent of exponential growth of *M. xanthus*. Two approaches were used. One involved the addition of vitamins singly and in combinations to the defined amino acid medium, and the other involved a comparison of growth in Difco Casitone and Difco vitamin-free Casitone (the latter is prepared by hydrolyzing acid-washed casein and is sufficiently vitamin-free to serve as a basal medium for vitamin assays). In neither case could any stimulatory effect be detected.

McDonald & Peterson (52) have recently reported a liquid medium which supports the growth of two species of *Archangium*, a genus in the so-called higher myxobacteria. While no quantitative evaluations of growth were made, the authors concluded that there was no detectable effect of the vitamins on the growth of these organisms.

Chase (53) could not demonstrate any effect of vitamins on the growth of *C. columnaris* in a defined amino acid medium.

In general, then, there has been no vitamin requirement demonstrated for the fruiting myxobacteria. There has been one report of the stimulation of growth in *M. virescens* by a number of vitamins (60), but this could not be demonstrated in *M. xanthus* (6), *Archangium* (52), or *C. columnaris* (53).

UTILIZATION OF MACROMOLECULES

A characteristic feature of the myxobacteria is their ability to hydrolyze macromolecules including proteins, starch, cell walls, glycogen, chitin, cellulose, and agar. Furthermore, while there is little quantitative data, there seems to be unanimous agreement that the presence of particular macromolecules stimulates the growth of myxobacteria.

Loebeck & Klein (4), using ^{14}C-labeled starch, showed that resting cells of *M. virescens* were able to oxidize significant quantities of the substrate to CO_2. Unfortunately, no measure was made of the amount of label incorporated into the cells.

Dworkin (6) demonstrated that purified glycogen stimulated the exponential rate of growth of *M. xanthus* in a defined, liquid medium. Furthermore, parallel determinations of total polysaccharide and total sugar in the medium indicated that, while the glycogen was hydrolyzed, the total sugars present remained constant, suggesting that the products of hydrolysis were not being assimilated.

Norén (60) reported that DNA and RNA served as sole sources of carbon and nitrogen for the growth of *M. virescens*, and that the RNA also stimulated growth in an otherwise complete medium. The RNA which was used was commercially prepared yeast RNA which is notoriously contaminated with all the components of the yeast cell. The probable lack of purity of the DNA is suggested by the fact that, in another report, exhaustively purified

DNA still contained 0.3 to 0.5 per cent amino acids (68). The effect of these macromolecules may therefore be attributed to the presence of other contaminating nutrients until otherwise demonstrated.

While no careful systematic survey has been made, it appears that the fruiting myxobacteria are usually capable of hydrolyzing starch, glycogen, protein, and bacterial cell walls. The hydrolysis of cellulose, has been demonstrated in some fruiting myxobacteria (22, 23, 61, 62, 66, 69), most cytophagas (2), and *Sporocytophaga* (2).

UTILIZATION OF SUBCELLULAR FRACTIONS

The ability of the fruiting myxobacteria to lyse protistal cells and to grow at the expense of the hydrolytic products was recognized by Pinoy (70) and has been utilized for their routine isolation and cultivation since. While there has been a considerable amount of work done on the lytic activity of the myxobacteria (See LYTIC FACTORS AND ANTIBIOTIC ACTIVITY), only Loebeck & Klein (4) have analytically investigated the utilization of subcellular fractions of bacteria. They totally labeled *E. coli* with ^{14}C, fractionated the cell into cell walls, cytoplasm, lipid, acid-soluble nucleic acid, and protein fractions. They then exposed these fractions to a liquid culture of a dispersed-growing variant of *M. virescens*, and collected and measured $^{14}CO_2$. There was considerable oxidation of the cytoplasmic fraction, lipid, and protein fractions, and negligible oxidation of the remaining fractions. Again, it is unfortunate that they did not measure the degree of assimilation of these various fractions.

METABOLISM

While there have been a few investigations of the intermediary metabolism of *Cytophaga* (71–73) and *Sporocytophaga* (74), the metabolism of only one fruiting myxobacterium has been examined. Watson & Dworkin have demonstrated the presence of citric acid cycle enzymes in extracts of vegetative cells and microcysts of *M. xanthus* (75, 76). On a per-cell basis, the enzyme activities of both types of cells are essentially the same with the exception of isocitric dehydrogenase, which is fivefold higher in microcysts than in vegetative cells. The extracts of vegetative cells also contained the following activities: glucose-6-phosphate dehydrogenase, phosphoglucomutase, aldolase phosphohexoseisomerase, fructose-1,6-diphosphatase, PEP carboxykinase, and malic enzyme. The following activities could not be detected: hexokinase, pyruvic kinase, glycerokinase, glycerol dehydrogenase, and lactic dehydrogenase (Watson, unpublished results). Microcyst extracts have not yet been examined for these activities.

Dworkin & Niederpruem (41) examined the terminal electron transport system of *M. xanthus* and found that the particulate subcellular fraction of both vegetative cells and microcysts could take up oxygen using $NADH_2$ as the substrate at equivalent rates, and that both vegetative cells and microcysts had a classical *Bacillus*-type cytochrome system with cytochromes *a*,

$a3$, b, and c-type components. The microcysts and vegetative cells differed by three parameters. One, while intact vegetative cells would metabolize acetate or casitone with a QO_2 of 9 and 12, respectively, intact microcysts had a QO_2 of 0 on all substrates tested. Two, the difference spectrum of the carbon monoxide-binding pigments were different for the two types of cells, and three, the microcysts had tenfold greater cytochrome c reductase and cytochrome oxidase activity than did the vegetative cells. It should be kept in mind, however, that while the vegetative cells were harvested from an exponentially growing, well-aerated liquid culture, the microcysts were harvested from fruiting bodies on the surface of two weeks-old petri dish cultures. It is quite possible that the differences reflect differences in the state of aerobiosis or conditions of cultivation rather than basic differences between the two types of cells. (All of the fruiting myxobacteria thus far described are obligate aerobes.) Now that it is possible to convert vegetative cells to microcysts quickly and synchronously (77), this point should be re-examined.

One member of the fruiting myxobacteria, therefore, seems to have a modified glycolytic pathway (pyruvic kinase and hexokinase are absent) as well as a tricarboxylic acid cycle and a terminal electron transport system in both vegetative cells and microcysts. In view of the inability of $M.$ $xanthus$ to oxidize carbohydrates, the presence of these glycolytic enzymes probably reflects a gluconeogenic function rather than a glycolytic one. This is consistent with the presence of the fructose, 1–6, diphosphatase activity.

Preliminary studies with ^{14}C-labeled acetate indicated that while glycerol-induced microcysts had a low QO_2 on acetate, they took it up almost as rapidly as did the vegetative cells and, like the vegetative cells, incorporated a significant proportion of the acetate into glutamic acid, aspartic acid, and proline of the cell protein (Watson, unpublished results). It is not clear why the microcysts have a reduced respiratory rate but the data suggest that this is not due to the absence of a citric acid cycle, the lack of a functional electron transport system or a general permeability barrier.

LIFE CYCLE AND MORPHOGENESIS

The life cycle of the fruiting myxobacteria includes colonial morphogenesis involving the aggregation of individual cells to form a rudimentary, multicellular structure called a fruiting body. Within the fruiting body, the individual rods undergo cellular morphogenesis, converting to refractile microcysts. Under the proper conditions these microcysts may then germinate to form the vegetative rods. In the higher myxobacteria (e.g., *Chondromyces*) the resting state is represented by the vegetative rods enclosed in a sac. The macrocyst, upon germination, releases the vegetative rods and initiates the swarm stage.

THE FRUITING BODY

The fruiting bodies of the myxobacteria vary from the simple mounds formed by *Myxococcus* to the elaborately sculptured forms found among the

Polyangiaceae. Within the fruiting body, the microcysts may occur in un-differentiated masses as in the Myxococcaceae or in cysts as in the Poly-angiaceae. The ability of some of the higher myxobacteria to enclose the vegetative rods within a macrocyst, which is then the unit structure of the resting stage, represents an additional and more complex dimension of the development cycle of the myxobacteria. Reichenbach has discussed the development of these macrocysts (78) and has done time lapse cinematography of macrocyst formation and germination in *Chondromyces apiculatus* (79).

There has not yet been a careful description of the morphological events occurring during fruiting body formation. We do not know, for example, at what stage of fruiting body formation the vegetative cells are converted to microcysts. Neither do we know the disposition of microcysts within the fruiting body. Are they dispersed throughout, peripherally arranged, or clustered in the center? We do not have any figures on the per cent conversion of vegetative cells to microcysts within the fruiting body nor are we sure whether the fruiting body is initiated by a vegetative cell or a microcyst. Finally, we have no clear idea of the function of the fruiting body.

EFFECT OF THE NUTRITIONAL MILIEU ON FRUITING BODY FORMATION

Quehl (54) first noted that, whereas low concentrations of peptone (0.5 per cent) stimulated the growth and fruiting body formation by *Myxococcus*, higher concentrations (1 to 3 per cent) tended to inhibit fruiting body formation. Since then, the observation that the nutritional milieu affects the extent and nature of fruiting body formation has been frequently made (19, 24, 44). The generalization that has emerged and which seems to apply both in the higher and lower fruiting myxobacteria is that high concentrations of growth media, while permitting rapid vegetative growth, inhibit subsequent fruiting body formation. That this effect is due to the presence of specific inhibitors of fruiting body formation was demonstrated by Dworkin (80, 81). A defined medium containing amino acids and salts would support exponential vegetative growth in liquid media. While it would not support colony formation from single cells on solid media (Dworkin, unpublished observation), considerable vegetative growth could be obtained with large inocula. When phenylalanine and tryptophan were omitted from the medium or were reduced in concentration from 1 mg/ml each to 0.4 mg/ml each, fruiting bodies were formed within 30 hours. The omission of no other amino acids from the medium had this effect. Subsequently, Leadbetter (82), using a different approach, confirmed the inhibitory effect of phenylalanine and tryptophan on fruiting body formation in *Myxococcus*. McCurdy (83) has recently succeeded in culturing *Chondromyces crocatus* in pure culture on a bacteria-free medium. He, too, has shown that phenylalanine and, to a lesser extent, tryptophan inhibited fruiting body formation by this organism and that the inhibitory effects of phenylalanine may be reversed by the addition of beta-2-thionyl-alanine or *p*-fluorophenylalanine. McCurdy has made the interesting suggestion that the previous inability to obtain fruiting body formation by *C. croca-*

tus in the absence of eubacterial contaminations (19, 70) may have reflected the destruction or inactivation by the contaminants of these inhibitors of fruiting body formation.

Fluegel (84) has developed a technique for inducing submerged fruiting bodies of *M. fulvus* in static liquid cultures. Using this technique, he has demonstrated an absolute requirement for divalent cations, e.g., calcium, magnesium, strontium. Vegetative cells grown on a complex medium were washed and resuspended in phosphate buffer. When calcium ions were added, fruiting body formation began and was completed after about 24 hours. It is of considerable interest that divalent cations are also required for glycerol induction of microcyst formation in *M. xanthus* (85).

CHEMOTAXIS

The apparent similarity between the life cycles of the fruiting myxobacteria and the Acrasiales has prompted a number of investigators to attempt to demonstrate that a chemotactic substance was involved in the aggregation process. Bonner (86) described some preliminary experiments which suggested that fruiting body formation by *C. crocatus* involved a directed migration of vegetative cells. It was not clear, however, that chemotaxis was involved. In 1954, Lev reported that fruiting bodies of *C. exiguus* and *M. xanthus* produced diffusible substances which stimulated fruiting body formation (87). A thin agar block containing a medium on which the test organism would not ordinarily fruit, was placed on top of fruiting bodies and inoculated with vegetative cells. After three days of incubation, the upper surface of the agar block contained fruiting bodies. There was no cross-induction between *Chondrococcus* and *Myxococcus*.

Jennings (88) reported an attempt to demonstrate and characterize the diffusible fruiting factor. A concentrated aqueous extract of *M. virescens* fruiting bodies was added to wells in a plate inoculated with *M. virescens*. Ordinarily, the medium would not support fruiting body formation, but fruiting bodies appeared around the wells containing the extract. The extract was chromatographed and compared to an extract of vegetative cells. A spot appeared on the chromatogram of the fruiting body extract which was absent from the vegetative cell extract. This spot, it was claimed, contained a steroid and would induce fruiting when the paper was laid on the agar plate. Details are almost completely missing from this note. There is no mention of the method of extraction of the fruiting bodies or vegetative cells, the growth medium for cultivating the vegetative cells, the solvent for chromatography, the methods used for visualizing the chromatographic spots, or the bioautographic experiment. In any case, the papers of Lev and Jennings suggested that a diffusible fruiting factor does exist but did not distinguish between an inactivator of a fruiting body inhibitor, e.g., phenylalanine, on the one hand, and the existence of an actual chemotatic substance on the other. That such an inactivator may exist has been suggested by McCurdy (83).

McVittie & Zahler (89) and Fluegel (90) have convincingly confirmed the existence of a chemotactic substance. McVittie & Zahler placed a cellophane membrane over fruiting bodies of *M. xanthus* and then spread vegetative cells over the surface of the cellophane. Fruiting bodies formed on top in direct juxtaposition to those beneath the cellophane. In order to eliminate the possibility that the orientation was caused by an elasticotactic response (91), glass beads approximately the same size as the fruiting bodies were placed under the membrane. There was no relationship between the location of the fruiting bodies formed on top of the membrane and the glass beads beneath it (89). Fluegel (90) also used the cellophane membrane to demonstrate that when a swarm of *M. fulvus* was induced to form fruiting bodies on one side of the membrane an equivalent swarm then placed on the other side would form juxtaposed fruiting bodies.

MICROCYST FORMATION

The microcysts are refractile cells which include the spheres of the Myxococcaceae and the ovoids and rods of the remaining families. Among the fruiting myxobacteria, their formation is normally associated with the formation of the fruiting body.

Thaxter, in 1897 (92), accurately described the morphological events leading to microcyst formation in *M. rubescens*. ". . . Sporulation consists in the direct transformation of single rods into single spores by a gradual inflation involving a shortening of the rod in the direction of its long axis. Even the longest individuals eventually assume a spherical form, and through the deposition of material on the inner surface of their walls are gradually converted into thick-walled refractile spores." Subsequent accounts of microcyst formation in *Myxococcus* (37, 77, 93–95) and in *Sporocytophaga* (96, 97) have merely confirmed the essentials of Thaxter's observations. By means of electron microscopy of thin sections of *M. xanthus*, Voelz & Dworkin (28) have examined changes in the fine structure during microcyst formation. They were unable to detect the thickening of the cell wall referred to by Thaxter, but showed, instead, the accumulation of a dense, adherent capsule. There was no detectable alteration in the organization of the cell wall.

In general, microcyst formation by the fruiting myxobacteria does not take place in liquid media in the absence of fruiting body formation. However, Adye & Powelson (42) reported a method for converting vegetative cells of *M. xanthus* into microcysts in a liquid medium containing sucrose, starch, beef extract, and salts. While the conversion was asynchronous and required three to four days, it did demonstrate that *Myxococcus* could form microcysts in liquid media, in a milieu not leading to the formation of fruiting bodies. A technique has recently been described for converting vegetative cells to microcysts rapidly (120 minutes), relatively synchronously, and quantitatively (77). The method consists of the addition of 0.5 M glycerol, or one of a variety of other primary alcohols, to an exponentially growing culture of *M. xanthus*. Prior to the addition of glycerol the cells are centrifuged, washed, and resuspended in the growth medium (divalent cations such as magnesium or calcium are absolutely required) containing no added sodium or potassium. It was found that the presence of monovalent cations interfered with the process, causing spheroplast formation.[6] A number of compounds with alcohol groups (e.g., erythritol, butanol, isopropanol, ethylene glycol, and phenethyl alcohol) will substitute for glycerol. A variety of other penetrating and nonpenetrating solutes were ineffective (85). Sadler & Dworkin (98) have recently described some aspects of macromolecular syntheses occurring during the glycerol-induced conversion of vegetative cells to microcysts. They found that DNA, RNA, and protein are synthesized during this process, and, on the basis of studies with chloramphenicol and actinomycin D, that RNA and protein syntheses are obligatory for microcyst development. They also examined the question of the mechanism of induction by glycerol and concluded that the inducer reacts with a peripheral structure of the cell and need not penetrate the cell in order to be effective. They have suggested that induction involves an alteration of a membrane-DNA complex.

Microcyst Germination

While Jahn described microcyst germination as occurring by elongation of spores into rods (99), most subsequent observations (2, 25, 37, 96) have been in essential agreement with those of Thaxter, who first described the germination processes (92). The steps Thaxter described were a slight swelling followed by a loss of refractility. The outer layer of the microcyst was then penetrated from within by a stout rod which elongated and left behind it an empty sheath. The Krzemieniewski's have clearly described this process in a number of species of *Myxococcus* as well as in one species of *Chondrococcus* (25). Dworkin & Voelz (37), using time lapse photomicrographs and phase contrast microscopy of spatially fixed germinating cells, observed all of the steps in single cells. While these authors could not detect the swelling which Thaxter referred to, the photographs support Thaxter's description. Voelz & Dworkin have examined the fine structure changes during germination of *M. xanthus* (28). The shell which is left behind the emerging rod appears to consist of both the capsular and wall material of the microcyst. The emergence of the vegetative cell is preceded by a shrinking away of the protoplast from the wall-capsule complex, followed by a localized rupture of the wall capsule.

Ramsey & Dworkin (100) have examined the germination of microcysts of *M. xanthus*, using both glycerol-induced microcysts of various ages as well as fruiting body microcysts. They found that 24-hour-old gycerol-induced microcysts would germinate in distilled water within about 120 minutes. As

---

[6] Studies with isolated cell walls have indicated the presence of a wall-lytic enzyme (system) which is monovalent cation-dependent (Dworkin, unpublished results). This may be the basis of the potassium-stimulated spheroplast formation and is consistent with the report by Mason & Powelson (5) that *M. xanthus* would lyse readily in the presence of low concentrations (0.02 M) of NaCl.

the microcysts aged, they required for germination either the presence of a high population density (at least 1.5×10^9 cells/ml), a distilled-water medium in which germination had taken place, or potasssium phosphate. The process was sensitive to chloramphenicol and resistant to levels of actinomycin D which effectively inhibited vegetative growth and which had been shown to penetrate the microcyst. This observation suggests that the microcyst, like the unfertilized sea urchin egg (101), contains (a) stable messenger RNA.

Morphogenetic Mutants

McVittie, Messik & Zahler (102) have described a number of nonfruiting mutants of *M. xanthus*. These mutants fall into two classes, the members of each class being able to interact with the other to form mixed fruiting bodies. The members of one class also lost the ability to make microcysts. Intraclass mixing never resulted in fruiting body formation nor was it possible to isolate a stable fruiter from the fruiting bodies formed by mixing the two classes. These data tend to rule out the possibility that genetic exchange is involved in fruiting body formation and suggest instead that some sort of phenotypic synergism is involved. Zahler has suggested that a number of types of lesions may be involved: (*a*) inability to form a chemotactic substance; (*b*) inability to respond to a chemotactic substance; (*c*) inability to destroy the chemotactic substance; (*d*) inability to make microcysts (102).

Morphogenetic mutants (strains vc and mc) of *M. xanthus* have also been described by Dworkin (6) and by Dworkin & Voelz (37). The vc mutant of *M. xanthus* does not form microcysts or fruiting bodies in response to the nutritional milieu, but can be induced to form microcysts by the glycerol technique. Strain mc does not form fruiting bodies but retains some capacity to form microcysts. Recently, Dworkin & Sadler (85) have reported a class of mutants selected for their inability to form microcysts in reponse to glycerol induction. It was of considerable interest that these mutants simultaneously lost the ability to form fruiting bodies. Three possible explanations for this relationship are: the portions of the genome concerning microcyst and fruiting body formation are on a coordinately regulated operon; both are located on an episomal particle; or fruiting body formation is a physiological consequence of microcyst formation.

RESISTANCE OF THE MICROCYST

There have been a number of general statements in the literature which suggest that the microcyst, while not as heat-resistant as the bacterial endospore, is a resistant cell. Baur (51) reported that, while the vegetative cells of *Myxococcus ruber* are killed at 50° C, the microcysts could tolerate 70° C for 30 minutes and dry heat at 100° C for 1 minute. Microcysts held at 60° C (dry heat) for 10 hours were still capable of germinating. Baur also measured the resistance of cells to desiccation and found that, while vegetative cells were no longer viable after remaining in the dried state for 30 minutes at room temperature, microcysts, on the other hand, were fully viable after four weeks of desiccation. After this period of time they began to lose viability and when six weeks had elapsed, Baur could no longer demonstrate any viable microcysts. Zeece has examined the resistance of vegetative cells and microcysts of *M. xanthus* to sonication, heat, and ultraviolet irradiation (103). Table I contains the results of these experiments, and indicates that the microcysts are considerably more resistant than vegetative cells to ultraviolet irradiation, heat, and sonication. Using the glycerol induction technique (77) for converting vegetative cells to microcysts, Zeece was able to show that resistance to sonication appeared as the immature microcyst began

TABLE 1

RESISTANCE OF VEGETATIVE CELLS AND MICROCYSTS OF *MYXOCOCCUS XANTHUS*

| | Logs/min decreases in viable cells | |
	Vegetative cells	Microcysts
Heat		
45 C	0.09	—
50 C	0.90	0
60 C	3.30	0.20
Sonic vibration (maximal slope)	15	0
Ultraviolet irradiation	2.1	0.7

to acquire refractility (103). It is not clear at this time whether the appearance of refractility reflects the formation of a capsule, a change in the cell wall structure, or in the state of hydration of the cell.

BACTERIOPHAGE

Bacteriophage have been described for two species of myxobacteria, *C. columnaris* (104) and *M. xanthus* (105, 106). This should not be taken to imply that bacteriophage do not exist for other myxobacteria but rather that the group has not been carefully examined in these terms. Furthermore, the inability of many of the myxobacteria to grow dispersed in liquid or as lawns on the surface of agar medium complicates the problem of detecting the phage.

Both the *C. columnaris* phages and the *M. xanthus* phage (MX-1) are double-stranded DNA phages, in no way unusual in terms of morphology, base composition, or life cycle. An interesting relationship between the infectivity of the MX-1 phage and the life cycle of the host has been described (106). During the glycerol-induced synchronous conversion of vegetative cells to microcysts, cells lost the ability to adsorb phage within a specific 10 to 15-minute period. It is not clear whether this reflects a loss or an alteration or a masking of an adsorption site. Furthermore, when cells were infected after having been allowed to proceed for about 15 or 20 minutes toward microcyst formation (there was not yet any morphological change or any loss of their adsorption sites) they completed microcyst formation. The microcyst thus formed contained the phage in an immature state so that, upon microcyst germination, the phages were released with a normal burst and the newly germinated vegetative cell lysed.

There have been no reports of any temperate phage systems among the myxobacteria. Again, this is certainly due to the difficulty in screening potential indicator strains.

PIGMENTS

The myxobacteria are invariably pigmented. The pigments are not diffusible and are red, orange, yellow, or green. Jahn (99) suggested that the pigments were carotenoids and subsequent analyses (107–110) have confirmed this. Woods, in 1948 (3), and Greene & Leadbetter in 1963 (108), reported that the nature of the pigmentation of *Myxococcus* was a function of whether the cells were grown in light or dark. [The photoinduction of carotenoids appears to be a generalized phenomenon (111) and must not be ignored in describing the carotenoids of the myxobacteria]. Burchard & Dworkin (110) have studied the kinetics of pigment synthesis in light-grown *M. xanthus* and have shown that both the photo-induced carotenoids as well as a diffusible photosensitizing pigment identified as protoporphyrin IX did not appear until the end of exponential growth. Furthermore, they have shown that the carotenoids in this organism serve a photo-protective function as originally described by Stanier's group for the Athiorhodaceae (112).

The genus *Myxococcus* is classified largely on the basis of its pigmentation. If this is to remain a legitimate taxonomic parameter in this group, a systematic analysis of the pigments of the organisms grown under standardized conditions is necessary.

PATHOGENICITY

Myxobacteria have been reported to be pathogenic for fish (113–115) and for man (38, 116, 117). Ordal & Rucker (113) isolated an organism which was responsible for an epizootic among blue-black salmon fingerlings. On the basis of typical myxobacterial morphology and motility, production of spherical microcysts and the ability to form columnar fruiting bodies in aqueous media, they assigned the organism to the new species *Chondrococcus columnaris*. Garnjobst (114) reported a myxobacterium isolated from infected bullheads. This organism, although similar in other respects to *C. columnaris*, was unable to form fruiting bodies or microcysts and was accordingly assigned by Garnjobst to the genus *Cytophaga* as *Cytophaga columnaris*. It is not clear whether this is a distinct organism from *C. columnaris* or whether it is the same. If the latter, either Garnjobst was unable to induce the organism to form fruiting bodies and microcysts, or it had lost this capacity naturally or as a result of continued laboratory cultivation. Since much of the classification of the myxobacteria is based on the formation and morphology of fruiting bodies and microcysts, the organisms which have lost the ability to form these structures constitute a difficult taxonomic group.

Gräf has isolated and described an anaerobic myxobacterium from the oral cavity of humans (38), and has shown that, like many other members of the normal oral flora, it is able to induce cytopathogenic effects when injected into bruised tissues (117) or into tissue cultures (116). Since it is not yet clear that these organisms can indeed induce any disease in man, it is premature to refer to them as pathogens. They are, however, clearly parasitic inhabitants of the normal oral flora. It is not clear what the relationship is between the organisms which Gräf has described and many of the fusobacteria which occur normally in the mouth.

MOTILITY

The motility of myxobacterial vegetative cells is of a gliding nature, depending on contact between the cell and a solid surface, and occurs in the absence of flagella. This sort of motility is not peculiar to the myxobacteria but is characteristic of the Cyanophyceae as well as a group of bacteria including the Beggiatoaceae and the Vitreoscillaceae.

Various suggestions to explain myxobacterial motility have been made. These included directed slime production (99), cellular contraction (118, 119), action of haustoria (120), and flexions of a mucilagenous band encircling the cells (35). The discovery of rhapidosomes in *Saprospira* (32), *Archangium* (33), *C. columnaris* (34), *Sporocytophaga myxococcoides* (35), and *M. xanthus*, all gliding bacteria, suggests a possible role of rhapidosomes in gliding motility. However, of 15 species of *Cytophaga* examined, only one, a cellulose utilizer, contained rhapidosomes (36). Gräf (35) has suggested that the rhapidosomes comprise a contractile tube surrounding the myxobacterial cell and, as such, are responsible for the gliding movement.

For a detailed account of the papers on myxobacterial motility in particular and gliding movement in general, the reader is referred to reviews on movement by Weibull (121) and by Jahn & Bovee (122). At the present moment there are no hypotheses which explain myxobacterial movement in mechanistic terms nor are there any which suggest an experimental approach.

LYTIC FACTORS AND ANTIBIOTIC ACTIVITY

There is a considerable amount of contradictory information available about lytic and antibiotic factors produced by myxobacteria. The contradictions probably stem from the failure to take at least three variables into account:

1. Norén (123) clearly showed a relationship between lytic activity on autoclaved staphylococcal cells and stage of life cycle of *M. virescens*. Although Norén attributed the differences in activity to differential rates of vegetative growth, the appearance of fruiting bodies were clearly concomi-

tant with a burst of lytic activity. Bender (124) found that lytic activity of *M. xanthus* against alcian blue-stained *Bacillus subtilis* appeared and then disappeared in a culture of vegetatively growing rods. It is obvious that future investigations of these activities must control the variables of culture age in vegetatively growing cultures as well as the stage of the life cycle in a developing culture.

2. There has often been a very casual attitude toward attributing the lytic activity of myxobacteria to "proteolytic" or "cell-wall lytic" factors without sufficient evidence. For example, so-called proteolytic activity on autoclaved cells (45, 46, 58, 124–126) should be (but usually is not) demonstrated by monitoring the appearance of free amino acids or peptides or by the disappearance of protein. Cell-wall lysis of Gram-positive organisms could be measured by the appearance of glucosamine, diaminopimelic acid, muramic acid, or larger fragments of murein. Lysis of Gram-negative cell walls could be measured by the same parameters in addition to looking for release of specific wall sugars (e.g., the 3,6-dideoxyhexoses) or lipids (phosphatides, phosphatidic acids). Furthermore, the use of isolated, purified walls of Gram-positive and Gram-negative cells as well as of purified subcellular fractions (e.g., protein, ribosomes, DNA) would considerably simplify the situation.

3. The physiological state of the host cells is undoubtedly of importance in determining their sensitivity to lysis by myxobacteria.

Lytic Activity

While the chemical nature of the hydrolytic activities of the myxobacteria has not yet been completely defined, a number of types of hydrolytic activities has been described, as follows:

1. Intact cells or culture filtrates of various fruiting myxobacteria will lyse autoclaved (12, 58, 123, 124, 126, 127), butanol-treated (124), or EDTA-treated (128) Gram-negative cells. Bender (124) concentrated a culture filtrate of *M. xanthus* and on the basis of a proteolytic activity of the extract against casein assumed that the lysis of autoclaved *E. coli* cells was also a reflection of the same proteolytic activity. Since there were no comparative determinations of specific activities with purification of the extract, comparisons of optima for activity against casein and the cells, or determinations of products of activity against the Gram-negative cells, it is difficult on the basis of the data presented to attribute the activity observed to proteolysis. An ingenious experiment by Margolith (50) has suggested, however, that the lytic activity of intact cells of *M. fulvus* against autoclaved *E. coli* may indeed be proteolytic. *Myxococcus fulvus* was grown on an agar medium containing casein with streaks of living and autoclaved *E. coli* made across the sites of inoculation. The zone of hydrolysis of the casein coincided with the zone of lysis of the autoclaved *E. coli*, but was considerably larger than the

zone of lysis of the living cells. Norén (126) has claimed to have demonstrated lysis of intact *Aerobacter* cells with an ammonium sulfate fraction of a concentrated dialyzed culture filtrate of *M. virescens* (U2D fraction). While this preparation clearly had activity against cells of *Aerobacter* disrupted by autoclaving or by freeze-thawing, the activity against so-called intact cells is equivocal. The cells were treated with merthiolate prior to exposure to the preparation, and lysis of a small percentage of the cells (15 per cent) required a 24-hour incubation period. The changes taking place in a suspension of merthiolate-treated cells incubated for 24 hours are difficult to evaluate. Norén was also unable to demonstrate extensive lysis of isolated *Aerobacter* cell walls by his U2D fraction, using reduction in optical density of the walls as a parameter of lysis. It is possible that treatment of the walls with EDTA would have sensitized them to lysis or that a more sensitive parameter, such as release of label from ^{14}C-labeled walls, or appearance of components of the wall in the supernatant, would have detected the lysis.

In any case, the lysis of disrupted Gram-negative cells (disrupted by autoclaving, freeze-thawing, or treatment with EDTA or 5 per cent butanol) by intact myxobacteria or by culture filtrates has been clearly demonstrated. While the precise nature of the lysis is still to be described, the activity is heat-labile, nondialyzable (124, 126), and precipitable with acetone (124) or ammonium sulfate (126). The properties of the lytic factor are consistent with its being an enzyme.

2. There have been a number of reports of the lysis of Gram-positive cells by culture filtrates of myxobacteria. Ensign & Wolfe (131, 132) isolated an extracellular enzyme from *Cytophaga* which lysed intact as well as heat-killed cells of *Arthrobacter*. Gillespie & Cook (128) also have described an extracellular enzyme from *Sorangium* which lysed intact *Arthrobacter* cells. In both cases, the enzymes were active against isolated Gram-positive walls. Ensign & Wolfe (131) reported that the enzyme was an amidase, splitting the murein into an oligosaccharide and a peptide. The *Sorangium* enzyme, on the other hand, appears to be a lysozyme-type enzyme, releasing Elson-Morgan-positive material but no free amino acids or small peptides from the murein (128). The *Cytophaga* enzyme was purified 60–fold but could not be separated from the proteolytic activity of the preparation. The *Sorangium* lytic enzyme, on the other hand, was clearly separated from an accompanying proteolytic enzyme.

Bender (124) used reduction in optical density of alcian-blue treated *B. subtilis* by culture filtrates of *M. xanthus* as a parameter of cell wall lysis. *B. subtilis* cells were referred to as viable cells, although no data were offered in support of this claim. In view of the propensity of vegetative cells of *B. subtilis* to lyse under a variety of conditions, it is not reasonable to assume that such cells treated with alcian-blue for 30 minutes at 40° C are still viable, without so demonstrating. While N-acetyl amino sugars were not detected as products of the lysis, only glutamic acid, alanine, and lysine were, suggesting that wall lysis may have occurred. Bender showed that the optima for activity against Gram-positive cells and heated Gram-negative cells were different. Furthermore, while the activity against heated Gram-negative cells reached a peak at about six days of cultivation and remained constant until 20 days had elapsed, the "wall-lytic" activity against *B. subtilis* reached a peak at seven days and was completely absent at 16 days. The activity was referred to as enzymatic but this was not demonstrated. Firstly, 90 per cent of the activity was lost upon dialysis. No test was made of the activity of the dialysate or of the ability of the dialysate to activate the residue. Secondly, the factor was referred to as heat-unstable, but was tested by exposing the extract and the substrate to elevated temperatures and noting the lack of lysis. This merely tested the temperature sensitivity of the lytic process, not the stability of the factor. Since Solnetzewa (129) and Singh (12) showed that lytic factors produced by a variety of myxobacteria against viable, intact bacteria, would pass through a cellophane membrane and that the factor was stable to 100° C for 15 minutes (129), it is entirely possible that one of the lytic factors against Gram-positive bacteria is a basic polypeptide antibiotic similar to bacitracin or gramicidin. A peptide antibiotic would be heat-stable, dialyzable, and precipitable with organic solvents. Furthermore, the production of bacitracin has been shown to be correlated with the process of spore formation in *Bacillus licheniformis* (130). Since the lytic activity of these types of antibiotics is expressed only on living, actively metabolizing cells it now becomes important to control the variable of the state of the host cells more carefully than has been done.

3. Lipolytic activity. The observation that treatment of Gram-negative cells with butanol sensitized them to lysis by a culture filtrate of myxobacteria (124), suggests that the dissociation or removal of a lipid component of the Gram-negative wall is necessary before lysis can take place. The inability to obtain this activity in cell-free filtrates and extracts is consistent with the observation that in order for living Gram-negative cells to be lysed by myxobacteria there must be direct cell to cell contact between the myxobacteria and the host (44–46). If the myxobacteria possess a nondiffusible, epicellular, lipolytic enzyme, it would be consistent with these observations. No such activity has yet been reported.

4. Bender (133) has demonstrated and characterized a polysaccharidase from *M. xanthus* which will lyse several species of yeast. Intact yeast cells were resistant to the enzyme; it was necessary either to treat the cells with cysteine- organic solvents (acetone, ethyl acetate, or alcohol-ether), or heat (98° C for 5 minutes). Undialyzable polysaccharides were the products of hydrolysis.

For a general discussion of bacteriolysis, the reader is referred to the recent review by Stolp & Starr (134).

Production of Antibiotics

Oxford (58) first demonstrated that cultures of myxobacteria (*M. virescens*) had antibiotic activity. Using inhibition of the growth of *Staphylococcus aureus* in liquid culture as a parameter of activity, Oxford showed that the antibiotic(s) appeared and then disappeared as the culture grew older. He was able to concentrate the material and to demonstrate that it was soluble in absolute alcohol. The antibiotic had no activity on Gram-negative bacteria. Woods (3) and Norén (135) were unable to repeat Oxford's observations, Norén finding that *M. virescens* produced an antibiotic against *A. aerogenes* but not against *S. aureus*. On the other hand, *C. coralloides* produced an antibiotic against *S. aureus* which had also weak, inhibitory activity against *A. aerogenes*. Norén & Raper, in a later publication (136), contradicted those findings. They reported that a variety of fruiting myxobacteria (*M. virescens*, *M. fulvus*, *M. stipitatus*, *M. lactiis*, *Chondrococcus lacticus*, and *C. crocatus*) produced antibiotics against a number of Gram-positive bacteria but none against Gram-negative bacteria. They concluded that since these myxobacteria could grow on and lyse intact Gram-negative bacteria, the production of an antibiotic against the host was not a prerequisite for lysis. Margolith (50) was also unable to demonstrate antibiotic activity of *M. fulvus* against *E. coli*. Finally, Kletter & Henis (48) were unable to detect any antibiotic activity against *A. aerogenes* or *S. aureus* in cell-free culture filtrates of *M. fulvus* and *M. virescens*.

Extracts prepared by grinding intact cells of *M. virescens* have been shown to inhibit hemagglutination by influenza viruses A and B and mumps virus (137). The active material was dialyzable and was partially purified by paper chromatography and electrophoresis (138). Furthermore, the dialyzed fraction when added to allantoic fluid infected with influenza A or B, reduced the ID_{50} to zero (139). Finally, the cytopathogenic effect of influenza A or B on embryonic heart muscle was completely reversed by the addition of the partially purified myxobacterial extract (139). These remarkable observations have not been pursued.

It is clear that the fruiting myxobacteria produce antibiotics against Gram-positive organisms and possibly against some Gram-negative organisms and viruses. The apparent instability of the antibiotics coupled with its production only at particular stages of the organisms' life cycle may have led to a certain amount of contradictory opinion regarding its existence and properties.

TAXONOMY

"The literary history of the *Myxobacteriaceae* thus bids fair to become as remarkable in its diversity as are the characters which make the order an anomaly among the plants which appear to be its nearest allies . . . and one can but look with no small interest, and perhaps with some misgivings, to such further taxonomic vicissitudes as may be in store for them" (140).

The taxonomy of the myxobacteria seems to involve three principal problems: 1. The classification of the genera *Cytophaga* and *Sporocytophaga*, vis-à-vis the fruiting myxobacteria on one hand and nonmyxobacterial gliding bacteria on the other. 2. The relationship between the myxobacteria which form the typical long, slender rods, round microcysts, and simple fruiting bodies (e.g., Myxococcaceae) and those whose vegetative cells are thick and relatively short, whose microcysts are refractile rods and which enclose the microcysts in large cysts (e.g., Sorangiaceae). 3. The parameters for species classification.

Jahn was the first to classify the myxobacteria formally (99). His description of a myxobacterium included the following characters: (*a*) long, thin vegetative rods; (*b*) production of carotenoid pigments; (*c*) formation of slime; (*d*) production of fruiting bodies containing either numerous spores formed by the shortening vegetative rods or cysts within which spores are borne.

Stanier's inclusion of *Cytophaga* and *Sporocytophaga* in the myxobacteria (2) focused attention on the cellular morphology of the myxobacteria and on their peculiar gliding motility. In order to include *Cytophaga* and *Sporocytophaga* as myxobacteria it was necessary to discard fruiting body formation as a requisite property of the myxobacteria. The parameters which Stanier suggested were mode of formation and structure of microcysts; lack of rigid cell walls; mode of locomotion; cell division by constriction; manner of colony growth. It might be useful now to re-examine some of these parameters and determine to what extent they still reflect the essential nature of the myxobacteria.

Microcyst formation is not limited to the myxobacteria. *Azotobacter* forms microcysts morphologically identical to those formed by myxobacteria. Furthermore, examination of the processes of microcyst formation and germination in *Azotobacter* (141) revealed that the processes are remarkably similar to those occurring in *M. xanthus* (28).

The notion that the cell walls of myxobacteria are somehow fundamentally different from those of other Gram-negative bacteria is not yet supported by any data. Mason & Powelson (29) and Adye & Powelson (42) have examined the walls of *M. xanthus* and found them to contain the same general chemical constituents found in other Gram-negative bacteria. Voelz & Dworkin (28) have examined thin sections of *M. xanthus* electron microscopically and have found the wall to be a typical Gram-negative cell wall. A considerable amount of emphasis has been placed on the flexibility of the myxobacterial cell. This flexibility is not a peculiar property of myxobacterial cells and, while it could be related to a low level of murein in the cell walls, it may also merely reflect a high length-to-thickness ratio of the cell. In fact, long cells of *Bacillus or Proteus* may be observed to bend and assume hairpin shapes when moving on agar, while cells of *M. xanthus*, when grown under conditions leading to a low length-to-thickness ratio, show none of the characteristic flexibility.

The gliding motility of the myxobacteria is a property shared by a large number of procaryotic protista including the Cyanophyceae, Beggiatoaceae, Spirochaetaceae, Vitreoscillaceae and others. In view of the lack of critical information pertaining to the mechanisms of gliding motility among this variety of organisms it cannot, however, be said, that these mechanisms are all similar. Similarly, the property of division by constriction is not restricted to the myxobacteria. A variety of other organisms such as *Flexibacter*, *Oscillatoria*, and *Microscilla* have been shown to lack cross-walls (142, 143).

It is certainly not necessary that the taxonomic characters used to define a group be peculiar to that group. It does seem unusual, however, to exclude the only property which is peculiar to the myxobacteria, namely, fruiting body formation.

There has recently become available figures for the molar percentages of guanine plus cytosine for a number of myxobacteria (144). These are listed as follows: *Myxococcus* (10 species), 68 to 71 per cent; *Sorangium* (2 species), 69 per cent; *Chondromyces* (1 species), 70 per cent; *Cytophaga* (5 species), 33 to 42 per cent; *Sporocytophaga* (2 species), 36 per cent. In addition, Mandel (145) has determined the following values: *Polyangium*, 67 per cent; *Archangium*, 68 per cent; *Sorangium*, 67 per cent. It is clear that *Cytophaga* and *Sporocytophaga* are in a separate category from the fruiting myxobacteria and that the parameter of G+C value may be used to distinguish *Cytophaga* and *Sporocytophaga* from morphogenetically deficient variants of the fruiting myxobacteria, e.g., strain vc of *M. xanthus* (6).

In Stanier's recent revision of the taxonomy of the myxobacteria in *Bergey's Manual* (7), the suggestion was made that the nonfruiting myxobacteria might properly be classified with the Beggiatoaceae, and other gliding bacteria. This proposal was not, however, incorporated into the manual. Soriano & Lewin, in a thoughtful review (142), have suggested that the nonfruiting myxobacteria be placed with the nonmyxobacterial gliding bacteria in the order Flexibacterales. (They have mistakenly included *Sporocytophaga*, presently a member of the Myxococcaceae, in the Cytophagaceae.) At an equal ordinal rank would be the Myxobacterales containing the fruiting myxobacteria. This seems a sensible proposal and would be consistent with the base ratio data.

It was completely unexpected that organisms as dissimilar as *Sorangium*, *Archangium*, *Chondromyces*, *Podangium*, and *Myxococcus* should have essentially the same G+C values, especially since the species of *Sorangium* tested were cellulose decomposers. These organisms differ in terms of their nutritional requirements, vegetative morphology, microcyst morphology, pigmentation, and shape of fruiting bodies and one would expect the G+C values to reflect these differences. The similarity of the G+C values does not, however, eliminate the possibility that another taxonomic problem may be lurking here. The degree of DNA homology between different species of bacteria has been determined by DNA hybridization experiments (146). This more sophisticated approach to determining taxonomic relatedness is being applied to the myxobacteria in a number of laboratories and should bring some additional critical data to bear on the problem.

The problem of the classification of the myxobacteria at the species level reflects in an exaggerated fashion the difficulty in classifying the bacteria in the absence of substantial information regarding their physiological and biochemical properties. Pigmentation, shape of fruiting body, and shape and dimensions of microcysts are essentially the only parameters used for classifying at the species level. However, as long as these are stable properties, they may serve a perfectly useful taxonomic function. The effects on these properties of nutrition and age of culture (19) have been well demonstrated and should be kept in mind. Ideally, one would hope to use such parameters as nutritional requirements, metabolic pathways, G+C ratios, DNA hybridization, and phage typing for specific classification. This ideal seems a long way off in the case of myxobacteria.

Gräf (38, 39) and Bauer (40) have described a series of so-called new genera and species of myxobacteria. These are *Sphaerocytophaga filiformis* and *S. fusiformis* (38), *Sporocytophaga cauliformis* (39), and *Sphaeromyxa xanthochlora* (40). The genera *Sphaerocytophaga* and *Sphaeromyxa* are based on the formation of "sphaeroids" which are claimed by the authors to be a part of a life cycle and to undergo germination. Not only is no evidence presented to document this claim, but the phase contrast and electron micrographs of the "spheroids" indicate clearly that these are sphaeroplasts. These organisms are obviously cytophagas which, like most myxobacteria, will form sphaeroplasts when old or under adverse conditions. (The "sphaeroids" are formed after a week or so in liquid culture or on blood agar plates.) Furthermore, Poindexter has examined Gräf's cultures of *S. cauliformis* described as a *Sporocytophaga* which goes through a life cycle involving a stalked form similar to *Caulobacter*. She has suggested that, ". . . the 'stalk' was nothing more than the slender, tapered end of the cell which persisted for some time after cell division had occurred" (147). The implication that *S. cauliformis* is therefore a combination of myxobacter and *Caulobacter* is unwarranted.

The creation of new genera and species on the basis of sphaeroplast formation and faulty morphological observations only confuses an already difficult taxonomic situation.

EPILOGUE AND CONCLUSIONS

One impression that emerges from a close examination of the myxobacteria is that the distinction between them and the eubacteria has been overemphasized. Furthermore, the only essential obstacle to handling these organisms as one does *E. coli* is the fact that, as a rule, they cannot be easily grown in a dispersed state in liquid media. Once, however, this difficulty is overcome, they appear to be amenable to the routine manipulations which have made bacteria an effective tool for biochemical and genetic research.

While most of the recent attention has been focused on the genus *Myxo-*

coccus, the ability of the so-called higher myxobacteria (e.g., *C. crocatus*) to form complex and elaborately sculptured fruiting bodies represents another exciting problem in developmental microbiology. It is to be hoped that an investigation of this type would be accompanied by a close scrutiny of their nutritional requirements, fine structure, intermediary metabolism, etc.

The conversion of myxobacterial rods to microcysts is a well-defined example of cellular morphogenesis, and now that it is possible to induce this conversion rapidly and synchronously (77) will certainly prove to be a valuable system for obtaining biochemical correlates of morphogenesis. Furthermore, the cellular aggregation of the fruiting myxobacteria culminates in a rudimentary kind of multicellularity and may be appropriate for examining the tactic processes and cell to cell interactions which are part of the multicellular state. Similar processes are indeed being studied in other protists (e.g., the Acrasiales). However, the relative simplicity of the procaryotic cell, coupled with the considerable amount of information available on the nature of bacterial cell walls considerably simplifies the task of causally relating changes in cell shape and function with changes in the macromolecular composition of the cell.

LITERATURE CITED[4]

1. Thaxter, R., *Botan. Gaz.*, **17**, 389–406 (1892)
2. Stanier, R. Y., *Bacteriol. Rev.*, **6**, 143–96 (1942)
3. Woods, N. A., *Studies on the myxobacteria* (Master's thesis, Univ. of Washington, Seattle, Wash., 1948)
4. Loebeck, M. E., and Klein, H. P., *J. Gen. Microbiol.*, **14**, 281–89 (1956)
5. Mason, D. J., and Powelson, D., *J. Gen. Microbiol.*, **19**, 65–70 (1958)
6. Dworkin, M., *J. Bacteriol.*, **84**, 250–57 (1962)
7. Breed, R. S., Murray, E. G. D., and Smith, N. R., *Bergey's Manual of Determinative Bacteriology*, 7th ed. (Williams & Wilkins, Co., Baltimore, Md., 1094 pp., 1957)
8. Starr, M. P., and Skerman, V. B. D., *Ann. Rev. Microbiol.*, **19**, 407–54 (1965)
9. Krzemieniewska, H., and Krzemieniewski, S., *Acta Soc. Botan. Polon.*, **4**, 3–54 (1926)
10. Krzemieniewska, H., and Krzemieniewski, S., *Ibid.*, **5**, 79–98 (1927)
11. Krzemieniewska, H., and Krzemieniewski, S., *Ibid.*, **7**, 250–73 (1930)
12. Singh, B. N., *J. Gen. Microbiol.*, **1**, 1–9 (1947)
13. McCurdy, H. D., Jr., *Can. J. Microbiol.*, **9**, 282–85 (1963)
14. Kofler, L., *Sitzber. Kais. Akad. Wiss. Wien. Mathem. Naturwiss. Klasse, Abt.* 1, **122**, 845–76 (1913)
15. Norén, B., *Botan. Tidskr.*, **46**, 446–53 (1952)
16. Singh, B. N., Mathew, S., and Sreenivasaya, M., *Symp. Antibiotics*, 1–4. (Sree Saraswatz Press, Ltd., Calcutta, India, 1958)
17. Brockman, E. R., and Boyd, W. L., *J. Bacteriol.*, **86**, 605–6 (1963)
18. Beebe, J. M., *Iowa State Coll. J. Sci.*, **15**, 307–18 (1941)
19. Kühlwein, H., *Arch. Mikrobiol.*, **14**, 678–704 (1950)
20. Krzemieniewska, K., and Krezemieniewski, S., *Acta Soc. Botan. Polon.*, **5**, 102–39 (1927)

[4] Supplementary bibliographic material (306 references) has been deposited as Document number 8751 with the ADI Auxiliary Publications Project, Photoduplication Service, Library of Congress, Washington, D. C. 20540. A copy may be secured by citing the document number and by remitting $7.50 for photoprints or $2.75 for 35 mm. microfilm. Advance payment is required. Make checks or money orders payable to: Chief, Photoduplication Service, Library of Congress.

21. Norén, B., *Nature*, **167**, 225–26 (1951)
22. Mishustin, E. N., *Mikrobiologiya*, **6**, 1274–92 (1937)
23. Mishustin, E. N., *Ibid.*, **7**, 427–44 (1938)
24. Vahle, C., *Zbl. Bakt. 2 Abt.*, **25**, 178–237 (1910)
25. Krzemieniewska, H., and Krzemieniewski, S., *Acta Soc. Botan. Polon.*, **5**, 46–90 (1928)
26. Imshenetsky, A. A., and Alferov, V. V., *J. Gen. Microbiol.*, **27**, 391–95 (1962)
27. Thimann, K. V., *The Life of Bacteria*, 2nd ed., 69. (The Macmillan Co., New York, N.Y., 909 pp., 1963)
28. Voelz, H., and Dworkin, M., *J. Bacteriol.*, **84**, 943–52 (1962)
29. Mason, D. J., and Powelson, D., *Biochim. Biophys. Acta*, **29**, 1–7 (1958)
30. Kühlwein, H., and Rossner, W., *Naturwissenschaften*, **50**, 339–40 (1963)
31. Voelz, H., *Arch. Mikrobiol.*, **51**, 60–70 (1965)
32. Correll, D. L., and Lewin, R. A., *Can. J. Microbiol.*, **10**, 63–74 (1964)
33. Reichenbach, H., *Arch. Mikrobiol.*, **50**, 246–55 (1965)
34. Pate, J. L., and Ordal, E. J., *Bacteriol. Proc.*, 32 (1965)
35. Gräf, W., *Arch. Hyg. Bakteriol.*, **149**, 518–26 (1965)
36. Ordal, E. J. (Personal communication, 1965)
37. Dworkin, M., and Voelz, H., *J. Gen. Microbiol.*, **28**, 81–85 (1962)
38. Gräf, W., *Arch. Hyg. Bakteriol.*, **145**, 405–59 (1961)
39. Gräf, W., *Ibid.*, **146**, 114 (1962)
40. Bauer, L., *Arch. Hyg. Bakteriol.*, **146**, 392–400 (1962)
41. Dworkin, M., and Niederpruem, D. J., *J. Bacteriol.*, **87**, 316–22 (1964)
42. Adye, J. C., and Powelson, D. M., *J. Bacteriol.*, **81**, 780–85 (1961)
43. Holt, J. G., and Powelson, D. M., *Bacteriol. Proc.*, 59 (1960)
44. Oetker, H., *Arch. Mikrobiol.*, **19**, 206–46 (1953)
45. Imshenetsky, A. A., and Kusuirina, L. A., *Mikrobiologiya*, **20**, 3–12 (1957)
46. Norén, B., *Botan. Tidskr.*, **54**, 550–60 (1960)
47. Nolte, E. M., *Arch. Mikrobiol.*, **28**, 191–218 (1957)
48. Kletter, B., and Henis, Y., *Can. J. Microbiol.*, **9**, 577–84 (1963)
49. Beebe, J. M., *Iowa State Coll. J. Sci.*, **15**, 319–37 (1941)
50. Margolith, P., *Nature*, **196**, 1335–36 (1962)
51. Baur, E., *Arch. Protistenk,.* **5**, 92–121 (1905)
52. McDonald, J. C., and Peterson, J. E., *Mycologia*, **54**, 368–73 (1962)
53. Chase, J. M., *Nutrition of some aquatic myxobacteria.* (Master's thesis, Univ. of Washington, Seattle, Wash., 1965)
54. Quehl, A., *Zbl. Bakt. 2 Abt.*, **16**, 9–34 (1906)
55. Solnetzewa, L., *Mikrobiologiya*, **9**, 217–31 (1940)
56. Solnetzewa, L., *Mikrobiologiya*, **10**, 505–25 (1940)
57. Clark, W. A., *J. Bacteriol.*, **67**, 589–92 (1954)
58. Oxford, A. E., *J. Bacteriol.*, **53**, 129–38 (1947)
59. Loebeck, M. E., *Studies on the terrestrial fruiting myxobacteria.* (Doctoral thesis, University of Washington, Seattle, Wash., 1954)
60. Norén, B., *Botan. Notiser*, **108**, 81–134 (1955)
61. Krzemieniewska, H., and Krzemieniewski, S., *Bull. Intern. Acad. Polon. Sci. Ltr., Ser. B., Sci. Nat.*, **75**, 11–31 (1937)
62. Krzemieniewska, H., and Krzemieniewski, S., *Ibid.*, **75**, 35–59 (1937)
63. Stanier, R. Y. (Personal communication, 1965)
64. Finck, G., *Arch. Mikrobiol.*, **15**, 358–88 (1950)
65. Beebe, J. M., *Iowa State Coll. J. Sci.*, **17**, 227–40 (1942)
66. Imshenetsky, A., and Solnetzewa, L., *Akad. Nauk. SSSR Izvest.*, **6**, 1115–72 (1936)
67. Norén, B., *Botan. Tidskr.*, **46**, 325–65 (1952)
68. Marmur, J., *J. Mol. Biol.*, **3**, 208–18 (1961)
69. Imshenetsky, A., and Solnetzewa, L., *Mikrobiologiya*, **6**, 3–15 (1937)
70. Pinoy, P. E., *Compt. Rend. Soc. Biol.*, **157**, 77–78 (1913)
71. Bachmann, B. J., *J. Gen. Microbiol.*, **13**, 541–51 (1955)
72. Anderson, R. L., and Ordal, E. J., *J. Bacteriol.*, **81**, 130–38 (1961)
73. Anderson, R. L., and Ordal, E. J., *Ibid.*, **81**, 139–46 (1961)
74. Starr, T. J., and Klein, H. P., *Arch. Mikrobiol.*, **20**, 235–42 (1954)
75. Watson, B. F., and Dworkin, M., *Bacteriol. Proc.*, 105 (1963)
76. Watson, B. F., and Dworkin, M., *Ibid.*, 85 (1965)

77. Dworkin, M., and Gibson, S. M., *Science*, **146**, 243–44 (1964)
78. Reichenbach, H., *Ber. Deut. Botan. Ges.*, **75**, 90–95 (1962)
79. Reichenbach, H., *Encyclopedia cinematographica #E797* Chondromyces apiculatus. (Inst. f. den Wissenschaftlichen Films, 34 Göttingen, Nonnensteig, 72, Germany)
80. Dworkin, M., *Bacteriol. Proc.*, 116 (1962)
81. Dworkin, M., *J. Bacteriol.*, **86**, 67–72 (1963)
82. Leadbetter, E. R., *Nature*, **200**, 1127–28 (1963)
83. McCurdy, H. D., Jr., *Can. J. Microbiol.*, **10**, 935–36 (1964)
84. Fluegel, W., *Proc. Minn. Acad. Sci.*, **31**, 114–15 (1964)
85. Dworkin, M., and Sadler, W., *J. Bacteriol.* (In press, 1966)
86. Bonner, J. T., *Morphogenesis.* (Atheneum, New York, 296 pp., 1963)
87. Lev, M., *Nature*, **173**, 501 (1954)
88. Jennings, J., *Nature*, **190**, 190 (1961)
89. McVittie, A., and Zahler, S. A., *Nature*, **194**, 1299–1300 (1962)
90. Fluegel, W., *Proc. Minn. Acad. Sci.*, **32**, 120–23 (1963)
91. Stanier, R. Y., *J. Bacteriol.*, **44**, 405–12 (1942)
92. Thaxter, R., *Botan. Gaz.*, **23**, 395–411 (1897)
93. Badian, J., *Acta Soc. Botan. Polon.*, **7**, 55–71 (1930)
94. Beebe, J. M., *J. Bacteriol.*, **42**, 193–223 (1941)
95. Klieneberger-Nobel, E., *J. Gen. Microbiol.*, **1**, 33–38 (1947)
96. Krzemieniewska, H., *Acta Soc. Botan. Polon.*, **1**, 507–19 (1930)
97. Grace, J. B., *J. Gen. Microbiol.*, **5**, 519–24 (1951)
98. Sadler, W., and Dworkin, M., *J. Bacteriol.* (In press, 1966)
99. Jahn, E., *Beiträge zur botanischer Protistologie. I. Die Polyangiden.* (Gebrüder Bortraeger, Leipzig, 107 pp., 1924)
100. Ramsey, S., and Dworkin, M., *Bacteriol. Proc.*, 17 (1966)
101. Gross, P. R., *J. Exptl. Zool.*, **157**, 21–38 (1964)
102. McVittie, A., Messik, F., and Zahler, S. A., *J. Bacteriol.*, **84**, 546–51 (1962)
103. Zeece, S., *Effect of heat, sonic vibration, and ultra-violet irradiation on vegetative cells and microcysts of Myxococcus xanthus*, (Summa cum laude thesis, Univ. of Minnesota, Minneapolis, Minn., 1965)
104. Anacker, R. L., and Ordal, E. J., *J. Bacteriol.*, **70**, 738–41 (1955)
105. Burchard, R. P., and Dworkin, M., *Bacteriol. Proc.*, 118–19 (1964)
106. Burchard, R. P., and Dworkin, M., *J. Bacteriol.*, **91**, 1305–13 (1966)
107. Greene, J. M., and Leadbetter, E. R., *Bacteriol. Proc.*, 34 (1962)
108. Greene, J. M., and Leadbetter, E. R., *Ibid.*, 54 (1963)
109. Greene, J. M., and Leadbetter, E. R., *Ibid.*, 17 (1964)
110. Burchard, R. P., and Dworkin, M., *J. Bacteriol.*, **91**, 535–45 (1966)
111. Batra, P. P., and Rilling, H. C., *Arch. Biochem. Biophys.*, **107**, 485–92 (1964)
112. Sistrom, W. R., Griffiths, M., and Stanier, R. Y., *J. Cell Comp. Physiol.*, **48**, 473–515 (1956)
113. Ordal, E. J., and Rucker, R. R., *Proc. Soc. Exptl. Biol. Med.*, **56**, 15–18 (1944)
114. Garnjobst, L., *J. Bacteriol.*, **49**, 113–28 (1945)
115. Nigrelli, R. F., and Hutner, S. H., *Zoologica*, **30**, 101–2 (1945)
116. Gräf, W., *Arch. Hyg. Bakteriol.*, **146**, 481–91 (1962)
117. Gräf, W., *Ibid.*, **146**, 492–500 (1962)
118. Mayer-Pietschmann, K., *Arch. Mikrobiol.*, **16**, 163–76 (1951)
119. Kühlwein, H., *Ber. Deut. Botan. Ges.*, **70**, 227–32 (1957)
120. Winogradsky, S., *Ann. Inst. Pasteur*, **43**, 549 (1929)
121. Weibull, C., Movement. In *The Bacteria, I. Structure*, 153–205. (Gunsalus, I. C., and Stanier, R. Y., Eds., Academic Press, Inc., New York, 513 pp., 1960)
122. Jahn, T. L., and Bovee, E. C., *Ann. Rev. Microbiol.*, **19**, 21–58 (1965)
123. Norén, B., *Botan. Tidskr.* **47**, 309–32 (1953)
124. Bender, H., *Arch. Mikrobiol.*, **43**, 262–79 (1962)
125. Oxford, A. E., and Singh, B. N., *Nature*, **158**, 745–46 (1946)
126. Norén, B., *Botan. Notiser*, **113**, 320–36 (1960)
127. Norén, B., *Svensk Botan. Tidskr.*, **49**, 282–94 (1955)
128. Gillespie, D. C., and Cook, F. D., *Can. J. Microbiol.*, **11**, 109–18 (1965)
129. Solnetzewa, L. I., *Mikrobiologiya*, **8**, 700–5 (1939)
130. Bernlohr, R. W., and Novelli, G. D., *Arch. Biochem. Biophys.*, **103**, 94–104 (1963)

131. Ensign, J. C., and Wolfe, R. S., *Bacteriol. Proc.*, 33 (1964)
132. Ensign, J. C., and Wolfe, R. S., *J. Bacteriol.*, **90**, 395–402 (1965)
133. Bender, H., *Arch. Mikrobiol.*, **45**, 407–22 (1963)
134. Stolp, H., and Starr, M. P., *Ann. Rev. Microbiol.*, **19**, 79–104 (1965)
135. Norén, B., *Botan. Tidskr.*, **47**, 402–10 (1953)
136. Norén, B., and Raper, K. B., *J. Bacteriol.*, **84**, 157–62 (1962)
137. Katzenberger, I., Kühlwein, H., and Kausche, G. A., *Zentr. Bakteriol. Parasitenk.*, *Abt. 2*, **109**, 478–81 (1956)
138. Katzenberger, I., and Kausche, G. A., *Naturwissenschaften*, **44**, 44–45 (1957)
139. Katzenberger, I., *Naturwissenschaften*, **46**, 607–8 (1959)
140. Thaxter, R., *Botan. Gaz.*, **37**, 405–16 (1904)
141. Wyss, O., Neumann, M. G., and Socolofsky, M. D., *J. Biophys. Biochem. Cytol.*, **10**, 555–65 (1961)
142. Soriano, S., and Lewin, R. A., *Antonie von Leeuwenhoek J. Microbiol. Serol.*, **31**, 66–80 (1965)
143. Steed, P., and Murray, R. G. E., *Can. J. Microbiol.* (In press, 1965)
144. Mandel, M., and Leadbetter, E. R., *J. Bacteriol.*, **90**, 1795–96 (1965)
145. Mandel, M. (Personal communication, 1965)
146. McCarthy, B. J., and Bolton, E. T., *Proc. Natl. Acad. Sci. U.S.*, **50**, 156–64 (1963)
147. Poindexter, J. (Personal communication, 1965)

THE RELATION OF THE PSITTACOSIS GROUP (CHLAMYDIAE)[1] TO BACTERIA AND VIRUSES[2,3,4]

By James W. Moulder

Department of Microbiology, The University of Chicago, Chicago, Illinois

Contents

INTRODUCTION... 108
MECHANISM OF REPRODUCTION.......................... 108
  DEVELOPMENTAL CYCLE..................................... 108
  GROWTH CURVES.. 109
  MECHANISM OF CELL DIVISION............................. 110
STRUCTURE AND CHEMICAL COMPOSITION............. 110
  CELL WALLS.. 111
  NUCLEIC ACIDS... 112
  PROTEIN... 113
  LIPIDS.. 113
  ANTIGENS.. 113
METABOLISM... 114
  GROWTH REQUIREMENTS...................................... 114
  ENDOGENOUS METABOLISM................................... 115
  ENERGY METABOLISM.. 115
  DNA METABOLISM.. 117
  RNA METABOLISM.. 119
  PROTEIN METABOLISM...................................... 120
  EFFECT ON HOST CELL METABOLISM......................... 120
TAXONOMIC POSITION OF THE PSITTACOSIS GROUP..... 121
  INTRA-GROUP RELATIONS................................... 121
  RELATION OF THE PSITTACOSIS GROUP TO THE BACTERIA.......... 123
  RELATION OF THE PSITTACOSIS GROUP TO THE VIRUSES.......... 126
CONCLUSION... 127

Un gros virus est un virus. Une petite bactérie est une bactérie.

A. Lwoff (72)

[1] Page (96) has proposed that all organisms of the psittacosis-lymphogranuloma venereum-trachoma group be gathered together in one genus, *Chlamydia* Jones, Rake, and Stearns 1945. This proposal is supported by the Subcommittee on the *Chlamydiaceae* of the Taxonomy Committee of the American Society for Microbiology.

[2] The survey of literature pertaining to this review was concluded on December 31, 1965.

[3] The following abbreviations will be used: RNA (ribonucleic acid); DNA (deoxyribonucleic acid); ATP (adenosine triphosphate); NAD (nicotinamide-adenine dinucleotide); NADP (nicotinamide-adenine dinucleotide phosphate).

[4] Original work cited was supported by grants from the National Institutes of Health and the Abbott Laboratories.

INTRODUCTION

The idea that viruses are degenerate evolutionary descendants of bacteria was first explicitly stated by Green (54) and Laidlow (64), and has more recently been supported by Burnet (29). If there is, as this hypothesis demands, an evolutionary continuity between bacteria and viruses, then, at some time in the past there must have arisen transitional forms exhibiting sets of properties that we would now recognize as partly bacterial and partly viral. The discovery of this kind of a borderline organism among the many present-day intracellular parasites would offer strong support for the hypothesis of degenerative evolution. Microorganisms of the psittacosis group have long been suspected of being just such intermediate organisms (18), and the purpose of this review is to examine this possibility in light of the large amount of new information that has accumulated since the group as a whole was last considered in these reviews (125). In the intervening eleven years we have gained a better understanding of the psittacosis group and a more precise delineation of the differences between viruses and bacteria. In examining the relationship of the psittacosis group to the bacteria and to the viruses, I shall proceed by first describing their principal properties and then speculating on the phylogenetic origin of these microorganisms and on the directions of evolution within the group.

The many members of the psittacosis group comprise an obvious natural taxon. They are nonmotile, Gram-negative, obligate intracellular parasites with an almost identical morphology and a common group antigen, and multiply in the cytoplasm of their host cells by means of a distinctive developmental cycle. They are usually differentiated one from another by the presence of specific antigens and by their pathogenic properties, although other differences are beginning to emerge. Some members of the group, the etiologic agents of psittacosis and ornithosis, are primarily parasites of birds but may also infect man and other mammals. Others of mammalian origin are commonly used laboratory strains, the agents of mouse pneumonitis, feline pneumonitis, and meningopneumonitis, for example. Still other mammalian members of the group are important pathogens of domestic herbivores. The causative agents of trachoma, inclusion conjuctivitis, and lymphogranuloma venereum may be passed from person to person without the intervention of animal reservoirs, and appear to be peculiarly human parasites.

MECHANISM OF REPRODUCTION
DEVELOPMENTAL CYCLE

Soon after the discovery of the etiologic agent of psittacosis, Bedson and his associates (15, 19, 20, 21, 25) concluded from microscopic observations on infected tissues that the psittacosis agent passes through a series of developmental forms while multiplying by binary fission, and introduced the term, "developmental cycle" to describe the sequence of events involved in the reproduction of the psittacosis agent in the cytoplasm of its host cell. With the advent of the electron microscope and the ultramicrotome, Bedson's observations were confirmed and extended. Two morphologically different developmental forms with a continuous gradation of intermediates between them were soon recognized (36, 47, 55, 66, 79, 80). One was a small cell about 0.3 μ in diameter, with an electron-dense nucleoid, and corresponding to the elementary body of light microscopy. The other was a large cell 0.5 to 1.0 μ in diameter, without a dense center, and equivalent to the initial body of the light microscopist. Thin sections of the infected host cells contained many forms apparently fixed in the act of binary fission (5–7, 44, 47, 55–57, 66–68, 77, 78, 100). In addition to these dividing forms, many workers also saw structureless matrices in the cytoplasm of host cells infected with the agents of meningopneumonitis and trachoma in which new agent cells were apparently being organized by some virus-like reproductive process (7, 23, 58, 77, 79, 100, 115). However, more recent work (6, 56) demonstrated that these matrices were artifacts resulting from the disruption of the fragile large developmental forms during fixation and embedding of the infected cell for thin-sectioning.

There appears to be no significant difference in morphology or developmental cycle among the various members of the psittacosis group, and a single generalized description applies to all. The following concept of the developmental cycle, based on the original concepts of Bedson, was suggested by Litwin and his associates (66, 68) and has been extended and put on a much firmer basis by the investigations of Armstrong & Reed (6) and Higashi (56).

The developmental cycle may be regarded as an orderly alternation of the small and large cell types. It is initiated by the highly infectious small cell which is taken into the host cell by phagocytosis. The engulfed small cell retains its morphological integrity in vacuoles bounded by membranes derived from the surface of the host cell, and there is no eclipse. Instead, without loss of individuality, the small cell is reorganized into a large cell which is the vegetative multiplying form of these organisms. Then, still within the membrane-bound vacuole, the large cell grows in size and multiplies by repeated binary fission. The developmental cycle is completed by the reorganization of most of the large cells into small ones which are then available for infection of new host cells. The time required for completion of a cycle varies from 24 to 48 hours, depending on the particular host-parasite system involved.

Growth Curves

One-step growth curves corresponding to a single developmental cycle have been obtained for a number of psittacosis group agents growing in the chorioallantoic ectoderm of the chick embryo (66, 68) or in cell cultures (23, 32, 56–58, 68, 93, 121). Earlier studies were discussed by Weiss (125). These curves may all be divided into early and late phases with the dividing line drawn at about 20 hours after infection. In the early phase there is no extracellular infectivity, and the intracellular infectivity is low and relatively constant. The late phase begins with the appearance of extracellular infectivity, and both extracellular and intracellular infectivity rise sharply and reach maxima near the end of the developmental cycle. The long lag before the rapid rise in infectivity at the beginning of the late phase has been interpreted as evidence that members of the psittacosis group pass through a virus-like eclipse during their developmental cycle. However, electron microscopic observations during the early phase show that there is no morphological eclipse and that the large agent cells are multiplying by binary fission throughout this period (6, 56, 66, 68). The long lag in the infectivity curve is due, not to the eclipse of the invading small particles but to their reorganization into the large vegetative cells instead, which are either completely noninfectious or only very weakly infectious. The rapid rise in infectivity at the beginning of the late phase of the growth curve coincides with the initiation of the reorganization of the large psittacosis group cells into the small, highly infectious ones (56, 66, 68).

Mechanism of Cell Division

Cell division in the large psittacosis group cells appears to proceed by the formation of cross-septa (56, 77). Large cells just finishing division were frequently connected by electron-dense bridges (44, 56). Structures of possibly similar nature occur inside large cells and may be situated on the plane of division. Higashi (56) has suggested that these structures are organelles acting as division centrums (45). Erlandson & Allen (44) saw complex internal membranes in large meningopneumonitis cells which they suggested might be mesosomes. They may be related to the structures seen by Higashi (56).

Large agent cells with two or more dense bodies that could be small cells at some stage in their development have been observed at infrequent intervals in thin sections of infected cells (5, 23, 47, 55, 56). These structures have been regarded as evidence that members of the psittacosis group may also multiply by multiple endosporulation (23, 47). However, they are found at such low frequencies that multiple endosporulation cannot be a quantitatively important method of multiplication in the psittacosis group.

The factors that initiate the reorganization of large cells into small ones are unknown. This reorganization "consists of marginal condensation and reduction in size accompanying differentiation of the nucleoid" (56). As will be discussed in the next section, the process is accompanied by a drastic reduction in the RNA/DNA ratio of the small cells as compared to the large ones.

STRUCTURE AND CHEMICAL COMPOSITION

Structural details of psittacosis group cells have been worked out by electron microscopic examination of thin sections of several different members of the group growing in appropriate host cells, while almost all data on chemical composition have been obtained with purified preparations of the meningopneumonitis agent. Preparations made from infected allantoic fluid were mixtures of small and large cells (82, 83). Suspensions consisting almost entirely of small meningopneumonitis cells were obtained by purifying the population released from L cells at the end of the developmental cycle (118), while homogeneous large cell preparations were made by lysing infected L cells 20 hours after infection, when the intracellular population was almost exclusively of the large cell type (117).

Cell Walls

Both large and small cells of the psittacosis group agents are surrounded by limiting membranes that are probably complete at all times. Reports of incomplete limiting structures appear to have been based on artifacts similar to those responsible for the formation of the matrices previously referred to. Erlandson & Allen (44) described a single unit membrane in both large and small meningopneumonitis cells, while Mitsui et al. (77) reported a double membrane around large trachoma cells and only a single membrane around the small ones. Armstrong & Reed (6) observed that large lymphogranuloma venereum cells "were bounded by an intact bilaminar envelope reminiscent of the combined cell wall and cytoplasmic membrane of bacterial cells." Anderson et al. (5) concluded that an ornithosis agent had a true cell wall under which there was a cytoplasmic membrane that was often poorly visualized.

Other evidence indicates that the envelope is homologous to the cell wall of Gram-negative bacteria. The multiplication of members of the psittacosis group was inhibited by penicillin (60, 124) and D-cycloserine (65, 87), antibiotics that inhibit the multiplication of bacteria by specifically interfering with the synthesis of the cell wall mucopeptide and are without effect on organisms lacking this structure (92). Agents growing in the presence of penicillin and D-cycloserine formed large irregularly shaped and vacuolated bodies that were probably analogous to bacterial spheroplasts (60, 83, 87, 116, 124). D-Alanine competitively reversed the growth inhibition of D-cycloserine in the psittacosis group (65, 87), just as it does in bacteria. Muramic acid, a unique constituent of bacterial cell wall mucopeptide, has been identified in four different members of the psittacosis group (98), and isolated envelopes of the meningopneumonitis agent were disintegrated by muramidase (74) although the intact meningopneumonitis cell was not (42, 74). All these observations are most simply interpreted by assuming that the limiting envelope of psittacosis group cells contains a mucopeptide layer similar to that of bacterial cell walls.

Cell walls of the meningopneumonitis agent were prepared from whole cells by treatment with deoxycholate and trypsin (61) or by sonic disintegration (74). The isolated envelopes were rigid enough to determine the size and shape of the intact cells from which they were derived. In electron micrographs, their resemblance to bacterial cell walls was striking. Meningopneumonitis cell walls resembled the cell walls of Gram-negative bacteria (104) in chemical composition. They contained only traces of nucleic acid, small amounts of carbohydrate, large amounts of lipid, and all of the amino acids of the whole cells (61, 84). Lysine was present and diaminopimelic acid was absent. Manire (74) observed that the isolated meningopneumonitis walls are morphologically complex. They consist of at least two layers, the inner of which is composed of highly ordered arrays of hexagonally packed units. Such structures have been seen in the walls of several different bacterial species (104).

Nucleic Acids

Both DNA and RNA were found in both large and small cells of the psittacosis group (61, 102, 117, 118, 129). In large cells DNA probably occurs in the form of twisted filaments distributed in irregular areas throughout the cytoplasm, whereas in the small cells the filaments are concentrated in the electron-dense nucleoids (5, 6, 44, 55, 77). Most of the RNA is probably contained in the ribosomes which may be seen in the cytoplasm of both large and small cells (5, 56).

The DNA of meningopneumonitis agent was extracted from populations of small (117) and mixed (42, 48) cell types by modifications of methods used for the extraction of DNA from poxviruses and bacteria. Both kinds of preparations had the properties of double-stranded DNA. Density gradient centrifugation and determination of thermal denaturation temperature indicated that the DNA from a mixed cell population had a guanosine plus cytosine content of 39 per cent (42). An earlier report (83) of a much lower guanosine plus cytosine content was in error. There was complete genetic homology between meningopneumonitis DNA and the DNA of four other members of the psittacosis group (48), as shown by the method of McCarthy & Bolton (76). It is therefore probable that the DNA of all psittacosis group agents is of approximately the same guanosine plus cytosine content, although that of the trachoma agent has been reported to be 44 per cent (24). Tamura (117) calculated from analysis of small cell populations of the meningopneumonitis agent that each cell contains 1.6×10^{-15} g DNA or 9.5×10^8 daltons. By comparison, a cell of *Escherichia coli* has 2.8×10^9 daltons of DNA (30), and a particle of vaccinia virus, 1.6×10^8 daltons (63).

Small meningopneumonitis cells had approximately equal amounts of RNA and DNA (118), but large cells taken from their L cell hosts 20 hours after infection contained four times as much RNA as DNA (117). Such a high RNA content is consistent with the rapid multiplication going on in the large cell population at that time. These large cells had at least three kinds of RNA, with sedimentation coefficients of 21S, 16S, and 4S, and guanosine plus cytosine contents of 52 per cent (119). The 21S and 16S RNA components were associated with 50S and 30S ribosomes, respectively (119). The guanosine plus cytosine content of trachoma agent RNA was the same as that of meningopneumonitis agent (24).

The high RNA content of the large immature psittacosis group cells probably accounts for the characteristic shifts in acridine orange staining of inclusions during the developmental cycle first observed by Starr et al. (112). The invading small cells are relatively rich in DNA and stain green. As the developmental cycle proceeds, the population shifts to the large cell type which is relatively rich in RNA, and stains red. Finally, at the end of the cycle the population again becomes a predominantly small one, rich in DNA, and staining green. The ribonuclease sensitivity of the RNA-rich early inclusions (38, 112) may be a property of the large cells themselves (106).

PROTEIN

Quantitative amino acid analysis by ion exchange chromotography was performed on small (117) and mixed (86) cell preparations of the meningopneumonitis agent. At least 18 different amino acids were present. About one fourth of the total alanine was the D-stereoisomer (86). The protein content of a small cell population was about 60 per cent (117).

LIPIDS

Microorganisms of the psittacosis group contain large amounts of as yet imperfectly characterized lipids. About one fourth of the total phosphorus of the meningopneumonitis agent was phospholipid phosphorus (83, 117, 118). The meningopneumonitis agent contained lecithin and neutral fats but no cholesterol (61). Cytidine diphosphate choline may also be present (106).

ANTIGENS

The antigenic composition of the psittacosis group is complex and poorly understood. The antigens fall into two categories (12, 16): group antigens whose antibodies react with all members of the psittacosis group, and specific antigens whose antibodies react only with the homologous strain and a limited number of closely related ones. Both types of antigen are probably located in the cell wall (46, 62, 103, 105). The group antigens are resistant to heat, nucleases, and proteinases but are inactivated by periodate and lecithinase A (11, 13, 22, 102), suggesting that their immunological activity resides in polysaccharide and lecithin moieties. The chemical nature of the specific antigens is unknown.

When cell walls are prepared from purified psittacosis group cell suspensions by treatment with deoxycholate and trypsin (61), most of the group antigens are extracted in the deoxycholate, leaving behind in the cell walls large amounts of specific antigens and only small amounts of group antigens. Fraser & Berman (46) studied these specific antigens by using cell walls as test antigens in complement fixation reactions with antiserum prepared against intact psittacosis group cells. They divided 14 different isolates into seven serological subgroups. Schachter (105) prepared antiserum against cell walls and reacted it with intact cell antigen in an immunofluorescent cross-absorption test with 11 different psittacosis group isolates. There were at least 11 different specific antigens, none of which was specific to a single organism. All were shared to different degrees by various psittacosis group agents. One antigen was found in all isolates from avian sources and never appeared in mammalian isolates. Another was found in strains of psittacine origin but not in other avian strains. Two antigens appeared only in mammalian isolates, one of them only in strains of human origin. All mammalian strains tested had one or both of these antigens. The possible evolutionary significance of these patterns of antigen distribution will be considered in a later section.

Members of the psittacosis group elaborate a soluble hemagglutinin that is related to the group antigens of the whole cell in antigenic specificity and in susceptibility to lecithinase A (49, 50, 59). The hemagglutinin of the 6BC strain of psittacosis contained lecithin, DNA, and protein (50). Psittacosis group hemagglutinins agglutinated mouse erythrocytes (59) and erythrocytes from some fowls but not from others, the individual distribution of susceptibility being identical to that for the poxvirus hemagglutinins (10), which also have a phosphatide as an active component (114).

METABOLISM
Growth Requirements

Since multiplication of psittacosis group agents has not been obtained outside other living cells, the investigator must examine the effect of changes in the nutritional state of infected host cell on the growth and multiplication of the parasite within, and from such effects hope to learn something about the nutritional requirements of these microorganisms. In this manner, Bader & Morgan (8, 9) established the minimum nutritional requirements of the 6BC strain of psittacosis growing in L cells maintained on a defined medium. No B vitamin or amino acid not required for L cell growth was essential for psittacosis multiplication, but two B vitamins and four amino acids essential for L cell multiplication were not required by the psittacosis agent.

The two B vitamins were folic acid and riboflavin (9). The lack of folic acid requirement was not surprising, because this vitamin is a constituent of psittacosis group cells (35), and sulfonamide-susceptible organisms, such as psittacosis 6BC, can synthesize folic acid (33, 34). The absence of a riboflavin requirement may reflect the absence of flavoprotein respiratory enzymes, as demonstrated for the meningopneumonitis agent by the use of a dual wavelength spectrophotometer (127).

The four amino acids not required by the psittacosis agent were arginine, histidine, lysine, and glutamine (8). The lack of any need for glutamine is hard to evaluate because it is more a coenzyme than a structural unit of proteins. However, its precursor, glutamate, is a constituent of 6BC protein (102). Arginine, histidine, and lysine are present in appreciable quantities in the proteins of the meningopneumonitis agent (86, 117) and are probably found in the protein of the psittacosis agent as well. It seems likely that the psittacosis agent can synthesize these three amino acids from precursors available in the infected L cells. A synthesis of lysine from diaminopimelate has been demonstrated in purified suspensions of the meningopneumonitis agent (88).

Ossowski et al. (95) determined the amino acid requirements of three trachoma strains, the lymphogranuloma venereum agent, and the 6BC strain of psittacosis in FL cell cultures. When the trachoma and lymphogranuloma venereum agents were cultured in FL cells growing in a medium containing Eagle's (43) 13 essential amino acids, the addition of serine, which was not needed by the FL cells, increased their multiplication 100-fold but was not needed for maximal growth of the 6BC agent. When arginine, histidine, and lysine were omitted from the medium, one trachoma agent and the lymphogranuloma venereum agent failed to grow, but their absence did not prevent the multiplication of the 6BC agent, as Bader & Morgan (8) had already observed in L cells. These experiments show that members of the psittacosis group differ among themselves in amino acid requirements and strengthen the assumption that the 6BC strain of psittacosis can actually synthesize arginine, histidine, and lysine.

Endogenous Metabolism

In the absence of nutrients, bacteria metabolize reserve materials and essential cell constituents such as RNA and protein and release the breakdown products into the suspending medium (40, 41). It has been suggested that this endogenous metabolism furnishes energy necessary for survival of the starving bacterial cell. The agent of meningopneumonitis has an endogenous metabolism similar in some respects to that of bacteria. When purified suspensions of this organism were held at 37° C in buffered saline, they enzymatically degraded part of their protein and RNA to peptides, amino acids, nucleosides, and nitrogen bases which were released into the medium (86). However, there was no indication that useful metabolic energy was generated endogenously or that the degradation of RNA and protein was in any way related to the death or survival of the isolated meningopneumonitis cells.

Energy Metabolism

Organisms of the psittacosis group did not oxidize glucose, pyruvate, the acids of the tricarboxylic acid cycle, glutamate, and other amino acids with either molecular oxygen or the pyridine nucleotides as the oxidants (3, 4, 91, 99). Their only oxidative reaction was the reoxidation of NADH by cytochrome c, ferricyanide, and 2,6-dichlorophenol indophenol (3, 4), or tetrazolium salts (2). Weiss & Kiesow (127) examined preparations of the meningopneumonitis agent with the dual wavelength spectrophotometer and found neither flavoproteins nor cytochromes. Reoxidation of reduced nicotinamide adenine dinucleotides was not observed.

The failure to find any evidence of an energy metabolism in the psittacosis group led to the suggestion that these organisms are energy parasites, depending on their hosts to generate ATP and other high-energy metabolites which they then appropriate for their own biosyntheses (82, 83). The validity of this concept was questioned when Weiss and his associates (128) found that purified preparations of six different members of the group degraded

C^{14}-labeled glucose with the liberation of CO_2 from the C_1 and $C_{3,4}$, but not C_6, positions. Comparable preparations from uninfected host tissues were without such activity. These results suggested that psittacosis group organisms metabolize glucose via the pentose cycle and by either the Embden-Meyerhof or Entner-Doudoroff pathways, reactions that are known to generate energy-rich compounds in other organisms.

The ability of the psittacosis group agents to attack glucose probably remained undetected for so long because it is small in magnitude (about 50 $m\mu M$ CO_2 liberated per mg cell protein per hour) and because it occurs at an appreciable rate only under an unusual set of conditions (126). For maximum liberation of CO_2 from glucose-1-C^{14}, meningopneumonitis cells purified from infected allantoic fluid had to be suspended in a medium containing inorganic phosphate and Mg^{++} and with a K^+:Na^+ ratio of greater than 1. The optimal concentrations of glucose, ATP, and NADP were all 1 to 5×10^{-3} M. There was virtually no CO_2 evolution from glucose in the absence of ATP, whereas its production was only halved in the absence of NADP. Adenosine diphosphate substituted for ATP but with much less efficiency. No effect was exerted by NAD. Glucose-1-C^{14}-6-phosphate was a better substrate for CO_2 production that glucose itself. Adenosine triphosphate did not increase CO_2 evolution from glucose-6-phosphate, but NADP induced increases of three- to fourfold.

Cell-free extracts of meningopneumonitis suspensions similar to those used by Weiss (126) contained the NADP-requiring glucose-6-phosphate and 6-phosphogluconate dehydrogenases in concentrations comparable to those present in extracts of some bacteria, and starch-gel electrophoresis showed that these dehydrogenases were qualitatively different from the corresponding enzymes of the uninfected chick embryo host (85). Vender & Moulder (123) found hexokinase in meningopneumonitis cell suspensions and extracts. Unlike glucose-6-phosphate dehydrogenase, the hexokinase was destroyed by incubating the intact cells with trypsin without loss of infectivity. When meningopneumonitis cells previously heated to destroy hexokinase were mixed with uninfected allantoic fluid, they adsorbed significant amounts of hexokinase that was not removed during the usual purification procedure. These results suggest that the meningopneumonitis agent has no hexokinase of its own but that it avidly adsorbs the enzyme of its host. If this is correct, then the first hexose to be metabolized by meningopneumonitis enzymes is glucose-6-phosphate, and the pathway from 1-C^{14}-glucose to $C^{14}O_2$ is probably:

$$\text{glucose} \xrightarrow{\text{ATP}} \text{glucose-6-P} \xrightarrow{\text{NADP}} \text{6-P-gluconate} \xrightarrow{\text{NADP}} \text{ribulose-5-P} + CO_2$$

host enzyme   meningopneumonitis enzymes

Meningopneumonitis extracts did not attack pentose phosphates (85).

This pathway accounts for the stimulation of CO_2 evolution in intact meningopneumonitis cells by ATP and NADP. Their requirement in amounts equivalent to the glucose added suggests that neither ATP nor NADP was regenerated during glucose oxidation in that organism. The generally accepted view is that nucleotides and other phosphorylated compounds do not enter bacterial cells, but the experiments just described indicate that NADP and glucose-6-phosphate penetrate intact cells of the psittacosis group. The conversion of hexose to pentose provides no metabolic energy for the psittacosis group, but it does provide specific examples of how the host may extend energetic assistance to the parasite in the form of phosphorylated glucose and NADP. It is possible that oxidation of glucose via glucose-6-phosphate provides the psittacosis group with synthetic intermediates such as pentose for nucleic acids and NADPH for fatty acids. Meningopneumonitis extracts also contain phosphohexose isomerase (85) which could generate fructose-6-phosphate as the precursor of glucosamine and muramic acid.

Members of the psittacosis group produced pyruvate from glucose (128) and liberated CO_2 from the C_1 positions of pyruvate and glutamate (127). Exogenous ATP was not needed for attack on pyruvate and glutamate. These reactions may possibly yield metabolically useful energy for the psittacosis group, but they have not been studied in detail.

Although most of the studies on carbohydrate metabolism in the psittacosis group have been done with the agents of meningopneumonitis and trachoma, five other organisms have also been studied (53, 128). All metabolized glucose in essentially the same manner, but there were minor and, as yet, imperfectly understood differences.

DNA METABOLISM

Synthesis of host DNA in the nucleus and parasite DNA in the cytoplasm could be distinguished by labeling both kinds of DNA with P^{32}-orthophosphate or H^3-cytidine and preparing autoradiograms (38, 81) or separating the infected cells into nuclear and cytoplasmic portions (106, 108). By these techniques, synthesis of DNA in an ornithosis agent growing in HeLa cells (38), and in the meningopneumonitis agent growing in L cells (81, 106, 108) was first detected 10 to 15 hours after infection. Since such organisms begin to divide by binary fission 7 to 10 hours after infection (56) and have generation times of 2 to 3 hours (100), each infecting agent cell could have undergone only a few divisions before new synthesis of DNA was evident. Synthesis of DNA in both the ornithosis and the meningopneumonitis agents continued throughout the developmental cycle. In the meningopneumonitis agent, the rate of DNA synthesis increased exponentially from 15 to 30 hours after infection and then declined, as if the L cell could not long support a maximal rate of meningopneumonitis multiplication. In the ornithosis agent, DNA synthesis was estimated to proceed at more than twice the rate of DNA synthesis in the HeLa cell host (38), whereas it was estimated that the maximal rate of synthesis of DNA in the meningopneumonitis agent was equal to that of the L cell in which it was growing (106).

Because 5'-fluorodeoxyuridine (121), aminopterin (101), and 5'-fluorodeoxycytidine (109) inhibited multiplication of psittacosis group agents when added to infected cells early in the developmental cycle but were unable to do so when added later than 15 to 20 hours after infection, it was concluded that most of the DNA of these organisms was made early in the growth cycle and that there was a lag between synthesis of DNA and the appearance of new infectious units. The experiments just described (38, 81, 106) show that this interpretation cannot be correct. The DNA synthesis in psittacosis group agents continued throughout the developmental cycle and was most rapid at a time when their multiplication was no longer affected by these drugs. Another explanation must be sought for this interesting change in drug susceptibility during the course of the growth cycle. Such a change is not limited to inhibitors of DNA synthesis. Meningopneumonitis multiplication in L cells was first susceptible and then resistant to inhibition by actinomycin D, which prevents DNA-directed RNA synthesis (119), and psittacosis multiplication in McCoy cells was similarly affected by p-fluorophenylalanine, an inhibitor of protein synthesis (120). It is possible that all of these observations have a common explanation.

Although exogenously supplied thymidine serves as a precursor of DNA in many different kinds of cells, autoradiograms of infected cells showed that H^3-thymidine did not significantly label the DNA of several different members of the psittacosis group (23, 38, 97, 113). Thymidine also failed to reverse the growth inhibition of aminopterin on a psittacosis agent (101). This unusual behavior of thymidine was investigated further by studying the availability of deoxyribonucleosides and ribonucleosides for synthesis of DNA and RNA in the meningopneumonitis agent and in its L cell host (122). This was done by measuring the incorporation of each tritiated compound into the nucleic acids of uninfected L cells and purified meningopneumonitis agent. The ribo- and deoxyribonucleosides of adenine and guanine were freely available for the synthesis of both DNA and RNA in the L cell and in the meningopneumonitis agent, as were cytidine and uridine. Deoxyuridine was not utilized by either host or parasite. The L cell incorporated thymidine and deoxycytidine exclusively into its DNA, but the meningopneumonitis agent did not incorporate them at all. Thus, the meningopneumonitis agent, unlike the L cell, was unable to utilize exogenous pyrimidine deoxyribonucleosides for synthesis of DNA, probably because it lacked the appropriate nucleoside kinases. Since L cells rapidly convert added thymidine to nucleotides, mainly thymidine triphosphate (31), the meningopneumonitis agent must also be unable to use the nucleotides of thymine as well as thymidine itself. If this is so, then thymine is probably incorporated into meningopneumonitis DNA by the following series of reactions, all of which occur within the meningopneumonitis cell itself.

uridine →   uridine   → deoxyuridine →   thymidine   → thymidine → DNA
          monophosphate   monophosphate monophosphate triphosphate

A comparable series of reactions would be involved in the incorporation of cytosine into meningopneumonitis DNA. This hypothesis requires that the meningopneumonitis cell be impermeable to the triphosphates of thymidine and deoxycytidine and yet able to pirate from its host the ATP required for phosphorylation of the nucleosides to the nucleoside triphosphates. Perhaps this is because the concentration of ATP in intracellular nucleotide pools is usually much higher than that of the deoxynucleoside triphosphates (73). In any event, the hypothesis (82, 83) that members of the psittacosis group make their nucleic acids from the nucleoside triphosphates of their host cell pool must be abandoned.

A functional host cell nucleus is not required for multiplication of these microorganisms. They grew in enucleate cytoplasmic fragments (37) and in colchicine-treated, micronucleated cells (111).

RNA Metabolism

Tamura & Iwanaga (119) studied the synthesis of RNA in uninfected L cells and in L cells infected with the meningopneumonitis agent. The base composition of the newly synthesized RNA in infected cells incubated with P^{32}-orthophosphate for 15 to 20 hours after infection was nearly identical with that of the RNA of the purified agent, and the 29S and 18S RNA components of the uninfected L cell were largely replaced by the 21S and 16S components characteristic of the meningopneumonitis agent itself. Synthesis of RNA characteristic of the meningopneumonitis agent was not inhibited by actinomycin D when the drug was added later than 5 to 10 hours after infection. Tamura & Iwanaga (119) concluded that a major portion of the RNA synthesized in L cells 10 to 20 hours after infection with the meningopneumonitis agent, was agent RNA.

Schechter (106) fractionated L cells labeled with H^3-cytidine and infected with the meningopneumonitis agent into nuclear, cytoplasmic, and agent fractions to show that the rate of synthesis of meningopneumonitis RNA closely paralleled that of agent DNA. Synthesis of RNA was first apparent at 15 hours, reached a maximum at about 25 hours, and declined slightly thereafter. The susceptibility of RNA synthesis in this organism to inhibition by actinomycin D in the early hours of the developmental cycle and its resistance to the same drug in the later stages of growth was confirmed (107). As pointed out by Tamura & Iwanaga (119), this could mean either that the meningopneumonitis agent can synthesize RNA without the use of a DNA template, or that the drug fails to penetrate the cytoplasmic vacuoles in which the meningopneumonitis agent is growing. As already pointed out, other inhibitors (101, 109, 120, 121) with unrelated modes of action, are also effective only when added early in the developmental cycle.

The metabolic functions of the different kinds of meningopneumonitis RNA have not been determined. The 21S and 16S components (119) are associated with 50S and 30S particles that are almost certainly ribosomes (117). These RNA species could be exclusively ribosomal in nature or they could include molecules with messenger activity. The 4S RNA could be transfer RNA or a degradation product of the larger molecules.

PROTEIN METABOLISM

As measured by the incorporation of C^{14}-lysine into the protein of the meningopneumonitis agent purified from labeled L cells (106), protein synthesis was first detected at the same time as that of agent DNA and RNA, and its rate of synthesis rose and fell with that of the meningopneumonitis nucleic acids. It is highly likely that this protein was synthesized in ribosomal systems analogous to those of bacteria. The meningopneumonitis agent contains 50S and 30S RNA-containing particles (117) and, like other members of the group, is susceptible to growth inhibition by chloramphenicol and tetracycline (125), antibiotics that inhibit bacterial multiplication by interfering with ribosomal synthesis of protein (92). In a system similar to that used to study protein synthesis in bacterial ribosomes, Alexander (1) found that intact meningopneumonitis cells incorporated the labeled amino acids of an algal hydrolyzate into trichloroacetic acid-insoluble forms at about the rate observed in typhus rickettsiae (26, 27).

EFFECT ON HOST CELL METABOLISM

When susceptible cell cultures were infected at high multiplicity with the agents of psittacosis (93) and meningopneumonitis (58), almost every cell infected was killed within the span of a single developmental cycle. Accelerated rates of host cell death were noticed as early as 10 to 15 hours after infection (58, 108). However, some infected cells multiplied to produce uninfected daughter cells or even "recovered" from successful infections without multiplication (94). Chronic infections have been produced in cell cultures (75, 94), and latent infections occur in both natural and experimental situations (83). Therefore, it must be remembered that the experiments to be described here were performed under conditions designed to maximize the effect of infection on host cell metabolism and that, in natural infections, interference with host metabolism is undoubtedly less severe.

The effect of infection with psittacosis group agents on the energy metabolism of host cells has not been adequately studied. There seems to be no effect on the overall rate of glucose dissimilation; uninfected L cells and L cells heavily infected with the agent of meningopneumonitis liberated $C^{14}O_2$ from the C_1 and $C_{3,4}$ positions of glucose-C^{14} at the same rates (90).

The studies of Tamura & Iwanaga (119) described in the previous section showed that, after infection of L cells with the meningopneumonitis agent, synthesis of host cell RNA was inhibited and largely replaced by synthesis of meningopneumonitis RNA. Autoradiography with H^3-cytidine demonstrated that most of the newly synthesized RNA was in the cytoplasmic inclusions of the meningopneumonitis agent.

Crocker et al. (38) studied DNA synthesis in HeLa cells infected with an ornithosis agent by making autoradiographs after labeling with H^3-thymidine and H^3-cytidine under a variety of conditions. When 40 per cent or more of the HeLa cells were infected, their generation times were prolonged. The entry of cells into the period of active DNA synthesis was retarded, and the duration of the period of DNA synthesis was doubled, although normal amounts of HeLa cell DNA were eventually synthesized. At infection rates greater than 90 per cent, the proportion of infected cells synthesizing DNA was normal at 15 to 18 hours after infection but had decreased by 15 to 21 hours. Cell division was inhibited early only when the cells were infected at high multiplicities.

By fractionating uninfected and infected L cells to which appropriate labeled intermediates had been added, Schechter and her associates (106,108) could distinguish between macromolecular syntheses of the L cells and of the meningopneumonitis agent growing within them. In one L cell line (108), DNA synthesis was almost completely inhibited 10 to 15 hours after infection and RNA synthesis was reduced by as much as 75 per cent. In a second L cell line derived from the first (106), DNA synthesis was depressed to only half the uninfected rate, and RNA synthesis was also less severely inhibited. These differences were in accord with the observation that meningopneumonitis multiplication in the second cell line was less rapidly lethal and longer sustained. It therefore appears that the degree to which a particular psittacosis group agent interferes with host cell metabolism may be highly dependent on the nature of the host cell itself. The absence of any detectable inhibition of protein synthesis in infected L cells (106) suggests that the inhibition of nucleic acid synthesis in infected host cells (38, 106, 108, 119) was relatively specific and not due to generalized depression of host cell metabolism.

Crocker et al. (38) gave two possible explanations for the inhibition of host DNA synthesis by members of the psittacosis group: (a) production, during cytoplasmic growth of the parasite, of a factor that blocks DNA synthesis in the host cell nucleus, or (b) a competition between host cell nucleus and psittacosis agent for cytoplasmic energy sources and precursors needed for DNA synthesis. They favored the second interpretation. Since the meningopneumonitis agent can use certain nucleosides for DNA synthesis but apparently cannot use nucleotides (122), the postulated competition may be for nucleoside precursors or for the energy needed to phosphorylate them to the nucleoside triphosphates. The moderate inhibitions of host DNA synthesis observed by Crocker et al. (38) and Schechter (106) may logically be explained on the basis of competition between host and parasite for precursors of DNA, but the almost complete inhibition of RNA synthesis seen by Tamura & Iwanaga (119) and the equally profound disruption of DNA synthesis reported by Schechter et al. (108) are difficult to explain on this basis, and the first explanation of Crocker et al. (38) appears to be more plausible.

TAXONOMIC POSITION OF THE PSITTACOSIS GROUP
INTRA-GROUP RELATIONS

A knowledge of the relation of different members of the psittacosis group to each other is essential to the understanding of their phylogenetic origin which, in turn, is essential to the establishing of their broad relationships to other life forms. Although only a handful of the many independent isolates of psittacosis group agents have been studied in any detail, the taxonomic relationships within the group are beginning to emerge and will undoubtedly stand out more clearly when a greater variety of characters in a larger number of isolates have been described. As more is learned about these organisms, their traditional classification on the basis of host origin and specific pathology will surely be replaced by one based on morphological, serological, and biochemical characters. A tentative but encouraging start in this direction has already been made.

Serological differentiation of psittacosis group isolates on the basis of their specific cell wall antigens has been initiated by Fraser & Berman (46) and by Schachter (105). Schachter's results suggest that isolates of avian and mammalian (including human) origin constitute major serological subgroups and that there are minor subdivisions within each; for example, a set of related psittacine strains within the avian group and a set of related human strains within the mammalian one.

Gordon & Quan (52) have divided 27 psittacosis group isolates into two subgroups on the basis of two characteristics: the degree of compactness or diffuseness of the cytoplasmic inclusion and the presence or absence of glycogen in the inclusion. The significance of glycogen in psittacosis group inclusions is not known. Its appearance is strongly inhibited by penicillin (14, 52), indicating that the synthesis of glycogen is almost certainly an activity of the parasite and not of the host. However, its production cannot be essential to the growth of these organisms because many of them do not produce it at all. In general, compact inclusions were characteristic of less virulent organisms, diffuse inclusions of the more virulent ones (28, 93, 94). Compact inclusions always contained glycogen (subgroup A); diffuse ones never did (subgroup B). Subgroup A contained only mammalian strains, but B contained strains of both mammalian and avian origin.

Lin & Moulder (65) investigated the homogeneity of the two subgroups of Gordon & Quan by examining 11 of their strains for susceptibility to sulfadiazine, susceptibility to D-cycloserine, and ease of reversal of the D-cycloserine inhibition with D-alanine (87, 89) (Table I). Subgroup A of Gordon & Quan appeared to be homogeneous. All four subgroup A isolates examined were sulfadiazine-sensitive, were highly susceptible to D-cycloserine, and the inhibition produced by 1 mole of D-cycloserine was reversed by 2 moles of D-alanine. Group B agents were typically sulfadiazine-resistant, much less susceptible to D-cycloserine, and the inhibition produced by 1 mole of D-cycloserine was reversed by only 0.02 mole of D-alanine.

Possible explanations of these differences in behavior toward D-cycloserine and D-alanine have been discussed elsewhere (39, 89). Sulfonamide-sensitive agents make their own folates (33, 34), whereas the resistant ones do not. Subgroup B was not homogeneous with respect to drug susceptibility; three strains deviated in one or more characters from the typical pattern. Two

TABLE I

Properties of the Subgroups A and B of Gordon & Quan

Agent	Nature of inclusion		Suscepti-bility to sulfadiazine (65)	Suscepti-bility to D-cyclo-serine (65)	Effective-ness of D-alanine in antagonizing D-cycloserine (65)
	Morphology (52)	Glycogen present (52)			
Subgroup A					
Lymphogranu-loma venereum	Compact	+	+	+++	+
Inclusion conjunctivitis	Compact	+	+	+++	+
Mouse pneumo-nitis	Compact	+	+	+++	+
Hamster	Compact	+	+	+++	+
Subgroup B					
Meningo-pneumonitis	Diffuse	0	0	+	+++
Feline pneumo-nitis	Diffuse	0	0	+	+++
Guinea pig con-junctivitis	Diffuse	0	0	+	+++
Ornithosis (pigeon)	Diffuse	0	0	+	+++
Psittacosis (6BC)	Diffuse	0	+	+	+++
Goat	Diffuse	0	0	+++	+
Bovine encephalo-myelitis	Diffuse	0	0	++	++

mutations involving these drug-susceptibility characters have been observed in the laboratory—the acquisition of sulfonamide resistance by the 6BC strain of psittacosis (51) and the mouse pneumonitis agent (69), and the shift from a subgroup A to subgroup B behavior toward D-cycloserine and D-alanine by a chlortetracycline-resistant strain of mouse pneumonitis (89). The drug-susceptibility characters are obviously not as stable as those concerned with the nature of the inclusion.

Relation of the Psittacosis Group to the Bacteria

The descent of the psittacosis group from the bacteria has never been disputed. It is the phylogenetic distance travelled in this descent that has been the source of argument. Have these organisms travelled a short evolutionary path and are simply obligately intracellular bacteria, or have they travelled so far that they are only remotely related to the bacteria? As a taxonomic entity, the bacteria and other procaryotic organisms are so diverse that a simple definition is difficult (110). However, it is generally agreed that there are properties that are highly characteristic of these life forms and some even unique to them. Organisms of the psittacosis group possess a number of these properties. Listed in the order in which they were discussed in earlier sections of this review, they are: (a) division by binary fission with the possible participation of mesosomes in cross-wall formation; (b) cell walls comparable in structure to those of Gram-negative bacteria and with the muramic acid-containing mucopeptide unique to the walls of procaryotic cells; (c) DNA-containing nucleoids with no membranes between them and the cytoplasm; (d) synthesis of folates by sulfonamide-susceptible agents; and (e) the presence of ribosomes with antibiotic susceptibilities characteristic of procaryotic ribosomes.

The meningopneumonitis agent, and probably other members of the group as well, shows no obvious defects in synthesis of its DNA, RNA, and protein. The one readily apparent metabolic defect is the complete or nearly complete absence of mechanisms for the production of metabolic energy. Regardless of what future investigations may reveal, this one biochemical lesion is sufficient to restrict these organisms to an intracellular existence.

What might the bacterial forebears of the psittacosis group have been like? This is a comfortable subject for speculation because there is no substantial evidence for or against any proposal, no matter how outrageous. Table II suggests a possible evolutionary history for the psittacosis group that does minimum violence to the few known facts. It seems most likely that the immediate ancestors of the psittacosis group were Gram-negative cocci which had already learned to grow inside host cells but were still facultatively intracellular parasites. Of present-day eubacteria, the Neisseriaceae most closely resemble these imagined progenitors (please note that it is not claimed that the Neisseriaceae are the ancestors of the psittacosis group).

The generic epithet, *Chlamydia*, proposed for the psittacosis group by Page (96) furnishes the convenient trivial name chlamydiae from which may be derived the concept of the protochlamydiae, the hypothetical first chlamydiae from which all others have descended. Of the presently existing chlamydiae, members of Gordon & Quan's subgroup A may most closely resemble the protochlamydiae. Subgroup A is a highly uniform collection of organisms, suggesting a comparatively recent common origin. Its members have at least two synthetic abilities that the subgroup B organisms do not—the ability to synthesize glycogen and folates. These properties suggest a closer relation to the hypothetical facultatively intracellular ancestor. In the scheme of Table II, the properties of the protochlamydiae are postulated as being essentially those of subgroup A, and its present-day representatives are visualized as being in the most direct line of descent from the proto-

TABLE II

SPECULATIONS ON THE EVOLUTIONARY ORIGIN OF THE
CHLAMYDIAE (PSITTACOSIS GROUP)

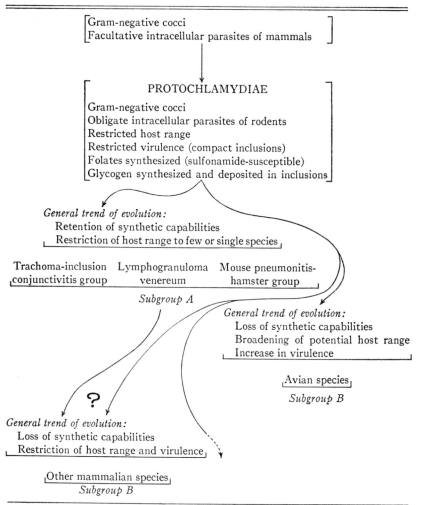

chlamydiae. The hosts of subgroup A organisms are either mice or men, and since mice were here before men, it is assumed that the protochlamydiae were parasites of rodents. Perhaps the agent of mouse pneumonitis most closely resembles the hypothetical protochlamydiae. The serological analyses of Schachter (105) suggest that the mammalian and avian organisms of subgroup B are separate branches of the evolutionary tree, and they are so indicated in Table II. Two equally probable (or improbable) origins of the mammalian strains of subgroup B are suggested.

Two main lines of evolution are pictured in Table II. One, characterized by retention of synthetic abilities and restriction of host range and virulence, has led to the evolution of subgroup A. The other, characterized by loss of synthetic ability and broadening of host range and increase in virulence, has its present termination in the avian strains of subgroup B. The mammalian strains of subgroup B may be considered as intermediate.

The possible relations of the psittacosis group to other small obligate and facultative intracellular parasites has been considered elsewhere (83).

RELATION OF THE PSITTACOSIS GROUP TO THE VIRUSES

If members of the psittacosis group are truly intermediate organisms, they must have properties characteristic, or at least reminiscent, of both bacteria and viruses, or, alternatively, the course of evolution within the group must show a discernible trend from the bacterial toward the viral. The definition of virus proposed by Lwoff (70–72) has been universally accepted. He lists four definitive viral characters which may be compared with the properties of the psittacosis group described in preceding pages.

1. Viruses possess only one kind of nucleic acid. Both the large and the small types of psittacosis group cells contain DNA and RNA.

2. Viruses are reproduced from their genetic material and they multiply in the form of their genetic material. When a member of the psittacosis group invades a host cell, its internal architecture changes, but it never loses its morphological integrity at any time during production of a new generation.

3. Viruses are unable to grow and to undergo binary fission. As pointed out by Bedson (17), psittacosis group cells grow in size in the hours immediately after invasion and decrease in size during the period of exponential multiplication. They reproduce by binary fission.

4. Viruses are devoid of enzymes that convert the potential energy of foodstuffs into the high-energy bonds needed for biological syntheses. Evidence for the formation of high-energy bonds in organisms of the psittacosis group is lacking. However, they do contain portions of enzyme systems that generate metabolically useful energy in other organisms. If it eventually turns out that the psittacosis group is completely unable to synthesize energy-rich compounds, then the loss of this ability must have occurred in comparatively recent evolutionary history.

Examination of the trends of evolution within the psittacosis group, as exemplified by the diversity of properties among the present members of the group, is not helpful because this group is so homogeneous that major diversities have not yet been described.

The properties of the psittacosis group have been compared with those of the poxviruses, the viruses they might be expected to resemble most closely, with the conclusion that there is no evidence of relationship (82).

Therefore, the decision whether or not to conclude that the members of the psittacosis group are in any way intermediate between bacteria and viruses rests on the interpretation of the significance of the apparent absence of energy-yielding reactions. My own feeling is that this is not sufficient reason to regard the members of the psittacosis group as borderline organisms.

CONCLUSION

The evaluation of any body of data is colored by the biases of the evaluator, and mine are well-known (82, 83). With this admission, my answer to the question posed in the title of this review is that the microorganisms of the psittacosis group are obligate intracellular bacteria without relationship to the viruses. To go one step further, I agree with Stanier (110) that the differences between viruses and bacteria are of such a nature that no truly intermediate stage of biological organization can be visualized.

LITERATURE CITED

1. Alexander, J. J. (Personal communication)
2. Allen, E. G., *J. Bacteriol.*, **90**, 1505–12 (1965)
3. Allen, E. G., and Bovarnick, M. R., *J. Exptl. Med.*, **105**, 539–47 (1957)
4. Allen, E. G., and Bovarnick, M. R., *Ann. N. Y. Acad. Sci.*, **98**, 229–33 (1962)
5. Anderson, D. R., Hopps, H. E., Barile, M. R., and Bernheim, B. C., *J. Bacteriol.*, **90**, 1387–1404 (1965)
6. Armstrong, J. A., and Reed, S. E., *Nature*, **201**, 371–73 (1964)
7. Armstrong, J. A., Valentine, R. C., and Fildes, C., *J. Gen. Microbiol.*, **30**, 59–73 (1963)
8. Bader, J. P., and Morgan, H. R., *J. Exptl. Med.*, **108**, 617–30 (1958)
9. Bader, J. P., and Morgan, H. R., *J. Exptl. Med.*, **113**, 271–81 (1961)
10. Barron, A. L., Zakay-Roness, Z., and Bernkopf, H., *Proc. Soc. Exptl. Biol. Med.*, **119**, 377–81 (1965)
11. Barwell, C. F., *Nature*, **162**, 460–61 (1948)
12. Barwell, C. F., *Brit. J. Expt. Pathol.*, **33**, 258–67 (1952)
13. Barwell, C. F., *Brit. J. Exptl. Pathol.*, **33**, 268–79 (1952)
14. Becker, Y., Mashiah, P., and Bernkopf, H., *Nature*, **193**, 271–72 (1962)
15. Bedson, S. P., *Brit. J. Exptl. Pathol.*, **14**, 267–77 (1933)
16. Bedson, S. P., *Brit. J. Exptl. Pathol.*, **17**, 109–21 (1936)
17. Bedson, S. P., *J. Roy. Inst. Public Health Hyg.*, **22**, 67–78 (1959)
18. Bedson, S. P., *J. Roy. Inst. Public Health Hyg.*, **22**, 131–43 (1959)
19. Bedson, S. P., and Bland, J. O. W., *Brit. J. Exptl. Pathol.*, **13**, 461–66 (1932)
20. Bedson, S. P., and Bland, J. O. W., *Brit. J. Exptl. Pathol.*, **15**, 243–47 (1934)
21. Bedson, S. P., and Gostling, J. V. T., *Brit. J. Exptl. Pathol.*, **35**, 299–308 (1954)
22. Benedict, A. A., and O'Brien, E., *J. Immunol.*, **76**, 293–300 (1956)
23. Bernkopf, H., Mashiah, P., and Becker, Y., *Ann. N. Y. Acad. Sci.*, **98**, 62–81 (1962)
24. Beskina, S. R., Ugoleva, N. A., and Shatkin, A. A., *Voprosy Med. Khim.*, **11**, 96–97 (1965)

25. Bland, J. O. W., and Canti, R. G., *J. Pathol. Bacteriol.*, **40**, 231–41 (1935)
26. Bovarnick, M. R., and Schneider, L., *J. Biol. Chem.*, **235**, 1727–31 (1960)
27. Bovarnick, M. R., Schneider, L., and Walter, H., *Biochim. Biophys. Acta*, **33**, 414–22 (1959)
28. Brown, A., *Ann. N. Y. Acad. Sci.*, **98**, 122–26 (1962)
29. Burnet, F. M., *Principles of Animal Virology*, 2nd ed., 445–58. (Academic Press, New York, 1960)
30. Cairns, J., *Cold Spring Harbor Symp. Quant. Biol.*, **28**, 43–45 (1963)
31. Cleaver, J. E., and Holford, R. M., *Biochim. Biophys. Acta*, **103**, 654–71 (1965)
32. Collier, L. H., *Ann. N. Y. Acad. Sci.*, **98**, 42–49 (1962)
33. Colón, J. I., *J. Bacteriol.*, **79**, 741–46 (1960)
34. Colón, J. I., *Ann. N. Y. Acad. Sci.*, **98**, 234–45 (1962)
35. Colón, J. I., and Moulder, J. W., *J. Infect. Diseases*, **103**, 109–19 (1958)
36. Constable, F. L., *Nature*, **184**, 474–75 (1959)
37. Crocker, T. T., and Eastwood, J. M., *Virology*, **19**, 23–31 (1963)
38. Crocker, T. T., Pelc, S. R., Nielsen, B. I., Eastwood, J. M., and Banks, J., *J. Infect. Diseases*, **115**, 105–22 (1965)
39. Curtiss, R., III, Charamella, L. J., Berg, C. M., and Harris, P. E., *J. Bacteriol.*, **90**, 1238–50 (1965)
40. Dawes, E. A., and Ribbons, D. W., *Ann. Rev. Microbiol.*, **16**, 241–64 (1962)
41. Dawes, E. A., and Ribbons, D. W., *Bacteriol. Rev.*, **28**, 126–49 (1964)
42. Dover, A. S., *Preparation and characterization of the deoxyribonucleic acid of the agent of meningopneumonitis.* (Master's thesis, Univ. of Chicago, 1965)
43. Eagle, H., *J. Biol. Chem.*, **214**, 839–52 (1955)
44. Erlandson, R. A., and Allen, E. G., *Virology*, **22**, 410–18 (1964)
45. Fitz-James, P., *Symp. Soc. Gen. Microbiol.*, **15**, 369–78 (1965)
46. Fraser, C. E. O., and Berman, D. T., *J. Bacteriol.*, **89**, 943–48 (1965)
47. Gaylord, W. H., *J. Exptl. Med.*, **100**, 575–80 (1954)
48. Gerloff, R. K., Ritter, D. B., and

Watson, R. O., *J. Infect. Diseases*, 116, 197–202 (1966)

49. Gogolak, F. M., *J. Infect. Diseases*, 95, 220–25 (1954)

50. Gogolak, F. M., and Ross, M. R., *Virology*, 1, 474–96 (1955)

51. Golub, O. J., *J. Lab. Clin. Med.*, 33, 1241–48 (1948)

52. Gordon, F. B., and Quan, A. L., *J. Infect. Diseases*, 115, 186–96 (1965)

53. Gordon, F. B., Weiss, E., Quan, A. L., and Dressler, H. R., *J. Infect. Diseases*, 116, 203–7 (1966)

54. Green, R. G., *Science*, 82, 443–45 (1935)

55. Higashi, N., *Ann. Rept. Inst. Virus Res. Kyoto Univ.*, 2, 1–21 (1959)

56. Higashi, N., *Exptl. Mol. Pathol.*, 4, 24–39 (1965)

57. Higashi, N., Notake, K., and Fukada, T., *Ann. Rept. Inst. Virus Res. Kyoto Univ.*, 2, 23–55 (1959)

58. Higashi, N., Tamura, A., and Iwanaga, M., *Ann. N. Y. Acad. Sci.*, 98, 100–21 (1962)

59. Hilleman, M. R., Haig, D. A., and Helmhold, R. J., *J. Immunol.*, 66, 115–30 (1951)

60. Hurst, E. W., Landquist, J. K., Melvin, P., Peters, J. M., Senior, N., Silk, J. A., and Stacey, G. J., *Brit. J. Pharmacol.*, 8, 297–305 (1953)

61. Jenkin, H. M., *J. Bacteriol.*, 80, 639–47 (1960)

62. Jenkin, H. M., Ross, M. R., and Moulder, J. W., *J. Immunol.*, 86, 123–27 (1961)

63. Joklik, W. K., *J. Mol. Biol.*, 5, 265–74 (1962)

64. Laidlow, P. P., *Virus Diseases and Viruses*. (Cambridge Univ. Press, London, 1938)

65. Lin, H. S., and Moulder, J. W., *J. Infect. Diseases*, 116, 372–76 (1966)

66. Litwin, J., *J. Infect. Diseases*, 105, 129–60 (1959)

67. Litwin, J., *Ann. N. Y. Acad. Sci.*, 98, 145–62 (1962)

68. Litwin, J., Officer, J. E., Brown, A., and Moulder, J. W., *J. Infect. Diseases*, 109, 251–79 (1961)

69. Loosli, C. G., Hamre, P., Grayston, T., and Alexander, E. R., *Antibiotics Ann.*, 490–503 (1954–55)

70. Lwoff, A., *J. Gen. Microbiol.*, 17, 239–53 (1957)

71. Lwoff, A., in *The Viruses*, 3, 187–20. (Burnet, F. M., and Stanley, W. M., Eds., Academic Press, New York, 1959)

72. Lwoff, A., *Rev. Biol. (Lisbon)*, 4, 55–60 (1963)

73. Mandel, P., in *Progress in Nucleic Acid Research and Molecular Biology*, 3, 299–334. (Davidson, J. N., and Cohn, W. E., Eds., Academic Press, New York, 1964)

74. Manire, G. P., *J. Bacteriol.*, 91, 409–13 (1966)

75. Manire, G. P., and Galasso, G. J., *J. Immunol.*, 83, 529–33 (1959)

76. McCarthy, B. J., and Bolton, E. T., *Proc. Natl. Acad. Sci. U.S.*, 50, 156–64 (1962)

77. Mitsui, Y., Fujimoto, M., and Kajima, M., *Virology*, 23, 30–45 (1964)

78. Mitsui, Y., Kajima, M., Nishimura, A., and Konishi, K., *Ann. N. Y. Acad. Sci.*, 98, 131–44 (1962)

79. Mitsui, Y., and Suzuki, A., *Arch. Ophthalmol. Chicago*, 56, 429–48 (1956)

80. Mitsui, Y., Suzuki, A., Hanabusa, J., Minoda, R., Ogata, S., Fukushima, S., and Miura, M., *Virology*, 6, 137–49 (1958)

81. Moore, D. E., *An autoradiographic study of DNA synthesis in L cells infected with the meningopneumonitis agent*. (Master's thesis, Univ. of Chicago, 1965)

82. Moulder, J. W., *The Biochemistry of Intracellular Parasitism*. (The Univ. of Chicago Press, Chicago, 1962)

83. Moulder, J. W., *The Psittacosis Group as Bacteria*. (Wiley, New York, 1964)

84. Moulder, J. W., and Grisso, D. L. (Unpublished results)

85. Moulder, J. W., Grisso, D. L., and Brubaker, R. R., *J. Bacteriol.*, 89, 810–12 (1965)

86. Moulder, J. W., Grisso, D. L., and Cho, G. J., *J. Infect. Diseases*, 115, 254–62 (1965)

87. Moulder, J. W., Novosel, D. L., and Officer, J. E., *J. Bacteriol.*, 85, 707–11 (1963)

88. Moulder, J. W., Novosel, D. L., and Tribby, I. I. E., *J. Bacteriol.*, 85, 701–6 (1963)

89. Moulder, J. W., Novosel, D. L., and Tribby, I. I. E., *J. Bacteriol.*, 89, 17–22 (1965)

90. Moulder, J. W., and Tribby, I. I. E. (Unpublished results)

91. Moulder, J. W., and Weiss, E., *J. Infect. Diseases*, 88, 56–67 (1951)

92. Newton, B. A., *Ann. Rev. Microbiol.*, 19, 209–40 (1965)

93. Officer, J. E., and Brown, A., *J. Infect. Diseases*, 107, 283–99 (1960)

94. Officer, J. E., and Brown, A., *Virology*, 14, 88–99 (1961)
95. Ossowski, L., Becker, Y., and Bernkopf, H., *Israel J. Med. Sci.*, 1, 186–93 (1965)
96. Page, L. A., *Intern. J. Systemat. Bacteriol.*, 16, 223–52 (1966)
97. Pelc, S. R., and Crocker, T. T., *Biochem. J.*, 78, 20p (1961)
98. Perkins, H. R., and Allison, A. C., *J. Gen. Microbiol.*, 30, 469–80(1963)
99. Perrin, J., *J. Gen. Microbiol.*, 6, 143–48 (1951)
100. Podolyan, V. Ya., Milyutin, V. N., Gudima, O. S., and Lukina, R. N., *Voprosy Virusologii*, 9, 208–12 (1964)
101. Pollard, M., and Tanami, Y., *Ann. N. Y. Acad. Sci.*, 98, 50–62 (1962)
102. Ross, M. R., and Gogolak, F. M., *Virology*, 3, 365–73 (1957)
103. Ross, M. R., and Jenkin, A. M., *Ann. N. Y. Acad. Sci.*, 98, 329–36 (1962)
104. Salton, M. R. J., *The Bacteriol Cell Wall*, 66–132. (Elsevier, Amsterdam, 1964)
105. Schachter, J., *Studies on Bedsonia antigens* (Doctoral dissertation, Univ. of California, Berkeley, 1965)
106. Schechter, E. M., *J. Bacteriol.*, 91, 2069–80 (1966)
107. Schechter, E. M., and Moulder, J. W. (Unpublished results)
108. Schechter, E. M., Tribby, I. I. E., and Moulder, J. W., *Science*, 145, 819–21 (1964)
109. Sharon, N., and Pollard, M., *Proc. Soc. Exptl. Biol. Med.*, 114, 344–47 (1963)
110. Stanier, R. Y., in *The Bacteria*, 5, 445–64. (Stanier, R. Y., and Gunsalus, I. E., Eds., Academic Press, New York, 1964)
111. Starr, T. J., *Texas Repts. Biol. Med.*, 21, 412–21 (1963)
112. Starr, T. J., Pollard, M., Tanami, Y., and Moore, R. W., *Texas Repts. Biol. Med.*, 18, 501–14 (1960)
113. Starr, T. J., and Sharon, N., *Proc. Soc. Exptl. Biol. Med.*, 113, 912–14 (1963)
114. Stone, J. D., *Australian J. Exptl. Biol. Med. Sci.*, 24, 191–96 (1946)
115. Tajima, M., Nomura, Y., and Kubota, V., *J. Bacteriol.*, 74, 605–20 (1957)
116. Tajima, M., Samijima, T., and Nomura, Y., *J. Bacteriol.*, 77, 23–34 (1959)
117. Tamura, A., *Ann. Rept. Inst. Virus Res. Kyoto Univ.*, 7, 1–13 (1964)
118. Tamura, A., and Higashi, N., *Virology*, 20, 596–604 (1963)
119. Tamura, A., and Iwanaga, M., *J. Mol. Biol.*, 11, 97–108 (1965)
120. Tanami, Y., and Pollard, M., *J. Bacteriol.*, 83, 437–42 (1962)
121. Tanami, Y., Pollard, M., and Starr, T. J., *Virology*, 15, 22–29 (1961)
122. Tribby, I. I. E., and Moulder, J. W., *J. Bacteriol.*, 91, 2362–67 (1966)
123. Vender, J., and Moulder, J. W. (Unpublished results)
124. Weiss, E., *J. Infect. Diseases*, 87, 249–63 (1950)
125. Weiss, E., *Ann. Rev. Microbiol.*, 9, 227–52 (1955)
126. Weiss, E., *J. Bacteriol.*, 90, 243–53 (1965)
127. Weiss, E., and Kiesow, L. A., *Bacteriol. Proc.*, 85 (1966)
128. Weiss, E., Myers, W. F., Dressler, H. R., and Chun-Hoon, H., *Virology*, 22, 551–62 (1964)
129. Zahler, S. A., and Moulder, J. W., *J. Infect. Diseases*, 93, 159–65 (1953)

STRUCTURE AND FUNCTION IN PROTOZOA[1]

By A. V. Grimstone

Department of Zoology, University of Cambridge, Cambridge, England

Contents

Introduction... 131
Nucleus... 132
Golgi Apparatus... 133
Food Vacuoles and Lysosomes.............................. 133
Cytoplasmic Microorganisms............................... 134
Cytoplasmic Organelles Containing DNA................... 135
Chromatoid Bodies... 136
Trichocysts, Ejectosomes, and Similar Bodies............... 137
Cilia, Flagella, Spindle Fibres, and Microtubules........... 138
Centrioles... 144
Problems Connected with the Formation of Cytoplasmic Organelles... 144

Introduction

This article discusses briefly some of the work published on protozoan cytology in the last three or four years. The review is not comprehensive, and the main criterion for inclusion of papers has been their relevance to an understanding of cell organization in general. This has led to the omission of much work on special topics in protozoan structure and function.

The merits of protozoa as material for cytological work are still not widely recognized, and one of the purposes which this article might serve is to draw attention to some of the organisms which deserve more detailed study. With some notable exceptions, much of the work being published at present is morphological in outlook; its supplementation by an experimental and biochemical approach would certainly pay dividends in many cases. The opportunities which protozoa offer for work on the correlation of fine structure with function, or for the experimental analysis of such topics as the control mechanisms involved in secretion, cell division or organelle formation, have scarcely been touched on so far. The fact that most protozoa are single cells ought to make them particularly valuable material for cytological research, if only because the complexities which arise from cell interactions in multicellular organisms are lacking.

Earlier work in this field has been reviewed in some detail (13, 52, 56, 111) and will not, for the most part, be reconsidered here.

[1] The survey of the literature pertaining to this review was concluded in December 1965.

Nucleus

Most of the recent work on protozoan nuclei has been brought together in a review by Grell (53).

The fine fibres commonly reported as making up protozoan chromosomes usually appear to be less than 100 Å in diameter. In the radiolarian, *Aulacantha*, for example, they are about 80 Å in diameter (54), and in *Amphidinium* and other dinoflagellates they are between 30 and 80 Å (43, 44). Giesbrecht (43) has drawn attention to possible similarities between the fine structure of dinoflagellate chromosomes and that of bacterial chromatin bodies. He has also proposed a model of chromosome structure in these flagellates, the main feature of which is that the DNA-containing fibres are thought to be not coiled but looped back and forth, the ends of the loops being attached to a continuous axis (45). In the chromosomes of *Aulacantha* there is evidence of the presence of an "axial complex," possibly comparable to that in some meiotic chromosomes (54). Apart from this, almost nothing is known about the fine-structural organization of protozoan chromosomes. The helices in the nucleus of *Amoeba proteus*, at one time thought to be part of the chromosomes, seem more probably to be nuclear products: they can apparently pass through the nuclear envelope and are found in the cytoplasm. They are possibly helical arrays of ribosomes (153), and may be comparable to the similar structures reported in the chromatoid bodies of *Entamoeba* (see below).

Several descriptions have been given of the fine structure of the nucleoli of protozoa (62, 63). It appears that in *Peridinium* the nucleolus has a Feulgen-positive core (62). Vivier (162) describes cyclical changes in the nucleoli of the macronucleus of *Paramecium* correlated with feeding.

The ciliate macronucleus continues to attract attention and there is now a considerable number of descriptions of its fine structure and cytochemistry in various organisms (31, 69, 70, 73, 128, 144, 163). It seems well established that DNA is localized in the smaller, dense bodies seen in electron micrographs (24), but it is not known whether these correspond to chromosomes or more complex genetic units. RNA typically occurs in larger, less dense bodies, probably to be regarded as nucleoli, but in *Tetrahymena* at least there is probably more than one kind of RNA-containing body in the macronucleus (31). Kluss (73) has confirmed earlier findings on the unravelling of the DNA-containing bodies prior to DNA replication in the reorganization bands of the macronucleus of *Euplotes*.

André & Vivier (7) have described remarkable deformations undergone by the migrating micronuclei of conjugants of *Paramecium*. The mechanism of movement of the nuclei is described by these authors as "amoeboid," and clearly the migrating nuclei develop large numbers of pseudopodial extensions.

In a series of studies, Feldherr (33–36) has shown that the pores in the nuclear envelope of amoebae are sites of entry of material into the nucleus. The passage of colloidal gold particles through the nuclear envelope is apparently restricted to narrow channels through the centre of the pores, and particles larger than about 125 Å in diameter are unable to enter. A different mechanism of nucleocytoplasmic interchange appears to operate in *Noctiluca*, in which Afzelius (2) finds that the nuclear envelope lacks pores over most of its area but that numerous vesicles with porous envelopes occur immediately below it. These may break open and become incorporated in the nuclear envelope, apparently liberating their contents into the cytoplasm.

Golgi Apparatus

The examination of an increasing number of protozoa confirms the view that their cytoplasmic membranes, like other features of their fine structure, are essentially comparable to those of metazoan cells. In one case, all membranes have been shown to have unit-membrane structure (20).

Studies of the Golgi apparatus, dictyosomes, and parabasal bodies (alternative terms for one kind of organelle), demonstrate that a considerable variety of formed products first becomes visible in Golgi vesicles. One of the clearest examples is provided by the surface scales of *Chrysochromulina*, *Heteromastix*, *Mesostigma*, and other flagellates. These have a distinctive shape and ornamentation and can be unequivocally identified in sections. They are formed in Golgi vesicles, apparently throughout the life cycle, and pass out in these towards the periphery of the cell, before being released onto the surface (83–85, 87, 89–91, 93). The chemical composition of the scales is, unfortunately, unknown. Somewhat similarly, the theca of *Platymonas* is produced by coalescence of small particles, also produced in Golgi vesicles (92). The ejectosomes of *Chilomonas* (see below) are a further example of an intricate structure arising in the Golgi apparatus (4), and the complex cytoplasmic rodlets of *Aulacantha*, which have been shown to contain polysaccharide, are another (134).

In such cases the Golgi vesicle presumably serves primarily as a site of accumulation of the constituent molecules of the structures in question, possibly ensuring a minimal concentration of those molecules, below which development would be unable to proceed. There is nothing to suggest that Golgi vesicles play a more active role in morphogenesis (i.e., by actually shaping the scales, ejectosomes, etc.), and, indeed, it is hard to envisage how they could.

In other protozoa the functions of the Golgi apparatus seem to be limited to the accumulation (which conceivably includes the prior synthesis, as well) of bulky secretory products. There are numerous descriptions of the fine structure of protozoan Golgi bodies [see, for example (20, 83)]. Such cytochemical work as is available is reviewed in an article by Nath & Dutta (105).

Food Vacuoles and Lysosomes

Digestion in protozoa is analogous to the breakdown of phagocytosed material in metazoan cells, and its study is therefore relevant to an understanding of lysosomes. In *Paramecium* it has been shown that the food vacuoles contain an esterase, lipase, ribonuclease, deoxyribonuclease, and acid phosphatase [(99, 103); reviews in (102, 140)], which are among the enzymes characterizing lysosomes. The appearance of these enzymes in food vacuoles seems not to be dependent on the presence of digestible food, since acid phosphatase, at least, is found in the vacuoles in quantity if ciliates, previously starved, are fed polystyrene latex particles (101). Assays show that in these experiments the total amount of acid phosphatase per cell does not increase following feeding, and its accumulation in food vacuoles must therefore result from a redistribution of enzyme previously present elsewhere in the cytoplasm (101). This agrees with the current hypothesis, derived from studies of mammalian cells, that one type of lysosome is a membrane-limited packet of hydrolytic enzymes which can be liberated at sites of intracellular digestion [see (28)]. Lysosomes do not as yet appear to have been isolated from protozoa or identified in electron micrographs. Ciliates such as *Paramecium* (and possibly other protozoa) would seem to form very suitable material for experimental work on the biochemistry and physiology of lysosomes, under more precisely controlled conditions than is usually possible in the case of metazoan cells.

Descriptions of the fine structure of food vacuoles have been given by several workers (68, 100, 140); Schneider's account (140) is a detailed one and includes a review of previous work. The intricate morphology of the cytopharynx of *Paramecium* has also been described by Schneider (139). The removal of digested products from food vacuoles into the cytoplasm commonly appears to take place by a form of pinocytosis. *Babesia rodhaini*, an intra-erythrocytic parasite, engulfs host cytoplasm into large food vacuoles (133), as does *Plasmodium* (132).

CYTOPLASMIC MICROORGANISMS

The bacteria and other microorganisms which live in or on protozoa exhibit relationships with their hosts of various degrees of intimacy. Externally located bacteria presumably participate less closely in their hosts' metabolism than do intracellular organisms. An extracellular location, however, does not preclude a close functional relationship, as is shown by the surface spirochaetes of *Mixotricha* which propel their host (20). All termite flagellates, it should be noted, like *Mixotricha*, appear to have bacteria or spirochaetes living in or on them.

Some infections with microorganisms appear to be accidental [e.g., (126)] and some hosts may tolerate a variety of intracellular organisms. *Paramecium bursaria*, for example, will form associations with several genera of algae and a yeast (15). There is evidence, however, that in this case the growth rates of the host vary with the nature of the infective organisms. In addition to obvious bacteria, which may or may not be present, the cytoplasm of *Amoeba proteus* sometimes contains bodies which are not definitely bacterial, but which can be seen to divide, and which incorporate labelled thymidine into DNA (170). It is not known whether these are at all closely integrated into their host's organization.

The partners in some associations are certainly very closely linked. Kappa, lambda, and mu, in *Paramecium*, all appear to be able to multiply only in host cells of certain genetic compositions [review in (71)]. *Crithidia oncopelti* contains supposed endosymbionts which are fairly constant in number and location and appear to be responsible for the "bacterial" pathway of lysine synthesis (via diaminopimelic acid) which this organism displays (46). The bacterial nature of the bodies in question has not, as yet, been unequivocally demonstrated, though this seems the most plausible hypothesis.

Participation of infective microorganisms in host-cell metabolism (and vice versa) could depend upon biochemical mechanisms of various degrees of intimacy. In brief, and to mention only three obvious possibilities, interdependence might be mediated by the interchange of substrates (e.g., amino acids), of enzymes necessary to metabolize such substrates, or of messenger RNA molecules necessary for enzyme synthesis. The latter mechanism, which would involve the protein-synthesizing machinery of one organism operating under instructions from another (cf. phage multiplication), would be worth looking for in some of the more persistent, supposedly symbiotic relationships. It is perhaps relevant here to note that the intracellular microorganisms of *Mixotricha* are commonly enveloped in rough-surfaced (ribosome-bearing) membranes of their host (20). The possibility that some cytoplasmic organelles may have originated as intracellular symbionts (see next section) suggests that a detailed study of the biochemical and genetic interactions of infective microorganisms and their hosts would be rewarding. In *Paramoeba* there is a body, the "Nebenkörper," which appears to be an accessory nucleus. It differs markedly in form and DNA content from the main nucleus of the cell, and neither type of nucleus can give rise to the other (51). Grell suggests that it may be the nucleus of a former parasite which has become closely integrated with a host cell and lost its own cytoplasm.

Cytoplasmic Organelles Containing DNA

A number of studies have demonstrated that the mitochondria of *Tetrahymena*, like those of some other cells, contain DNA (108, 154, 155). It has been shown that incorporation of thymidine into this is independent of nuclear DNA synthesis (108), and there are indications that the mitochondrial DNA is shared among successive generations of mitochondria, which would be consistent with the hypothesis of mitochondrial division (107).

The trypanosome kinetoplast-mitochondrion complex can be regarded as a mitochondrion in which the DNA is segregated in a distinct, Feulgen-positive region, the kinetoplast [review in (97)]. The extent and development of the mitochondrion varies, and is related to the environmental conditions and hence to the form of respiratory metabolism [review by Vickerman (161)]. In trypanosomes living in the blood stream of the vertebrate host,

Krebs cycle enzymes and cytochromes are absent and terminal respiration follows an alternative pathway. The mitochondrion in such forms is simple and there are few cristae. Trypanosomes in the insect host, on the other hand, have a normal respiratory pathway and the mitochondrion is correspondingly well developed, with numerous branches and abundant cristae. Vickerman (160, 161) suggests that the posterior growth of the mitochondrion from the kinetoplast may be responsible for the relative changes in position of organelles in the insect form. The proliferation of the mitochondrion depends on the presence of the kinetoplast DNA. In so-called akinetoplastic forms (which may arise spontaneously or be induced) the kinetoplast DNA (though not the rest of the organelle) is lost (95, 96, 98), and such forms can survive only in the blood stream. They are unable to develop an extensive mitochondrion and are not able to grow in insect hosts. It is a tenable hypothesis that the kinetoplast DNA contains information necessary for synthesis of the mitochondrial enzymes (151). Similar results have been obtained in the case of the leptomonad-leishmania transformation in *Leishmania* (118, 131, 158). Whether a similar situation exists in the case of the kinetoplast-mitochondrion of *Bodo* (110) is not known.

The DNA in the trypanosome kinetoplast occurs as 25 Å fibrils and is not associated with histones (152). In these aspects it resembles the DNA of mitochondria, plastids, bacteria, and blue-green algae, and differs from that of most nuclei, which contain larger fibrils of DNA-histone. Kinetoplast DNA is also more sensitive to acriflavine than is nuclear DNA. These similarities and differences have led Ris to postulate that organelles such as kinetoplasts may be the descendants of former bacterial endosymbionts (124).

Plastid DNA in *Chlamydomonas* (125) has been reviewed by Sager (136, 137) and will not be discussed here. The possible occurrence of DNA in ciliate basal bodies is considered below. In view of the increasing interest in these topics it is worth noting, finally, that thymidine cannot always be used as a specific precursor of DNA (135).

CHROMATOID BODIES

The chromatoid bodies of *Entamoeba invadens* consist of dense masses of ribonucleoprotein. They can be isolated and have been found to dissociate into two kinds of small particles: one about 150 Å in diameter, the other about 230 to 280 Å (9–11). Barker (10, 11) obtained similar particles from a microsomal fraction from *Entamoeba* and suggests that chromatoid bodies are made of ribosomes. The bodies arise in early cysts or in precystic stages by aggregation of small particles and disperse in late cysts (11, 12). The ribosomes are arranged with great regularity in the chromatoid bodies, which have a polycrystalline structure. It has been suggested that the basic elements in this are helical arrays of ribosomes (145, 146). The micrographs on which this interpretation is based are not of sufficiently high resolution to demonstrate this unequivocally. If it is correct, there is a possible parallel between chromatoid bodies and the helical arrays of ribosomes in differentiating cells (146). It will be interesting to know whether chromatoid bodies are sites of protein synthesis. Barker & Svihla (12) regard them as "stores" of ribosomes, held pending an active phase of growth on excystation.

Trichocysts, Ejectosomes, and Similar Bodies

Explosive or ejectile organelles occur in most groups of protozoa. They vary widely in form and apparent mode of functioning. The mechanism of discharge of the trichocysts of ciliates such as *Paramecium*, which appears to depend on the rapid transformation of an amorphous mass of protein into a crystalline thread [see (56)], appears to be quite unlike that of the ejectosomes of *Chilomonas* (4, 66, 67), in which the trichocyst thread exists in complete but telescoped form in the undischarged state; and both of these are different from the mechanism found in the polar capsules of the Cnidosporidia which, like the nematocysts of the Cnidaria, contain a complete, invaginated thread (114, 115) [it is becoming increasingly evident that the Cnidosporidia are probably not protozoa at all (48)]. In spite of the diversity of form and apparent mechanism of discharge, it is tempting to regard all forms of explosive organelles as the elaborate evolutionary derivatives of the much simpler muciferous bodies which occur in both flagellates (26, 76, 86, 88) and ciliates (18, 50, 157), just below the cell surface, and which discharge their contents to the exterior. [In some organisms the contents of these may contribute to the formation of cyst membranes (50).] In both trichocysts and muciferous bodies, the contents of a membrane-delimited organelle are expelled to the exterior by a process which appears to involve the swelling or molecular reorganization of the contents.

Recent work (26) has shown that trichocysts similar to those of ciliates occur in a variety of dinoflagellates (*Oxyrrhis*, *Amphidinium*, etc.). These are found in addition to muciferous bodies. They differ from ciliate trichocysts in that they exhibit an extremely regular rectangular substructure in the undischarged state.

The trichocysts of both *Paramecium* (29, 171) and *Frontonia* (172) develop in small vesicles, randomly located in the cytoplasm and unrelated to the ciliary basal bodies of the cell cortex. The material which forms the trichocyst body is lamellar in texture during the early stage of development but subsequently becomes homogeneous. Since a periodic structure, of a different kind from that present in the initial stage, reappears in the extruded shaft, it would seem that the trichocyst material can exist in at least three different states. In the course of development the trichocyst vacuoles move from the interior of the cytoplasm to take up their precise location in the cell cortex. The fact that depletion of trichocysts by electrical stimulation is followed by large-scale synthesis of new ones (171), suggests that trichocyst formation is controlled by a negative feedback mechanism. The formation of the muciferous bodies of *Tetrahymena* has recently been described in detail (157). They form in vacuoles and, as with trichocysts, the contents display a crystalline structure at one phase in development, which later disappears. The ejecto-somes of *Chilomonas* also develop in vacuoles, but in this case in vacuoles of the Golgi apparatus (4).

CILIA, FLAGELLA, SPINDLE FIBRES, AND MICROTUBULES

This topic has been repeatedly reviewed and discussed in recent years [see, for example (3, 32, 65, 106, 113, 148)] and only some of the more recent literature will be considered here. The static, somewhat uninformative morphological picture of cilia and flagella, derived from the study of thin sections, is now being supplemented by a growing body of information about their molecular structure and biochemistry. This relates in particular to the properties and distribution of the ciliary ATPase, the mode of interaction of ATP with ciliary components, and the substructure of ciliary fibres. The re-sults published so far do not permit the formulation of a molecular hypothesis of ciliary movement but it is clear that the data for such a hypothesis are now being assembled. In addition to the biochemical work, observations on flagellar mutants and the comparative study by conventional techniques of a range of cilia and flagella and comparable organelles, are both providing use-ful information.

Much of the recent work on the fractionation of cilia has been carried out on isolated cilia of *Tetrahymena*, which can be obtained in bulk (113, 167). Following removal of the membranes with digitonin or other agents, various protein components can be brought into solution under mild conditions. About 50 per cent of the protein passes into solution as soon as the mem-branes are removed. The residual protein consists chiefly of central and outer fibres, which commonly retain their normal arrangement (38). The residual protein can be totally dissolved in moderately strong salt solutions (e.g., $0.6M$ KCl), or, more instructively, it can be fractionated by dialysis against a chelating agent (EDTA) at low ionic strength. Under these conditions the ATPase activity of the preparation goes into solution, and so does about 30 per cent of the protein. The insoluble residue consists of outer fibres lacking arms. The arms will return to their normal location if Mg^{++} is added to the preparation and about 50 per cent of the ATPase activity then once again becomes sedimentable. This suggests that the arms must be the site of at least part of the ciliary ATPase activity (38).

This conclusion has been substantiated by further study of the ATPase itself (42). Density-gradient centrifugation separates this into two fractions, with sedimentation constants of 14S and 30S. Electron microscopic examina-tion of the 14S fraction shows it to consist of particles (probably single ATPase molecules) about 90 Å by 140 Å, with an estimated molecular weight of about half a million. The 30S fraction consists of linear aggregates of the 14S particles, up to 0.5μ long. These show a repeating structure along their length with a periodicity approximately the same as the spacing of the arms along the outer fibres, as seen in longitudinal sections (41). It therefore seems likely that the 14S units represent individual arms, which are ordinarily linked together along the length of the outer fibres. The ciliary ATPase has been termed "dynein." It resembles in some respects the protein, myxomyosin, thought to be involved in the movements of slime moulds, but is dissimilar to any of the muscle proteins. This dissimilarity is emphasized by the fact that the reactivation of glycerol-extracted *Tetrahymena* cilia by ATP does not require the presence of Ca^{++} (39).

The interaction of ATP with ciliary proteins has been studied by Gibbons (40), using light scattering to follow the reaction. The addition of ATP to the residual protein fraction causes an immediate fall in light scattering. This is also brought about by ADP, but other nucleotides are ineffective [Brokaw (17) found a similar nucleotide specificity in the activation of isolated *Polytoma* flagella]. Dynein must be present in order for ATP to produce its effect, and in reconstituted systems the 30S dynein fraction is essential and cannot be replaced by the 14S (supposedly monomeric) fraction. There is evidence that the fall in light scattering results from an increase in the degree of hydration of the outer fibres, in which respect the ciliary proteins appear to behave differently from actomyosin, which contracts and expels water by syneresis in the presence of ATP.

Observations on the substructure of flagellar fibres by negative staining were first made on sperm tails (6, 109), and have recently been extended to protozoan flagella (60). The most important finding is that the outer fibres are made up of filaments, approximately 40 Å in diameter, about 12 of which form the wall of each subfibre. The filaments appear to run straight along the length of the fibres and each of them consists of a single chain of globular units about 40 Å in diameter (60). The spacing and arrangement of the filaments and their subunits as they appear in electron micrographs have been analyzed by optical diffraction methods (72), which confirm the main longitudinal periodicity of 40 Å (the spacing of the subunits), but also reveal additional complexities.

The two central fibres appear to be more fragile than the outer ones and are not usually preserved following negative staining. When they do survive they show the same 40 Å periodicity as the outer fibres, but the diffraction patterns obtained from the micrographs show a number of differences which suggest that the detailed organization of the two is not identical (60).

Neither fractionation nor negative staining has clarified the nature of the structures which lie between the central and outer fibres, which is unfortunate since these structures are not well understood at present. The secondary fibres described from sections (41) in some flagellates are not always obvious in other material, but radial links (or spokes), originally described by Afzelius (1), have been found rather commonly (37). Both secondary fibres and spokes are less than 50 Å thick, and it is not difficult to think of reasons why one should appear more prominent than another in different materials. If a single structure had to be proposed for all cases on the basis of the available evidence, the most likely one would be a set of nine secondary fibres linked by radial fibres to both the central and outer fibres (5, 37). There is a need, however, for more careful study of this problem than has so far been attempted.

Of the additional structures which may be present in some flagella, a preliminary study of certain Chrysophycea has shown that the mastigonemes are complex structures, in which negative staining reveals a number of sub-filaments (16). In *Heteromastix* and related organisms, the surface of the flagella may be covered by close-packed scales (89, 93). X-ray diffraction data on the ciliary membrane itself have been presented by Silvester (147).

A number of recent observations give indirect information about the mechanism of ciliary movement. It is now clear, for example, that ciliary membranes are not essential for movement, since isolated cilia of *Tetrahymena*, lacking membranes, can be activated by ATP (39). (The basal bodies are probably also missing in these isolated cilia.) Studies of the nonmotile mutants of *Chlamydomonas* are also relevant. Lewin's original study of these paralyzed organisms revealed a multiplicity of genetically controlled factors implicated in motility, but none of the mutations could be shown to be correlated with any structural lesion (77). More recently, a proflavine-induced nonmotile mutant of *Chlamydomonas reinhardii* has been found which lacks central fibres (122). This character segregates at meiosis following crosses with wild-type organisms. The finding suggests that the central fibres play a key role in flagellar movements.

The basal bodies of cilia and flagella display a greater range of structural variation than do cilia and flagella themselves. In some pigmented flagellates there is what appears in transverse section to be a nine-pointed star within the cylinder of fibres (75). According to Manton (80), this "star" is made up of a fibril, or series of fibrils, running helically around the inside of the basal body and connecting alternate outer fibres. Manton points out that with an odd number of outer fibres (e.g., nine) each fibre will be linked to every other one by this arrangement, which would not be the case with an even number.

Basal bodies of various degrees of purity have been isolated in bulk from *Tetrahymena* and there are some preliminary data on their composition (8, 61, 138, 142). As might be expected, protein is the major constituent, but preparations also commonly contain about 2 per cent RNA. There is not, as yet, good evidence that this does not arise by contamination with ribosomes, and the reported demonstration of protein synthesis by basal bodies (143) must at present be viewed with some scepticism. The finding of about 3 per cent DNA in basal body preparations (142) almost certainly results from contamination, and in more highly purified preparations the amount of DNA is very much less, if it is present at all (8, 61). Whether DNA is a genuine constituent of basal bodies remains to be determined. Randall & Disbrey (120) have reported cytochemical and autoradiographic evidence for its presence, again in *Tetrahymena*, and give some preliminary estimates of the possible amount per basal body [see also (119)]. These observations, like those on bulk isolates, have all been made on disrupted cells, and the possibility of contamination has not been completely excluded. The proposed amount of DNA lies on the limit of sensitivity of the methods used for its detection, and it seems permissible, for the time being, to view the results with some caution. More convincing evidence might be provided by electron auto-radiography of cells grown in tritiated thymidine. Possible functional roles of basal body DNA, are discussed by Randall & Disbrey (120).

The production of new basal bodies and their surrounding membranous ciliary corpuscles has been studied recently in *Paramecium* by Dippell (25). Ciliary corpuscles apparently arise from pre-existing ones by elongation and growth, and the basal bodies form in close association with old ones. Not un-expectedly, these findings partly contradict earlier reports by some other workers (29, 123). Roth & Shigenaka (129) have described stages in the production of new cilia in *Diplodinium* and have produced evidence to show that the fibres are randomly distributed when first produced and sub-sequently take up their characteristic arrangement. A preliminary descrip-tion of the formation of new basal bodies and flagella in *Trypanosoma equi-perdum* has been given by Grassé (49). New basal bodies arise close to pre-existing ones, but there is no evidence of division. In *Naegleria* there is some evidence that bundles of flagellar fibres are formed in the cytoplasm and subsequently extruded. Possible intracellular precursors of the flagella have been seen (141).

Numerous descriptions have appeared of the fibrous structures attached to, and in some cases linking together, basal bodies [see (112, 113, 129)]. The obvious suggestion, that these are involved in the co-ordination of ciliary or flagellar activity, lacks proof in almost all cases. In *Euplotes*, however, experi-mental evidence has been presented to show that the co-ordination of the anal cirri with the activity of the adoral membranelles depends on the in-tegrity of bundles of microtubules connecting the basal bodies of the two sets of structures (47). The co-ordination of these organelles, which perform intri-cate, intermittent movements, is possibly more complex than, and therefore different in kind from, the co-ordination of the repetitive movements of ad-jacent cilia or flagella covering the body in organisms such as *Paramecium* or *Trichonympha*. An analysis in hydromechanical terms by Machin (78) shows that structures such as flagella, undulating in proximity, will tend automat-ically to synchronize their movements. That this may indeed be a major factor in the co-ordination of body cilia, is suggested by observations on *Mixotricha*. This flagellate is propelled by the activity of thousands of spirochaetes attached to its body surface (20). The movements of the spiro-chaetes are precisely co-ordinated, and well-defined metachronal waves are produced. The possibility that this co-ordination depends on a system within the flagellate itself is remote, since the spirochaetes are simply adherent to the body surface and do not penetrate into the cell.

Fibres similar to those in cilia and flagella, appearing tubular in cross-section, are found in a variety of situations, both in protozoa and in the cells of higher plants and animals. In the latter they are commonly termed micro-tubules, and frequently seem to be concerned in cell movements. The comparative study of these structures is of some interest, but no useful purpose would be served by a comprehensive review at the present time. Only certain examples will be discussed.

There are a few cases among the protozoa in which it seems safe to identify the fibres as intrinsically contractile or extensible elements. The most striking examples are the axostyles of some of the flagellates of termites, notably, members of the Pyrsonymphidae such as *Saccinobaculus*. The axostyle is, in these organisms, a broad rod or ribbon running through the cytoplasm and, by its active undulations, changing the shape of the cell (58). It is composed of up to 5000 longitudinal fibres, arranged in parallel rows and morphologically indistinguishable from the central fibres of flagella. (The axostyles of other flagellates, such as *Trichomonas*, which can bend but do not undulate, are commonly hollow cylinders with a wall made up of a single layer of similar fibres.) The axostyle of *Saccinobaculus*, propagating undulatory waves along its length, resembles a flagellum in its movements yet displays no comparable elaboration of structure. There is only one type of fibre, and there are no arms (though fine cross-connexions are present). This suggests that the complexity of structure of cilia and flagella is not essential for the generation of undulatory waves.

Apart from cases such as this, there is a large number of examples in which fibres seem to be involved in cell movements but where the evidence for intrinsic contractility is less clear. The haptonemata of *Prymnesium* and other flagellates form one example. These are appendages similar in dimensions to flagella but capable only of attaching to the substrate and coiling into a tight helix. They contain six or seven longitudinal, single fibres or tubules, which are not arranged in any characteristic pattern (85, 88). In the bases of these organelles the number of fibres increases to nine (82). Unlike flagella, haptonemata have multiple membranes: below the plasma membrane there is a long membrane-bounded cavity, the "haptonema space," dividing the contents into central and outer regions joined only by small bridges. Manton (82) discusses the possibility that turgor pressure may be involved in the changes in form of these organelles, but while this may be a factor it would seem more likely that the fibres play a primary role.

Other cases in which fibres of similar dimensions and appearance appear to be involved in movement were reviewed previously (56). Among examples which have been described since may be mentioned the fibrils surrounding the contractile vacuole pore in *Tetrahymena* (30), the subpellicular fibres of gregarines (165), and a range of fibrillar structures in ciliates [see (21, 129)]. In these cases, as with haptonemata, it is reasonable to suggest that the fibres are intrinsically contractile. There are other situations in which fibres seem to be connected with cell movement but in which it seems highly unlikely that they shorten or elongate actively themselves. The fibres of the mitotic spindle are a case in point [for amoebae see (22, 127); for radiolaria

(54); and for flagellates (81); similar fibres are present in ciliate micronuclei (129, 159), and the large bundles of fibrils described in the macronuclei of some strains of *Paramecium caudatum* (163, 164) are probably also spindle fibres]. It would seem likely that in the anaphase movements of chromosomes, the centromeres move along spindle fibres, rather than being dragged to the poles by shortening of the fibres. The dimensions involved, and the speed of the movements make the latter explanation unlikely. Elongation of the central spindle, by growth, is, of course, in some cases a contributing factor in anaphase movements. Roth & Shigenaka (129) have discussed the resemblances between spindle fibres and those occurring in cilia and other organelles.

There is growing evidence for the involvement of fibres in amoeboid movement [(23, 27, 74); reviewed in (168, 169)]. There appears, however, to be a considerable range in the dimensions of the structures involved, and some of them seem to be different from the standard type of microtubule. Nachmias (104), for example, finds fibres 70 to 80 Å in diameter in the cytoplasm of *Chaos chaos* if the amoebae are fixed whole, but larger fibres (150 Å) if the plasmalemma is torn before fixation. McManus & Roth (94) have described three kinds of fibrous structure in the cytoplasm of various slime moulds. It is relevant here to note that the contractile element of the stalks of peritrichs (the "spasmoneme") is fibrillar, but the fibrils are only about 50 Å in diameter (121).

The possibility that fibres or microtubules, apparently of the standard type, may be skeletal in function is suggested by de Puytorac (117) on the basis of a review of their occurrence in a range of ciliates. There seem to be few cases, however, among the examples quoted, in which the fibres could not also be concerned in cell movement. The two supposed functions, are not, of course, mutually exclusive. In the tentacles of Suctoria, for example, the cylinder of fibres which runs their length could well be concerned both with maintaining rigidity and with the movement of ingested food down the central canal (130). A similar argument applies to the microtubules in the axopodia of Heliozoa (64).

The situation as it appears at the moment can be summarized by saying that there is a range of tubular elements in the cytoplasm which in general appear to be relatively rigid, and may therefore play an important role in the maintenance or alteration of cell shape, and which are also involved in cell movements, by virtue either of their intrinsic contractility or of the occurrence of shearing movements between their surfaces and the surroundings. The extent to which the two functions are developed could vary in different cases, and might depend on the spacing or mutual arrangement of the tubules, or on the presence or absence of additional components (such as arms).

Finally, it is worth noting that there appear to be some contractile organelles which are not built of fibres or microtubules of any kind, but have a completely different structure. The costa of some species of *Trichomonas* is one such case: this is composed of fine, longitudinal lamellae, with a periodic structure repeating at about 760 Å (57). A somewhat similar structure has been found in the supposedly skeletal fibres of the ciliate, *Mesnilella* (116).

CENTRIOLES

Typical (basal-body-like) centrioles, not connected to cilia or flagella, have apparently not been found so far at the poles of the mitotic spindle of any protozoon [see, for example (127)]. No study, however, has as yet been sufficiently exhaustive to demonstrate their absence conclusively. A typical centriole has apparently been found so far in only one protozoon, *Trichonympha*, and here it is not known to participate in mitosis (59). In some flagellates the spindle fibres seem to develop in loose association with the flagellar basal bodies (81).

The complex behaviour and functions of the large centrioles of termite flagellates have been reviewed by Cleveland (19). Only two of these organisms, *Trichonympha* and *Pseudotrichonympha*, have so far been studied in detail (59). The former, as already noted, has a typical centriole, not known to play any part in division, but in addition it has an elaborate centriolar apparatus which is functional in mitosis. The gross organization and fine structure of this apparatus is quite different from that of a typical centriole, and also from that of the equally elaborate centriolar apparatus of *Pseudotrichonympha*. The only features in common in the two organisms seems to be the presence of dense, finely fibrous material, to which spindle fibres attach. In *Pseudotrichonympha*, spindle fibres persist throughout interphase, attached to a layer of this dense material lining the inside of the rostral tube.

PROBLEMS CONNECTED WITH THE FORMATION OF CYTOPLASMIC ORGANELLES

Discussions of the formation of new cytoplasmic structures for the most part still tend to take place within an antiquated conceptual and theoretical framework. Terms such as "morphogenesis," "crystallization," "autonomy," and "self-replication" are used uncritically and without detailed analysis of their content. It seems commonly to be assumed that "the replication of cytoplasmic organelles" is a single, though peculiarly difficult, problem. Perhaps this is one reason for the present state of almost complete ignorance about the events responsible for the formation of any type of organelle, in protozoa or any other kind of cell.

Perhaps it would be more profitable to begin by making no assumptions about the uniformity or nonuniformity of the processes involved, and to be prepared for what would at present appear to be wide variations in the mechanisms producing a given type of organelle (for example, mitochrondria) in different cells, or even in the same type of cell at different stages in its life history. Each case, it is suggested, should be considered separately, the temptation to generalize should be resisted for the time being, and a series of specific, limited questions formulated about the processes involved. For example, if we are considering the formation of trichocysts in *Paramecium* it would be reasonable to begin by asking some of the following questions: What types of molecule enter into the composition of trichocysts? Which of these are peculiar to trichocysts and which are common to a number of cytoplasmic structures? Where in the cell is the information specifying the structure of these molecules located? What factors control the synthesis of the molecules and at what level is control exercised? Is synthesis continuous or intermittent? Are all of the types of molecule synthesized simultaneously, and is their synthesis under common control? Are molecules synthesized at the sites where new trichocysts will begin to form, or elsewhere? In either case, what determines where synthesis occurs? What determines where new trichocysts begin to develop? What is the nature of the intermolecular bonds involved in trichocyst formation? How far do molecular properties account for the form of the organelle, and what other factors, if any, are involved in shaping structure? Are pre-existing trichocysts or any other type of organelle involved in formation of new trichocysts, and if so in what way? What determines the number of trichocysts in a cell? Is trichocyst formation continuous or intermittent? (this is distinct from the question of the synthesis of constituent molecules). If the rate of trichocyst formation is controlled by the rate of trichocyst discharge (see above), at what level does the control system operate? How can an organelle, or the lack of it, act as a signal controlling production of that organelle? Why do trichocysts originally appear deep in the cytoplasm and subsequently move to the surface? How do they move? Is their formation complete before they reach the surface? What factors are responsible for bringing them to their precise locations at the cell cortex?

The list of questions could obviously be extended indefinitely, and the answer to any of them would almost certainly lead to new questions, or to a reformulation of old ones. Some of the questions will no doubt seem foolish or wrongly framed in the light of further knowledge. In some cases existing knowledge (for example, of control mechanisms in bacteria) could profitably be applied to the more complex situations in eucells. Almost none of the questions posed looks answerable by direct observation with the electron microscope. What does seem highly probable is that an attempt to answer almost any of these questions could hardly fail to produce dividends in the form of precise, much-needed information.

Some of the available information about organelle formation and subcellular morphogenesis has been briefly discussed in the preceding sections of this article, and several more extensive reviews and discussions are available (55, 136, 150, 156). It is clear that in some cases the extreme hypothesis, that organelle formation is exclusively under nuclear control, and that the generation of cytoplasmic structures depends solely on the "spontaneous" assembly of molecules whose composition is specified by nuclear genes, is no longer tenable. It could be argued, in any case, that what is generated by spontaneous assembly of molecules is "material" rather than "form," and that some other agency must always be postulated to account for complex morphology. There is strong evidence for the involvement of a nonchromosomal (extranuclear), genetic system in chloroplast formation, and at a more complex level Sonneborn (14, 150) has produced convincing evidence that abnormal cortical patterns in *Paramecium* may be inherited independently of nuclear genetic control [see also (156)]. In these cases the cytoplasm clearly contributes "morphogenetic information."

To refer to cases in which organelle formation depends on pre-existing cytoplasmic structure as examples of "patterned growth" (137) may serve to draw attention to the continuity of new structure with old, but as an explanatory concept it does not take us far. Here, as with some other terms [for example, "crystallization," "condition-generated forms" (166)], "what is to be explained is already put into the definition of the concepts serving for explanation" [(79); see also (149)].

LITERATURE CITED

1. Afzelius, B. A., *J. Biophys. Biochem. Cytol.*, **5**, 269–78 (1959)
2. Afzelius, B. A., *J. Cell Biol.*, **19**, 229–38 (1963)
3. Allen, R. D., and Kamiya, N., Eds., *Primitive Motile Systems in Cell Biology.* (Academic Press, New York, 642 pp., 1963)
4. Anderson, E., *J. Protozool.*, **9**, 380–95 (1962)
5. André, J., *J. Ultrastruct. Res.*, **5**, 86–108 (1961)
6. André, J., and Thiery, J., *J. Microscop.*, **2**, 71–80 (1963)
7. André, J., and Vivier, E., *J. Ultrastruct. Res.*, **6**, 390–406 (1962)
8. Argetsinger, J., *J. Cell Biol.*, **24**, 154–57 (1965)
9. Barker, D. C., in *Proc. Intern. Congr. Electron Microscopy, 5th, Philadelphia, 1962*, **2**, UU-9 (1962)
10. Barker, D. C., *Exptl. Cell Res.*, **32**, 272–79 (1963)
11. Barker, D. C., *Z. Zellforsch.*, **58**, 641–59 (1963)
12. Barker, D. C., and Svihla, G., *J. Cell Biol.*, **20**, 389–98 (1964)
13. Beams, H. W., and Anderson, E., *Ann. Rev. Microbiol.*, **15**, 47–68 (1961)
14. Beisson, J., and Sonneborn, T. M., *Proc. Natl. Acad. Sci. U.S.*, **53**, 275–82 (1965)
15. Bomford, R., *J. Protozool.*, **12**, 221–24 (1965)
16. Bradley, D. E., *Quart. J. Microscop. Sci.*, **106**, 327–31 (1965)
17. Brokaw, C. J., *Exptl. Cell Res.*, **22**, 151–62 (1961)
18. Cheissin, E. M., and Mosevich, T. N., *Arch. Protistenk.*, **106**, 181–200 (1962)
19. Cleveland, L. R., in *The Cell in Mitosis* 3–53. (Levine, L., Ed., Academic Press, New York, 274 pp., 1963)
20. Cleveland, L. R., and Grimstone, A. V., *Proc. Roy Soc., London*, Ser. B, **159**, 668–86 (1964)
21. Daniel, W. A., and Mattern, C. F. T., *J. Protozool.*, **12**, 14–27 (1965)
22. Daniels, E. W., and Roth, L. E., *J. Cell Biol.*, **20**, 75-84 (1964)
23. Danneel, S., *Naturwissenschaften*, **15**, 368–69 (1964)
24. Dippell, R. V., *J. Cell Biol.*, **19**, 20A–21A (1963)
25. Dippell, R. V., in Progress in Protozoology (Abstracts of papers).

26. Dragesco, J., and Hollande, A., *Compt. Rend.*, **260**, 2073–76 (1965)
27. Dugas, D. J., and Bath, J. D., *Protoplasma*, **54**, 421–31 (1962)
28. de Duve, C., in *Lysosomes*, 1–31. (Reuck, A. V. S. de, and Cameron, M. P., Eds., J. & A. Churchill, London, 446 pp., 1963)
29. Ehret, C. F., and Haller, G. de, *J. Ultrastruct. Res.*, Suppl. 6, 1–42 (1963)
30. Elliott, A. M., and Bak, I. J., *J. Protozool.*, **11**, 250–61 (1964)
31. Elliott, A. M., Kennedy, J. R., and Bak, I. J., *J. Cell Biol.*, **12**, 515–31 (1962)
32. Fauré-Fremiet, E., *Biol. Rev.*, **36**, 464–536 (1961)
33. Feldherr, C. M., *J. Cell Biol.*, **12**, 159–67 (1962)
34. Feldherr, C. M., *J. Cell Biol.*, **14**, 65–72 (1962)
35. Feldherr, C. M., *J. Cell Biol.*, **25**, 43–52 (1965)
36. Feldherr, C. M., and Marshall, J. M., *J. Cell Biol.*, **12**, 640–45 (1962)
37. Gibbons, I. R., *J. Biophys. Biochem. Cytol.*, **11**, 179–205 (1961)
38. Gibbons, I. R., *Proc. Natl. Acad. Sci. U. S.*, **50**, 1002–10 (1963)
39. Gibbons, I. R., *J. Cell Biol.*, **25**, 400–2 (1965)
40. Gibbons, I. R., *J. Cell Biol.*, **26**, 707–12 (1965)
41. Gibbons, I. R., and Grimstone, A. V., *J. Cell Biol.*, **7**, 697–716 (1960)
42. Gibbons, I. R., and Rowe, A. J., *Science*, **149**, 424–26 (1965)
43. Giesbrecht, P., *Zentr. Bakteriol. Parasitenk., Abt. I. Orig.*, **187**, 452–98 (1962)
44. Giesbrecht, P., *Z. Naturforsch.*, **20b**, 927–28 (1965)
45. Giesbrecht, P., *Zentr. Bakteriol. Parasitenk., Abt., I. Orig.*, **196**, 516–19 (1965)
46. Gill, J. W., and Vogel, H. J., *J. Protozool.*, **10**, 148–52 (1963)
47. Gliddon, R., in Progress in Protozoology (Abstracts of papers). *Intern. Conf. Protozool., 2nd, London, 1965*, 246 (1965)
48. Grassé, P. P., *Compt. Rend.*, **251**, 2638–40 (1960)
49. Grassé, P. P., *Compt. Rend.*, **252**, 1–6 (1961)

50. Grassé, P. P., and Mugard, H., *Compt. Rend.*, **253**, 31–34 (1961)
51. Grell, K. G., *Arch. Protistenk.*, **105**, 303–12 (1961)
52. Grell, K. G., *Fortschr. Zool.*, **14**, 1–85 (1962)
53. Grell, K. G., in *The Cell*, **6**, 1–79. (Brachet, J., and Mirsky, A. E., Eds., Academic Press, New York, 564 pp., 1964)
54. Grell, K. G., and Ruthmann, A., *Chromosoma*, **15**, 185–211 (1964)
55. Grenson, M., *Intern. Rev. Cytol.*, **16**, 37–59 (1964)
56. Grimstone, A. V., *Biol. Rev.*, **36**, 97–150 (1961)
57. Grimstone, A. V. (Unpublished observations, 1965)
58. Grimstone, A. V., and Cleveland, L. R., *J. Cell Biol.*, **24**, 387–400 (1965)
59. Grimstone, A. V., and Gibbons, I. R., *Phil. Trans. Roy. Soc., Ser. B.* (In press, 1966)
60. Grimstone, A. V., and Klug, A., *J. Cell Sci.* (In press, 1966)
61. Hoffman, E. J., *J. Cell Biol.*, **25**, 217–28 (1965)
62. Hollande, A., Cachon, J., and Cachon-Enjumet, M., *Compt. Rend.*, **256**, 3193–95 (1963)
63. Hollande, A., and Cachon-Enjumet, M., *Compt. Rend.*, **249**, 167–69 (1959)
64. Hovasse, R., *Protistologica*, **1**, 81–88 (1965)
65. Jahn, T. L., and Bovee, E. C., *Ann. Rev. Microbiol.*, **19**, 21–58 (1965)
66. Joyon, L., *Ann. Fac. Sci. Univ. Clermont*, **22**, 1–96 (1963)
67. Joyon, L., *Arch. Zool. Exptl. Gen.*, **102**, 199–200 (1963)
68. Jurand, A., *J. Protozool.*, **8**, 125–30 (1961)
69. Jurand, A., Beale, G. H., and Young, M. R., *J. Protozool.*, **9**, 122–31 (1962)
70. Jurand, A., Beale, G. H., and Young, M. R., *J. Protozool.*, **11**, 491–97 (1964)
71. Kimball, R. F., in *Biochemistry and Physiology of Protozoa*, **3**, 243–75. (Hutner, S. H., Ed., Academic Press, New York, 616 pp. 1964)
72. Klug, A., and Berger, J. E., *J. Mol. Biol.*, **10**, 565–69 (1964)
73. Kluss, B. C., *J. Cell Biol.*, **13**, 462–65 (1962)
74. Komnick, H., and Wohlfarth-Bottermann, K. E., *Z. Zellforsch.*, **66**, 434–56 (1965)
75. Lang, N. J., *J. Cell Biol.*, **19**, 631–34 (1963)
76. Leedale, G. F., Meeuse, B. J. D., and Pringsheim, E. G., *Arch. Mikrobiol.*, **50**, 68–102 (1965)
77. Lewin, R. A., *J. Gen. Microbiol.*, **11**, 358–63 (1954)
78. Machin, K. E., *Proc. Roy. Soc., London, Ser. B.* **158**, 88–104 (1963)
79. Mainx, F., in *International Encyclopedia of Unified Science*, **1**, No. 9 (Chicago Univ. Press, Chicago, Ill., 86 pp., 1955)
80. Manton, I., *J. Roy Microscop. Soc.*, **82**, 279–85 (1963)
81. Manton, I., *J. Roy, Microscop. Soc.*, **83**, 317–25 (1964)
82. Manton, I., *Arch. Mikrobiol.*, **49**, 315–30 (1964)
83. Manton, I., and Ettl, H., *J. Linnean Soc.* (*Botan*), **59**, 175–84 (1965)
84. Manton, I., and Leedale, G. F., *Phycologia*, **1**, 37–57 (1961)
85. Manton, I., and Leedale, G. F., *J. Marine Biol. Assoc., U. K.*, **41**, 519–26 (1961)
86. Manton, I., and Leedale, G. F., *J. Marine Biol. Assoc. U. K.*, **41**, 145–55 (1961)
87. Manton, I., and Leedale, G. F., *Arch. Mikrobiol.*, **47**, 115–36 (1963)
88. Manton, I., and Leedale, G. F., *Arch. Mikrobiol.*, **45**, 285–303 (1963)
89. Manton, I., Oates, K., and Parke, M., *J. Marine Biol. Assoc. U. K.*, **43**, 225–38 (1963)
90. Manton, I., Parke, M., *J. Marine Biol. Assoc. U.K.*, **39**, 275–98 (1960)
91. Manton, I., and Parke, M., *J. Marine Biol. Assoc. U.K.*, **42**, 565–78 (1962)
92. Manton, I., and Parke, M., *J. Marine Biol. Assoc. U.K.*, **45**, 743–54 (1965)
93. Manton, I., Rayns, D. G., Ettl, H., and Parke, M., *J. Marine Biol. Assoc. U.K.*, **45**, 241–55 (1965)
94. McManus, M. A., and Roth, L. E., *J. Cell Biol.*, **25**, 305–18 (1965)
95. Mühlpfordt, H., *Z. Tropenmed. Parasitol.*, **14**, 475–501 (1963)
96. Mühlpfordt, H., *Z. Tropenmed. Parasitol.*, **14**, 357–98 (1963)
97. Mühlpfordt, H., *Z. Tropenmed. Parasitol.*, **15**, 289–323 (1964)
98. Mühlpfordt, H., and Bayer, M., *Z. Tropenmed. Parasitol.*, **12**, 334–46 (1961)
99. Müller, M., *Acta Biol. Acad. Sci. Hung.*, **13**, 283–97 (1962)
100. Müller, M., and Röhlich, P., *Acta. Morphol. Acad. Sci. Hung.*, **10**, 297–305 (1961)

101. Müller, M., Röhlich, P., and Törö, I., *J. Protozool.*, **12**, 27–34 (1965)
102. Müller, M., Röhlich, P., Tóth, J., and Törö, I., in *Lysosomes*, (Reuck, A. V. S. de, and Cameron, M. P., Eds., J. & A. Churchill, London, 446 pp., 1963)
103. Müller, M., Tóth, J., and Törö, I., *Nature*, **187**, 65 (1960)
104. Nachmias, V. T., *J. Cell Biol.*, **23**, 183–88 (1964)
105. Nath, V., and Dutta, G. P., *Intern. Rev. Cytol.*, **13**, 323–55 (1962)
106. Newton, B. A., and Kerridge, D., *Symp. Soc. Gen. Microbiol.*, **15**, 220–49 (1965)
107. Parsons, J. A., *J. Cell Biol.*, **23**, 70A (1964)
108. Parsons, J. A., *J. Cell Biol.*, **25**, 641–46 (1965)
109. Pease, D. C., *J. Cell Biol.*, **18**, 313–26 (1963)
110. Pitelka, D. R., *Exptl. Cell Res.*, **25**, 87–93 (1961)
111. Pitelka, D. R., *Electron-microscopic Structure of Protozoa* (Pergamon Press, Oxford, 269 pp., 1963)
112. Pitelka, D. R., *J. Microscop.*, **4**, 373–94 (1965)
113. Pitelka, D. R., and Child, F. M., in *Biochemistry and Physiology of Protozoa.* **3**, 131–98. (Hutner, S. H., Ed., Academic Press, New York, 616 pp., 1964)
114. de Puytorac, P., *J. Microscop.*, **1**, 39–46 (1962)
115. de Puytorac, P., *Compt. Rend.*, **256**, 1594–96 (1963)
116. de Puytorac, P., *J. Microscop.*, **2**, 189–96 (1963)
117. de Puytorac, P., in *Progress in Protozoology* (Abstracts of papers). *Intern. Conf. Protozool.*, *2nd*, *London, 1965*, 246 (1965)
118. Pyne, C. K., *Compt. Rend.*, **251**, 2776–78 (1960)
119. Rampton, V. W., *Nature*, **195**, 195 (1962)
120. Randall, Sir John, and Disbrey, C., *Proc. Roy. Soc. London, Ser. B*, **162**, 473–91 (1965)
121. Randall, Sir John, and Hopkins, J. M., *Phil. Trans. Roy. Soc., Ser. B*, **245**, 59–79 (1962)
122. Randall, Sir John, Warr, J. R., Hopkins, J. M., and McVittie, A., *Nature*, **203**, 912–14 (1964)
123. Randall, Sir John, Watson, M. R., Silvester, N. R., Alexander, J. B., and Hopkins, J. M., *Proc. Linnean Soc.*, **174**, 37–40 (1963)

124. Ris, H., in *Proc. Intern. Congr. Electron Microscopy, 5th, Philadelphia, 1962*, **2**, XX-1 (1962)
125. Ris, H., and Plaut, W., *J. Cell Biol.*, **13**, 383–91 (1962)
126. Roth, L. E., and Daniels, E. W., *J. Cell Biol.*, **9**, 317–23 (1961)
127. Roth, L. E., and Daniels, E. W., *J. Cell Biol.*, **12**, 57–78 (1962)
128. Roth, L. E., and Minick, O. T., *J. Protozool.*, **8**, 12–21 (1961)
129. Roth, L. E., and Shigenaka, Y., *J. Cell Biol.*, **20**, 249–70 (1964)
130. Rudzinska, M., *J. Cell Biol.*, **25**, 459–77 (1965)
131. Rudzinska, M. A., d'Alesandro, P. A., and Trager, W., *J. Protozool.*, **11**, 166–91 (1964)
132. Rudzinska, M. A., and Trager, W., *J. Biophys. Biochem. Cytol.*, **6**, 103–12 (1959)
133. Rudzinska, M. A., and Trager, W., *J. Protozool.*, **9**, 279–88 (1962)
134. Ruthmann, A., and Grell, K. G., *Z. Zellforsch.*, **63**, 97–119 (1964)
135. Sagan, L., *J. Protozool.*, **12**, 105–9 (1965)
136. Sager, R., in *Biochemistry and Physiology of Protozoa*, **3**, 297–318. (Hutner, S. H., Ed., Academic Press, New York, 616 pp., 1964)
137. Sager, R., *Symp. Soc. Gen. Microbiol.*, **15**, 324–42 (1965)
138. Satir, B., and Rosenbaum, J. L., *J. Protozool.*, **12**, 397–405 (1965)
139. Schneider, L., *Z. Zellforsch.*, **62**, 198–224 (1964)
140. Schneider, L., *Z. Zellforsch.*, **62**, 225–45 (1964)
141. Schuster, F., *J. Protozool.*, **10**, 297–313 (1963)
142. Seaman, G. R., *Exptl. Cell Res.*, **21**, 292–302 (1960)
143. Seaman, G. R., *Biophys. Biochim. Acta*, **55**, 889–99 (1962)
144. Seshachar, B. S., *J. Protozool.*, **11**, 402–9 (1964)
145. Siddiqui, W. A., and Rudzinska, M. A., *Nature*, **200**, 74–75 (1963)
146. Siddiqui, W. A., and Rudzinska, M. A., *J. Protozool.*, **12**, 448–59 (1965)
147. Silvester, N. R., *J. Mol. Biol.*, **8**, 11–19 (1964)
148. Sleigh, M. A., *The Biology of Cilia and Flagella.* (Pergamon Press, Oxford, 229 pp., 1962)
149. Smith, S., *Symp. Soc. Exptl. Biol.*, **14**, 214–29 (1960)
150. Sonneborn, T. M., in *The Nature of Biological Diversity*, 165–221.

(Allen, J. M., Ed., McGraw Hill, New York, 304 pp., 1963)

151. Steinert, M., *J. Biophys. Biochem. Cytol.*, **8**, 542–46 (1960)

152. Steinert, M., *Exptl. Cell Res.*, **39**, 69–73 (1965)

153. Stevens, A. R., and Prescott, D. M., *Exptl. Cell Res.*, **40**, 204–7 (1965)

154. Stone, G. E., and Miller, O. L., *J. Cell Biol.*, **23**, 89A (1964)

155. Stone, G. E., and Prescott, D. M., *J. Protozool.*, **11**, Suppl. 24 (1964)

156. Tartar, V., *The Biology of Stentor.* (Pergamon Press, Oxford, 413 pp., 1961)

157. Tokoyasu, K., and Scherbaum, O. H., *J. Cell Biol.*, **27**, 67–81 (1965)

158. Trager, W., and Rudzinska, M. A., *J. Protozool.*, **11**, 133–45 (1964)

159. Tucker, J. B. (Unpublished observations, 1965)

160. Vickerman, K., *Trans. Roy. Soc. Trop. Med. Hyg.*, **56**, 487–95 (1962)

161. Vickerman, K., *Nature*, **208**, 762–66 (1965)

162. Vivier, E., *Compt. Rend.*, **250**, 205–7 (1960)

163. Vivier, E., *Compt. Rend. Soc. Biol.*, **155**, 494–97 (1961)

164. Vivier, E., and André, J., *Compt. Rend.*, **252**, 1848–50 (1961)

165. Vivier, E., and Schrevel, J., *J. Microscop.*, **3**, 651–70 (1964)

166. Waddington, C. H., *New Patterns in Genetics and Development.* (Columbia Univ. Press, New York and London, 271 pp., 1962)

167. Watson, M. R., Alexander, J. B., and Silvester, N. R., *Exptl. Cell Res.*, **33**, 112–29 (1964)

168. Wohlfarth-Bottermann, K. E., *Intern. Rev. Cytol.*, **16**, 61–131 (1964)

169. Wolpert, L., *Symp. Soc. Gen. Microbiol.*, **15**, 270–93 (1965)

170. Wolstenholme, D. R., and Plaut, W., *J. Cell. Biol.*, **22**, 505–13 (1964)

171. Yusa, A., *J. Protozool.*, **10**, 253–62 (1963)

172. Yusa, A., *J. Protozool.*, **12**, 51–60 (1965)

YEAST GENETICS[1]

By Robert K. Mortimer

Division of Medical Physics, Donner Laboratory, University of California, Berkeley, California

AND

Donald C. Hawthorne

Department of Genetics, University of Washington, Seattle, Washington

Contents

Life Cycles.. 151
Recombination.. 152
Tetrad and random spore analysis; procedures........................ 152
Chromosome maps.. 153
Interference, chiasma, and chromatid................................ 153
Gene conversion, interallelic recombination.......................... 154
Mitotic segregation.. 154
Mutation.. 155
Techniques, induction, and mutant enrichment...................... 155
Spontaneous mutation.. 156
Induced mutation.. 156
Suppressors and suppressible mutations............................. 157
Mutant characterization.. 158
Resistance and morphological mutants.............................. 159
Gene Action.. 160
Gene-enzyme relationships.. 160
Regulation.. 161
Respiration-Deficient Mutants.. 162
Transformation.. 164

Two reviews by the pioneers of yeast genetics, Lindegren (1) and Winge & Roberts (2), cover the early literature and provide a full description of the life cycles of yeast. Since the appearance of the latter review, there has been a wide acceptance of yeast as an organism for genetic studies with a resultant extensive literature. We have not attempted a complete review of these publications. Rather, we have selected a portion of the literature for review with emphasis on the more recent reports.

Life Cycles

While a number of different yeasts have been used in genetic studies, i.e., *Hansenula wingeii* (3, 4), *Saccharomyces lactis* (5), *Saccharomyces fragilis* (6, 7), *Zygosaccharomyces dobzhanskii* (7), only two species, *Saccharomyces cerevisiae* and *Schizosaccharomyces pombe* have been subjected to extensive genetic analysis.

[1] The survey of the literature pertaining to this review was concluded in January 1966.

Schizosaccharomyces pombe normally has a haploid vegetative phase with only a transistory diploid state. The formation of the diploid zygote from two haploid cells is followed immediately by meiosis and sporulation. Both heterothallic and homothallic stocks are available. The mating type alleles, + and −, are allelic with a locus conferring homothallism and, in fact, a complex locus is indicated since homothallic segregants can be obtained by recombination of the + and − alleles (8).

The *Saccharomyces* interbreeding stock which, besides *Saccharomyces cerevisiae*, includes *S. carlsbergensis*, *S. chevalieri*, *S. chodati*, *S. diastaticus*, and *S. italicus*, is diploid in the vegetative phase (1). Meiosis and sporulation yield haploid spores. Unless individual spores are isolated they will fuse with their complementary neighbors to restore the diploid state. In heterothallic strains, single spore clones will remain haploid for many generations. However, diploid cell lines can arise from haploid cultures either through endomitosis or as a consequence of mutation of the mating type locus.

Rapid diploidization of haploid spore progeny is a characteristic of homothallic strains. This property was first shown to be under genetic control by the analysis of a hybrid formed from spores of heterothallic *S. cerevisiae* and homothallic *S. chevalieri* (2). These strains differ in a single gene, D, which controls diploidization and segregates independently of the mating type alleles a and α. Gene D is interpreted to behave as a "mutator gene" that causes mutation of the mating type gene to its complementary allele (9, 10). This effect may be in the nature of a regulatory mechanism since there is evidence that the mating type locus is a complex with cistrons for both a and α products (9, 11). Additional genes for homothallism have been isolated from other strains of *Saccharomyces* (12). In one case, the tetrad ratios of homothallism : heterothallism, i.e., 0:4, 1:3, and 2:2, suggested the presence of complementary genes controlling homothallism, with one of the genes closely linked to the α mating type allele (13).

As discussed above, genetic strains of yeast normally alternate between the haploid and diploid phases. However, polyploid strains can originate through a variety of events in the cell cycle (14). The deliberate construction of polyploids is possible and all stages of ploidy up to hexaploid have been obtained (15–17). The genotype of such polyploids can be confirmed by genetic analysis (15, 18, 19). Triploids have characteristically low spore viability (15, 17, 20). (Spore viability patterns and segregation ratios characteristic of triploids have been observed in the analysis of brewing yeast, 21, 22). Tetraploids, on the other hand, produce diploid spores with normal viability. Sets of tetraploid hybrids can be constructed that differ in the number of dominant genes for particular loci, and such sets have been used to estimate the effect of gene dosage in the production of galactokinase (23) and cytochrome c (24).

RECOMBINATION

Tetrad and random spore analysis; procedures.—Genetic analysis of both *Saccharomyces cerevisiae* and *Schizosaccharomyces pombe* is possible by either tetrad or random spore analysis. In the former, the isolation of tetrads has been facilitated by the use of enzymatic digestion of the ascus wall followed by micromanipulation (25). Random spore suspensions also have been prepared for this organism by a variety of procedures (21, 26, 27). Methods devised to disperse the spores and enrich them relative to the unsporulated diploid cells include sonication, phase-separation, and selective killing. With *S. pombe*, the procurement of random spore suspensions is simplified by virtue of properties of this yeast. Spores are released from the asci after incubation at low temperature and can be enriched by killing of parental cells with alcohol (28).

While four-spore asci normally are used in tetrad analysis, it is possible to use asci with only two or three spores and obtain normal segregation ratios among the spores (29, 30). This is particularly relevant in random spore studies of hybrids that yield incomplete asci. With most hybrids, spore viability is greater than 90 per cent. Low spore viability occasionally is encountered and can be explained by polysomy, triploidy, translocations, lethal mutations, or interactions between genes.

The extent of linkage of a gene with its centromere can be determined by three independent methods. As with *Neurospora*, sister spores, and hence centromere-linked genes, are arranged in characteristic patterns in linear asci, *AAaa* for *Schizosaccharomyces pombe*, and *AaAa* for *Saccharomyces cerevisiae* (31). The latter yeast, however, rarely yields linear asci, and centromere segregation is usually determined from the segregation of known centromere-linked genes deliberately included in the hybrid (32). Another method involves the use of tetraploid hybrids, for which the distribution of segregation ratios of a gene in duplex condition depends on its distance from the centromere (15, 17, 31, 33).

Chromosome maps.—Mapping of mutants in *S. cerevisiae* has progressed considerably and at present 14 linkage groups, each identified by an independently segregating centromere, are known (32, 34–37). Additional linkage groups might be expected since a recent cytological study has reported 18 bivalents in first meiotic metaphase (38). The chromosome maps now exceed 1300 centimorgans and contain approximately 100 genes. Mapping has been carried out primarily by tetrad analysis of diploid hybrids, although mitotic segregation and trisomic analysis have also been used to screen markers for location on particular chromosomes (34).

Interference, chiasma, and chromatid.—For exchanges in adjacent intervals on one side of the centromere, positive chiasma interference has been observed, while for exchange in intervals across the centromere no interference occurs (32). The relative frequencies of two-strand, three-strand, and four-strand double cross-overs have been determined for a number of adjacent intervals. Exceptions are more prevalent than agreements with the 1:2:1 ratios expected on conventional models of crossing-over, and are generally in the direction of a deficiency of three-strand exchanges or an excess of two-strand exchanges, or both (32, 39, 40).

A number of examples of preferential segregation of genes in different linkage groups have been reported (35, 41). The point of preferential segregation has been identified with the centromere. The mode of preferential segregation, whether involving parental or nonparental combinations, varies with the hybrid. One apparent example of preferential segregation in another study (32) can be explained by selective elimination of certain tetrads as a consequence of a chromosome structural alteration.

Gene conversion, interallelic recombination.—Deviations from the expected 2:2 segregation ratios are frequently encountered in tetrad analysis of yeast. Some of these irregular segregations can be explained through conventional genetic mechanisms, i.e., polyploidy, polysomy, multiple gene control (complementary or polymeric), mitotic recombination preceding meiosis, and suppressors. Even when these explanations do not apply, 3:1 and 1:3 ratios are found in the order of 1 per cent for most makers (42). These irregular segregations have been attributed to "gene conversion," first described in yeast by Lindegren (1). Two recent reviews deal specifically with this topic (42, 43).

Diploid hybrids that contain two noncomplementing mutant alleles at a locus have been used in many studies of gene conversion. Such heteroallelic diploids are found to revert to wild type at a much higher frequency than the corresponding homoallelic diploids (44–48). The revertant diploids generally are found to be heterozygous for one or the other input allele which suggests a nonreciprocal event, and only rarely is the double negative recovered (42, 48). The frequency of this heteroallelic reversion is increased by ultraviolet (49) or X rays (50). The sensitivity to X ray-induced heteroallelic reversion has been used as a measure of the distance between mutant alleles, and a detailed map of one locus has been determined in this manner (50, 51). Reversion in a diploid heteroallelic at a locus that confers both an adenine and histidine requirement is suppressed by the presence of histidine in the medium (52, 53).

Sporulation of heteroallelic diploids also greatly stimulates the production of revertants. The time dependence of the appearance of revertants in a culture undergoing sporulation suggests two separate events in heteroallelic recombination (54). From the frequency of revertant spores it is possible to construct fine structure maps (8, 28, 55–59). Irradiation of diploid cells prior to meiosis results in a large increase in the frequency of irregular segregation ratios in tetrads formed by the irradiated cells (11).

A copy-choice model of DNA replication has been proposed to explain the nonreciprocal recombination observed in heteroallelic diploids (45), and regular chromatid exchange can account for the reciprocal recombinants (8). A recent model of crossing-over which involves DNA synthesis predicts both reciprocal and nonreciprocal events (43).

Mitotic segregation.—Mitotic recombination can result in the segregation of genetic markers in vegetatively propagated diploid cells. This may result in sectored colonies, the size of the sector depending on the division at which mitotic segregation occurs. Ultraviolet (60–62) and X rays (63, 64) induce a relatively high frequency (up to 5 per cent)of mitotic segregation in the division immediately following treatment. Mitotic segregation also occurs spontaneously but at a frequency in the order of 10^{-5} to 10^{-4} per cell division (65).

Various mechanisms have been proposed for the segregation of genetic markers in vegetative cells, including mitotic crossing-over at the four-strand stage, crossing-over followed by meiotic centromere disjunction and restitution of diploidy, and mitotic nondisjunction (60, 62). For the first two of these mechanisms, reciprocal products are expected in opposite sectors. For nondisjunction, the negative sector may be monosomic. Genetic analyses of both sides of sectored colonies have shown them to be predominantly reciprocal, i.e., one side is homozygous dominant, the other homozygous recessive (60). Linked markers also tend to segregate together. An exception to these observations has been reported in which opposite sectors were not reciprocal (64). These results could be interpreted to be due either to deletion at the locus or to mitotic nondisjunction, and it is of interest that chromosome I, for which spontaneous aneuploids have been reported (32, 66), may be involved.

A critical observation that bears on the above mechanisms of mitotic segregation is the dependence of sectoring frequency of a gene on its distance from the centromere. Proximal genes have been reported to segregate less frequently than more distal ones in both spontaneous (65) and induced (60, 67) segregation, favoring conventional mitotic crossing-over. However, a lack of correlation between the frequency of ultraviolet-induced sectoring and centromere distance of a group of genes has been reported (62) which is more consistent with meiotic centromere disjunction, or nondisjunction. Failure to observe the expected magnitude of homozygosis of other markers argues against this interpretation (48), and the lack of correlation with centromere distance could be due to multiple crossing-over induced by the relatively high ultraviolet exposure used.

Coincidence of mitotic exchange of markers on different linkage groups is much higher than might be expected if exchanges were occurring randomly (67). This is evidence for a condition, possibly partial or complete synapsis, necessary for mitotic recombination that is present in only a portion of the cells.

MUTATION

Techniques, induction, and mutant enrichment.—While isolation of revertants or of resistance mutants is technically straightforward, the procurement of large numbers of yeast auxotrophs until recently has been difficult because of lack of suitable selection procedures. Mutants can be recovered by total isolation using replica plating although this procedure is relatively inefficient. A procedure for enriching for spontaneously arising adenine mutants has been described (57, 65). Certain adenine blocks in both *Saccharomyces cerevisiae* and *Schizosaccharomyces pombe* result in red-pigmented colonies. A second mutation at one of several other loci controlling earlier steps in the adenine biosynthetic pathway blocks the pigment formation and results in a white colony. In culture, the mutant white cells grow more rapidly than do the red cells, and are enriched. Procedures analogous to the penicillin technique for bacteria are available for the isolation of yeast mutants. Actidione (68, 69), nystatin (68), and deoxyglucose (70, 71) kill growing cells and can be used to enrich for all or particular classes of mutants in a treated population of cells. Allyl alcohol is toxic to yeast and provides a selective environment for alcohol dehydrogenase mutants which have a low affinity for this compound (72). The inhibition of inositol-less death by an additional nutritional block has been used to select for mutants in *S. pombe* (73).

Spontaneous mutation.—Our understanding of the molecular mechanism of spontaneous mutation in meiotic organisms has been advanced by recent studies with yeast. Certain yeast mutants revert more readily in meiosis than in mitosis and reversion of these mutants is associated with recombination of outside markers. These "meiotic effect" mutants are proposed to result from base addition or deletion changes and the reversion to arise through unequal crossing over that restores the normal reading frame. The meiotic effect is eliminated when the mutant allele is placed opposite a deletion, supporting the proposal that pairing and crossing-over is involved in reversion. Mutants known to be associated with base-pair substitution fail to show the meiotic effect (74–77).

Induced mutation.—There are relatively few reports of mutagenic action of base analogues on yeast. 2-6-Diaminopurine and 5-bromouracil act synergistically with ultraviolet but alone are relatively ineffective (69, 78). 5-Fluorouracil is an effective agent for inducing cytoplasmic petites (79, 80).

Acridine was shown to be mutagenic in yeast if applied during meiosis but to have an antimutagenic effect during mitosis. This effect is related to a requirement for pairing and recombination in reversion of reading-frame type mutants (81).

Nitrous acid has been shown to be an effective mutagen in yeast (82–87). Both sectored and whole mutant colonies are observed following treatment with this agent (86). The distribution of nitrous acid-induced mutants at two loci in *Schizosaccharomyces pombe* is different than that found for ultraviolet- or X ray-induced mutants (55, 88). The alkylating agent ethylmethanesulfonate has been used to obtain auxotrouphs in *Saccharomyces cerevisiae*. A relatively high percentage of unstable and leaky mutants was recovered (89). Mutants of the $ad_{5,7}$ locus of *S. cerevisiae* recovered following ethylmethanesulfonate ultraviolet treatment were compared with spontaneously arising mutants for interallelic complementation. The percentage of complementing mutants for ethylmethane and ultraviolet light was about 50 per cent, but only 8 per cent of the spontaneous mutants were in the complementing class (90, 91). Ultraviolet light is effective for inducing both forward and reverse mutation and has been used to obtain auxotrophs for a number of genetic studies in yeast (32, 34, 92).

A series of X ray-induced mutations affecting growth rate have been characterized for effect in haploids (93) and in heterozygotes (94). The expression of these mutations is modified by genetic background (95) and environment (96), and their relative frequencies depend on dose (97). Radiation-induced dominant and recessive lethals in yeast have been described (98–101). Various aspects of radiation genetics of yeast are included in a recent review (102).

Different mutagens have been compared for their abilities to induce reversion in auxotrophic strains of yeast. Considerable variation in mutagenicity of a series of alkylating agents was observed for reversion of an adenine auxotroph (103). The advantage of using a number of mutant alleles in such experiments is illustrated by another study in which a series of mutants at an adenine locus in *S. pombe* showed striking specificities with regard to reversion by ultraviolet or nitrous acid. Also, the extent of reversion by outside suppressors was allele- and mutagen-dependent (82). In this system, methionine was found to exert an antimutagenic effect (104, 105). Since reversion of an auxotroph may arise through a number of genetic changes which themselves may show mutagen specificity (82, 84), it is worthwhile to determine the mechanisms of reversion for each system studied. It has been demonstrated a number of times that suppressors are involved in reversion (63, 82, 84, 87, 103, 106–109). By studying reversion of mutant alleles that were present in homozygous condition in cells of different ploidy it was possible to distinguish between reversions caused by recessive suppressors and dominant suppressors or back mutation (110, 111). Reversions induced in yeast by ultraviolet or other radiations have been studied with respect to the comparative action of different radiations or modification of expression by different post-irradiation conditions (63, 87, 112–115).

Suppressors and suppressible mutations.—The suppressors obtained by selection of mutations to prototrophy may be classified as either locus- or allele-specific. The former class is presumed to include mutations which present alternate pathways to bypass the genetic block. The latter class of suppressors have, in general, proved to be super-suppressors which are effective in suppressing given alleles at many different loci (106).

Examples of locus-specific suppressors have been found for several of the mutants in the isoleucine-valine biosynthetic pathway in yeast. A mutational block which imposes only an isoleucine requirement (is_1) can be either completely alleviated by one suppressor or can be satisfied by threonine when another suppressor is present (108). From isoleucine-valine mutants, is_2, is_3, and is_5, suppressors which alleviate only one of the requirements can be obtained (83). With is_2 and is_3 stocks, the "half-revertants" are isoleucine-dependent. The is_5 "half-revertants" are valine-dependent. Another case of a half-revertant has been described for the ad_3 mutation which imposes both a histidine and an adenine requirement. The revertant strain is histidine independent (87).

The allele-specific super-suppressors are analogous to the amber suppressors in *Escherichia coli* and its bacteriophages. The super-suppressors act upon a wide variety of mutant phenotypes: amino acid, purine, and pyrimidine requirements, and fermentation and respiratory deficiencies. The suppressible mutants are ubiquitous, both in their occurrence throughout the genome and at sites within a given gene (51,106). The suppressible alleles, for the most part, are found in the noncomplementing class of alleles at a given locus. The few suppressible alleles that do participate in intragenic complementation have a polarized complementation pattern. They complement only mutants toward one side in the fine structure map of the locus. Thus, no two suppressible alleles are found to complement each other. The above observations on the super-suppressible mutants are consistent with the interpretation applied to the amber mutants and suppressors—i.e., these mutants have as a common defect a nonsense codon which causes the termination of the polypeptide chain by an interruption of translation. The suppressors causes translation of the nonsense codon and synthesis of the complete polypeptide chain.

In some strains, a super-suppressor failed to act on known suppressible alleles. This property which renders the suppressor inactive segregated as a cytoplasmically-determined trait, which suggests a self-replicating cytoplasmic system in suppression (116).

Mutant characterization.—A corollary of problems of intra-allelic recombination or mutagenesis involving the selection of prototrophs is the classification of the available alleles with respect to the nature of the defect in the DNA in terms of changes that lead to mis-sense codons, nonsense codons, reading-frame shifts, and gross deletions or other irreparable aberrations. While the mutants with reading-frame shifts can only be detected in the course of reversion trials by the 'meiotic effect' (77), it is often expedient to first test the available alleles for properties characteristic of mis-sense and nonsense mutants. Super-suppressible alleles appear to be mutants in the latter category and it is our experience that they can be expected to occur at every locus at a frequency of about one in four for ultraviolet-derived material (51,106). The properties associated with mis-sense mutants are temperature sensitivity, osmotic remediability (see below), and ability to complement other mutants within the locus (if one is dealing with a locus where inter-allelic complementation occurs). Although loci showing interallelic complementation are not uncommon in *Saccharomyces*, complementation data are available for only two loci, tr_5 (51), and $ad_{5,7}$ (90,91). A similar situation applies for *Schizosaccharomyces pombe*, in which, again, two loci have been studied in this respect, ad_6 (56, 88) and ad_8 (58).

The designation "osmotic remedial" has been suggested for a type of conditional auxotrophic mutant which will grow without the usual supplement when the osmotic pressure of the minimal medium is raised by the addition of KCl or organic solutes such as sorbitol or diethyleneglycol (117). About one in seven (36/231) of the nutritional mutants of *Saccharomyces* have this property. Many of the osmotic-remedial mutants could also be classified as temperature-sensitive, and still others showed an interdependence of temperature and osmotic pressure in providing optimum conditions for growth. Osmotic remedial mutants at loci where complementation occurs are nearly always found in the complementing class of alleles. From these coincidences with the properties of temperature sensitivity and intragenic complementation, it has been argued that the osmotic remedial mutants represent mis-sense mutants which cause an abnormally folded protein as a consequence of a single amino acid substitution.

Resistance and morphological mutants.—The analogue of arginine, canavanine, inhibits the growth of yeast. Recessive mutations that confer resistance to this agent can be isolated (118), and appear to be the result of inactivation of a gene that produces a permease for arginine (119). Certain ethionine-resistant mutants are affected in a relatively nonspecific fashion in their ability to accumulate amino acids (120). Another general amino acid permease system in yeast has been characterized. Mutation at a single locus decreases the permease activity and confers resistance to several amino acids analogues.(121). The fungicide, actidione, irreversibly inhibits the growth of yeast at levels of 0.5 ppm. Mutations, both dominant and recessive, that permit growth at levels from 2 to 20 ppm are found at eight genetic loci (34, 122, 123), and certain combinations of these confer resistance to 1000 ppm (123). Analogues of actidione are equivalent to actidione with regard to the relative response of different mutants (124). A mutant resistant to 2-deoxyglucose was found to be partially deficient in hexokinase and unable to utilize glucose (71). Resistance to allyl alcohol has been associated with mutation of a locus controlling alcohol dehydrogenase synthesis (72). Four genes are involved in resistance of yeast to 5-fluorouracil. One of these is linked to a structural gene in the uracil pathway (80, 125). Mutations that confer resistance to relatively high levels of copper have been studied (32, 35, 126). Cells grown on copper-containing medium may develop a brown pigment that is associated with excessive production of hydrogen sulfide, but this is not a requisite of copper resistance (127). Resistance genes for a variety of additional chemical agents including cadmium (128), lithium (129), Roccal (34), and other compounds (39) have been utilized as genetic markers in studies on recombination. Those genes that confer resistance in a recessive fashion are particularly useful to select changes from a heterozygous to homozygous or hemizygous condition. They have been used in mitotic segregation studies (130) and for selection of haploid spores from a mixture of spores and parental diploid cells (54).

A variety of mutagenic agents induce mutations that decrease the sensitivity of yeast to ionizing radiations. The mutations are recessive and occur at a number of loci. The frequency of such mutants among survivors can be as high as 80 per cent. One of the possible explanations offered is that the loci involved in determining radioresistance regulate repair processes in the cells (85).

Mutants of yeast that affect colony morphology are relatively rare and have been limited to the genes in the adenine (44, 65) or lysine (131) pathways that control pigment formation, or to genic petites (132). Another class of colony variants is obtained after prolonged culture of cells on lactic acid or ethanol. These "smooth colony" mutants are also characterized by more rapid growth on lactate and can arise by mutation at a minimum of seven loci (133, 134).

GENE ACTION

Gene-enzyme relationships.—Approximately fifty genetic loci in *Saccharomyces* have been identified with particular enzymatic steps. Relatively complete determination of the gene-enzyme relationships for the synthetic pathways of histidine (135), uracil (136, 137), tryptophan (51, 109, 138), homoserine (139), and isoleucine-valine (140), and for the utilization of galactose (141, 142), have been presented. In addition, some of the enzymes involved in the synthesis of adenine (143, 144), arginine (137, 145), glutamic acid (146, 147), lysine (148, 149), methionine (139, 150), and tryosine and phenylalanine (151) have been identified with particular genes. Also determined are gene-enzyme relationships for steps in the adenine (8, 56, 58, 143) and uracil (152) pathways of *Schizosaccharomyces pombe*. There are at least 13 genes derived from various *Saccharomyces* species which control the fermentation of α-glucosides (92, 153–158). Some of these can be distinguished by the phenotype of the intact cells in response to maltose, α-methylglucoside, isomaltose, and melezitose. However, a comparison of the α-glucosidases from six strains with different maltose genes showed that they were similar in all the properties investigated: substrate specificity, heat inactivation, antiserum inactivation, and chromatographic separation (159).

In yeast, as in *Neurospora*, the genes controlling the consecutive steps of a biosynthetic pathway generally are not linked. There are only a few cases of clustering of functionally related genes reminiscent of the operons in *E. coli* and *Salmonella*. The five genes controlling the synthesis of tryptophan from chorismic acid are unlinked (34); the first and fourth reactions in this pathway are catalyzed by an aggregate of the products of two of the genes (138). Seven of the ten histidine pathway enzymes are controlled by independently segregating genes. The remaining enzymes in this pathway are formed by a set of three cistrons located at an eighth locus (34, 135). Four of the five isoleucine and isoleucine-valine genes can be associated with enzymes, but the fifth mutant gives extracts which have all of the individual activities. It is postulated that this gene is concerned with the organization of the enzymes on a particle (140). The four known reactions between glutamic acid and homoserine have been identified with four independently segregating genes (139). There are at least ten genes involved in the synthesis of lysine (92). Thus far, only five have been genetically mapped and they are unlinked (34). Two genes, ly_9 and ly_1, have been identified with the terminal steps in lysine biosynthesis controlling the synthesis of saccharopine reductase and saccharopine dehydrogenase, respectively (148). Cultures carrying the ly_9 block develop a yellow pigment, presumably due to the accumulation of a precursor of lysine (131). Two other genes have a double requirement for lysine and glutamic acid and also segregate as genetic petites. One of these has been shown to lack aconitate hydratase that controls the synthesis of alpha-keto glutarate in the Krebs cycle. Another gene also lacks this enzyme but requires only glutamic acid (146, 147). The biosynthesis of arginine in *Saccharomyces* has been studied extensively (137, 145, 160–162). Mutants responsible for the enzymes N-α-acetyl-ornithinase (145), ornithine transcarbamylase (137), and carbamoyl phosphate synthetase have been identified (137). Four genes are known for the enzymes in the uracil pathway after carbamoyl phosphate (136).

Regulation.—The mechanisms regulating enzymatically controlled reactions in yeast appear to parallel those observed in other organisms. The arginine and uracil pathways have been studied extensively in this regard. Carbamoyl phosphate, a precursor of both arginine and uracil, in *Saccharomyces* is synthesized separately by genes specific for each of these pathways. Uracil and uridine triphosphate strongly inhibit the activity of the enzyme specific for the pyrimidine pathways. This feedback control is eliminated in certain mutants selected for resistance to 5-fluorouracil. Arginine causes only a slight inhibition of the arginine-specific carbamoyl phosphate synthetase activity (137, 163). Enzymes that are responsible for subsequent steps in pyrimidine synthesis are inducible by precursors in this pathway (136). At least two of the steps in ornithine synthesis are repressible by arginine (145, 162) and the enzyme that couples ornithine and carbamoyl phosphate, ornithine transcarbamylase, is subject to both feedback inhibition by arginine (164) and control by a regulator gene (161). Evidence for a specific binding protein involved in the regulation of this enzyme has been presented (160). Another example of regulation in a branched pathway is that presented for threonine and methionine synthesis. Three steps between aspartate and homoserine are common for the two biosynthetic pathways and threonine represses the activity of the first enzyme, methionine that of the third (139).

The regulation and linkage relationships of the genes involved in galactose utilization have several of the aspects of the operon model. The genes ga_1, ga_7, and ga_{10}, for the first three enzymes in the Leloir pathway, galactokinase, transferase, and epimerase, are closely linked (141). These enzymes are induced simultaneously when the wild-type yeast is exposed to galactose (165). An unlinked recessive mutation, i^-, causes the constitutive synthesis of these enzymes, (166). However, no definitive operator mutant linked to the structural genes has been found. Instead, the 0^0 phenotype, the abolition of all three activities, is obtained by a mutation, ga_4, of another unlinked gene (141).

The study of another inducible enzyme system, the respiratory system, has led to a novel model of regulation (24). Two physiologically similar cytochrome c species, iso-1 and iso-2, are found in a ratio of about 10:1 in fully grown aerobic cultures. However, if the kinetics of their synthesis during adaption to aerobic growth is followed, it is seen that the minor species, iso-2 cytochrome c, appears first. It is proposed that the polypeptide chain of iso-2 cytochrome c, without the heme group, may function as a repressor of the synthesis of iso-1 cytochrome c. The addition of the heme group to the polypeptide to form the iso-2 molecule relieves this repression and permits the synthesis of iso-1 cytochrome c. Further evidence on the sequential induction of the cytochromes was obtained in studies on glucose repression of cytochrome a synthesis in various "cy" mutants which control levels of cytochrome c in aerobic cultures (167).

RESPIRATION–DEFICIENT MUTANTS

Respiratory-deficient variants of *Saccharomyces*, the small colony or "petite" strains, as defined by their inability to utilize nonfermentable carbon sources for growth, may be classified as vegetative (cytoplasmic) petites or segregational (genic) petites (132, 168). All of the vegetative petites are characterized by a loss of a galaxy of enzymatic activities. For the most part, the segregational petites mimic this phenotype. However, low temperature spectrophotometry has revealed differences in cytochrome content among the various genic petites and even between some vegetative petites (169).

The evidence for the cytoplasmic factor in the inheritance of respiratory sufficiency has been documented by Ephrussi (168). Briefly, the observations were that crosses of petite by grande (respiratory-sufficient) haploids gave grande diploids which, when sporulated, yielded only grande progeny. Subsequent studies with crosses involving vegetative petites showed that this was atypical. Generally, petite by grande crosses give a high proportion of petite diploid clones. It was proposed that the normal cytoplasmic factor was supplanted or suppressed by the defective factor from the petite (170). The petite clones which behaved this way were termed suppressive petites as opposed to the neutral petites, the original class of petites.

Given petite isolates can be characterized as to their degree of suppressiveness (171). This can range from 0 for neutral petites to nearly 100 for the highly suppressive petites. Strains with intermediate values have been investigated to see if they were composed of a mixture of highly suppressive and neutral petites or were homogeneous with the intermediate degree of suppressiveness reflecting the probability the particular defective factor will prevail in descendants from petite by grande zygotes. The latter interpretation was favored by subcloning experiments which showed a strong mother-daughter correlation (172).

Since the various enzyme activities which are missing in the petite are associated with the mitochondria in yeast as well as in higher organisms it was natural to equate the cytoplasmic factor with the mitochondria (168, 173). However, the loss of the cytoplasmic factor in the vegetative petites does not mean the loss of the mitochondria; they are found in petite strains, albeit deformed, as revealed by electron microscopy (174). The mitochondrial fraction isolated from the vegetative petites lacks the cytochromes a, a_3, and b, as expected, but has much less cytochrome c activity than expected on the basis of the spectrophotometry of the intact cells (175, 176).

Cytochemical investigations of petites, "near-petites," and wild-type strains for cytochrome oxidase and succinic dehydrogenase activities have shown that different mitochondrial populations can persist in the same cell (177, 178). Of particular interest were the near-petites, isolated after acriflavine treatment and scored as petite by the tetrazolium assay, but still respiratory-sufficient. These variants had reduced numbers of cytochrome oxidase-positive mitochondria and generally more succinic dehydrogenase positive ones. The classical petite strains have no cytochrome oxidase-positive mitochondria, and the number of succinic dehydrogenase-positive mitochondria is the same as that of the wild type.

Vegetative petites occur spontaneously at rates much higher than those expected of gene mutations. A wholesale induction of petites occurs in cultures subjected to various treatments. An essential feature of these treatments is to provide conditions which permit the growth of the culture. Chemicals that can be used for petite induction, include acriflavine and its derivatives, tetrazolium chloride, actidione, caffeine, copper sulfate, manganese chloride, and 5-fluorouracil (79, 80, 179). Acriflavine treatment is particularly useful since essentially 100 per cent of new buds are petite concentrations that cause no detectable killing (180). Growth at elevated or reduced temperatures also is a highly efficient means of producing petite cells (181, 182), and could be used in place of the acriflavine treatment to distinguish between the mother cells and the progeny (183).

Irradiation with ultraviolet light is another means of inducing vegetative petites. Experiments with monochromatic light have implicated a nucleic acid in this process (184, 185). Reports that this process of ultraviolet induction is sensitive to photoreactivation support this conclusion (186, 187). A comparison of the ultraviolet dosage curves for the induction of petites in anerobically and aerobically grown haploid cultures indicates that a single hit suffices in the former while multiple events are required with the latter (185). The above observations are still consistent with the interpretation that the mitochondria are the targets since DNA has been found in these organelles (188, 189).

At least 15 different genes with the petite phenotype have been reported (34, 132, 167, 176), and one expects many more since there have been few repeats. Some of the genes are pleiotropic and cause requirements for lysine and glutamic acid in addition to the respiratory block. Strains with the lysine mutations ly_6 and ly_8 have been shown to be lacking the cytoplasmic factor (132). Other genic petites, p_3 and p_{12}, also fail to complement neutral petites and form grande zygotes, indicating absence of the cytoplasmic factor. Most mutant strains maintain the cytoplasmic factor although in only a fraction of the cells of a population. The genic petite strains have also been characterized for suppressiveness, but unless they lacked the cytoplasmic factor they were not suppressive (171). Differences in cytochrome content and in levels of the associated enzyme activities have been demonstrated for several of the mutants (169. 176).

A relationship between the cytoplasmic factor and given petite genes has been demonstrated by a study of the onset of respiration in synchronized populations of zygotes from crosses of genic petites p_1, p_5, and p_7 and a neutral vegetative petite (190). Each cross gives a characteristic lag, 0.5 hour (p_5), 4.8 hour (p_7), and 9.7 hour (p_1). When two genic petites are crossed, the lag observed is that of the parent with the shortest lag. Thus, the gene mutation influences the physiological state of the associated cytoplasmic factor.

Besides the genic petites there is a class of respiratory mutants which affects the production of cytochrome c (24, 191). A structural gene cy_1, for the major iso-1-cytochrome c has been identified and five other genes, cy_2 to cy_6, have been found which reduce the levels of both iso-1-cytochrome c and iso-2-cytochrome c. Spectroscopic screening was used in the detection of these mutants since most are able to grow on nonfermentable substances.

TRANSFORMATION

There has been a report on the transformation of yeast cells grown in nutrient medium containing DNA fractions from a donor strain (192, 193). However, this work is subject to other interpretations and efforts by others to repeat it have not been successful (194, 195). In another attempt at transformation, protoplasts of the recipient cells were used but without success (Roman and Friis, personal communication). The rationale behind the use of protoplasts was to eliminate the thick cell wall as a possible barrier of the transfer of DNA. Spheroplasts were used as recipients in the transformation of vegetative petites to the grande phenotype by mitochondrial preparations from respiratory-sufficient cells (196). However, the assessment of this experiment is difficult because of inadequate controls.

LITERATURE CITED

1. Lindegren, C. C., *The Yeast Cell, Its Genetics and Cytology.* (Educational Publ., Inc., St. Louis, Mo., 1949)
2. Winge, O., and Roberts, C., in *Chemistry and Biology of Yeasts*, 123–56. (Cook, A. H., Ed., Academic Press, New York, 763 pp., 1958)
3. Wickerham, L. J., *Compt. Rend. Trav. Lab. Carlsberg*, 26, 423–43 (1956)
4. Brock, T. D., *J. Bacteriol.*, 78, 59–68 (1959)
5. Wickerman, L. J., and Burton, K. A., *J. Bacteriol.*, 71, 290–95 (1956)
6. Gorman, J., Taruo, P., LaBerge, M., and Halvorson, H. O., *Biochem. Biophys. Res. Commun.*, 15, 43–49 (1964)
7. Wickerham, L. J., and Burton, K. A., *J. Bacteriol.*, 71, 296–302 (1956)
8. Leupold, U., *Cold Spring Harbor Symp. Quant. Biol.*, 23, 161–70 (1958)
9. Hawthorne, D. C., *Genetics*, 48, 1727–29 (1963)
10. Oeser, H., *Arch. Mikrobiol.*, 44, 47–74 (1962)
11. Takahashi, T., *Bull. Brewing Sci.*, 10, 11–22 (1964)
12. Takahashi, T., Saito, H., and Ikeda, Y., *Genetics*, 43, 251–60 (1958)
13. Takahashi, T., *Genetics*, 43, 705–14 (1958)
14. Roman, H., in Recent Progress Microbiology. *Symp. Intern. Congr. Microbiol.*, *8th, Montreal, 1962,* 306–12. (Univ. of Toronto Press, Toronto, Canada, 1961)
15. Roman, H., Phillips, M. M., and Sands, S. M., *Genetics*, 40, 546–61 (1955)
16. Laskowski, W., *Z. Naturforsch.*, 15b, 495–506 (1960)

17. Mortimer, R. K., *Radiation Res.*, **9**, 312–26 (1958)
18. Leupold, U., *J. Genet.*, **54**, 411–26 (1956)
19. Leupold, U., *J. Genet.*, **54**, 427–39 (1956)
20. Takahashi, T., *Japan J. Genet.*, **34**, 392–400 (1959)
21. Emeis, C. C., and Windisch, S., *Z. Naturforsch.*, **15b**, 702–6 (1960)
22. Johnston, J. R., in *European Brewery Conv.*, *Brussels*, *1963*, 412–21. (Elsevier Publ. Co., Amsterdam, 1964)
23. Nelson, N. M., and Douglas, H. C., *Genetics*, **48**, 1585–91 (1963)
24. Slonimski, P. P., Acher, R., Péré, G., Sels, A., and Somlo, M., in *Mécanismes de Régulation des Activités Cellulaires chez les Microorganismes*, No. 124, 435–61. (Eds. Centre Natl. Rech. Sci., Paris, 1965)
25. Johnston, J. R., and Mortimer, R. K., *J. Bacteriol.*, **78**, 272 (1959)
26. Emeis, C. C., and Gutz, H., *Z. Naturforsch.*, **13b**, 647–50 (1958)
27. Zakharov, I. A., and Inge-Vechtomov, S. G., *Issled. Genet., Leningr. Univ.*, **2**, 134–39 (1964)
28. Leupold, U., *Allgem. Pathol. Bakteriol.*, **20**, 535–44 (1957)
29. Takahashi, T., *Bull. Brewing Sci.*, **8**, 1–9 (1962)
30. Takahashi, T., and Akamatsu, K., *Seiken Zihô*, **15**, 54–58 (1963)
31. Hawthorne, D. C., *Genetics*, **40**, 511–18 (1955)
32. Hawthorne, D. C., and Mortimer, R. K., *Genetics*, **45**, 1085–1110 (1960)
33. Leupold, U., *Compt. Rend. Trav. Lab. Carlsberg, Ser. Physiol.*, **26**, 221–50 (1956)
34. Mortimer, R. K., and Hawthorne, D. C., *Genetics*, **53**, 165–73 (1966)
35. Lindegren, C. C., Lindegren, G., Shult, E., and Hwang, Y. L., *Nature*, **194**, 260–65 (1962)
36. Hwang, Y. L., Lindegren, G., and Lindegren, C. C., *Can. J. Genet. Cytol.*, **5**, 290–98 (1963)
37. Hwang, Y. L., Lindegren, G., and Lindegren, C. C., *Can. J. Genet. Cytol.*, **6**, 373–80 (1964)
38. Tamaki, H., *J. Gen. Microbiol.*, **41**, 93–98 (1965)
39. Desborough, S., Shult, E. E., Yoshida, T., and Lindegren, C. C., *Genetics*, **45**, 1467–80 (1960)
40. Desborough, S., and Shult, E. E., *Genetica*, **33**, 69–78 (1962)
41. Shult, E. E., Desborough, S., and Lindegren, C., *Genet. Res.*, **3**, 196–209 (1962)
42. Roman, H., in *Methodology in Basic Genetics*, 209–27. (Burdette, W. J., Ed., Holden Day, San Francisco, 1963)
43. Holliday, R., *Genet. Res.*, **5**, 282–304 (1964)
44. Roman, H., *Cold Spring Harbor Symp. Quant. Biol.*, **21**, 175–85 (1956)
45. Roman, H., *Ann. Genet.*, **1**, 11–17 (1958)
46. Roman, H., and Jacob, F., *Cold Spring Harbor Symp. Quant. Biol.*, **23**, 155–60 (1958)
47. Kakar, S. N., *Genetics*, **48**, 957–66 (1963)
48. Hurst, D. D., and Fogel, S., *Genetics*, **50**, 435–58 (1964)
49. Roman, H., and Jacob, F., *Compt. Rend.*, **245**, 1032–34 (1957)
50. Manney, T. R., and Mortimer, R. K., *Science*, **143**, 581–83 (1964)
51. Manney, T. R., *Genetics*, **50**, 109–21 (1964)
52. Clavilier, L., Luzzati, M., and Slonimski, P. P., *Compt. Rend. Soc. Biol.*, **154**, 1970–74 (1960)
53. Luzzati, M. M., Clavilier, L., and Slonimski, P. P., *Compt. Rend.*, **249**, 1412–14 (1959)
54. Sherman, F., and Roman, H., *Genetics*, **48**, 255–61 (1963)
55. Gutz, H., *Nature*, **191**, 1124–25 (1961)
56. Leupold, U., *Arch. Julius Klaus-Stift. Vererbungsforsch. Sozialanthropol. Rassenhyg.*, **36**, 89–117 (1961)
57. Leupold, U., *Arch. Julius Klaus-Stift. Vererbungsforsch. Sozialanthropol. Rassenhyg.*, **30**, 506–16 (1955)
58. Megnet, R., and Giles, N. H., *Genetics*, **50**, 967–71 (1964)
59. Clarke, C. H., *Experientia*, **21**, 582–83 (1965)
60. James, A. P., and Lee-Whiting, B., *Genetics*, **40**, 826–31 (1955)
61. Parry, J. M., and Cox, B. S., *J. Gen. Microbiol.*, **40**, 235–41 (1965)
62. Wilkie, D., and Lewis, D., *Genetics*, **48**, 1701–16 (1963)
63. Mortimer, R. K., Brustad, T., and Cormack, D. V., *Radiation Res.*, **26**, 465–82 (1965)
64. Yamasaki, T., Ito, T., and Matsudaira, Y., *Japan. J. Genet*, **39**, 147–50 (1964)
65. Roman, H., *Compt. Rend. Trav. Lab. Carlsberg. Ser. Physiol.*, **26**, 299–314 (1956)
66. Cox, B. S., and Bevan, E. A., *New Phytologist*, **61**, 342–55 (1962)

67. Fogel, S., and Hurst, D. D., *Genetics*, 48, 321–28 (1963)
68. Moat, A. G., Peters, N., Jr., and Srb, A. M., *J. Bacteriol.*, 77, 673–77 (1959)
69. Pittman, D., Shult, E., Roshanmanesh, A., and Lindegren, C., *Can. J. Microbiol.*, 9, 103–9 (1963)
70. Megnet, R., *Mutation Res.*, 2, 328–31 (1965)
71. Megnet, R., *J. Bacteriol.*, 90, 1032–35 (1965)
72. Megnet, R., *Pathol. Microbiol.*, 28, 50–57 (1965)
73. Megnet, R., *Experientia*, 20, 320 (1964)
74. Magni, G. E., and von Borstel, R. C., *Genetics*, 47, 1097–1108 (1962)
75. Magni, G. E., *Proc. Natl. Acad. Sci. U.S.*, 50, 975–80 (1963)
76. Magni, G. E., *J. Cellular Comp. Physiol.*, 64, Suppl. 1, 165–72 (1964)
77. Magni, G. E., *Atti Assoc. Genet. Ital.*, *Pavia*, 10, 3–26 (1965)
78. Takahashi, T., and Shinmyo, A., *Bull. Brewing Sci.*, 10, 79–80 (1964)
79. Moustacchi, E., and Marcovich, H., *Compt. Rend.*, 256, 5646–48 (1963)
80. Lacroute, F., *Compt. Rend.*, 257, 4213–16 (1963)
81. Magni, G. E., von Borstel, R. C., and Sora, S., *Mutation Res.*, 1, 227–30 (1964)
82. Clarke, C. H., *Genet. Res.*, 6, 433–41 (1965)
83. Kakar, S. N., Zimmermann, F., and Wagner, R. P., *Mutation Res.*, 1, 381–86 (1964)
84. Loprieno, N., and Clarke, C. H., *Mutation Res.*, 2, 312–19 (1965)
85. Moustacchi, E., *Mutation Res.*, 2, 403–12 (1965)
86. Nasim, A., and Clarke, C. H., *Mutation Res.*, 2, 395–402 (1965)
87. Zimmermann, F. K., and Schwaier, R., *Z. Vererbungslehre*, 94, 253–60 (1963)
88. Leupold, U., and Gutz, H., in Genetics Today, *Proc. Intern. Congr. Genet.*, *10th, The Hague*, 31–35. (Geerts, S. J., Ed., Pergamon Press, London, 1965)
89. Lindegren, G., Hwang, Y. L., Oshima, Y., and Lindegren, C. C., *Can. J. Genet. Cytol.*, 7, 491–99 (1965)
90. Costello, W. P., and Bevan, E. A., *Genetics*, 50, 1219–30 (1964)
91. Dorfman, B., *Genetics*, 50, 1231–43 (1964)
92. Carbondale Yeast Genetics Conference, *Microbial Genet. Bull.*, 19 (Suppl.) (1963)
93. James, A. P., *Genetics*, 44, 1309–24 (1959)
94. James, A. P., *Genetics*, 45, 1627–48 (1960)
95. Müller, I., and James, A. P., *Genetics*, 46, 1721–33 (1961)
96. Kivi, E. I., and James, A. P., *Hereditas* 48, 247–63 (1963)
97. James, A. P., MacNutt, M. M., and Morse, P. M., *Genetics*, 52, 21–29 (1965)
98. Laskowski, W., and Haefner, K., *Biophysik*, 1, 407–12 (1964)
99. Laskowski, W., and Haefner, K., *Nature*, 200, 795–96 (1963)
100. Mortimer, R. K., *Brookhaven Symp. Biol.*, 14, 62–75 (1961)
101. Owen, M. E., and Mortimer, R. K., *Nature*, 177, 625–26 (1956)
102. James, A. P., and Werner, M. M., *Radiation Botany*, 5, 359–82 (1965)
103. Marquardt, H., Zimmermann, F. K., and Schwaier, R., *Z. Verebungslehre*, 95, 82–96 (1964)
104. Clarke, C. H., *J. Gen. Microbiol.*, 31, 353–63 (1963)
105. Clarke, C. H., *J. Gen. Microbiol.*, 39, 21–31 (1965)
106. Hawthorne, D. C., and Mortimer, R. K., *Genetics*, 48, 617–20 (1963)
107. Inge-Vechtomov, S. G., *Vest. Leningr. Univ.*, *Ser. Biol.*, No. 9, 112–17 (1964)
108. Kakar, S. N., *Genetics*, 48, 967–79 (1963)
109. Parks, L. W., and Douglas, H. C., *Genetics*, 42, 283–88 (1957)
110. Haefner, K., *Biophysik*, 1, 413–17 (1964)
111. Haefner, K., *Z. Naturforsch.*, 19b, 451–55 (1964)
112. Haefner, K., and Laskowski, W., *Z. Naturforsch.*, 18b, 301–9 (1963)
113. Heslot, H., *Abhandl. Deut. Akad. Wiss. Berlin, Kl. Med.*, 1, 98–105 (1961)
114. Heslot, H., *Abhandl. Deut. Akad. Wiss. Berlin, Kl. Med.*, 1, 193–228 (1962)
115. Hrishi, N., and James, A. P., *Can. J. Genet. Cytol.*, 6, 357–63 (1964)
116. Cox, B. S., *Heredity*, 20, 505–21 (1965)
117. Hawthorne, D. C., and Friis, J., *Genetics*, 50, 829–39 (1964)
118. Srb, A. M., *Compt. Rend. Trav. Lab. Carlsberg*, 26, 363–80 (1956)
119. Wiame, J. M., Bechet, J., Mousset, M., and De Deken-Grenson, M., *Arch. Intern. Physiol. Biochim.*, 70, 766–67 (1962)
120. Sorsoli, W. A., Spence, K. D., and

Parks, L. W., *J. Bacteriol.*, **88**, 20–24 (1964)

121. Surdin, Y., Sly, W., Sire, J., Bordes, A. M., and de Robichon-Szulmajster, H., *Biochim. Biophys. Acta*, **107**, 546–66 (1965)
122. Middlekauf, J. E., Hino, S., Yang, S. P., Lindegren, G., and Lindegren, C. C., *Genetics*, **42**, 66–71 (1957)
123. Wilkie, D., and Lee, B. K., *Genet. Res.* **6**, 130–38 (1965)
124. Lee, B. K., and Wilkie, D., *Nature*, **206**, 90–92 (1964)
125. Lacroute, F., and Slonimski, P. P., *Compt. Rend.*, **258**, 2172–74 (1964)
126. Seno, T., *Japan. J. Genet.*, **37**, 207–17 (1962)
127. Seno, T., *Mem. Coll. Sci.*, *Univ. Kyoto*, *Ser. B.*, **30**, 1–8 (1963)
128. Middlekauf, J. E., Hino, S., Yang, S. P., Lindegren, G., and Lindegren, C. C., *J. Bacteriol.*, **72**, 796–801 (1956)
129. Laskowski, W., *Genetics*, **41**, 98–106 (1956)
130. Holliday, R., *Genetics*, **50**, 323–35 (1964)
131. Bhattacharjee, J. K., and Lindegren, G., *Biochem. Biophys. Res. Commun.*, **17**, 554–58 (1964)
132. Sherman, F., *Genetics*, **48**, 375–85 (1963)
133. Galzy, P., *Heredity*, **19**, 731–33 (1964)
134. Galzy, P., and Bizeau, C., *Heredity*, **20**, 31–36 (1965)
135. Fink, G. R., *Science*, **146**, 525–27 (1964)
136. Lacroute, F., *Compt. Rend.*, **258**, 2884–86 (1964)
137. Lacroute, F., Pierard, A., Grenson, M., and Wiame, J. M., *J. Gen. Microbiol.*, **40**, 127–42 (1965)
138. DeMoss, J. A., *Biochem. Biophys. Res. Commun.*, **18**, 850–57 (1965)
139. de Robichon-Szulmajster, H., Surdin, Y., Karassevitch, Y., and Corrivaux, D., in *Mécanismes de Régulation des Activités Cellulaires chez les Microorganismes*, No. 124, 255–269. (Eds. Centre Natl. Rech. Sci., Paris, 1965)
140. Kakar, S. N., and Wagner, R. P., *Genetics*, **49**, 213–22 (1964)
141. Douglas, H. C., and Hawthorne, D. C., *Genetics*, **49**, 837–44 (1964)
142. Tsoi, A., and Douglas, H. C., *Biochim. Biophys. Acta*, **92**, 513–20 (1965)
143. Demain, A. L., *J. Bacteriol.*, **86**, 339–45 (1964)
144. Levinthal, M., Fogel, S., and Hurst, D., *Genetics*, **47**, 967 (1962) (Abstract)
145. De Deken, R. H., *Biochim. Biophys. Acta*, **78**, 606–16 (1963)
146. Ogur, M., Coker, L., and Ogur, S., *Biochem. Biophys. Res. Commun.*, **14**, 193–97 (1964)
147. Ogur, M., Roshanmanesh, A., and Ogur, S., *Science*, **147**, 1590 (1965)
148. Jones, E. E., and Broquist, H. P., *J. Biol. Chem.*, **240**, 2531–36 (1965)
149. Mattoon, J. R., and Haight, R. D., *J. Biol. Chem.*, **237**, 3486–90 (1962)
150. Pigg, C. J., Spence, K. D., and Parks, L. W., *Arch. Biochem. Biophys.*, **97**, 491–96 (1962)
151. Lingens, F., and Hellmann, H., *Z. Naturforsch.*, **13**, 462–63 (1958)
152. Megnet, R., *Arch. Julius Klaus-Stift. Vererbungsforsch. Sozialanthropol. Rassenhyg.*, **33**, 299–334 (1959)
153. Hawthorne, D. C., *Heredity*, **12**, 273–84 (1958)
154. Oeser, H., and Windisch, S., *Naturwissenschaften*, **51**, 122 (1964)
155. Ouchi, S., and Lindegren, C. C., *Can. J. Genet. Cytol.*, **5**, 257–67 (1963)
156. Oshima, Y., *J. Ferment. Technol.*, **38**, 521–31 (1960)
157. Takahashi, T., and Ikeda, Y., *Z. Vererbungslehre*, **90**, 66–73 (1959)
158. Terui, G., Okada, H., and Oshima, Y., *Technol. Rept. Osaka Univ.*, **9**, 237–59 (1959)
159. Halvorson, H. O., Winderman, S., and Gorman, J., *Biochim. Biophys. Acta*, **67**, 42–53 (1963)
160. Bechet, J., and Wiame, J. M., *Biochem. Biophys. Res. Commun.*, **21**, 226–34 (1965)
161. Bechet, J., Wiame, J. M., and Grenson, M., *Arch. Intern. Physiol. Biochim.*, **73**, 137–39 (1965)
162. De Deken, R. H., *Biochem. Biophys. Res.*, **8**, 462–66 (1962)
163. Lacroute, F., *Compt. Rend.*, **259**, 1357–59 (1964)
164. Bechet, J., Wiame, J. M., and De Deken-Grenson, M., *Arch. Intern. Physiol. Biochim.*, **70**, 564–65 (1962)
165. de Robichon-Szulmajster, H., *Science*, **127**, 28–29 (1958)
166. Douglas, H. C., and Pelroy, G., *Biochim. Biophys. Acta*, **68**, 155–56 (1963)
167. Reilly, C., and Sherman, F., *Biochim. Biophys. Acta*, **95**, 640–51 (1965)
168. Ephrussi, B., *Nucleo-Cytoplasmic Relations in Microorganisms*. (Clarendon Press, Oxford, 1953)

169. Sherman, F., and Slonimski, P. P., *Biochim. Biophys. Acta*, **90**, 1–15 (1964)

170. Ephrussi, B., Hottinguer, H., and Roman, H., *Proc. Natl. Acad. Sci. U.S.*, **41**, 1065–71 (1955)

171. Sherman, F., and Ephrussi, B., *Genetics*, **47**, 695–700 (1962)

172. Ephrussi, B., and Grandchamp, S., *Heredity*, **20**, 1–7 (1965)

173. Wilkie, D., *The Cytoplasm in Heredity*. (Methuen & Co., Ltd., London, 1964)

174. Yotsuyanagai, Y., *J. Ultrastruct. Res.*, **7**, 141–58 (1962)

175. Mahler, H. R., Mackler, B., Grandchamp, S., and Slonimski, P. P., *Biochemistry*, **3**, 668–77 (1964)

176. Mackler, B., Douglas, H. C., Will, S., Hawthorne, D. C., and Mahler, H. R., *Biochemistry*, **4**, 2016–20 (1965)

177. Avers, C. J., Pfeffer, C. R., and Rancourt, M. W., *J. Bacteriol.*, **90**, 481–94 (1965)

178. Avers, C. J., Rancourt, M. W., and Lin, F. H., *Proc. Natl. Acad. Sci. U.S.*, **54**, 527–34 (1965)

179. Nagai, S., Yanagashima, N., and Nagai, H., *Bacteriol. Rev.*, **25**, 404–26 (1961)

180. Marcovich, H., *Ann. Inst. Pasteur*, **85**, 443–52 (1953)

181. Sherman, F., *J. Cellular Comp. Physiol.*, **54**, 37–52 (1959)

182. Ogur, M., Ogur, S., and St. John, R., *Genetics*, **45**, 189–94 (1960)

183. James, A. P., *Can. J. Genet. Cytol.*, **3**, 128–34 (1961)

184. Raut, C., and Simpson, W. L., *Arch. Biochem. Biophys.*, **57**, 218–28 (1955)

185. Wilkie, D., *J. Mol. Biol.*, **7**, 527–33 (1963)

186. Sarachek, A., *Cytologia Tokyo*, **23**, 143–58 (1958)

187. Pittman, D., Ranganathan, B., and Wilson, F., *Exptl. Cell. Res.*, **17**, 368–77 (1959)

188. Mahler, H. R., and da Silva Pereira A., *J. Mol. Biol.*, **5**, 325–47 (1962)

189. Schatz, G., Haslbrunner. E., and Tuppy, H., *Biochem. Biophys. Res. Commun.*, **15**, 127–32 (1964)

190. Jakob, H., *Genetics*, **52**, 75–98 (1965)

191. Sherman, F., *Genetics*, **49**, 39–48 (1964)

192. Oppenoorth, W. F. F., *European Brewery Conv.*, **1961**, 172–204. (Elsevier Publ. Co., Amsterdam)

193. Oppenoorth, W. F. F., *Nature*, **193**, 706 (1962)

194. Harris, G., and Thompson, C. C., *Nature*, **188**, 1212–13 (1960)

195. Laskowski, W., and Lochmann, E. R., *Naturwissenschaften*, **48**, 225 (1961)

196. Tuppy, H., and Wildner, G., *Biochem. Biophys. Res. Commun.*, **20**, 733–38 (1965)

DEVELOPMENTAL CHANGES DURING THE FORMATION AND BREAKING OF THE DORMANT STATE IN BACTERIA[1,2,3]

By Harlyn O. Halvorson, James C. Vary, and William Steinberg

Department of Bacteriology, University of Wisconsin, Madison, Wisconsin

Contents

SPOROGENESIS.. 170
Metabolic Regulation.. 171
Transcriptional Products...................................... 172
Protein Synthesis... 173
 Changes in the spore-forming machinery...................... 173
 Synthesis of spore-specific components...................... 173
Morphological and Physiological Stages........................ 175
Genetic Control... 175
INITIATION OF GERMINATION...................................... 177
Multiplicity of Trigger Mechanisms............................ 177
Woese Hypothesis.. 178
The l-Alanine-Induced Trigger................................. 179
General Nature of the Initiator System........................ 179
OUTGROWTH.. 180
Absence of Stable mRNA in Spores.............................. 180
Development of Biosynthetic Capacity.......................... 181
 Protein-synthesizing system................................ 181
 Transcription and translation.............................. 181
Ordered Protein and Enzyme Synthesis.......................... 182
DNA Synthesis... 183
Relationship Between Transcription and DNA Replication........ 183

Dormant spores represent both an end point and a beginning in biology. The dormant spore has a specialized and complex structure whose formation results from a morphogenic change during vegetative growth. Under appropriate conditions the spore can germinate and synthesize the structures and macromolecules characteristic of vegetative cells, thereby beginning its life cycle anew.

[1] The survey of the literature pertaining to this review was concluded in December 1965.

[2] The following abbreviations are used: ALD (l-alanine dehydrogenase); NAD (nicotinamide-adenine dinucleotide); UDP (uridine diphosphate); UDPG (uridine diphosphate glucose).

[3] The preparation of this review was supported in part by grants from the Public Health Service (GM 265 and GM 12332).

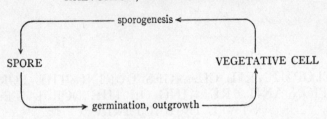

The return to vegetative growth involves two stages. First, following appropriate stimulation, the dormant state is rapidly broken by a series of degradative reactions collectively called "germination." The second stage, "outgrowth," is a period dependent upon the synthesis of new macromolecules, and the spore gradually develops into a vegetative cell. All of the events (genetic, morphological, biochemical, and physiological) leading to the conversion of a vegetative cell into a spore comprise the period of "sporogenesis." "Sporulation" involves only those stages of sporogenesis in which the synthesis and assembly of spore components takes place. These processes, sporogenesis, germination, and outgrowth, are examples of intracellular differentiation during which morphological and biochemical changes occur in response to appropriate environmental stimuli.

During the past 15 years, the primary interest in bacterial spores involved the development of techniques for preparing and isolating clean spores, comparing the chemical and physical properties of spores and vegetative cells, and examining the nature of dormancy. The emergence of the field from a strictly descriptive phase began about 1960 when it was realized that the biosynthetic events occurring during sporulation and outgrowth were ordered processes (1, 2), and with the demonstration that the ability to form spores can be restored by transformation in asporogenous mutants of *Bacillus subtilis* (3).

This review will not attempt to cover the broad field of interest in bacterial spores; many of these areas have been covered in recent reviews and symposia (1, 4–8). We shall deal mainly with the biochemical and genetic studies on sporogenesis, outgrowth, and the recent developments in our understanding of the trigger mechanism present in spores for initiating germination. For additional details of sporogenesis and, to some extent, of outgrowth, the reader is referred to several reviews (9–13). We shall assume that the reader has an understanding of the regulatory mechanisms functioning in microorganisms (14).

SPOROGENESIS

Early in sporogenesis, a compartmentalized cell is created (15). After the forespore septum is produced, the cell is divided into two compartments, one enclosing the developing "forespore" (primordial spore), the other the larger portion of the cell, the "sporangium." Biochemical studies on sporogenesis (protein turnover, mRNA synthesis, etc.) have not always distinguished between these two. Although each compartment receives half of the cellular DNA (16), the two are essentially different metabolic systems. Replication of the DNA in the forespore ceases, whereas in the sporangium, depending upon the strain of *Bacillus*, DNA replication may continue until lysis occurs. Vegetative components continue to be produced in the sporangium (17, 18), while in the forespore (see below) the products of biosynthesis are spore-specific.

METABOLIC REGULATION

Sporogenesis involves the function of a large number of spore genes. It is therefore not surprising that a large number of environmental factors affect the actual phenotypic expression. The optimum conditions for sporogenesis differ in each species from those required for vegetative growth (5, 7), and limitations in a variety of substances in the medium can initiate the process of sporogenesis (19). Such limitations are known to influence both the metabolism and regulatory systems of bacteria (13), but their role in initiating sporogenesis is unclear. Shifts in cellular metabolism (21), levels of intracellular metabolites (22), and extensive turnover of protein and RNA (17, 22–26) take place during spore formation. Schaeffer et al. (12) proposed that sporogenesis is controlled by the intracellular concentration of nitrogen-containing catabolite(s) which may affect the synthesis of a single spore-specific enzyme. A protease, repressed by amino acids (27, 28), has been a popular candidate for regulating sporogenesis (12, 25, 29, 30).

Although parallels between catabolic repression and sporogenesis exist (12, 20), it is presently difficult to make a careful analysis of the metabolic regulation of sporogenesis. However, several generalizations may be made on the overall effects of nutrients on spore formation. Sporogenesis is strongly influenced by the carbon and nitrogen sources available (5, 12, 19). Metabolizable nitrogen compounds, and glucose in the presence of an available supply of nitrogen, effectively repress sporogenesis. Rapidly metabolized carbon sources favor vegetative growth, whereas slowly metabolized carbon sources stimulate spore formation.

A specific factor for initiating sporogenesis has recently been described (31). During the initial phases of sporogenesis this small molecular weight factor is produced which permits the endotrophic spore formation of washed vegetative cells when transferred to mineral medium. The active principal, called "sporogen," has been crystallized (32). Its identification and the study of its mode of action is one of the most promising leads to an understanding of the regulation of sporogenesis. It will be of interest to determine whether there is any relationship between this factor and N-succinyl glutamic acid which is known to appear during sporogenesis and which stimulates sporulation in *B. subtilis* (33, 34).

There have been several attempts to obtain bacterial populations in which sporulation occurs in a synchronous manner (35). An improved technique for obtaining synchronous sporulation has recently been described (36). When germinated spores of *Bacillus cereus* (which had developed to the stage of elongation and initiated DNA synthesis) were transferred to a medium deficient in nutrients, new sporangia were formed without intermediate cell division and fully dormant spores matured in about 10 to 12 hours.

TRANSCRIPTIONAL PRODUCTS

The participation of many spore genes in the formation of the spore is evident from an examination of the products of transcription and translation. Sporogenesis is accompanied by extensive RNA and protein turnover (22–26, 37), and it is dependent upon new protein and RNA synthesis. If inhibitors of protein (15, 38–42), RNA (24, 25, 43, 44), or cell wall and cell membrane (40, 41, 43, 45) synthesis are added early in sporogenesis, macromolecular synthesis stops and spore formation is inhibited. From a consideration of turnover rates, it appears that the proteins which are incorporated into the spore are synthesized *de novo* (11, 22).

The formation of the spore can be considered as a process in which a number of specific genes, which are repressed during vegetative growth, are activated and new gene products appear. Molecular studies on the RNA formed during sporogenesis support this concept. Ribonucleic acid synthesis in sporulating cells is similar to that in exponentially growing cultures; all fractions of RNA, including stable (transfer RNA and ribosomal RNA) and labile (mRNA), are formed (24, 26, 43, 46). Interesting shifts in the ratios of RNA components during sporogenesis have been reported. Doi & Igarashi (47) noted that the ratio of tRNA to rRNA rose during this period, with tRNA reaching 30 per cent in the dormant spore. This shift is probably due to the fact that during spore formation the number of ribosomes and polysomes steadily declines (43), although some stable membrane-bound polysomes may survive (48). From prolonged RNA labeling experiments (9, 26, 43), ribosomal RNA turnover has been detected which may modify calculations of the quantity of mRNA from pulse-labeling and chase experiments.

The classes of mRNA formed during sporogenesis (in both the sporangium and prespore) differ in several respects from that produced during vegetative (step down) growth or during outgrowth from germinated cells. First, although the base compositions of rRNA and tRNA from vegetative cells and spores are identical, sporulation mRNA has a different ratio of bases from vegetative mRNA (49). Second, direct evidence for the transcription of the spore genome during sporogenesis was provided by Doi (49, 50) and Aronson (51), who employed competition experiments for RNA-DNA hybrid formation. Common gene products were observed in all RNA populations tested; however, competition was more complete in homologous RNA preparations. According to Doi (49, 50), the mRNA produced during sporulation is more complex than mRNA formed in vegetative cells or during outgrowth. That produced during outgrowth, which one would expect to resemble the transcriptional products of the vegetative genome, effectively competes for hybrid formation with vegetative but not sporulation mRNA. From similar competition experiments, sporulating cells were found to contain transcription products common to vegetative cells (in part possibly rRNA and sporangium mRNA) as well as mRNA specific to sporulation.

Aronson (51), in examining the mRNA population of sporulating cells, observed that it was less heterogeneous than in vegetative cultures. Competition experiments indicated that although the kinds of mRNA changed, a common fraction persisted throughout sporulation. In addition, the finding that actinomycin D, added late in sporulation, was not inhibitory to the completion of sporulation (44, 52) suggested that during sporogenesis long-lived messengers were produced. Since actinomycin D does inhibit sporulation when added during the period of active synthesis of spore proteins, these conclusions were questioned (53). Aronson (48) has recently re-examined this question following the discovery that a portion of the spore mRNA is found tightly bound to the cytoplasmic membrane. In cultures committed to sporogenesis, 20 per cent of the hybridizable pulse-labeled RNA persists after chasing and this is present almost exclusively in the membrane fraction as polysomes which survive in the presence of actinomycin D. In hybridization experiments, this fraction does not compete with rRNA. Aronson suggested the interesting possibility that this stable mRNA may function in the synthesis of spore coat proteins.

Protein Synthesis

Sporogenesis, in cells of *Bacillus* (11) and *Clostridium* (54), is accompanied by major shifts in both the number and kind of proteins synthesized. Some of these shifts are associated with (*a*) the mechanism controlling the production of the spore, and (*b*) the final components of the spore itself.

Changes in the spore-forming machinery.—The terminal pathways of acetate oxidation are nonfunctional in vegetative cells grown in a complex medium with glucose as the main carbon source (55, 56). During the early stages of sporogenesis, the cells induce the formation of a functional tricarboxylic acid cycle (55, 57–59). Mutants which are blocked in the production of aconitase, one of the key enzymes of acetate oxidation, fail to sporulate but continue to grow vegetatively in the presence of glutamate (60). Further, repression of the synthesis of enzymes of the tricarboxylic acid cycle inhibits spore formation (61). It appears that sporulation requires a rich supply of intermediates as well as energy from the tricarboxylic acid cycle for the synthesis of spore-specific components. Evidence that these enzymes are not specific spore components was furnished by Szulmajster & Hanson (62), who observed that when sporulating cells are disrupted by lysozyme (17), the enzymes of the tricarboxylic acid cycle remain in the sporangium and are not incorporated into the spore at significant levels.

Synthesis of spore-specific components.—During sporulation, dipicolinic acid synthesized in the sporangium (63) and specific proteins are incorporated into the spore. Consequently, spores differ from vegetative cells not only in the pattern of enzyme activities present (7, 54), but also in the nature of the proteins which catalyze the same reactions in spores and vegetative cells (11).

The extent to which unique species of macromolecules are produced during sporulation and incorporated into the spore is indicated by the appearance of numerous surface and soluble spore-specific antigens (64–68). Immunoelectrophoretic techniques have detected at least 12 soluble antigens in spores. Four of these were common to the heat-resistant proteins of the vegetative cell, five were new heat-resistant proteins and three were new heat-sensitive proteins. A number of heat-sensitive antigens, which are observed in extracts of vegetative cells, disappear during sporulation.

In only a few cases has the same enzyme from spore and vegetative cell been sufficiently characterized to permit a physical chemical comparison. One of these, catalase, is attached to particles in the spore and is heat-resistant (69). Catalase from vegetative cells is soluble and heat-sensitive (70). The two catalases differ in their kinetic properties (71) and are immunologically distinct (66, 70). During sporulation, the appearance of the antigenically active spore catalase is coupled with a decrease in the vegetative form of the enzyme (66). Another enzyme which differs substantially in spores and vegetative cells is the soluble NADH oxidase. Simmons & Costilow (54) purified a heat-stable NADH oxidase from spores of *Clostridium botulinum*. Green & Sadoff (72) purified the spore and vegetative enzyme to the same specific activity and observed numerous differences in their properties. The spore enzyme is heat-stable and has a molecular weight of over 200,000, whereas the vegetative enzyme is rapidly denatured at 70° C and has a molecular weight of 100,000. The two enzymes can be separated from each other by gel filtration or by chromatography on diethylaminoethyl cellulose and are also immunologically distinct. Some spore-like enzyme is present in vegetative cells, whereas spores contain only the heat-stable enzyme.

Differences between spore and vegetative enzymes which are based solely on heat resistance may be misleading (73). An example of this is the glucose dehydrogenase of spores of *B. cereus* which loses heat stability *in vivo* during germination. Sadoff et al. (74) have purified the enzyme 500-fold from the spores and showed that it underwent a reversible dissociation under the influence of pH and salts. Decrease in molecular size was coupled with increases in thermal stability.

From the studies with antigens and purified enzymes, it can be seen that numerous differences exist between the related protein molecules in spores and vegetative cells. If these reflect differences in primary structure (yet to be established), one possible explanation is that they are due to changes in the translational mechanism. The selection of structural gene mutants for an enzyme in vegetative cells (e.g., heat-sensitive enzyme) should be extremely useful in determining whether separate cistrons exist for the vegetative and spore enzymes.

Morphological and Physiological Stages

Differentiating biological systems are committed at a given point in time to the synthesis of new specific macromolecules; the time at which each of these appears differs for each macromolecule. In sporulation, an ordered series of cytological changes occurs, indicating that the synthesis of the new structural elements which accompany these events are ordered (43, 75–77). Six morphological stages have been recognized during sporulation in *B. subtilis* Marburg (75). Numerous mutants, blocked at various morphological stages, have been isolated and examined with the electron microscope (78). Fitz-James (43) has described a similar sequence of events, including a mutant blocked in cortex formation, for sporulation of *B. cereus*. In the earliest two stages, an axial filament of chromatin material is observed, part of which is destined for the spore. Its appearance follows the synthesis of spore-specific DNA (9). Subsequently, the inward folding of the cell membrane occurs to form the forespore septum. This event coincides with the compartmentalization of DNA. Continued growth of the membrane and enclosure of the forespore leads in the next stage to the prespore. Stage IV, the formation of the cortex, is one of the critical stages in sporulation. During this period, diaminopimelic acid, a constituent of the cortex (45), and cysteine, a constituent of the spore coat (79), are incorporated. This stage is followed by the completion of the spore coat (stage V), accumulation of dipicolinic acid, uptake of calcium (75), and the final development of the cortex and heat resistance of the spore. During the last stage, the mature spore appears within the sporangium. Lysis of the sporangium and the concomitant liberation of the mature spore represents the terminal stage of sporulation.

We do not as yet have a systematic study of the time at which various physiological and biochemical properties appear in any one sporulating system. It is clear, however, that these events do not occur at the same time but are ordered (9, 11). For example, in *B. cereus* T, the spore-specific glucose dehydrogenase appears at the end of maximal growth (80) when sporogenesis commences, whereas the spore-specific alanine racemase appears six hours later (81). In *Bacillus megaterium*, the synthesis of spore adenosine deaminase precedes the synthesis of spore ribosidase by several hours (82). Many other specific products, such as antibiotics (29, 75, 83–85), proteases (25, 29, 30), and lytic enzymes (86–88), appear at different intervals in the sporulation cycle. Furthermore, sporulating cells develop resistance to treatment by X rays two hours before they become heat-resistant. Heat resistance appears about the time that the sporulating cell is synthesizing dipicolinic acid and is accumulating calcium (40, 79). X-ray resistance occurs simultaneously with the synthesis of a structure rich in disulfide bonds but the significance of this is not clear (89).

Genetic Control

A system as complex as sporogenesis must be controlled by a number of regulatory and structural genes. Mutants of sporogenesis can be obtained either spontaneously or else by treatment with a mutagenic agent such as ultraviolet light (3, 90, 91). Two types of mutants have been isolated, both of which can lead to blocks at various stages of the sporulation cycle (75): (a) Asporogenous (Sp$^-$); mutants which are incapable of producing dormant spores; (b) Oligosporogenous (Osp); mutants which produce only low frequency of spores (e.g., 10^{-5}) under normal conditions of sporogenesis.

The largest class of mutants isolated comprises those which have blocks in the initial stages of sporulation (75, 92). Two classes of mutants are included in this group, (i) those with defects in metabolism essential for supporting the biosynthesis of spore components (spore-synthesizing machinery), and (ii) those defective in the genetic expression of spore-specific elements. For example, as previously discussed, the function of the tricarboxylic acid cycle is essential for sporogenesis. This cycle can be induced in vegetative cells without leading to sporulation and is present in a number of asporogenic mutants and therefore is part of the vegetative machinery (9). Mutants which are defective in one or more of the enzymes of the tricarboxylic acid cycle fail to initiate sporogenesis and appear as Stage I mutants (60). Analysis of the biochemical deficiencies in the various mutants from each stage may provide a clearer understanding of the process of sporogenesis. For example, biochemical defects in Stage I mutants could indicate those events essential to the initiation of intracellular differentiation. Some of the defects described in Stage I mutants include the loss of ability to synthesize NADH oxidase (93), an antibiotic, and a proteolytic enzyme (75, 92). In *B. cereus*, mutant blocks in the synthesis of cortex or normal spore coats have been identified with later stages (43).

Relatively little information is available on the genetics of sporogenesis. Several investigators, taking advantage of the fact that *B. subtilis* Marburg is transformable (94) and transducible (95, 96), have started to map the spore genes. Although the results to date are only fragmentary, some generalizations can be made: (a) a large number of spore genes exist in the vegetative cell (75); (b) several genes which regulate the first stage in sporogenesis are closely linked (92); (c) some spore genes appear scattered over the vegetative chromosome (75, 97, 98).

Estimation of the number and distribution of genes directly involved in the production of the spore is presently difficult for several reasons. First, since the genes described represent all of the determinants for sporogenesis, including the spore-forming machinery, it is not clear whether the structural genes controlling the synthesis of spore-specific components are clustered or scattered over the chromosome. Sporulation is sensitive to physiological conditions and a variety of mutations that do not affect spore proteins or spore-specific functions, but may indirectly result in asporogeny or oligosporogeny. Secondly, a degree of selection may exist during isolation. Spizizen (92), employing irradiation of wild-type cultures, found Sp$^-$ markers primarily linked to a gene for competence. On the other hand, Takahashi (97, 98) observed that when auxotrophic strains were used, in each case asporogenic mutants were obtained which were linked to the auxotrophic marker employed.

Noting that functions associated with sporogenesis are not necessarily essential to normal cellular functions, and can be irreversibly lost, Jacob et al. (99) suggested that spore formation may be controlled by an episome; a suggestion which was later withdrawn (75). Recent support for the episome hypothesis has come from the laboratory of Slepecky. It is based on the high frequency of stable asporogenous mutants from early-log cultures treated with acriflavin (100), and on the ability of cultures during outgrowth to revert directly to spore formation (36). By CsCl buoyant-density centrifugation, a satellite band of DNA which disappears during outgrowth, has recently been observed in spores of *B. cereus* (101). There is no direct evidence that this is involved in sporulation.

INITIATION OF GERMINATION

Germination is an irreversible process in which a number of simultaneous events takes place shortly after exposure of activated spores to specific stimulants. After the usual lag period following the addition of a germinating agent, the spore sequentially loses its heat resistance, dipicolinic acid, impermeability to dyes, Ca^{++}, refractility, and optical density to visible light (102). An equation has been derived (103, 104) which accurately describes the kinetics of the latter two properties in *B. cereus* spores (105). Electron micrographs of *B. subtilis* spores indicate a progressive swelling of the cortex and appearance of fine nuclear fibrils during the initial stages of germination (77, 106). Collectively, germination is a degradative process and probably involves a number of enzymatic reactions. Since spores will germinate normally in the presence of inhibitors of protein and nucleic acid synthesis, the enzymes responsible for germination must also be specific components which are built into the structure of the spore (107).

MULTIPLICITY OF TRIGGER MECHANISMS

Bacterial spores are endowed with multiple mechanisms for breaking the cryptobiotic state. In addition to simple sugars and amino acids whose action can be explained either by the pyruvate hypothesis (108, 109) or by other pathways of amino acid metabolism (110, 111), germination may be initiated by salts and mechanical disruption (112), metal chelates (113–116) and, in certain strains of spores, by straight- or branched-chained C_3 to C_9 hydrocarbons (117, 118). This diversity of initiators may represent, on the one hand, multiple pathways of germination or, on the other, an extremely basic mechanism capable of being initiated by several methods.

Selective modification of triggering systems designed to examine the mechanism(s) of germination in spores has been little exploited. Several new approaches have recently appeared. First, Campbell et al. (119) have found that supra-optimal heating of spores of *Bacillus stearothermophilus* destroys the capacity to germinate on a minimal medium, presumably by denaturation of some enzymes, but initiation may then be caused by the addition of glutamate or lysine, possible intermediates in a catenary pathway. Second, spores produced under varying conditions have different germination responses (120, 121). For instance, it has recently been demonstrated that in spores of *B. megaterium* grown in the presence of high amounts of glucose, L-alanine-induced germination is inhibited by increasing temperatures of heat activation, whereas the reciprocal results are found in the controls grown in low glucose concentrations (122). Third, Freese & Cashel (123) found that spores produced by mutants of *B. subtilis* devoid or low in alanine dehydrogenase (ALD$^-$), respond differently to calcium dipicolinate and to L-alanine than do normal spores.

Woese Hypothesis

In the past few years several workers have attempted to provide a theoretical approach to the mechanism of germination. One proposed by Woese (124) is summarized below.

Spores contain a "germination enzyme" which, in some manner, initiates the sequence of degradative reactions in germination. There are a certain number of the enzymes in every spore and the number per spore is Poissonally distributed in the population. Theoretically, one could divide up this heterogeneous population into a finite number of homogeneous fractions in which each spore contained exactly the same number of enzymes as other spores of that same fraction. Heterogeneity in spore populations has recently been demonstrated (105, 125).

This enzyme catalyzes the production of some product, P (or, equally, the degradation of some inhibitor) which must attain a certain critical concentration (P_c) before initiation occurs. The time (t_c) to reach this concentration level will depend on the number of enzyme molecules (n) present in the spore; therefore, in spores with the same n, t_c will be the same and germination should occur at the *same* time for all of those spores. A frequency distribution of the number of spores with the same t_c vs. t_c generates a Poisson distribution with statistics identical to those experimentally observed (105). By simply assuming different values for m (the average number of enzyme molecules per spore), that Poisson distribution which corresponds to $n = 15$ to 20 resembles the time derivatives of germination curves, and closely approximates the germination distributions described by Vary & Halvorson (125). This would imply that the average number of germination enzymes per spore in *B. cereus* strain T is 15 to 20; it is interesting to note that for the same strain, the number of ALD molecules per spore has been estimated as 14 (120). Woese suggested that triggering of germination may involve an allosteric effection by normal germination substances. For example, the enzyme would not function until the allosteric site(s) is saturated (e.g., by L-alanine).

The predictions for this model are those which have been commonly observed: (a) with increasing concentrations of L-alanine (assumed to be the effector), germination proceeds more rapidly and completely up to the point of saturation; (b) for the rate at which spores germinate, there is an optimal temperature (expected in any enzymatic reaction); (c) the length of heat activation times also show an optimum, increasing as more molecules of enzyme are activated [possibly by Riemann's proposal (126) of disrupting a Ca-dipicolinic acid-enzyme complex] and decreasing after long periods of heating by eventual denaturation.

THE L-ALANINE-INDUCED TRIGGER

A primary candidate for the L-alanine-induced trigger enzyme is one known to utilize L-alanine and its analogues. The arguments that this involves L-alanine dehydrogenase have recently been summarized (108) and will not be reviewed here.

Clearly, the isolation of mutants devoid of ALD would resolve the question of the necessity of ALD for germination. In fact, such mutants of *B. subtilis* have been isolated by Freese and co-workers (127) and the comparison of L-alanine-induced germination in both ALD⁻ and ALD⁺ spores demonstrates the necessity of ALD for complete L-alanine-induced germination. Whereas 100 per cent germination was obtained in ALD⁺ spores, only a small fraction (10 per cent) of ALD⁻ spores germinated in the presence of L-alanine. In further studies with ALD⁻ spores prepared by centrifugation through CsCl, it was found that more than 10 per cent of the spores eventually germinated, i.e., 50 per cent of the control within 100 minutes (123). It is difficult to compare these data with the above since Cs⁺ is known to activate spores (128) and may also activate other enzymatic reactions. This residual activity was explained by the proposal that L-alanine, or an analogue, was capable of initiating some trigger mechanism for the endogenous release of L-alanine or an L-alanine derivative (e.g., pyruvate) in a fraction of the population of ALD⁻ spores. The possibility that such mutants contain low levels of L-alanine dehydrogenase has not been excluded. That spores with low ALD-specific activity germinate very rapidly in the presence of L-alanine has been demonstrated by McCormick & Halvorson (120).

GENERAL NATURE OF THE INITIATOR SYSTEM

Since germination is primarily degradative, it is probable that a hydrolytic enzyme is involved in its initiation. This was first proposed by Powell & Strange (129) who isolated an enzyme from spores which hydrolyzes vegetative cell walls. Several laboratories have extended this approach. Gould & Hitchins (130, 131) demonstrated that if a wide variety of spores are preincubated in disulfide bond reducing agents and 8 *M* urea, a treatment known to imitate heat activation (132), subsequent treatment with lysozyme caused phase darkening. Although the pretreatment of these spores was lethal, the authors proposed that a lytic system may exist in spores which is activated following enzymatic disulfide cleavage. This lytic system could solubilize the spore cortex, permitting increased permeability and the onset of metabolism. A possible candidate for this lytic enzyme was demonstrated by Gould & Hitchins (133) to be similar to the Strange & Dark S-enzyme (134), and it was suggested that the activation of this enzyme may be by reduction of intramolecular disulfide bonds. It should be noted that the substrate for the partially purified enzyme was nonviable spores, indicating that the characteristic germination properties observed here may have been the result of a physical reaction rather than a metabolic response by the spore. And indeed it has been shown that a strong proteinase (Subtilopeptidase A) can cause the characteristic changes associated with spore germination (135, 136) presumably by degrading the spore coat and thereby weakening the structural integrity of the spore. Sensitization of spores by the Gould & Hitchins method (130, 131) which imitates heat activation had no effect on the rate of subtilisin-induced changes.

A more convincing approach to enzymatically initiated, physiological germination would be the isolation of an initiatory from spores which could cause viable spores to germinate. Extracts of *B. cereus* strain T spores contain such an initiator which has properties analogous to the properties of germinating spores (137). This component can be isolated from the dormant spore in an inactive form and activated by heat (72° C for 10 minutes). Its pH, temperature, ionic, and stability properties are analogous to those of heat-activated spores.

OUTGROWTH

The period of development after germination until the beginning of the first cell division is called "outgrowth" (138) or "postgerminative development" (139). Following dissolution of the spore cortex and rupture of the spore coat, the spore core membrane becomes the cell wall of the emerging vegetative cell which then elongates and divides (77). The conditions for outgrowth are usually different from those supporting germination. Germination and outgrowth have different temperature optima, and most spores need nutrients for outgrowth which are not required for germination (140, 141). Outgrowth is characterized by a period of active biosynthetic activity. Inhibition of the energy supply (142) or the addition of antibiotics which block cell wall and macromolecular synthesis (143–146), inhibit outgrowth. During this period increases in dry weight and swelling occur (147), vegetative-specific antigens appear (68) and progressive changes are noted in the pattern of RNA synthesis (49, 148, 149), classes of ribosomal particles (150), metabolic activity (56, 139, 145), structures (77, 146, 151), and DNA replication (152–154).

ABSENCE OF STABLE mRNA IN SPORES

Although overall differentiation in various systems is dependent upon RNA and protein synthesis, in several instances, such as developing sea urchin eggs (155, 156), seeds (157), embryonic chick down-feathers, and chick lens tissue (158, 159), stable mRNAs (polysomes) have been demonstrated, some of which support limited protein synthesis. If a stable mRNA produced during sporulation was incorporated into the spore, one would expect that it would be available for protein synthesis during outgrowth. This now seems unlikely for the following reasons: (a) Detectable levels of mRNA are not carried over into the dormant spore during sporulation (46, 49). (b) When spores are germinated in the presence of actinomycin D, RNA and protein synthesis are completely inhibited (26, 144, 145). (c) Polysomes are absent in extracts of spores (43, 150, 160, 161). (d) Extracts of spores fail to incorporate amino acids into protein unless supplemented with mRNA (162). Collectively, these findings, like those in ascospores of *Neurospora* (163), conidiospores of *Penicillium* (164) and peanut seeds (165) suggest that bacterial spores are devoid of stable mRNA and that protein synthesis is dependent upon initial transcription of the genome.

DEVELOPMENT OF BIOSYNTHETIC CAPACITY

Protein-synthesizing system.—Dormant spores contain a defective protein-synthesizing system (162). In addition to the absence of mRNA discussed above, both the supernatant and ribosomes are defective. As judged from *in vitro* incorporation experiments, repair of the protein-synthesizing system *in vivo* occurs in the absence of protein synthesis (161). Heat treatment of spores partially restores the activity of the supernatant fraction. The low capacity of the ribosomal particle fraction is primarily attributed to the low concentration of active monosomes (70S particles) in spores. Dormant spores of *B. cereus* T contain 30S, 50S, and 70S RNA particles (161). However, in *B. subtilis* and *B. megaterium*, only 50S and 70S particles have been found (150), 160). In germinated spores, the 70S particles are fully active in protein synthesis, and from quantitative considerations it appears that the rate-limiting step in protein synthesis during outgrowth is the synthesis of mRNA (161).

Transcription and translation.—Protein synthesis during outgrowth is dependent upon new mRNA transcription. When spores are germinated in a medium supporting vegetative multiplication, RNA synthesis begins at the end of the germination period, followed several minutes later by the onset of protein synthesis (144, 162). Throughout the period of outgrowth, as well as during vegetative growth, the addition of actinomycin D immediately blocks further RNA synthesis and, after a delay of several minutes, protein synthesis as well (26, 144, 145, 162). The RNA synthesized early in outgrowth includes all three classes of RNA (149), has the same base composition as vegetative RNA, and effectively competes with pulse-labeled vegetative RNA in hybridization experiments (49, 50). The emergence of biosynthetic activity in several systems, e.g., ascospores of *Neurospora* (163), conidiospores of *Penicillium* (164) and *Aspergillus* (166), and seeds (167, 168), is associated with functional polyribosome formation, and hence, indirectly on the synthesis of mRNA. Several attempts have been made to correlate the biosynthetic activity of outgrowing spores with the maturation of ribosomal system. Woese and co-workers (150) observed in *B. subtilis* that during outgrowth both ribosomal precursors (25S and 35S) as well as 100S ribosomes (polysomes) were formed. A ribosomal system capable of supporting *in vitro* protein synthesis has recently been detected during outgrowth of spores of *B. cereus* (162).

From the above results, it appears that the polymerase for synthesizing mRNA pre-exists in the spore. Two findings support this view. First, spores germinated in the presence of chloramphenicol can synthesize RNA. Secondly, for the first time a DNA-dependent RNA polymerase has been detected in spores of *B. subtilis* (169). All four trinucleotides are utilized and the product has been isolated and identified as a heteropolymer of RNA.

ORDERED PROTEIN AND ENZYME SYNTHESIS

The sequential replication of the chromosome which accompanies outgrowth of bacterial spores provides a readily available model system for studying the transcriptional and translational events occurring during differentiation (152, 162, 170, 171). Since the dormant spore can be regarded as essentially devoid of functional messenger RNA, the conversion to vegetative growth requires transcription and *de novo* synthesis of vegetative components. The system therefore permits a measurement of the degree of order which exists in the synthesis of macromolecules. Specifically, one may ask whether the appearance of new protein species is a sequential or an ordered event, or whether the entire genome is accessible to RNA polymerase activity once outgrowth begins. Several observations have been made with *B. cereus* T spores which suggest that the controls operating during outgrowth insure an ordered process. Halvorson (11) examined extracts of germinated spores labeled with H^3-leucine and C^{14}-leucine at two intervals in outgrowth. The radioactivity profiles obtained from a chromatographic procedure indicated that different classes of protein were synthesized during the two intervals. A more conclusive demonstration of ordered synthesis employing acrylamide gel electrophoresis is reported by Kobayashi et al. (162). They observed that some proteins characteristic of the vegetative cell were synthesized early in outgrowth while others appeared at later intervals. Further, the syntheses of basal levels of several enzymes (α-glucosidase, alkaline phosphatase) are ordered during outgrowth (145). Since during this same period, mRNA has a half life of a few minutes, it was inferred that the ordered protein synthesis must reflect differences in the time of transcription of the corresponding portion of the genome. This periodicity of enzyme synthesis during outgrowth was subsequently repeated over several division cycles in vegetative growth (162), suggesting that similar transcriptional and translational controls operate during both phases of development. During outgrowth, there was no difference in the time at which a brief period of both basal and induced α-glucosidase and histidase synthesis occurred (128). These enzymes were synthesized during a period when there is no net DNA synthesis. Similar discontinuous enzyme synthesis has been reported for L-alanine dehydrogenase in germinating spores of *Penicillium* (164), for alanine-glutamic acid transaminase in germinating spores of *Aspergillus niger* (172), and for UDP-galactose polysaccharide transferase and UDPG synthetase during development in *Dictyostelium discoidium* (173, 174). For a more general survey of enzyme synthesis in developing systems, see the reviews by Baldwin & Rusch (175), Allen (176), and Gottlieb (177).

DNA Synthesis

The presence of DNA polymerase and enzymes involved in the synthesis of deoxyribonucleotides in spores has recently been demonstrated (178). The experiments of Yoshikawa (153) and Oishi et al. (152) on the regulation of DNA synthesis during outgrowth indicate that the DNA contained within the bacterial spore is in the completed form. Marker frequency analysis in DNA transformation studies has been used to demonstrate that the replication of the *B. subtilis* chromosome during outgrowth occurs in an ordered sequential fashion (152, 170, 171). From the study made by Oishi et al. (152), it appears that the genes replicate in the same order during outgrowth as that observed in the vegetative cell.

Yoshikawa (153) has demonstrated that a significant amount of DNA synthesis occurs when *B. subtilis* spores are germinated in the presence of chloramphenicol. The tentative assumption has been made that this represents repair synthesis. The data of Donnellan & Setlow (179) and Smith & Yoshikawa (180) on the formation of thymine photo products in irradiated bacterial spores indicate that spores ". . . have a very effective repair mechanism. . ." (179), and that the physical state of the DNA in spores is significantly different from that which is found in vegetative cells. There are several other indications that a repair mechanism does become operative followin the initiation of germination (143, 181). During the early stages of outgrowth of spores of *B. cereus*, the disappearance of a satellite band of DNA (101) occurs during a period of thymidine incorporation equivalent to about 1 per cent of the total DNA (182). This incorporation is sensitive to mitomycin (182) and to caffeine (128), an inhibitor of host cell reactivation in *E. coli* (183).

Relationship Between Transcription and DNA Replication

The dependence of outgrowth on ordered transcription provides an ideal system for determining whether transcription is ordered by or related to DNA replication. The independence of at least initial transcription during outgrowth was demonstrated recently by germination in the presence of mitomycin C (184). It is well known also that bacteria undergoing thymineless death do not produce DNA but are still capable of synthesizing induced enzymes (185).

Assuming that the order of the synthesis of individual mRNA follows the replication of the genome, then if only transcriptional operations regulated developmental changes, a correspondence between the genetic map and the appearance of individual enzymes would be expected (186–188). If this is actually the situation for the spore system, then the gene order on the chromosome will reflect the sequence of those activities necessary for the return to vegetative growth (152).

A systematic study of the order of enzyme synthesis during outgrowth has not as yet been conducted. In *B. cereus*, the order of appearance of several enzymes is the same as that during synchronous growth (145, 162). In *B. subtilis*, the synthesis of different classes of RNA appears to be ordered. Oishi & Sueoka (189), from hybridization studies of the RNA synthesized during outgrowth, have tentatively identified the cistrons responsible for the synthesis of 16S and 23S RNA. The loci for the ribosomal fraction are confined to a restricted region adjacent to the *ade* marker, the origin of DNA replication. By similar experiments, Dubnau et al. (190) identified the cistrons of rRNA with the first 10 per cent of the bacterial chromosome of the same organism. They have suggested that the doubling in the rate of r- and sRNA synthesis observed by Donnellan et al. (149) during outgrowth of *B. subtilis* spores may be attributed to the duplication of this region of the genome.

LITERATURE CITED

1. *Spores II*, a symposium. (Halvorson, H. O., Ed., Burgess Publ. Co., Minneapolis, Minn., 1961)
2. Woese, C. R., and Forro, J. R., *J. Bacteriol.*, **80**, 811–17 (1960)
3. Schaeffer, P., Ionesco, H., and Jacob, F., *Compt. Rend.*, **249**, 481 (1959)
4. *Spores III*, a symposium. (Campbell, L. L., and Halvorson, H. O., Eds., Am. Soc. Microbiol., Ann Arbor, Mich., 1965)
5. Murrell, W. G., in Microbial reaction to environment, *Symp. Soc. Gen. Microbiol.*, **11**, 100–51 (1961)
6. *Cryptobiotic stages in biological systems*, a symposium. (Grossowicz, N., Hestrin, S., and Keynan, A., Eds., Elsevier Publ. Co., Amsterdam, 1961)
7. Halvorson, H. O., in *The Bacteria*, **IV**, 223–64. (Gunsalus, I. C., and Stanier, R. Y., Eds., Academic Press, New York, 1962)
8. Sussman, A. S., and Halvorson, H. O., *Microbial Dormancy*. (Harper & Row, New York, in press, 1966)

9. Szulmajster, J., *Bull. Soc. Chim. Biol.*, **46**, 443–81 (1964)
10. Robinow, C. F., in *The Bacteria*, **I**, 207–48. (Gunsalus, I. C., and Stanier, R. Y., Eds., Academic Press, New York, 1961)
11. Halvorson, H. O., in Function and structure of microorganisms, *Symp. Soc. Gen. Microbiol.*, **15**, 343–68 (1965)
12. Schaeffer, P., Millet, J., and Aubert, J.-P., *Proc. Natl. Acad. Sci. U. S.*, **54**, 704–11 (1965)
13. *Mécanismes de Régulation des Activités Cellulaires Chez les Microorganisms*, an international symposium. (Centre National de la Recherche Sci., Paris, 1965)
14. Synthesis and structure of macromolecules, *Cold Spring Harbor Symp. Quant. Biol.*, **28** (1963)
15. Fitz-James, P. C., *J. Biophys. Biochem. Cytol.*, **8**, 507–28 (1960)
16. Young, I. E., and Fitz-James, P. C., *J. Biophys. Biochem. Cytol.*, **6**, 467–82 (1959)

17. Aubert, J.-P., and Millet, J., *Compt. Rend.*, **256**, 1866–68 (1963)
18. Aubert, J.-P., and Millet, J., *Compt. Rend.*, **256**, 5442–45 (1963)
19. Grelet, N., *J. Appl. Bacteriol.*, **20**, 315–24 (1957)
20. Foster, J. W., *Quart. Rev. Microbiol.*, **31**, 102–18 (1956)
21. Nakata, H. M., and Halvorson, H. O., *J. Bacteriol.*, **80**, 801–10 (1960)
22. Leitzmann, C., and Bernlohr, R. W., *J. Bacteriol.*, **89**, 1506–10 (1965)
23. Monro, R. E., *Biochem. J.*, **81**, 225–32 (1961)
24. Spotts, C. R., and Szulmajster, J., *Biochim. Biophys. Acta*, **61**, 635–38 (1962)
25. Balassa, G., *Biochem. Biophys. Res. Commun.*, **15**, 236–39 (1964)
26. Balassa, G., *op. cit.* (Ref. 13, 565–82)
27. Chaloupka, J., and Kreckova, P., *Biochem. Biophys. Res. Commun.*, **8**, 120–24 (1962)
28. Millet, J., and Aubert, J.-P., *Compt. Rend.*, **259**, 2555–58 (1964)
29. Spizizen, J., Reilly, B., and Dahl, B., in *Proc. Intern. Congr. Genet., 11th, The Hague, 1963*, 31
30. Bernlohr, R. W., *J. Biol. Chem.*, **239**, 538–43 (1964)
31. Srinivasan, V. R., and Halvorson, H. O., *Nature*, **197**, 100–1 (1963)
32. Srinivasan, V. R., *op. cit.* (Ref. 4, 64–74)
33. Millet, J., and Pineau, E., *Compt. Rend.*, **250**, 1363–65 (1960)
34. Aubert, J.-P., Millet, J., Pineau, E., and Milhaud, G., *Biochim. Biophys. Acta*, **51**, 529–37 (1961)
35. Halvorson, H. O., *J. Appl. Bacteriol.*, **20**, 305–14 (1957)
36. Vinter, V., and Slepecky, R. A., *J. Bacteriol.*, **90**, 803–7 (1965)
37. Young, I. E., and Fitz-James, P. C., *J. Biophys. Biochem. Cytol.*, **6**, 483–98 (1959)
38. Foster, J. W., and Perry, J. J., *J. Bacteriol.*, **67**, 295–302 (1954)
39. Nakata, D., Matsushiro, A., and Miwatoni, T., *Med. J. Osaka Univ.*, **6**, 1047–60 (1956)
40. Ryter, A., and Szulmajster, J., *Ann. Inst. Pasteur*, **108**, 640–51 (1965)
41. Vinter, V., *Folia Microbiol.*, **9**, 58–72 (1964)
42. Canfield, R. E., and Szulmajster, J., *Nature*, **203**, 526–98 (1964)
43. Fitz-James, P. C., *op. cit.* (Ref. 13, 529–44)
44. Del Valle, M. R., and Aronson, A. I., *Biochem. Biophys. Res. Commun.*, **9**, 421–25 (1962)
45. Murrell, W. G., and Warth, A. D., *op. cit.* (Ref. 4, 1–24)
46. Doi, R., and Igarashi, R. T., *J. Bacteriol.*, **87**, 323–28 (1964)
47. Doi, R., and Igarashi, R. T., *Nature*, **203**, 1092–94 (1964)
48. Aronson, A. I., *J. Mol. Biol.*, **13**, 92–104 (1965)
49. Doi, R., and Igarashi, R. T., *Proc. Natl. Acad. Sci. U. S.*, **52**, 755–62 (1964)
50. Doi, R., *op. cit.* (Ref. 4, 111–24)
51. Aronson, A. I., *J. Mol. Biol.*, **11**, 576–88 (1965)
52. Aronson, A. I., and Del Valle, M. R., *Biochim. Biophys. Acta*, **87**, 267–76 (1964)
53. Szulmajster, J., Canfield, R. E., and Blicharska, J., *Compt. Rend.*, **256**, 2057–60 (1963)
54. Simmons, R. J., and Costilow, R. N., *J. Bacteriol.*, **84**, 1274–81 (1962)
55. Hanson, R. S., Srinivasan, V. R., and Halvorson, H. O., *J. Bacteriol.*, **86**, 45–50 (1963)
56. Goldman, M., and Blumenthal, H. J., *J. Bacteriol.*, **87**, 387–90 (1964)
57. Hanson, R. S., Srinivasan, V. R., and Halvorson, H. O., *J. Bacteriol.*, **85**, 451–60 (1963)
58. Megraw, R. E., and Beers, R. J., *J. Bacteriol.*, **87**, 1087–93 (1964)
59. Pepper, R. E., and Costilow, R. N., *J. Bacteriol.*, **87**, 303–10 (1964)
60. Hanson, R. S., Blicharska, J., and Szulmajster, J., *Biochem. Biophys. Res. Commun.*, **17**, 1–7 (1964)
61. Hanson, R. S., Blicharska, J., Arnaud, M., and Szulmajster, J., *Biochem. Biophys. Res. Commun.*, **17**, 690–95 (1964)
62. Szulmajster, J., and Hanson, R. S., *op. cit.* (Ref. 4, 162–73)
63. Kondo, M., Takeda, Y., and Yoneda, M., *Biken's J.*, **7**, 153–56 (1964)
64. Tomcsik, J., and Baumann-Grace, J. B., *J. Gen. Microbiol.*, **21**, 666–75 (1959)
65. Norris, J. R., and Wolf, J., *J. Appl. Bacteriol.*, **24**, 42–56 (1961)
66. Baillie, A., and Norris, J. R., *J. Appl. Bacteriol.*, **26**, 10—16 (1963)
67. Baillie, A., and Norris, J. R., *J. Bacteriol.*, **87**, 1221–26 (1964)
68. Walker, P. D., and Batty, I., *J. Appl. Bacteriol.*, **28**, 194–96 (1965)
69. Lawrence, N. L., and Halvorson, H. O., *J. Bacteriol.*, **68**, 334–37 (1954)

70. Sadoff, H. L., *op. cit.* (Ref. 1, 180–94)
71. Sadoff, H. L. (Personal communication)
72. Green, J. H., and Sadoff, H. L., *J. Bacteriol.*, **89**, 1499–1505 (1965)
73. Yoshida, A., and Freese, E., *Biochim. Biophys. Acta*, **96**, 248–62 (1965)
74. Sadoff, H. L., Bach, J. A., and Kools, J. W., *op. cit.* (Ref. 4, 97–110)
75. Schaeffer, P., Ionesco, H., Ryter, A., and Balassa, G., *op. cit.* (Ref. 13, 553–63)
76. Takagi, A., Kawata, T., Yamamoto, S., Kubo, T., and Okita, S., *Japan. J. Microbiol.*, **4**, 137–55 (1960)
77. Kawata, T., Inoue, T., and Takagi, A., *Japan. J. Microbiol.*, **7**, 23–42 (1963)
78. Ryter, A., Ionesco, H., and Schaeffer, P., *Compt. Rend.*, **252**, 3675–77 (1961)
79. Vinter, V., *op. cit.* (Ref. 1, 127–41)
80. Bach, J. A., and Sadoff, H. L., *J. Bacteriol.*, **83**, 699–707 (1962)
81. Stewart, B. J., and Halvorson, H. O., *J. Bacteriol.*, **65**, 160–66 (1953)
82. Powell, J. F., and Hunter, J. R., *Biochem. J.*, **62**, 381–87 (1956)
83. Bernlohr, R. W., and Novelli, G. D., *Nature*, **184**, 1256–57 (1959)
84. Bernlohr, R. W., and Novelli, G. D., *Arch. Biochem. Biophys.*, **103**, 94–104 (1963)
85. Balassa, G., Ionesco, H., and Schaeffer, P., *Compt. Rend.*, **257**, 986–88 (1963)
86. Greenberg, R. A., and Halvorson, H. O., *J. Bacteriol.*, **69**, 45–50 (1955)
87. Strange, R. E., and Dark, F. A., *J. Gen. Microbiol.*, **17**, 525–37 (1957)
88. Tomcsik, J., and Bouille, M., *Ann. Inst. Pasteur*, **100**, 25–36 (1961)
89. Bott, K. F., and Lundgren, D. G., *Radiation Res.*, **21**, 195–211 (1964)
90. Lundgren, D. G., and Beskid, G., *Can. J. Microbiol.*, **6**, 135–51 (1960)
91. Spizizen, J., *op cit.* (Ref. 1, 142–48)
92. Spizizen, J., *op. cit.* (Ref. 4, 125–37)
93. Szulmajster, J., and Schaeffer, P., *Biochem. Biophys. Res. Commun.*, **6**, 217–23 (1961)
94. Spizizen, J., *Proc. Natl. Acad. Sci. U. S.*, **44**, 1072–78 (1958)
95. Takahashi, I., *Biochem. Biophys. Res. Commun.*, **5**, 171–75 (1961)
96. Thorne, C. B., *J. Bacteriol.*, **83**, 106–11 (1962)
97. Takahashi, I., *J. Bacteriol.*, **89**, 294–98 (1965)
98. Takahashi, I., *J. Bacteriol.*, **89**, 1065–67 (1965)
99. Jacob, F., Schaeffer, P., and Wollman, E. L., in Microbiol genetics, *Symp. Soc. Gen. Microbiol.*, **10**, 67–91 (1960)
100. Rogolsky, M., and Slepecky, R. A., *Biochem. Biophys. Res. Commun.*, **16**, 204–8 (1964)
101. Douthit, H. A., and Halvorson, H. O., *Federation Proc.*, **25**, 707 (1966)
102. Levinson, H. S., and Hyatt, M. T., *Bacteriol. Proc.*, 36 (1965)
103. McCormick, N. G., *Biochem. Biophys. Res. Commun.*, **14**, 443–46 (1964)
104. McCormick, N. G., *J. Bacteriol.*, **89**, 1180–85 (1965)
105. Vary, J. C., and McCormick, N. G., *op. cit.* (Ref. 4, 188–98)
106. Mayall, B. H., and Robinow, C. F., *J. Appl. Bacteriol.*, **20**, 333–41 (1957)
107. Keynan, A., and Halvorson, H. O., *op. cit.* (Ref. 4, 174–79)
108. Halvorson, H. O., O'Connor, R., and Doi, R., *op. cit.* (Ref. 6, 71–95)
109. Hermier, J., *Ann. Inst. Pasteur*, **102**, 629–43 (1962)
110. Hermier, J., Siegenthaler, P.-A., Blondel-Quéroix, J., and Bergére, J.-L., *Bull. Soc. Chim. Biol.*, **47**, 1217–34 (1965)
111. Krask, B. (Personal communication)
112. Rode, L. J., and Foster, J. W., *Proc. Natl. Acad. Sci. U. S.*, **46**, 118–28 (1960)
113. Riemann, H., and Ordal, Z. J., *Science*, **133**, 1703–4 (1961)
114. Keynan, A., and Halvorson, H. O., *J. Bacteriol.*, **83**, 100–5 (1962)
115. Fleming, H. P., and Ordal, Z. J., *J. Bacteriol.*, **88**, 1529–37 (1964)
116. Jaye, M., and Ordal, Z. J., *J. Bacteriol.*, **89**, 1617–18 (1965)
117. Rode, L. J., and Foster, J. W., *J. Bacteriol.*, **81**, 768–79 (1961)
118. Rode, L. J., and Foster, J. W., *Proc. Natl. Acad. Sci. U. S.*, **53**, 31–37 (1965)
119. Campbell, L. L., Richards, C. M., and Shiff, E. E., *op. cit.* (Ref. 4, 55–63)
120. McCormick, N. G., and Halvorson, H. O., *Ann. N.Y. Acad. Sci.*, **102**, 763–72 (1963)
121. Levinson, H. S., and Hyatt, M. T., *J. Bacteriol.*, **87**, 876–86 (1964)
122. Holmes, P. K., Nags, E. H., and Levinson, H. S., *J. Bacteriol.*, **90**, 827–28 (1965)
123. Freese, E., and Cashel, M., *op. cit.* (Ref. 4, 144–51)
124. Woese, C. R. (To be submitted)
125. Vary, J. C., and Halvorson, H. O., *J. Bacteriol.*, **89**, 1340–47 (1965)
126. Riemann, H., *op. cit.* (Ref. 1, 24–48)

127. Freese, E., Park, S. W., and Cashel, M., *Proc. Natl. Acad. Sci. U. S.*, **51**, 1164–72 (1964)
128. Steinberg, W. (Unpublished results)
129. Powell, J. F., and Strange, R. E., *Biochem. J.*, **54**, 205–9 (1953)
130. Gould, G. W., and Hitchins, A. D., *Nature*, **197**, 622 (1963)
131. Gould, G. W., and Hitchins, A. D., *J. Gen. Microbiol.*, **33**, 413–23 (1963)
132. Keynan, A., Evenchik, Z., Halvorson, H. O., and Hastings, W. J., *J. Bacteriol.*, **88**, 313–18 (1964)
133. Gould, G. W., and Hitchins, A. D., *op. cit.* (Ref. 4, 213–21)
134. Strange, R. E., and Dark, F. A., *J. Gen. Microbiol.*, **16**, 236–49 (1957)
135. Sierra, G., *Can. J. Microbiol.*, **10**, 929–31 (1964)
136. Sierra, G., *Can. J. Microbiol.* (In press, 1966)
137. Vary, J. C., *Bacteriol. Proc.*, 37 (1965)
138. O'Brien, R. T., and Campbell, L. L., *Bacteriol. Proc.*, 46 (1956)
139. Levinson, H. S., and Hyatt, M. T., *J. Bacteriol.*, **72**, 176–83 (1956)
140. Demain, A. L., and Newkirk, J. F., *J. Bacteriol.*, **79**, 783–88 (1960)
141. Levinson, H. S., and Hyatt, M. T., *Ann. N.Y. Acad. Sci.*, **102**, 773–88 (1963)
142. Treadwell, P. E., Jann, G. J., and Salle, A. J., *J. Bacteriol.*, **76**, 549–58 (1958)
143. Stuy, J., *Antonie van Leeuwenhoek, J. Microbiol. Serol.*, **22**, 337–49 (1956)
144. Higa, A., *Synthesis and decay of messenger RNA in bacteria.* (Doctoral thesis, Massachusetts Institute of Technology, Cambridge, 1964)
145. Steinberg, W., Halvorson, H. O., Keynan, A., and Weinberg, E., *Nature*, **209**, 710–11 (1965)
146. Vinter, V., *op. cit.* (Ref. 4, 25–37)
147. Hitchins, A. D., Gould, G. W., and Hurst, A.., *J. Gen. Microbiol.*, **30**, 445–53 (1963)
148. Uchiyama, H., *J. Gen. Appl. Microbiol.*, **11**, 233–42 (1965)
149. Donnellan, J. E., Nags, E. H., and Levinson, H. S., *op. cit.* (Ref. 4, 152–61)
150. Woese, C. R., Langridge, R., and Morowitz, H. J., *J. Bacteriol.*, **79**, 777–82 (1960)
151. Fitz-James, P. C., *Can. J. Microbiol.*, **1**, 525–48 (1955)
152. Oishi, M., Yoshikawa, H., and Sueoka, N., *Nature*, **204**, 1069–73 (1964)
153. Yoshikawa, H., *Proc. Natl. Acad. Sci. U. S.*, **53**, 1476–83 (1965)
154. Young, I. E., and Fitz-James, P. C., *Nature*, **183**, 372–73 (1959)
155. Gross, P. R., *J. Exptl. Zool.*, **157**, 21–38 (1964)
156. Monroy, A., Maggio, R., and Rinaldi, A. M., *Proc. Natl. Acad. Sci. U. S.*, **54**, 107–11 (1965)
157. Dure, L., and Waters, L., *Science*, **147**, 410–72 (1965)
158. Bell, E., Humphreys, T., Sayter, H. S., and Hall, C. E., *Science*, **148**, 1739–41 (1965)
159. Reeder, R., and Bell, E., *Science*, **150**, 71–72 (1965)
160. Chaloupecky, V., *Folia Microbiol.*, **9**, 232–37 (1964)
161. Kobayashi, Y. (Unpublished results)
162. Kobayashi, Y., Steinberg, W., Higa, A., Halvorson, H. O., and Levinthal, C., *op. cit.* (Ref. 4, 200–12)
163. Henney, H. R., and Storck, R., *Proc. Natl. Acad. Sci. U. S.*, **51**, 1050–55 (1964)
164. Kornfeld, J., *Structure and physiological aspects of germination of conidia of* Penicillium chrysogtenum. (Doctoral thesis, Univ. of Wisconsin Madison, 1961)
165. Marcus, A., and Feeley, J., *Proc. Natl. Acad. Sci. U. S.*, **51**, 1075–79 (1964)
166. Horikoshi, K., Ohtaka, Y., and Ikeola, Y., *Agr. Biol. Chem. (Japan)*, **29**, 724–27 (1965)
167. Marcus, A., and Feeley, J., *J. Biol. Chem.*, **240**, 1675–80 (1965)
168. Chroboczek, H., and Cherry, J. H., *Biochem. Biophys. Res. Commun.*, **20**, 774–79 (1965)
169. Kerjan, P., and Szulmajster, J., *Compt. Rend.*, **262**, 312–16 (1966)
170. Yoshikawa, H., O'Sullivan, A., and Sueoka, N., *Proc. Natl. Acad. Sci. U. S.*, **52**, 973–80 (1964)
171. Wake, R. G., *Biochem. Biophys. Res. Commun.*, **13**, 67–70 (1963)
172. Takabe, I., and Yanagita, T., *Plant Cell Physiol. (Tokyo)*, **1**, 17–28 (1959)
173. Wright, B. E., and Anderson, M. L., *Chemical basis of development*, a symposium, 296–314. (McElroy, W. D., and Glass, B., Eds., Johns Hopkins Press, Baltimore, Md., 1958)
174. Sussman, M., and Osborn, M. J., *Proc. Natl. Acad. Sci. U. S.*, **52**, 81–87 (1964)
175. Baldwin, H. H., and Rusch, H. P., *Ann. Rev. Biochem.*, **34**, 365–94 (1965)

176. Allen, P. J., *Ann. Rev. Phytopathol.*, **3**, 313–42 (1965)
177. Gottlieb, D., *Endeavour*, **23**, 85–89 (1964)
178. Falaschi, A., Spudich, J., and Kornberg, A., *op. cit.* (Ref. 4, 88–96)
179. Donnellan, J. F., and Setlow, R. B., *Science*, **149**, 308–9 (1965)
180. Smith, K. C., and Yoshikawa, H. (Personal communication)
181. Irie, R., Yano, N., Morichi, T., and Kembo, H., *Biochem. Biophys. Res. Commun.*, **20**, 389–91 (1965)
182. Steinberg, W., *The sequence of biochemical events accompanying out-outgrowth of spores of* Bacillus cereus *strain T* (Master's thesis, Univ. of Wisconsin, Madison, 1965)
183. Sauerbier, W., *Biochem. Biophys. Res. Commun.*, **14**, 340–46 (1964)
184. Steinberg, W., Halvorson, H. O., and LaBerge, M., *Bacteriol. Proc.*, **14** (1965)
185. Hanawalt, P., and Wax, R., *Science*, **145**, 1061–63 (1964)
186. Cutler, R. G., and Evans, J. E., *Biophys. Soc.*, Abstr., **10**, 160 (1965)
187. Masters, M., and Pardee, A. B., *Proc. Natl. Acad. Sci. U. S.*, **54**, 64–70 (1965)
188. Halvorson, H. O., Gorman, J., Taruo, P., Epstein, R., and LaBerge, M., *Federation Proc.*, **23**, 1002–8 (1964)
189. Oishi, M., and Sueoka, N., *Proc. Natl. Acad. Sci. U. S.*, **54**, 483–91 (1965)
190. Dubnau, D., Smith, I., and Marmur, J., *Proc. Natl. Acad. Sci. U. S.*, **54**, 724–30 (1965)

BIOSYNTHETIC MODIFICATIONS INDUCED BY DNA ANIMAL VIRUSES[1,2]

By Maurice Green

Institute for Molecular Virology, St. Louis University School of Medicine, St. Louis, Missouri

Contents

INTRODUCTION.. 189
MAJOR ANIMAL VIRUS GROUPS AND THE DIVERSITY OF ANIMAL VIRUSES..... 190
  Experimental virology, its variables and pitfalls: cells, viruses, isotopes, inhibitors, and enzymes... 191
BIOSYNTHETIC MODIFICATIONS INDUCED BY DNA ANIMAL
VIRUSES... 193
PAPOVAVIRUSES... 194
  Polyoma virus-cytocidal infection.................................. 194
  SV40 virus-cytocidal infection..................................... 197
  Transformation of cells in vitro.................................... 198
  Polyoma virus-transformation...................................... 198
  SV40 virus-transformation... 200
  The adenovirus-SV40 so-called "hybrid"............................ 203
ADENOVIRUSES... 204
  Virus replication... 206
  Macromolecular synthesis.. 207
  Enzyme induction... 207
  Adenovirus transformation... 208
HERPESVIRUSES.. 209
  Replication of pseudorabies....................................... 209
  Replication of herpes simplex virus................................ 211
POXVIRUSES... 211
  Poxvirus "uncoating".. 212
  Viral replication... 212
  Macromolecular biosynthesis....................................... 213
  Enzyme induction... 214
OPEN QUESTIONS... 216

INTRODUCTION

An understanding of the biosynthetic processes induced[3] by infection with animal viruses is important for progress in several areas of biological and

---

[1] Literature survey completed in January 1966.

[2] The following abbreviations are used: dAMP (deoxyadenylic acid); dCMP (deoxycytidylic acid); C (cytosine); FUDR (5-fluorodeoxyuridine); G (guanine); dGMP (deoxyguanylic acid); PFU (plaque-forming units); TdR (thymidine); dTMP (deoxythymidylic acid); DNase (deoxyribonuclease).

[3] "Induced" is used here to denote a metabolic alteration accompanying virus infection, no mechanism being implied.

medical science. First, from the purely medical point of view, about 60 per cent of all illnesses are estimated (1) to be caused by viral infection. Yet, clinically effective drugs are not available for viral diseases, and the meager results of over 20 years of empirical searching for antiviral agents indicate that further knowledge of the fine structure of viral components and the molecular events involved in viral replication and virus-induced cell damage are required in order to select and design effective agents for the treatment of viral diseases.

Secondly, an understanding of the cancer cell and the neoplastic process in molecular terms, a hopeless pursuit several years ago, is now a realistic research goal for those studying tumorigenic viruses and the mechanism of virus-induced cell transformation. Because tumor-producing viruses can now be obtained in highly purified form and suitable "normal" cells in culture can be transformed into "neoplastic" cells, experimental systems are becoming available for a rational analysis of the molecular basis of neoplasia (2).

Thirdly, and fundamentally most important, is the use of viruses as tools for the analysis of cell function. During the past ten years, the tremendous increase in biochemical knowledge of the structure and replication of the macromolecular constituents of living systems, i.e., RNA, DNA, and protein, has resulted in the development of a new discipline, molecular biology, and further has cultivated a new frontier—"cell biology"—ripe for biochemical exploitation. The workings of the complex mammalian cell in the synthesis and regulation of macromolecules, and the function of cell organelles, e.g., the nucleus, nucleolus, and cell membrane in these processes, comprise today's challenges for modern biology.

The mammalian cell, containing more than a million genes, with thousands of different proteins being synthesized at any one time, presents an extremely difficult system for the analysis of transcription and translation of specific macromolecules. Presently it is impossible to isolate and identify a specific cellular gene, its corresponding messenger RNA, and its protein product. The great potential of animal viruses is that they provide unique footholds within the mammalian cell for attacking these complex problems, for which other approaches may be virtually nonexistent. Virus infection is the only experimental procedure available by which a defined segment of genetic material can be introduced into a mammalian cell. Since viruses contain only a limited number of genes, from three to several hundred, and viral nucleic acid can be isolated in highly purified and undamaged form, it is technically feasible to analyze in detail the transcription and translation of specific viral macromolecules, and the intracellular controls of these processes, employing the virus-infected cell for experimental analysis.

Major Animal Virus Groups and the Diversity of Animal Viruses

More than 500 animal viruses of various sizes and degrees of chemical complexity have been described, containing either DNA or RNA, and multiplying or maturing in different parts of the cell. However, most animal viruses have been classified into eight groups on the basis of biochemical and biophysical properties of the virion (the extracellular mature virus particle) (3): four DNA-containing groups, the papovaviruses, adenoviruses, herpesviruses, and poxviruses; and four RNA-containing groups, the picornaviruses, reoviruses, arboviruses, and myxoviruses. Viral DNAs range in size from 3 million to 160 million daltons, are double-stranded,and either circular (papovaviruses) or linear. Viral RNAs have molecular weights ranging from 2 million for the picornaviruses to over 10 million for the reoviruses, the latter uniquely being double-stranded. This great variety in chemical composition (4), structure, and site of replication, presumably reflecting as well differences in replicative patterns and induced cellular modifications, endow animal viruses with a unique role in dissecting cellular function in molecular terms: by infecting homogeneous cell cultures one can experimentally insert viral genetic material of different types and sizes into defined intracellular regions and study the ensuing biosynthetic events.

Excellent reviews of the biochemistry of virus multiplication by Darnell (5), Joklik (6), Levintow (7), and Tamm & Eggers (8) have appeared during the past two years. The RNA viruses have been particularly well covered and reports published during the past two years have reinforced but not altered substantially our understanding of the biosynthesis of these viruses. Recently, much new work on the DNA viruses has appeared. Accordingly, this review covers in detail the biosynthesis of DNA animal viruses.

Experimental virology, its variables and pitfalls: cells, viruses, isotopes, inhibitors, and enzymes.—It is often difficult to evaluate the validity and significance of reported virus-induced biosynthetic modifications. Modern virus research makes many demands on the investigator, insisting that he be not only a rigorous biologist capable of dealing quantitatively with cell cultures and viruses, but also be well trained in biochemical methodology and concepts in order to study effectively the virus-infected cell. It is not surprising that numerous conflicting reports confuse the literature on virus-induced biosynthetic modifications [e.g., see (9)], and that reported observations are often not further developed or substantiated. Several possible causes of these discordant results, evaluated in retrospect, are briefly discussed below.

The host cell employed for virus infection, whether it is a primary culture or an established line, whether it is in the stationary or exponential phase of growth, and the specific medium employed, represent variables which may determine the cellular response to virus infection. For example, infection with pseudorabies virus will stimulate or depress DNA synthesis depending upon whether the cells are in stationary or exponential phase of growth prior to infection (10). The need to define carefully the physiological state of the host cell before and during virus infection is obvious. Although exponentially growing cells appear most suitable for biochemical analysis of virus infection, mainly because this condition is readily defined and reproduced experimentally, workers have often preferred to use "nongrowing" cells, rationalizing that such cells possess decreased metabolic levels (as compared to exponentially growing cells), thus providing a conveniently low base line for the detection of virus-induced modifications. These considerations emphasize the need to determine the relevance of a viral-induced biosynthetic modification to the process of viral replication. However, evaluating the relationship to virus replication of a particular metabolic change is often difficult. An important approach is illustrated by studies of thymidine kinase induction in vaccinia virus-infected cells. Virus mutants have been isolated (11) which lack the ability to induce thymidine kinase, yet replicate normally. This example suggests that some virus-induced alterations are not essential for virus replication in a particular cell culture, although perhaps required for virus growth in other cell types which may be restricted normally in certain metabolic activities. Virus-induced biosynthetic changes may be due also to nonspecific cell damage accompanying viral infection. In view of these variables it seems wise to maintain an open mind with regard to conflicting results and the relevance of viral-associated biosynthetic alterations to virus replication.

The purity of the virus inoculum used to infect cells for experimental analysis and the number of virus particles adsorbed per cell (multiplicity of infection), are variables often not analyzed or understood with regard to virus-induced modifications and their detection. Ideally, *all* cells should be infected simultaneously. Otherwise, if the major proportion of cells is uninfected, specific biosynthetic alterations may be missed, or asynchrony of infection may distort the temporal sequence of biosynthetic events. Also, in mixed populations, products of infected cells possibly may affect uninfected cells, producing metabolic changes wrongly attributed to virus replication. To achieve complete infection, large virus inocula are generally employed, giving input multiplicities of 100 to 1000 PFU per cell. However, high input multiplicities alone are no guarantee that all cells are infected and produce virus; the important parameter, the proportion of cells infected, is often not stated or determined. For example, infection of a majority of mouse embryo cells in culture by polyoma virus is difficult, even with input multiplicities of 1000 PFU per cell (12), and this disturbing fact clouds the interpretation of recent important results.

An additional consideration, only occasionally examined, is the effect of the multiplicity of infection on cellular metabolism. The introduction of one, ten, or 1000 viral particles into a cell may be expected to modify the temporal sequence of biosynthetic events (13).

Commonly, crude virus stocks are employed to infect cells for experimental use. Such preparations are composed mainly of disrupted cell material which possibly may produce nonspecific effects unrelated to virus infection. This problem may be avoided by using chemically purified virus, preferably of clonally derived virus strains.

A large amount of biochemical research on virus-infected cells uses radioisotopes in experiments to study (*a*) the intracellular localization and the rate of synthesis of RNA, DNA, and protein; (b) viral precursor relationships; and (c) the intracellular fate of labeled viral components. It is not known to what extent conflicting reports in the literature may be due to the uncritical use of isotopic techniques. For example, the rate of synthesis of RNA, DNA, or protein in infected and uninfected cells is usually determined by adding radioactive precursors to the medium and measuring the amount of radio-activity incorporated into RNA, DNA, or protein after an empirical period. However, the controls necessary to validate the assumption that incorpora-tion of isotope reflects net synthesis of macromolecules are often not run, i.e., is incorporation linear and does it remain so during the incorporation period and is the intracellular pool rapidly saturated? Further, is the size and spe-cific activity of the pool the same in infected and uninfected cells?

Inhibitors, such as FUDR, actinomycin D, and puromycin, are widely used to study the synthesis of DNA, RNA, and protein in virus-infected cells. The concentration of inhibitor effective in blocking macromolecular synthesis and that level causing toxic and other undefined side effects, may depend upon the cell type and medium employed. However, often the spe-cificity and effectiveness is assumed rather than carefully established for each virus-cell system, and the interpretation of such studies is necessarily ambig-uous.

The initial demonstration by Flaks & Cohen (14) of bacteriophage induced enzyme synthesis has spurred the search for similar phenomena in animal virus-infected cells. Increases in enzyme activity have been demon-strated thus far in cells infected with members of six of the eight major ani-mal virus groups, illustrating the generality of this phenomenon. The virolo-gist, now studying enzymes in virus-infected cells, must learn the techniques and pitfalls of enzyme chemistry, if he is not to contribute more misinforma-tion than useful data to the literature.

BIOSYNTHETIC MODIFICATIONS INDUCED
BY DNA ANIMAL VIRUSES

The virions of the four major DNA-virus groups differ widely in size, composition, and DNA content (4, 15). They range in diameter from $45 m\mu$ for the comparatively simple papovaviruses to approximately 300 mμ for the complex poxviruses, with corresponding DNA sizes of 3 to 160 million daltons (4, 15). The biosynthesis of representative members of the four DNA groups has been studied during the past four years and appears generally to involve the following series of events: (a) attachment of the virus to the host cell and subsequent transport to nuclear or cytoplasmic sites (16); (b) intra-cellular "uncoating" of the viral DNA; (c) transcription of specific regions of parental DNA; (d) attachment of the transcribed product, viral messenger RNA, to cytoplasmic or nuclear (?) ribosomes; (e) synthesis of viral-specific enzymes and other "early" proteins; (f) replication of viral DNA, presum-ably by the cellular or viral-coded DNA polymerase; (g) a second wave of transcription involving parental or progeny viral DNA or both; (*h*) translation of these viral messenger RNAs to viral capsid proteins and other viral-specific proteins, some involved in regulatory functions; and (*i*) the final construction of the virion, believed to occur by a process of self-assembly at least with the simpler viruses (17).

While the overall replication pattern of the DNA viruses may be similar, the individual biosynthetic steps can differ greatly. This is not surprising in view of the radically different intracellular sites of multiplication, chemical composition, and especially the wide range of information content. The characteristic biosynthetic pattern of each DNA-virus group would be expected to differ considerably and accordingly each group is discussed separately below.

PAPOVAVIRUSES

This group of small tumor-producing viruses (45 and 55 mμ in diameter) containing DNA and protein (4, 15), include polyoma, simian virus-40 (SV 40), Shope rabbit papilloma, human papilloma (wart), and several other animal papilloma viruses. Toolan H-1 (18), Kilham rat (19), and X-14 (20) viruses, although tentatively grouped with the papovaviruses, are only about 20 mμ in diameter and clearly form a new virus group. Papovavirus DNAs are small (3 to 5 million daltons), double-stranded, circular, and infectious; of the four DNA virus groups, only the papovaviruses have yielded infectious DNAs. The base compositions of papovavirus DNAs (43 to 49 per cent G+C) are similar to those of mammalian cell DNAs (42 to 44 per cent), suggesting a possible relationship between oncogenicity and base composition (15). The structure and mode of replication of the papovaviruses and the biosynthetic alterations induced by infection are of particular interest since virus-cell interaction can lead to either (*a*) cytocidal infection resulting in viral replication and cell death, or (*b*) neoplastic transformation of "normal" to "cancer" cells. Furthermore, both phenomena can be studied in cells cultured *in vitro*. Because viruses are the only carcinogens active *in vitro*, where the neoplastic process can be analyzed in molecular terms, their study provides an extremely important experimental approach for the study of cancer and the regulation of cell growth (21). The papovaviruses contain only three to eight genes, and it is a reasonable expectation that the identification of each gene function will lead to an understanding of the mechanism of cell transformation.

Polyoma virus-cytocidal infection.—The replication of polyoma virus has been studied mainly in mouse embryo cell cultures, where unfortunately even with high multiplicities it is difficult to infect all cells (12). Viral capsid protein (22) and viral DNA (23) accumulate, but are not necessarily synthesized, in the cell nucleus, as shown by immunofluorescence and autoradiography. The time of formation of viral protein, viral DNA, and infectious virus has been studied, using puromycin to inhibit protein synthesis and an infectious DNA assay (24): early proteins required for virus and viral DNA formation are first formed at 8 to 9 hours after infection, viral DNA is made starting at 12 to 14 hours, the full complement of protein needed for virus maturation first appears at 14 hours, and virus maturation begins at 22 to 24 hours after infection. The time when virus maturation is complete was not established, presumably because of the uncertainties involved in a nonsynchronous, incompletely infected cell system. Similar sequences of biosynthetic events, differing in time scale, have been reported for representative members of the three other DNA animal virus groups and with the T-even bacterial viruses.

Little was known about macromolecular metabolism in polyoma virus-infected cells until the past year when several provocative although somewhat conflicting reports appeared, bearing on the mechanism of virus transformation as well. Minowada (25) initially detected an increased proportion of cells synthesizing DNA at three to five days after polyoma virus infection, by autoradiographic analysis of thymidine incorporation; however, the small proportion of infected cells and the slow rate of virus formation made interpretation of these results difficult. DNA synthesis during polyoma virus infection was studied in detail by Dulbecco, Hartwell, and Vogt (26, 27). Dense monolayers of mouse kidney cells, initially possessing low rates of DNA synthesis and low DNA enzyme activities, were infected with polyoma virus under conditions where only 50 to 60 per cent of cells became virus producers, as judged by immunofluorescent analysis of virion protein formation. Under these conditions infectious DNA is synthesized from about 24 to 36 hours, while mature virus is formed from 24 to 55 hours after infection. DNA synthesis is stimulated tenfold between 16 and 30 hours after infection, as measured by the incorporation of H^3-thymidine and P^{32}-phosphate; there is a 25 per cent increase in the DNA content of the culture. The DNA synthesized during this time consists of about two thirds cell DNA and one third viral DNA as shown by chromatography, infectious DNA assay, and hybridization measurements. It was concluded that polyoma virus uniquely induces the synthesis of cellular DNA, a function thought to be related to viral carcinogenesis, and not reported with any other DNA virus.

Similar findings were reported independently by Weil and co-workers (28) who found a large increase in thymidine incorporation 20 to 45 hours after infection (80 to 90 per cent of the mouse kidney cells are stated to be virus producers). Sedimentation velocity analyses disclosed that most of the newly synthesized DNA is cellular. Recent studies by Winocour and co-workers (29, 30) have further confirmed the increased DNA synthesis and thymidine incorporation, and also demonstrated enhanced formate and methionine incorporation into polyoma-infected cultures.

The hypothesis that polyoma virus can induce cellular DNA synthesis has been challenged by several recent studies (12, 31, 32). Molteni and co-workers (31) confirmed the stimulated thymidine uptake in polyoma-infected cell cultures, but since only 5 per cent of the cells were infected in their experiments, they concluded that increased DNA synthesis occurs mainly in uninfected cells. In this regard, it would seem profitable to test whether medium from, and extracts of, infected cells will stimulate DNA synthesis in uninfected cells. Sheinin & Quinn (12), employing a virus-cell system un-complicated by the presence of uninfected cells, suggest that polyoma virus inhibits rather than stimulates the synthesis of host cell DNA. Infection of exponentially growing mouse embryo cells with a polyoma virus variant pro-duced 100 per cent infection at high input multiplicities (1000 PFU per cell). Under these conditions, cell mitosis is inhibited, viral protein is made starting at 14 hours, and virus maturation occurs between 14 and 36 hours after in-fection. By autoradiographic analysis of uninfected cultures, it was shown that 30 per cent of uninfected cells synthesize DNA at any one time, as ex-pected with an asynchronous exponentially growing culture. The same pat-tern occurs during the first 12 hours of infection. A dramatic change takes place, however, between 12 to 20 hours after infection: the fraction of cells synthesizing DNA increases to 90 per cent but less DNA appears to be made in each cell, as judged from the intensity of nuclear labeling. The authors conclude that cell DNA synthesis ceases at 12 hours and only viral DNA is made after this time. Although quantitative data and criteria for distinguishing host DNA from viral DNA were lacking in these investiga-tions, later experiments in which host cell and viral DNA were separated by chromatography support the conclusion that cellular DNA synthesis in ex-ponentially growing cells is inhibited by polyoma virus infection (32).

A possibly important factor in the above studies may be the growth state of the cells. Stationary phase cells were used when stimulated DNA synthesis was found, while exponentially growing cells were employed when inhibition of cell DNA synthesis was claimed. A somewhat similar situation holds with pseudorabies infection (10). These interesting findings concerning the stimulation of DNA and obviously require further cytological and bio-chemical studies to establish their relevance to viral replication and carcino-genesis.

In an attempt to elucidate the mechanism of cellular DNA induction, the DNA-synthesizing enzymes were assayed in extracts of uninfected and in-fected cells (26, 27). Starting at 16 hours after infection, the activities of three enzymes increased sharply, TdR kinase and dCMP deaminase rose to levels ten to 15 times higher, and DNA polymerase three to seven times higher than those of uninfected cells. No changes in dCMP and dAMP kinase activity were detected. Only infectious virus induces an increase in enzyme activity; empty capsids are ineffective. The synthesis of DNA continues for 40 hours, but the increase in enzyme activity ceases at 28 hours, presumably due to the operation of a viral-induced regulatory mechanism, such as that described for vaccinia virus (33) and T2 bacteriophage (34). Studies on mechanism lead to the conclusion (27) that polyoma virus induces an increase in the rate of synthesis of TdR kinase and dCMP deaminase since (a) viral-induced enzyme activation appears to be unlikely because infected cell extracts do not stimulate the enzyme activity of uninfected cell extracts; (b) viral-induced stabilization of labile enzyme molecules is not supported by the results of enzyme stability studies; and (c) simultaneous protein synthesis is essential for increased activity. Frearson and co-workers (35) independently reported a three- to sixfold increase in TdR kinase and a twofold increase in thymidylic acid synthetase late after infection with polyoma virus. A recent report (36) further confirms the increased TdR kinase activity. A comparison of several properties of TdR kinase and dCMP deaminase in crude extracts of infected and uninfected cells disclosed no substantial differences (27), but differences in rate constants between viral-induced and cellular TdR kinase were reported (36).

An important question is whether polyoma-induced enzymes are coded for by viral or cell genes. Polyoma virus contains about 3×10^6 daltons of DNA, corresponding to about 4500 nucleotide pairs of molecular weight 660. According to present coding theories, groups of three nucleotide pairs code for each amino acid; thus, there is sufficient genetic information in polyoma DNA to code for only 1500 amino acids. Since proteins generally range in molecular weight from 20,000 to 50,000, the polyoma genome may code for as few as three proteins of molecular weight 50,000 (500 amino acids each) or as many as seven to eight proteins of molecular weight 20,000 (200 amino acids each). Several viral genes probably are required for capsid proteins, and others may code for the viral-specific transplantation (37, 38) and tumor antigens (39) found in polyoma-induced tumor cells. It seems unlikely therefore that sufficient coding capacity is present in the viral genome to code for all of the induced enzyme activities as well. One may speculate that the virus affects a key control mechanism which derepresses a block of host cell enzymes involved in DNA synthesis.

Host cell DNA is not degraded following polyoma virus infection (12, 28), nor is there any change in DNA configuration or base composition (28).

Autoradiographic measurements on the incorporation of radioactive leucine (40) suggest an increased synthesis of nuclear and nucleolar proteins in polyoma-infected cells. However, the overall rate of protein and RNA synthesis in stationary phase mouse embryo cells was stated to be unaffected by infection (26).

Under conditions in which FUDR prevents both the synthesis of infectious virus and the incorporation of cytidine into DNA, "normal" amounts of viral protein and empty virus particles are formed (41), suggesting that the parental virus genome codes for the formation of viral protein. However, this conclusion may not be valid since, as with most inhibitor experiments, the synthesis of a few progeny DNA molecules in each infected complex cannot be ruled out.

SV40 virus-cytocidal infection.—To date, very little definitive information is available on the kinetics of synthesis of viral DNA and protein and the effects of SV40 virus on cellular biosynthetic processes. This is unfortunate, since this tumor-producing virus, initially found as a contaminant of the poliovirus vaccine (42), may provide key systems for studying virus-induced neoplasia.

Cytological studies provide evidence for the nuclear synthesis or accumulation of SV40 virus and for a possible late cytoplasmic phase (43). Virus is made between 24 and 72 hours after infection of African green monkey cells; the formation of both infectious virus and viral protein is suppressed by FUDR, implying that progeny DNA codes for the synthesis of capsid protein (44), a result differing from that reported with polyoma virus (41). Infection of monkey kidney and human diploid cells does not alter the rate of RNA or protein synthesis (45), as is also the case with polyoma virus. Cells infected in the stationary phase produce virus and lyse, while replicating green monkey kidney cells upon infection continue to replicate, produce low yields of virus, and may be transformed (45). Clearly, these curious phenomena should be more clearly defined at a cellular level.

Thymidine kinase, present in low levels in monkey kidney cells, is increased eight- to twelvefold after infection with SV40 virus (46); actinomycin D prevents this stimulation, implicating DNA-dependent RNA synthesis in thymidine kinase induction.

Transformation of cells in vitro.—Several papovaviruses can permanently transform "normal" cells in culture into "cancer" cells (47, 48). Cellular alterations, which often but not always accompany transformation, include loss of contact inhibition ["contact inhibition" refers to the arrest of growth when cell-to-cell contact is made in monolayer culture], changed morphology, altered chromosome number and shape, and increased growth rate (49). Transformed cells generally produce tumors in appropriate animals and usually are recognized and assayed by their ability to form dense, multi-layered colonies (21), easily scored by simple cloning procedures. The continued synthesis of at least two new viral-specific antigens, the "tumor" and "transplantation" antigens, is a consistent feature of virus-transformed cells.

Information on the mechanism of viral transformation and the biosynthetic alterations accompanying this process are fragmentary and limited mainly to polyoma and SV40 viruses. Because only a small proportion of cells in culture generally are transformed by these viruses (50–52), biochemical analysis of the transformation process has not been feasible; what is urgently needed for biochemical studies is a virus-cell system permitting synchronous transformation of all or most cells in a population.

Very little has been done on the comparative biochemical analysis of the neoplastic end product, the virus-transformed cell, with the normal cell of origin. Such information also may provide clues concerning the nature of the neoplastic process.

Polyoma virus-transformation.—Infection of newborn hamsters, mice, and rats with polyoma virus usually produces fatal tumors. *In vitro* infection of mouse and hamster embryo cells or a permanent hamster cell line leads to transformation of only a small proportion of the cells, a maximum of 5 to 10 per cent under optimal conditions (50, 51). This upper limit is not due to genetically insusceptible cells, since similar transformation rates are found for a number of clonally derived hamster fibroblast cultures (53). Viral DNA induces tumors in animals (54) and transforms cells in culture (55).

Polyoma-transformed cells do not require the presence or synthesis of infectious virus to maintain their neoplastic properties (56). Attempts to detect alternative viral forms including "transforming" virus, incomplete virus (by immunological methods), infectious DNA, or a "provirus" state (using induction techniques successful with lysogenic bacteria), have proven negative (56).

Virus-free polyoma tumors and transformed cells contain two new viral-specific antigens unrelated to the structural antigens of the virion (37–39): (a) the transplantation antigen, detected by its ability to induce resistance to tumor transplantation, and (b) the "tumor" antigen, demonstrated by complement fixation or immunofluorescence with serum from tumor-bearing animals. Viral-specific tumor antigens have been previously found in tumors induced also by SV40 virus (57) and adenovirus type 12 (58). These immunological data provide indirect evidence for the continued presence of at least a portion of the viral genome in the tumor cell.

Direct experimental proof of the presence of polyoma DNA in virus-transformed cells is lacking, however (56). This question of critical importance for deciphering the mechanism of viral carcinogenesis is very difficult to answer experimentally. A single copy of the polyoma genome in a tumor cell would represent only a very small portion of the total cellular DNA, about one part in two million, and if only a single viral gene were present, about one part in ten million. Nucleic acid hybridization techniques currently in use provide the necessary specificity for recognizing the viral genome by means of virus-specific nucleotide sequences; however, the sensitivity necessary for its detection is difficult to attain, requiring (a) the preparation of viral DNA, viral messenger RNA, or synthetic viral "complementary" RNA of very high specific radioactivity (200,000 to 1,000,000 counts per minute/μg nucleic acid), and (b) hybridization techniques with high efficiencies and very low background "noise" levels. Studies attempting to detect viral DNA in polyoma-induced tumor cells have yielded enigmatical results. Winocour (59), in a detailed analysis using DNA-RNA hybrid formation, did not detect hybridization between tumor DNA and polyoma "complementary" RNA (made on a polyoma DNA template with the *Escherichia coli* DNA-dependent RNA polymerase). Based on reconstruction experiments, these results indicate that fewer than 20 copies of the viral genome are present per tumor cell. Axelrod, Habel & Bolton (60), on the other hand, using DNA-DNA hybrid formation, detected complementary nucleotide sequences between polyoma DNA and normal mouse DNA but found increased complementarity between polyoma DNA and polyoma-induced tumor DNA. These data are compatible with the integration of the viral genome into the tumor cell. The number of viral genomes per cell, although not given, may be estimated from the reported degree of hybridization to be between 5 and 25. More recently. Winocour reported that synthetic "complementary" RNA made on a mouse DNA template shows considerable homology with polyoma DNA, but not with DNA from rabbit papilloma virus, vaccinia virus, bacteriophage T4, or *Escherichia coli* (61). The homology between polyoma DNA and mouse DNA confirms the previous results reported by Axelrod et al. (60). However, increased homology between polyoma DNA and synthetic RNAs made on templates of polyoma-induced tumor DNAs was not observed by Winocour (61), in contrast to the previous results using DNA-DNA hybrid measurements (60).

Complementary nucleotide sequences were detected also between rabbit synthetic RNA and both rabbit papilloma DNA and polyoma DNA (61); however, the nucleotide sequences homologous to cell DNA in these two viruses appear to be different. The extent of nucleotide sequence homology between virus and cell DNAs could not be quantitated since the completeness of transcription of the *in vitro*-transcribed RNAs is not known. The existence of natural homology, i.e., nucleotide sequences held in common between cell and tumor virus DNA, may be important for the postulated interaction between viral and cell DNA leading to carcinogenesis. A mechanism analogous to bacterial lysogeny may be involved since the DNAs of bacteriophage lambda and its host cell, *E. coli*, also possess nucleotide sequences in common (62, 63). The presence of natural homology between animal virus and cell DNAs, although extremely interesting, complicates the already formidable task of detecting the viral genome in the tumor cell. Alternative approaches are needed, for example, the analysis of the messenger RNA fraction of transformed cells for viral information.

The base compositions of tumorigenic adenovirus types 12 and 18 and the papovaviruses are similar (64) and overlap that of mammalian cell DNA. This may suggest the possible existence of a nucleotide sequence common to the tumorigenic virus DNAs which may be complementary to a portion of the cell genome. Evidence concerning these prospects is fragmentary. Tumorigenic adenoviruses possess large nucleotide sequences in common (65, 66); however, it is not known to what extent these reflect viral cistrons concerned with carcinogenesis. No homology was detected between synthetic polyoma RNA and the DNAs of rabbit papilloma and SV40 viruses (59).

The transforming ability of polyoma virus is destroyed at about one half the rate of its reproductive ability by four different methods of inactivation (67, 68), indicating that only 50 per cent of the genome or at most four genes (assuming a total of eight), are involved in transformation. This suggests that viral transformation is a simpler process than viral replication, involving fewer gene functions. One may speculate that two genes are required to specify the viral-specific transplantation and tumor antigens, and a third gene to synthesize the thick coat of acid mucopolysaccharide associated with polyoma virus-transformed cells (69). It should be understood that no definitive information is yet available on the function of the several genes responsible for cell transformation by polyoma virus, but the intriguing possibilities suggest many interesting experiments.

SV40 virus-transformation.—Simian virus-40, found naturally in monkeys, is similar to mouse polyoma virus in several ways, including the possession of a ring-shaped DNA molecule of 3×10^6 molecular weight (70), which is both infectious (71, 72) and oncogenic (73, 74). This virus seems ideally suited for biochemical studies on viral oncogenesis since it can be grown in established monkey cell lines, is readily purified (75), and can transform cells *in vitro* with efficiencies approaching 50 per cent (76). To date, however, very little biochemical information about SV40-induced transformation is available.

Thus far, SV40 virus has been found to induce tumors only in hamsters, but transformation *in vitro* has been demonstrated with hamster, rabbit, mouse, porcine, and bovine cells (73, 77). It uniquely transforms human cells in culture (78–80), often producing specific chromosomal alterations.

Infectious virus has been detected in some SV40-induced tumors and transformed cells, but not in others, but it seems clear that the presence of infectious virus is not essential for maintaining the transformed state (81). Two puzzling reports (82, 83) on the "induction" of small amounts of infectious virus in SV40-transformed cells need further examination at a single cell level before their significance can be evaluated. SV40-induced tumor and transformed cells synthesize a viral-specific complement-fixing antigen (tumor antigen) (57) presumed to be identical to the intranuclear antigen detected in SV40-transformed cells by immunofluorescence (84, 85) (using serum from hamsters carrying SV40 tumors); virion antigens are absent from transformed cells. The presence of the SV40 tumor antigen in five species of transformed cells (84) supports the concept that the tumor antigen is coded for by the viral genome; the alternative mechanism that a cellular gene, common to five different species, is activated by virus infection seems less likely. Of further significance, the SV40 tumor antigen is found also during the normal viral replication cycle in green monkey cells (84, 86, 87), prior to the formation of virion antigens.

Recent studies have provided additional information on the localization, chemical nature, and mechanism of formation of the SV40 tumor antigen. The antigen is present in 100 per cent of the nuclei of transformed cells, bound in some manner to nuclear RNA (as inferred by the elimination of fluorescent staining by RNase treatment of fixed cell preparations), and is absent from the nucleoli (88). As studied in crude tumor cell extracts, the antigen is a soluble protein (i.e., digested by trypsin) with a sedimentation coefficient of 18S (as determined by zone centrifugations in sucrose gradients) indicating a relatively high molecular weight, about 600,000 (88). Immunologically, it is distinct from viral coat protein, and antibodies against the tumor antigen do not react with chemically degraded virus particles, indicating also that the antigen is not an internal component of the virion (88).

Studies on the formation of the tumor and viral antigen during the replication cycle of SV40 virus show that the DNA antagonists, arabinosyl cytosine and FUDR (88, 89, 90) block the synthesis of viral coat protein, but not tumor antigen, while actinomycin prevents synthesis of both viral and tumor antigens (90). An obvious interpretation is that during viral replication a messenger RNA molecule transcribed from a specific portion of the parental viral genome codes for the synthesis of the tumor antigen. Furthermore, this implies that the segment of viral DNA and its corresponding messenger RNA species are present in every SV40-induced tumor cell. The proof of this mechanism may require the isolation of viral-specific messenger RNA from tumor cells and the demonstration of its homology with viral DNA and its messenger activity for tumor antigen synthesis in an *in vitro* protein-synthesizing system. Alternatively, the tumor antigen may be a product of a cellular gene which is activated or "derepressed" by virus infection. Although this hypothesis is considered unlikely, mainly because the tumor antigen is virus-specific and not cell species-specific, it may be not too far-fetched in view of (*a*) the large number of genes shared by different mammalian species (91), and (*b*) the likelihood that only a small proportion of the total genome in any particular cell population is actually expressed. Tumor antigen formation is induced also by infection with SV40 DNA (92), eliminating a possible role of viral coat protein in a derepression mechanism, and further supporting a coding function for viral DNA in antigen synthesis.

The biological function of the tumor antigen in the transformation process is completely unknown. The isolation and characterization of this material may aid significantly in establishing its role.

Much less is known concerning the transplantation antigen found in SV40-induced tumors (93–95). Recent studies suggest that this antigen is located on the cell surface and is distinct from the nuclear tumor antigen (96, 97). Its role in oncogenesis is unknown.

The established mouse cell line, 3T3, is readily transformed by SV40 virus without cytocidal complications, thus providing a very useful system for the analysis of *in vitro* transformation (98). The growth of uninfected cells is arrested at a low cell density, due to a high degree of contact inhibition, in stage G1 of the growth cycle, i.e., prior to DNA synthesis (99). SV40 virus is able to transform a large fraction of the cell population, releasing growth control, and as a consequence transformed cells grow to densities 10 to 25 times higher than that of normal 3T3 (98). The same cell can be transformed successively by both polyoma and SV40 viruses (100, 101). The doubly transformed cell produces both viral-specific tumor antigens, suggesting the existence of multiple cellular sites for interaction with different oncogenic virus genomes. The frequency of SV40-induced transformation is increased in the presence of iodeoxyuridine and bromodeoxyuridine (102); possibly the incorporation of these thymidine analogues into cellular DNA opens up single-stranded sites capable of interacting with viral DNA, thus facilitating transformation.

Evidence that replicative infection with polyoma virus of nongrowing cell populations stimulates host cell DNA synthesis (26, 28), a function suggested to be related to viral oncogenesis, has already been discussed. In contrast, recent incisive experiments with the SV40-3T3 system (103) do not support this mechanism, at least with SV40-induced transformation. The SV40 virus does not initiate DNA synthesis, cell growth, or transformation in a strictly nongrowing population of 3T3 cells. However, if, after the addition of virus, one division of cells is permitted (by a 1:2 dilution of a confluent monolayer), transformation occurs at the normal frequency. It may be postulated that one cycle of cell division is essential to fix the genetic change involved in transformation, suggesting that transformation involves the interaction of the viral genome with cellular DNA during the active replication of cellular DNA.

The adenovirus-SV40 so-called "hybrid."—The parasitism of some adenoviruses by SV40 genetic material, discovered by Huebner and co-workers (104), is a surprising and not yet fully understood phenomenon. A strain of human adenovirus type 7, once contaminated with but later freed of SV40 virus, was found to induce hamster tumors which contain the complement-fixing tumor antigen specific for SV40. Furthermore, the SV40 nuclear tumor antigen was produced also during cytocidal infection of several cell species (105, 106) with this virus. Since the SV40 antigen-inducing capacity could not be separated from the adenovirus particle by several methods (105, 107), it was concluded that SV40 genetic material was enclosed in an adenovirus capsid. The term "adenovirus-SV40 hybrid" has been coined to describe this virus; however, it is not known whether SV40 DNA is chemically linked with the much larger adenovirus DNA (molecular weight 23 million) as a true hybrid, or whether it is "free" within the virion. Only a portion of the SV40 genome is carried by the "hybrid" since neither SV40 virus nor capsid protein is synthesized by infected cells.

Attempts to isolate pure lines of "hybrid" virus have proven negative and a two-hit relationship was established between virus dilution and plaque induction (108, 109). On the basis of these findings, it was postulated that the adenovirus type 7–SV40 "hybrid" consists of a population of two types of particles, fully infectious "normal" adenovirus particles ("helper" particles) and defective "hybrid" particles. Cells infected with "hybrid" particles alone cannot produce virus unless infected also with nonhybrid adenovirus "helper" particles. The helper adenovirus induces the synthesis of the coat protein which encloses the SV40 genetic material of the "hybrid."

The SV40 genome in the adenovirus 7–SV40 "hybrid" is readily transferred to other adenoviruses including human types 2, 3, 4, 5, and 12 by means of dual infection with "hybrid" and normal adenoviruses (110, 111). Similar yields of "hybrid" virus of both serotypes are produced, suggesting the independent replication of the SV40 genetic component and its random incorporation into adenovirus capsids. These findings suggest that the SV40 genetic material is loosely or not at all linked to adenovirus DNA. However, the actual makeup of the "hybrid" particle is far from clear. It consists of an adenovirus capsid containing at least one incomplete SV40 genome, but is adenovirus genetic material also present? A complete adenovirus genome is unlikely since the "hybrid" is defective and cannot reproduce infectious adenovirus. The presence of only a few SV40 genomes and no adenovirus DNA also seems improbable since a particle of this composition would possess a lower buoyant density that nonhybrid particles and should separate from the latter during density gradient centrifugation. Density gradient separation has not been effective, however (108). An adenovirus capsid containing a large number of incomplete SV40 genomes sufficient to give a DNA content compatible with the buoyant density of the adenoviruses (112) is a possibility, as is also the occurrence of a true genetic hybrid between incomplete adenovirus and SV40 genomes. Clarification of this problem may require the physical isolation of pure "hybrid" particles and the characterization of its DNA components by homology measurements with SV40 and adenovirus DNAs.

The tumors induced by the adenovirus type 7–SV40 "hybrid" appear to be specified by the SV40 genetic information and not by that of adenovirus type 7 which is itself weakly oncogenic. The "hybrid" virus induces tumors sooner and at a higher frequency than does normal adenovirus type 7. In addition, the "hybrid" transforms human cells *in vitro* (113), a property characteristic of SV40 but not adenovirus. However, the most convincing evidence to indicate that the incomplete SV40 genome contains the potential for tumor production is that an artificially produced adenovirus type 2–SV40 hybrid is oncogenic (114), while normal adenovirus type 2 is not oncogenic.

Human adenoviruses generally grow poorly or not at all in monkey kidney cultures, but their growth is greatly enhanced by simultaneous infection with SV40 virus (115). Similarly, the "hybrid" potentiates the growth of adenovirus in monkey kidney cells (111), indicating that the genetic determinant for this function also resides in the "hybrid."

In summary, it appears that the adenovirus 7–SV40 "hybrid" carries the SV40 genetic determinants for tumor antigen synthesis, neoplastic transformation, and the potentiation of adenovirus growth in monkey kidney cells, but it is a defective particle since it cannot synthesize capsid protein, a function which must be supplied by a "helper" adenovirus.

A new type of adenovirus–SV40 "hybrid," differing from that discussed above has been reported recently with types 4 and 12 (116, 117), and appears to involve the incorporation of a complete, infectious SV40 genome within an adenovirus capsid.

ADENOVIRUSES

This group of medium sized (65 to 85 mμ diameter), DNA-containing viruses consists of 48 immunological types (118), 17 from lower animals and 31 of human origin (Types 1 through 31 refer to the human adenoviruses). Several human adenoviruses are of particular interest since they are carcinogenic in newborn animals, and are the first human viruses shown to possess neoplastic properties. Human adenovirus types 1 to 28 have been well characterized chemically (112, 119). They contain from 11.6 to 13.5 per cent DNA (112) and chemical and mass determinations on eleven types (120) indicate that DNA and protein are the sole constituents of the virion.

A surprisingly wide range of DNA base compositions, from 48 to 60 per cent G+C, is found in the human adenoviruses (112). Piña & Green discovered a correlation between base composition and tumorigenicity (112): highly oncogenic (121, 122) adenovirus types 12 and 18 possess the lowest G+C content, 48 to 49 per cent (64), values similar to those of the oncogenic papovaviruses and closer to that of cell DNA (42 to 44 per cent G+C). Types 3, 7, 11, 14, 16, and 21 have somewhat higher G+C contents, 50 to 53 per cent (112); of these, types 3 (120, 123), 7 (124), 14 (120), 16 (120), and 21 (120) appear to be weakly oncogenic. The remaining human adenoviruses contain 55 to 60 per cent G+C (112); none of these has been reported thus far to be oncogenic.

To explain this correlation, it may be postulated that tumorigenic adenoviruses must possess DNA segments complementary to that of the cell; these DNA segments necessarily possess the same base composition. Although the DNAs of the tumorigenic adenoviruses and the cell differ by 5 to 10 per cent in G+C content, their broad thermal denaturation profiles (50 per cent of the DNA melts over a 5° C range) indicate considerable intramolecular heterogeneity in G+C content (125) and suggest that stretches of viral and cell DNA overlap in G+C content. The higher G+C content of the nontumorigenic adenoviruses (>55 per cent G+C) may exclude such overlap.

DNA homology measurement reveals surprising large differences in the genetic makeup of the oncogenic and nononcogenic human adenoviruses (65, 66, 126). Highly oncogenic types 12 and 18 are closely related to each other (80 per cent nucleotide sequence homology) but quite unrelated to nononcogenic types 2 and 4 and to weakly oncogenic types 3, 7, 14, 16, and 21 (10 to 20 per cent homology). Adenovirus DNAs have molecular weights of 21 to 23 million as determined both by sedimentation velocity and electron microscopy measurements and may contain a minimum of 23 genes (127). (The report of a circular DNA of molecular weight five million (128) has not been confirmed by several laboratories (127). The 10 to 20 per cent of the nucleotide sequences common to the highly oncogenic adenovirus types 12 and 18 and the weakly oncogenic adenoviruses would represent from two to six viral cistrons, which may possibly code both for the common features of the adenoviruses and for their tumorigenic capacity. These considerations suggest that if the carcinogenic potential of adenovirus types 3, 7, 14, 16, 21, 12, and 18 lies in the possession of nucleotide sequences common to these viruses, these regions represent a small portion of the total adenovirus genome, approximately one to three viral cistrons.

In view of these large differences in genetic information, one may expect the metabolic alterations induced by infection with adenovirus type 12 and 18 to be quite distinct from those of the other adenoviruses. Information on adenovirus biosynthesis has been obtained mainly with adenovirus types 2, 4, and 5, very little comparative information being available for the oncogenic adenoviruses.

Virus replication.—As visualized by electron microscopy (129), adenovirus particles after adsorption, penetration, and engulfment within phagocytic inclusions, are released near or within the cell nucleus. It is not known whether viral DNA is uncoated in the nucleus of cytoplasm. A brief report (130) suggests that the uncoating process is carried out rapidly by pre-existing host enzymes. Older cytological and cytochemical studies point to a nuclear site for adenovirus formation (118); however, as with other nuclear DNA viruses, it is not known whether viral protein is synthesized in the nucleus or in the cytoplasm and subsequently transferred to the nucleus. However, as discussed below, the presence of adenovirus messenger RNA in cytoplasmic polyribosomes (131) provides evidence for a cytoplasmic site for adenovirus protein synthesis.

The time course of formation of viral DNA, viral protein, and mature virus has been studied in HeLa cell monolayer (132, 133) infected with adenovirus type 5, and in exponentially growing suspension cultures of KB cells infected with adenovirus type 2 (134, 135). Using fluorophenylalanine and 5-fluorodeoxyuridine to inhibit protein and DNA synthesis, the following sequence of events in the replication of adenovirus type 2 was established (134, 135): (*a*) protein(s) essential for viral DNA synthesis are made at about 4 hours after infection; (*b*) viral DNA synthesis begins at 6 to 7 hours; (*c*) the synthesis of viral coat proteins commences at 10 hours; and (*d*) virus maturation occurs between 13 to 28 hours after infection. Over 10,000 PFU, corresponding to 200,000 virus particles, are formed per cell nucleus. Concurrent protein synthesis is needed for continued viral DNA synthesis (135), a requirement not further studied. Direct analysis of the incorporation of radioactive thymidine and valine into adenovirus have confirmed the time course of viral DNA and viral protein synthesis obtained by the more indirect inhibitor studies cited above (135). A similar sequence of biosynthetic events in adenovirus type 5-infected HeLa cultures has been demonstrated by inhibitor studies (133); the time of onset of each event is delayed by 4 hours, probably reflecting differences in virus type or in cell growth state.

Experiments in which pyrimidine analogues (136) and actinomycin D (136, 137) were used disclosed that RNA synthesis is essential during the latent period for subsequent formation of adenovirus types 2 and 5. An increasing proportion of the pulse-labeled RNA formed after infection with adenovirus type 2 is complementary to viral DNA (131, 138), indicating that it is the viral messenger RNA. Pulse-labeled RNA, complementary to adenovirus type 2 DNA, is found in cytoplasmic polyribosomes starting between 6 and 12 hours after infection and reaching a maximum level at about 18 hours

(131); polyribosomes loaded with adenovirus-specific messenger RNA actively incorporate radioactive amino acids, suggesting that some, if not all, adenovirus proteins are made in the cytoplasm.

Synthesis of DNA (132, 139) is required for the formation of viral structural proteins, implying that progeny viral DNA codes for viral coat proteins.

The time of synthesis of viral-specific macromolecules in cells infected with the tumor-producing adenoviruses has not been determined. Viral growth measurement (140) indicate that highly oncogenic types 12 and 31 (a new oncogenic human adenovirus) possess longer latent periods and slower growth rates than adenovirus type 2.

Macromolecular synthesis.—Exponentially growing suspension cultures of KB cells infected with adenovirus type 2 or highly oncogenic adenovirus types 12 or 31 stop dividing but continue to synthesize and accumulate protein, DNA, and RNA, as measured by direct chemical analysis (140, 141). At about 30 hours after infection, the content of these macromolecules per infected cell is from 1.5 to 2 times that of uninfected cells. The protein and DNA content of infected cells increases slightly after this time while the RNA content drops considerably (140); the fate of this "labile" RNA has not been studied. Infected cells do not lyse for as long as 60 hours after infection and virus remains mainly cell-associated. Similar increases in macromolecular content for adenovirus type 4-infected HeLa cells were reported earlier (142).

Pulse-labeling experiments with adenovirus types 2, 12, and 31 infected KB cells indicate that the rate of DNA, RNA, and protein synthesis per infected cell is 1 to 1.5 times that of uninfected cells until about 24 hours after infection, when it declines (140). In general, the net synthesis of macromolecules in adenovirus-infected cells appears to be unaffected until late after infection. The rate of incorporation per cell of radioactive valine, thymidine, and uridine into the acid-soluble pool is stimulated greater than twofold by 12 hours after infection, reflecting, perhaps, the increased size of the infected cells (140).

When type 5 "fiber" antigen is added to uninfected cells, macromolecular synthesis is inhibited, suggesting the hypothesis (143) that the accumulation of this material is responsible for the inhibition of cellular macromolecule synthesis observed late after infection.

Only 19 per cent of the DNA and 6 per cent of the protein made after infection with adenovirus type 2 are incorporated into mature virus (144). Of the excess protein and DNA in type 5-infected cells, a considerable amount is believed to be viral antigenic protein (145) and viral DNA (118). Whether this holds for other adenoviruses, especially the oncogenic types which appear to possess a slow growth rate, remains to be determined.

Enzyme induction.—Infection of exponentially growing KB cells with adenovirus type 2 does not alter the activities of several enzymes concerned in DNA synthesis, including DNA polymerase, TdR, dTMP, dAMP, dCMP, and dGMP kinases (9, 144); in contrast infection of KB cells with vaccinia virus under identical conditions produces three- and eightfold increases in DNA polymerase and TdR kinase activities (9, 144). Thus, of the four DNA virus groups (see later sections), only the adenoviruses appear to lack the ability to stimulate DNA polymerase and thymidine kinase activities. Possibly adenovirus type 2 is unique, or a modest increase in enzyme activity is masked by the normally high enzyme levels present in exponentially growing cells. Recently, a simian adenovirus has been reported to stimulate thymidine kinase activity in monkey kidney cells (46). Perhaps the defectiveness of human adenoviruses in monkey kidney cells is related to their inability to induce certain enzyme activities, and the potentiation by SV40 virus is due to enzyme induction.

Large increases in several DNase activities are induced by infection with poxviruses and herpesviruses, but not with adenoviruses (146).

A two- to threefold increase in aspartic acid transcarbamylase activity is detected at 18 hours after infection of HeLa cells with adenovirus type 5 (147, 148), but only when nongrowing cells are used. Evidence has been presented suggesting that the elevation in activity is caused by a release from feedback inhibition resulting from the depletion of cellular pyrimidine derivatives utilized for viral DNA synthesis (148).

Adenovirus transformation.—"Highly oncogenic" human adenovirus types 12 and 18 produce tumors in a large proportion of newborn hamsters (121, 122) within one or two months after inoculation, while "weakly oncogenic" types, 3, 7, 14, 16, and 21 (120, 123, 124) produce tumors in a much smaller proportion of animals after longer time periods; tumors are produced also in newborn rats and mice. Purified adenovirus type 12 induces tumors within three weeks after inoculation of newborn hamsters and 0.2 μg of virus is effective (125). Transformation *in vitro* of hamster, rat, and rabbit cells by adenovirus type 12 occurs at a low frequency (149–151).

Infectious virus has not been detected in adenovirus-induced tumors (122, 152), but adenovirus-specific, complement-fixing tumor antigens, distinct from virion antigens, are found in virus-induced tumors and transformed cells (123, 153), and antigenically similar or identical T antigens (referred to as "T" antigen when found in cells during cytocidal infection) are synthesized by infected cells (154). Two distinct categories of tumor and T antigens are produced by the adenoviruses: a common cross-reacting antigen shared by 12, 18, and 31 (123, 153), and a different cross-reacting antigen shared by types 3, 7, 11, 14, 16, and 21 (114, 123).

The T antigen is detected in the cell nucleus early after infection with adenovirus types 12 and 18, prior to the synthesis of virion antigens (154, 155). Like the SV40 T antigen, the adenovirus antigen is formed when viral DNA synthesis is blocked (155), suggesting again that the parental viral genome codes for T antigen formation. T antigen partially purified from infected cells is smaller than viral structural proteins (155); in contrast, SV40 T antigen is reported to be much larger (88).

Possibly the adenovirus T antigen is an early enzyme induced by virus infection. The persistence of the immunologically related tumor antigen in adenovirus-induced tumors and transformed cells suggests the integration of part of the viral genome in the tumor cell. Recent studies have provided direct evidence for the presence of functional viral DNA in adenovirus type 12 tumor and transformed cells (156, 157). A large proportion of the rapidly labeled mRNA fraction in the polyribosomes, about 2 to 5 per cent, was shown to be complementary to adenovirus type 12 DNA (156). This RNA species is absent from normal cells and from polyoma and SV40 virus tumor and transformed cells. The rapid synthesis, location in polyribosomes, presence in small quantities, homology with viral DNA, and specificity with regard to cellular origin of RNA and viral origin of DNA, support the conclusion that this material is viral-specific mRNA.

Hybridization measurements (157) between synthetic RNA complementary to adenovirus type 12 DNA and tumor cell DNA, indicate that less than one part of viral DNA is present in 10^5 of cell DNA. Yet, one part in 20 to 50 (2 to 5 per cent) of the mRNA in the polyribosomes of adenovirus type 12 tumor and transformed cells is viral coded (156). It therefore appears that this small amount of viral DNA is preferentially transcribed. The mechanism of selective transcription operative in viral carcinogenesis may represent a specialized case of a more general phenomenon occurring during cell differentiation. These data (156, 157) further suggest that a large amount of viral-specific protein is synthesized by adenovirus type 12 tumor and transformed cells. It seems likely that some of these proteins are involved in the induction and maintenance of the neoplastic state and that they may be identical to the tumor antigens discovered by Huebner and his associates (58, 122). It is important to isolate and characterize these proteins to establish their role in carcinogenesis.

HERPESVIRUSES

These moderately large (120 to 180 mμ diameter), lipid-containing viruses appear to form two distinct classes according to DNA base composition (4): (a) herpes simplex, pseudorabies, and infectious rhinotracheitis possessing an ususually high G+C content, 68 to 74 per cent; and (b) equine abortion, LK, and human cytomegalovirus containing 56 to 58 per cent G+C. The large genome of the herpesviruses, consisting of 70 to 90 million daltons of DNA (4), is two to three times larger than that of the adenoviruses. Like the papovaviruses and adenoviruses, the formation of herpesvirus (158) and its DNA (159) appears to take place in the nucleus. Of the herpesvirus group, the biosynthesis of only herpes simplex and pseudorabies viruses has been studied in depth.

Replication of pseudorabies.—Kaplan and co-workers, in a series of interesting experiments, investigated the replication of pseudorabies virus in exponentially growing and stationary phase rabbit kidney monolayer cultures. Viral DNA is synthesized between 2 and 8 hours (160), viral structural proteins between 2.5 and 10 hours (161), and mature virus from 3 to 10 hours (160); the formation of nonstructural viral-specific proteins, detected by immunological means (161), and of virus-induced enzymes (162) occurs between 1 and 6 hours after infection.

Virus infection affects DNA synthesis differently depending upon the physiological state of the cells. The overall rate of DNA synthesis is stimulated 20-fold in stationary phase cells but is inhibited in exponential phase cells (10). Stationary phase cells synthesize only viral DNA after infection (163). In exponential phase cells, the synthesis of cellular DNA is inhibited starting at 2 hours after infection and is blocked completely by 7.5 hours, while the rate of viral DNA synthesis progressively increases during this period (160).

Studies on the mechanism of inhibition of cellular DNA synthesis by pseudorabies virus indicate: (a) competition between cellular and viral DNA for replication is not involved since reduction in the level of intracellular viral DNA (by FUDR treatment and reversal with thymidine) does not affect the subsequent inhibition of cellular DNA synthesis (164); (b) a greater affinity of DNA polymerase from infected cells for viral DNA than cellular DNA is not the cause, as shown by *in vitro* enzyme tests (164); (c) degradation of cellular DNA after infection does not occur (160); but (d) since puromycin stops the inhibitory process, it was proposed that a specific viral-induced protein blocks cellular but not viral DNA synthesis by an unknown regulatory mechanism (164).

Pseudorabies DNA replicates semiconservatively (165). However, a decreasing amount of viral DNA synthesized during the infectious process undergoes replication, a large portion being converted into a form resistant to DNase action, presumably a viral precursor (166). As with most virus systems, viral DNA is made in excess and only part (20 per cent) of the total viral DNA formed is incorporated into mature virus particles (163).

Infection of stationary phase cells inhibits not only cellular DNA synthesis but cellular protein synthesis as well (161). Although the total rate of protein synthesis remains unchanged after infection, the formation of normal cellular proteins progressively decreases and the synthesis of two new classes of proteins, viral structural proteins and viral-specific nonstructural proteins progressively increases, as detected by immunological analysis (161).

Three enzymes, TdR kinase, dTMP kinase, and DNA polymerase, present in stationary phase cells at barely detectable levels prior to infection, are stimulated greatly within 1 hour after infection, while the levels of dCMP, dGMP, and dAMP kinases remain high and unchanged (162). Enzyme inhibition tests, using gamma globulin prepared against extracts of uninfected and infected cells, suggest that the induced thymidine kinase is a new protein species distinct from the cellular thymidine kinase, while the DNA polymerase and dAMP kinase are antigenically similar or identical to host enzymes (162). A recent brief report (167) indicates that the increased dTMP kinase activity is due to a unique virus-induced stabilization of the enzyme.

Uridine incorporation is inhibited by virus infection of both exponentially growing and stationary cells (10), suggesting that virus specifically blocks RNA synthesis.

The role of progeny DNA in the control of the infectious process was examined (168). When defective progeny viral DNA was formed by the incorporation of 5-bromodeoxyuridine, two effects were noted: (a) the cutoff of enzyme synthesis which normally occurs at 6 hours after infection was prevented, leading to uncontrolled enzyme synthesis, and (b) the normal loss of enzyme activity occurring at 10 to 14 hours, due to leakage of enzymes from infected cells, was also interfered with. It was concluded that progeny viral genomes code for the synthesis of specific proteins which control enzyme synthesis and cell premeability. Bromodeoxyuridine-substituted viral DNA transmits incorrect information, thus interfering with these late viral regulatory processes.

Replication of herpes simplex virus.—Inhibitors studies (169, 170) with infected HEp-2 cells (an established human cell line) show that viral DNA is made between 4 and 14 hours, while virus maturation occurs between 6 and 15 hours after infection. Protein synthesis is required prior to viral DNA formation, presumably reflecting the synthesis of enzymes for viral DNA synthesis. The rates of synthesis of DNA, RNA, and protein, as determined by pulse-labeling experiments, are inhibited after infection, protein synthesis being the least affected (171).

In infected BHK-21 cells (an established hamster cell line), virus is made between 4 and 9 hours (1000 particles per cell), viral structural proteins from 2 to 9 hours, and increases in DNA polymerase and DNase activities occur between 2 and 6 hours after infection; the largest increments in enzyme activity appear to occur in the nuclear fraction (172, 173). Striking increases are found in two DNase activities (146).

It is not known whether these viral-induced enzymes are coded for by the viral or cell genome. TdR kinase activity, barely detectable in a mutant strain of mouse fibroblast cells, is induced by infection with herpes simplex virus (174). This demonstration and the isolation of herpes simplex mutants lacking in thymidine kinase-inducing activity (175), strongly suggest that the viral genome codes for TdR kinase. Furthermore, as noted previously, cells infected with pseudorabies virus (162) induce TdR kinase which is immunologically distinct from the normal cellular enzyme.

Poxviruses

The large, chemically complex, poxviruses (4) are the only DNA viruses which replicate exclusively within the cytoplasm (176). Their large complement of DNA, 160 million daltons, is about one fifteenth the size of the *E. coli* chromosome and suggests that they code for many viral-induced functions, an expectation borne out by recent studies.

The DNAs of vaccinia, rabbitpox, cowpox, ectromelia, and fowlpox (15) possess similar G+C contents, 35 to 37 per cent, which are the lowest of the DNA viruses. Among all the DNA viruses, the replication of vaccinia virus has been studied in greatest detail.

Poxvirus "uncoating."—Uncoating is experimentally defined as the intracellular release of viral DNA from the virion in a form digestible by DNase. Biochemical studies by Joklik (177, 178) have provided a detailed picture of the complex "uncoating" of rabbitpox DNA consistent, in the main, with Dale's electron microscopic studies (179). Purified virus, isotopically labeled specifically in its DNA, protein, and phospholipid moieties, was used to infect cells (177, 178). After rapid adsorption and uptake of whole virus particles into phagocytic vacuoles (179), a two-stage process occurs, as investigated by following the subsequent intracellular fate of the labeled viral constituents (177, 178).

During the first step, the outer membranes of the virion are disrupted, releasing the entire viral phospholipid and 50 per cent of the viral protein and producing DNase-resistant (177) "viral cores" [as visualized by thin section electron microscopy (179)]. This process is thought to involve the action of pre-existing cellular enzymes since it occurs without lag and takes place in the presence of inhibitors of protein and RNA synthesis.

The second step, which releases viral DNA from its core, occurs after a 30- to 60-minute lag, and is dependent upon: (*a*) a functional host cell genome (ultraviolet irradiated cells will not uncoat cores); (*b*) prior RNA synthesis; (*c*) prior protein synthesis; and (*d*) virus particles with undamaged proteins (heat-inactivated particles cannot initiate the uncoating mechanism even though their genome is intact). In the light of these requirements and the view that viral DNA within a DNase-resistant core cannot be transcribed, it has been proposed (178) that a "viral inducer protein" released from the virion during the first step in the uncoating process, derepresses a specific region of the host cell genome, leading to the synthesis of the cytoplasmic "uncoating protein." The uncoating protein digests viral cores, releasing functional poxvirus DNA. The hypothetical uncoating protein is then a proteolytic enzyme, coded for by a cellular gene normally inactive, but perhaps playing a role during some stage of differentiation (6). The hypothetical viral inducer protein and uncoating protein have not yet been isolated and characterized.

Viral replication.—The time course of vaccinia virus DNA and protein formation was studied, using specific inhibitors of DNA and protein synthesis and immunological techniques to detect viral-specific proteins. In vaccinia virus-infected HeLa cells, viral DNA is synthesized from 1.5 to 7 hours after infection (FUDR studies), viral structural proteins from 2 to 14 hours (detected immunologically), the last protein species required for virus formation from 4 to 14 hours (as determined by fluorophenylalanine inhibition), and mature virus from 5 to 14 hours after infection (180, 181). Large amounts of viral-specific protein, including the group-specific nucleoprotein antigen and the "LS" antigen, are formed in the absence of viral DNA synthesis (182–

184), implying that the parental viral genome normally codes for the synthesis of viral structural protein; however, the synthesis of several progeny DNA molecules is difficult to rule out.

Joklik & Becker (185) studied the replication and coating of vaccinia DNA in HeLa cells by direct biochemical analysis of the cytoplasmic fraction. The parental viral genome attaches to large cytoplasmic "aggregates" (185) that are thought to be identical to the viral "factories" observed microscopically (176, 179). As detected by short pulses of C^{14}-thymidine, viral DNA replicates in the aggregates between 1.5 to 4.5 hours after infection at a rate several times the rate of cellular DNA in uninfected cells (185). The total amount of viral DNA synthesized is quite large, amounting to 50 per cent of the total-cellular DNA present. Starting at about 4 hours after infection, when viral DNA synthesis is nearly complete, the stepwise coating of DNA takes place via intermediate DNase-sensitive and DNase-resistant subvirions. Mature virions are formed starting at 5 hours. As with other DNA viruses, only part (about one third) of the viral DNA formed is incorporated into virions. Protein synthesis is required for viral DNA synthesis, presumably reflecting the induction of a new DNA polymerase after uncoating. The aggregates or "factories" in which viral DNA is replicated and coated do not contain messenger RNA, polyribosomes, or a lipid membrane (185) (i.e., they are deoxycholate-insensitive) and therefore differ in these respects from the "virus synthesizing bodies" in which poliovirus is formed (186).

Macromolecular biosynthesis.—Both inhibition and stimulation of DNA synthesis have been reported in vaccinia virus-infected cells [see (9) for example]. An explanation may be provided by recent studies (185) which suggest a rapid inhibition of host DNA synthesis followed by a burst of viral DNA synthesis—the net result being a stimulation. Whether host DNA inhibition or viral DNA synthesis predominates may depend upon the particular system and the environmental conditions. Host DNA is not degraded after infection (187).

The formation of nuclear RNA is unaffected until 3 to 4 hours after infection, at which time marked inhibition occurs (188, 189): ribosomal and transfer RNA are not degraded. The mechanism of inhibition of cell RNA synthesis has not been studied, but it does not appear to be caused by degradation of the cell DNA template (187). In contrast, cytoplasmic RNA synthesis is stimulated, and the newly synthesized cytoplasmic RNA is mainly viral messenger RNA as judged by the following criteria: (*a*) a base composition which matches vaccinia DNA; (*b*) the ability to hybridize with vaccinia DNA; and (*c*) its presence in polyribosomes. The size of viral messenger RNA shifts from about 10S to 20S during the infectious cycle, presumably reflecting sequential transcription of different segments of the viral genome (188). Vaccinia messenger RNA, within 30 to 60 seconds after its formation, becomes associated with 40S subribosomal particles and is subsequently incorporated into polyribosomes (190), a process thought to play a role in the normal cellular formation of polyribosomes. Immunologically identifiable vaccinia protein has been isolated from polyribosomes (191).

An unsolved problem is the question of the enzyme which synthesizes viral messenger RNA; is it the host DNA-dependent RNA polymerase or a new viral-induced enzyme? There are difficulties with either view: vaccinia messenger RNA is made in the cytoplasm, but the cellular RNA polymerase is present in the nucleus (192, 193), bound to DNA in a supposedly non-diffusable form. An alternate mechanism, the viral induction of a new RNA polymerase in the cytoplasm, is also difficult to contemplate since the induction process itself requires a functional RNA polymerase.

Unexplained also are the mechanisms of inhibition of host cell RNA, DNA, and protein synthesis. Since inhibition of DNA synthesis occurs in the absence of protein synthesis and is induced by ultraviolet-inactivated virus, it has been suggested that a viral structural protein directly inhibits DNA formation (185).

A peculiar phenomenon is the instability of the major portion of vaccinia messenger RNA (194, 195): treatment of infected cells with actinomycin results in the rapid degradation of viral polyribosomes under conditions in which uninfected cell polyribosomes are stable (195), and further, the synthesis of immunologically detectable viral proteins is blocked, whereas protein synthesis in uninfected cells continues (194). In sharp contrast, messenger RNA for several viral-induced early enzymes appears to be unusually stable (196, 197), as discussed below.

Enzyme induction.—Poxvirus DNA is made in the cytoplasm, whereas cellular DNA is synthesized normally in the nucleus; therefore, the induction of new enzymes for viral DNA synthesis is not surprising. Several enzyme activities are increased after vaccinia virus infection, including DNA polymerase (9, 144, 197–199), TdR kinase (9, 144, 200–202), and several DNases (146, 203, 204). Virus-induced increases in TdR kinase, DNA polymerase, and DNases are detected by two hours after infection (9, 197, 200). In each case new protein synthesis is required for enzyme induction (196, 197, 205), and the involvement of DNA-dependent RNA synthesis is assumed but not clearly demonstrated.

At 4 to 7 hours after infection, depending upon the particular virus-cell system, enzyme induction is shut off (9, 33, 197, 200). McAuslan (33, 196) demonstrated that the late "repression" of thymidine kinase formation requires three events: (a) the aminopterin-sensitive synthesis of progeny viral DNA; (b) the actinomycin-sensitive synthesis of a "repressor" RNA; and (c) the puromycin-sensitive synthesis of a "repressor" protein. Repression of all three induced enzymes is prevented when progeny viral DNA synthesis is blocked by FUDR (197), and enzyme activity continues to increase for at least 5 hours. The messenger RNA's coding for these early enzymes appear to be very stable in contrast to the marked lability of the bulk of viral messenger RNA (194, 195). These experiments lead to the conclusion that progeny viral cistrons code for the synthesis of proteins which block the function of the messenger RNAs for early enzyme synthesis. Why the parental viral cistron is blocked in this capacity is unexplained, but a similar "switch off" of early enzyme formation is known with bacteriophage-infected cells (34).

A crucial question is whether these virus-induced enzymes are coded for by the host or viral genome. Four possible mechanisms may be proposed to explain virus-induced enzyme increases: (a) the activity of an existing host enzyme is stimulated, e.g., by an allosteric mechanism; (b) a normally functioning host cell gene is further "derepressed" or induced to synthesize increased amounts of the same enzyme species; (c) a nonfunctioning host cell gene is derepressed, producing a new enzyme species not present normally in the cell, although other enzyme molecules (isozymes) with similar activities may be present; or (d) a viral gene codes directly for the synthesis of a new enzyme molecule, although again cellular enzymes with similar activities may be present. It is a formidable task to distinguish rigorously among these alternatives. A dependence upon protein and RNA synthesis may eliminate (a) but not differentiate (b) from (c) or (d). If properties of the new enzyme differ from those of the normal host enzyme, e.g., heat stability, pH optimum etc., then alternatives (c) or (d) are indicated and (b) is eliminated. However, the distinction between alternative (d), in which the viral genome determines the enzyme structure, and (c) in which the cell's genetic potential for making an enzyme remains unexpressed until virus infection, is extremely difficult to decide experimentally. Unequivocal proof of viral coding may require the cell-free synthesis of enzyme activity using viral messenger RNA as a template.

Infection with ultraviolet-irradiated virus, which presumably cannot be uncoated, induces TdR kinase but not DNA polymerase and DNase activities (197). These data suggest that the increase in TdR kinase activity may result from a derepression of a cellular gene by a virion protein. Thymidine deoxyribose kinase of infected cells differs in several properties from that of uninfected cells (196, 206), but this is not proof of viral coding and may merely indicate that the enzyme species increased by infection differs from that of the normal host cell, i.e., the cell may have several enzyme species. However, the isolation of vaccinia mutants lacking in TdR kinase-inducing activity, and the differences in properties of TdR kinase induced by vaccinia and by herpes simplex viruses (206), provide a strong argument for viral coding. The question of viral or cell coding for poxvirus-induced thymidine kinase therefore is far from settled.

Vaccinia virus-induced DNA polymerase also has several properties that differ from that of the host cell (197). Here, it may be more reasonable to expect the induction of a viral-coded enzyme since vaccinia DNA is made in the cytoplasm rather than in the nucleus where cellular DNA is replicated. Furthermore, of the nine enzymes of the DNA synthesizing enzyme complex, DNA polymerase appears to be the rate-limiting activity (9). However, with both DNA polymerase and DNase, definitive evidence for viral coding is not yet available.

Wild speculations are in order to explain several unusual findings involved in vaccinia virus replication: (a) the origin of the cytoplasmic RNA polymerase which synthesizes vaccinia messenger RNA; (b) the unusual stability of the "supposed messenger RNA" involved in early enzyme formation; and (c) the role of the induced DNase active on single-stranded DNA. It may be postulated that a small portion of the viral DNA functions directly as a messenger. This DNA segment, necessarily single stranded, may form polyribosomes shortly after infection and code for the formation of a new RNA polymerase, TdR kinase, DNA polymerase, DNase, and other early enzymes. The functions of nucleases are unknown, but possibly vaccinia-induced DNase serves a regulatory role, destroying the single-stranded DNA on the polyribosomes at late times after infection, thus accounting for the observed "switch off" of early enzyme formation. Inconsistent with this scheme is the early appearance of DNase at 1.5 hours after infection, but perhaps this enzyme is inactive intracellularly until the presumed "repressor protein," whose function would involve the activation of DNase, is synthesized later. This would also explain the unusual stability of early enzyme formation in the presence of actinomycin, resulting from a "messenger DNA" and not RNA. Of course, several alternative schemes are also feasible, such as: (a) the virion contains an RNA polymerase molecule; (b) the virion contains a messenger RNA coding for polymerase formation; (c) the transfer of RNA polymerase from the nucleus to cytoplasm; or (d) the migration of a small segment of viral DNA from the cytoplasm to the nucleus which codes for the viral RNA polymerase. Some clever experimentation will obviously be required to decide these questions.

OPEN QUESTIONS

The replication of DNA animal viruses is only beginning to be understood in molecular terms, a number of important questions remain to be answered and several important problems have hardly been touched, as listed below: (a) Practically nothing is known about the mechanism of virus adsorption to host cell and the receptor sites involved. (b) Although the uncoating process has been well studied with the poxviruses, comparable information about the other three DNA virus groups is virtually nonexistent. (c) Where does viral protein synthesis take place in cells infected with the nuclear DNA virus groups (i.e., the papovaviruses, adenoviruses, and herpesviruses)—in the nucleus as cytological evidence would suggest, or in the cytoplasm as is the case with most cellular protein? (d) What selective advantage does viral-directed inhibition of host cell DNA, RNA, and protein synthesis serve for the invading virus? These inhibitions appear to be mediated by proteins in several cases, but the molecular mechanisms involved are obscure. (e) The mechanism of synthesis of viral DNA is not clear. Although poxvirus DNA, which is synthesized in the cytoplasm, is thought to be replicated by a viral-induced DNA polymerase, it is not known whether the viral DNAs of the nuclear viruses are synthesized by the cellular or viral-induced DNA polymerases.

(*f*) Increases in DNA polymerase and thymidine kinase activities have been found in cells infected with poxviruses, herpesviruses, and papovaviruses, but not with human adenoviruses; however, the significance of these enzyme increases is not clear and the role of the ubiquitous thymidine kinase is unknown. (*g*) The possible existence of replicative forms of viral DNA has not been examined, although such intermediates are found in bacteriophage-infected cells. (*h*) Direct experimental proof of viral coding for induced enzymes has not been attempted as yet. (*i*) There is no evidence available as to whether new RNA polymerase enzymes are induced for the transcription of viral DNAs. (*j*) Are specific virus synthesizing structures formed for each of the different DNA viruses as appears to be the case with the poxviruses and picornaviruses? (*k*) Present evidence indicates that the parental viral genome codes for early viral functions while progeny genomes code for the synthesis of virion constituents and for viral control mechanism. The molecular mechanism for selective and sequential transcription of the viral genome during the infectious cycle is completely obscure at the present time. (*l*) What is the mechanism of growth control by DNA tumor-producing viruses? (*m*) What does the natural homology between some tumor virus DNAs and cellular DNA signify? (*n*) The identity and role of the tumor antigen in viral carcinogenesis is only speculative at present. (*o*) The functions of the large number of viral genes, from 3 to perhaps 500, are hard to imagine. Are all viral gene functions expressed during infection?

The queries and unsolved problems listed above suggest that a complete understanding of virus infection in molecular terms will require not only considerably more incisive studies on virus multiplication, but also a fuller insight into cell function in general.

LITERATURE CITED

1. Horsfall, F. L., in *Viral and Rickettsial Infections of Man*, Chap. 1, 1–10. (Horsfall, F. L., Jr., and Tamm, I., Eds., J. B. Lippincott, Philadelphia, 1282 pp., 1965)

2. Watson, J. D., in *Molecular Biology of Gene*, 441–70. (W. A. Benjamin, New York, 494 pp., 1965)

3. Green, M., in *Viral and Rickettsial Infections of Man*, Chap. 2, 11–18. (Horsfall, F. L., Jr., and Tamm, I., Eds., J. B. Lippincott, Philadelphia, 1282 pp., 1965)

4. Green, M., *Am. J. Med.*, **38**, 651–68 (1965) (Virus Symp.)

5. Darnell, J. E., in *Viral and Rickettsial Infections of Man*, Chap. 9, 233–66. (Horsfall, F. L., Jr., and Tamm, I., Eds., J. B. Lippincott, Philadelphia, 1282 pp., 1965)

6. Joklik, W. K., in *Progress in Medical Virology*, 44–96. (Melnick, J. L., Ed., Hafner Publ. Co., Inc., New York, 376 pp., 1965)

7. Levintow, L., in *Annual Review of Biochemistry*, 487-526. (Luck, J. M., and Boyer, P. D., Eds., Annual Reviews, Inc., Palo Alto, 700 pp., 1965)

8. Tamm, I., and Eggers, H. J., *Am. J. Med.*, **38**, 678–98 (1965) (Virus Symp.)

9. Green, M., Piña, M., and Chagoya, V., *J. Biol. Chem.*, **239**, 1188–97 (1964)

10. Kaplan, A. S., and Ben-Porat, T., *Virology*, **11**, 12–27 (1960)

11. Dubbs, D. R., and Kit, S., *Virology*, **22**, 214–25 (1964)

12. Sheinin, R., and Quinn, G., *Virology*, **26**, 73–84 (1965)

13. Penman, S., and Summers, D., *Virology*, **27**, 614–20 (1965)

14. Flaks, J. G., and Cohen, S. S., *Biochim. Biophys. Acta*, **25**, 667–68 (1957)

15. Green, M., in *Viral and Rickettsial Infections of Man*, Chap. 6, 145–74 (Horsfall, F. L., Jr., and Tamm, I., Eds., J. B. Lippincott, Philadelphia, 1282 pE., 1965)

16. Dales, S., in *Progress in Medical Virology*, 1–37. (Melnick, J. L., Ed., Hafner Publ. Co., Inc., New York, 376 pp., 1965)

17. Casper, D. L. D., in *Viral and Rickettsial Infections of Man*, Chap. 4, 51–93. (Horsfall, F. L., Jr., and Tamm, I., Eds., J. B. Lippincott, Philadelphia, 1282 pp., 1965)

18. Greene, E. L., and Karasaki, S., *Proc. Soc. Exptl. Biol. Med.*, **119**, 819–22 (1965)

19. Vasquez, C., and Brailovsky, C., *Exptl. Mol. Pathol.*, **4**, 130–40 (1965)

20. Payne, F. E., Beals, T. F., and Preston, R. E., *Virology*, **23**, 109–13 (1964)

21. Dulbecco, R., *Science*, **142**, 932–36 (1963)

22. Henle, G., Deinhardt, F., and Rodriguez, J., *Virology*, **8**, 388–91 (1959)

23. Williams, M. G., and Sheinin, R., *Virology*, **13**, 368–90 (1961)

24. Gershon, D., and Sachs, L., *Virology*, **24**, 604–9 (1964)

25. Minowada, J. *Exptl. Cell Res.*, **33**, 161–75 (1964)

26. Dulbecco, R., Hartwell, L. H., and Vogt, M., *Proc. Natl. Acad. Sci. U. S.*, **53**, 403–10 (1965)

27. Hartwell, L. H., Vogt, M., and Dulbecco, R., *Virology*, **27**, 262–72 (1965)

28. Weil, R., Michel, M. R., and Ruschmann, G. K., *Proc. Natl. Acad. Sci. U. S.*, **53**, 1468–75 (1965)

29. Winocour, E., Kaye, A. M., and Stollar, V., *Virology*, **27**, 156–69 (1965)

30. Gershon, D., Hausen, P., Sachs, L., and Winocour, E., *Proc. Natl. Acad. Sci. U. S.*, **54**, 1584–92 (1965)

31. Molteni, P., DeSimone, V., Grosso, E., Polli, E., and Bianchi, P. A., *Biochem. J.*, **98**, 78–81 (1966)

32. Sheinin, R., *Virology*, **28**, 621–32 (1966)

33. McAauslan, B. R., *Virology*, **20**, 162–68 (1963)

34. Dirksen, M. L., Wiberg, J. S., Koerner, J. F., and Buchanan, J. M., *Proc. Natl. Acad. Sci. U. S.*, **46**, 1425–30 (1960)

35. Frearson, P. M., Kit, S., and Dubbs, D. R., *Cancer Res.*, **25**, 737–44 (1965)

36. Sheinin, R., *Virology*, **28**, 47–55 (1966)

37. Habel, K., *Proc. Soc. Exptl. Biol. Med.*, **106**, 722–25 (1961)

38. Sjogren, H. O., Hellstrom, I., and Klein, G., *Cancer Res.*, **21**, 329–37 (1961)

39. Habel, K., *Virology*, **25**, 55–61 (1965)

40. Minowada, J., *Gann*, **55**, 267–76 (1964)

41. Sheinin, R., *Virology*, **22**, 368–76 (1964)

42. Sweet, B. H., and Hilleman, M. R.,

Proc. Soc. Exptl. Biol. Med., **105,** 420–27 (1960)

43. Mayor, H. D., Stinebaugh, S. E., Jamison, R. M., Jordon, L. E., and Melnick, J. L., *Exptl. Mol. Pathol.*, 1, 397–416 (1962)

44. Melnick, J. L., Stinebaugh, S. E., and Rapp, F., *J. Exptl. Med.*, **119,** 313–26 (1964)

45. Carp, R. I., and Gilden, R. V., *Virology*, **28,** 150–62 (1966)

46. Kit, S., Dubbs, D. R., DeTorres, R. A., and Melnick, J. L., *Virology*, **27,** 453–57 (1965)

47. Melnick, J. L., in *Viral and Rickettsial Infections of Man*, Chap. 39, 841–59. (Horsfall, F. L., Jr., and Tamm, I., Eds., J. B. Lippincott, Philadelphia, 1282 pp., 1965)

48. Noyes, W. F., *Virology*, **25,** 358–63 (1965)

49. Koprowski, M., *Am. J. Med.*, 716–25 (1965) (Virus Symp.)

50. Vogt, M., and Dulbecco, R., *Proc. Natl. Acad. Sci. U. S.*, **46,** 365–70 (1960)

51. Stoker, M., and Abel, P., *Cold Spring Harbor Symp. Quant. Biol.*, **17,** 375–86 (1962)

52. Todaro, G. J., and Green, H., *Virology*, **23,** 117–19 (1964)

53. Black, P. H., *Virology*, **24,** 179–85 (1964)

54. Orth, G., Atanasiu, P., Boiron, M., Rebiere, J. P., and Paoletti, C., *Proc. Soc. Exptl. Biol. Med.*, **115,** 1090–95 (1964)

55. Crawford, L., Dulbecco, R., Fried, M., Montagnier, L., and Stoker, M., *Proc. Natl. Acad. Sci. U. S.*, **52,** 148–52 (1964)

56. Vogt, M., and Dulbecco, R., *Virology*, **16,** 41–51 (1962)

57. Black, P. H., Rowe, W. P., Turner, H. C., and Huebner, R. J., *Proc. Natl. Acad. Sci. U. S.*, **50,** 1148–56 (1963)

58. Huebner, R. J., Rowe, W. P., Turner, H. C., and Lane, W. T., *Proc. Natl. Acad. Sci. U. S.*, **50,** 379–89 (1963)

59. Winocour, E., *Virology*, **25,** 276–88 (1965)

60. Axelrod, D., Habel, K., and Bolton, E. T., *Science*, **146,** 1466–69 (1964)

61. Winocour, E., *Virology*, **27,** 520–27 (1965)

62. Cowie, D. B., and McCarthy, B. J., *Proc. Natl. Acad. Sci. U. S.*, **50,** 537–43 (1963)

63. Green, M. H., *Proc. Natl. Acad. Sci. U. S.*, **50,** 1177–84 (1963)

64. Green, M., and Piña, M., *Proc. Natl.*

Acad. Sci. U. S., **50,** 44–46 (1963)

65. Lacy, S., Sr., and Green, M., *Proc. Natl. Acad. Sci. U. S.*, **52,** 1053–59 (1964)

66. Lacy, S., Sr., and Green, M., *Science*, **150,** 1296–97 (1965)

67. Benjamin, T. L., *Proc. Natl. Acad. Sci. U. S.*, **54,** 121–24 (1965)

68. Basilico, C., and diMayorca, G., *Proc. Natl. Acad. Sci. U. S.*, **54,** 125–27 (1965)

69. Defendi, V., and Gasic, G., *J. Cellular Comp. Physiol.*, **62,** 23–32 (1963)

70. Crawford, L. V., and Black, P. H., *Virology*, **24,** 388–92 (1964)

71. Gerber, P., *Virology*, **16,** 96–98 (1962)

72. Boiron, M., Paoletti, C., Thomas, M., Rebiere, J. P., and Bernard, J., *Compt. Rend.*, **254,** 2097–99 (1962)

73. Diderholm, H., Stenkvist, B., Ponten, J., and Wesslen, T., *Exptl. Cell Res.*, **37,** 452–59 (1965)

74. Black, P. H., and Rowe, W. P., *Proc. Natl. Acad. Sci. U. S.*, **54,** 1126–33 (1965)

75. Black, P. H., Crawford, E. M., and Crawford, L. V., *Virology*, **24,** 381–87 (1964)

76. Todaro, G. J., and Green, H., *Virology*, **28,** 756–59 (1966)

77. Black, P. H., and Rowe, W. P., *Proc. Soc. Exptl. Biol. Med.*, **114,** 721–27 (1963)

78. Koprowski, H., Ponten, J. A., Jensen, F., Raodin, R. G., Moorehead, P. S., and Saksela, E., *J. Cellular Comp. Physiol.*, **59,** 281–92 (1962)

79. Shein, H. M., and Enders, J. F., *Proc. Natl. Acad. Sci. U. S.*, **48,** 1164–72 (1962)

80. Todaro, G. J., Wolman, S. R., and Green, H., *J. Cellular Comp. Physiol.*, **62,** 257–65 (1963)

81. Melnick, J. L., Khera, K. S., and Rapp, F., *Virology*, **23,** 430–32 (1964)

82. Sabin, A. B., and Koch, M. A., *Proc. Natl. Acad. Sci. U. S.*, **50,** 407–17 (1963)

83. Gerber, P., *Science*, **145,** 833 (1964)

84. Pope, J. H., and Rowe, W. P., *J. Exptl. Med.*, **120,** 121–28 (1964)

85. Rapp, R., Butel, J. S., and Melnick, J. L., *Proc. Soc. Exptl. Biol. Med.*, **116,** 1131–35 (1964)

86. Rapp, F., Kitahara, T., Butel, J. S., and Melnick, J. L., *Proc. Natl. Acad. Sci. U. S.*, **52,** 1138–42 (1964)

87. Sabin, A. B., and Koch, M. A., *Proc. Natl. Acad. Sci. U. S.*, **52,** 1131–38 (1964)

88. Gilden, R. V., Carp, R. I., Taguchi,

F., and Defendi, V., *Proc. Natl. Acad. Sci. U. S.*, **53**, 684–92 (1965)

89. Rapp, F., Melnick, J. L., and Kitahara, T., *Science*, **147**, 625–27 (1965)

90. Rapp, F., Butel, J. S., Feldman, L. A., Kitahara, T., and Melnick, J. L., *J. Exptl. Med.*, **121**, 935–44 (1965)

91. Hoyer, B. H., McCarthy, B. J., and Bolton, E. T., *Science*, **144**, 959–67 (1964)

92. Black, P. H., and Rowe, W. P., *Virology*, **27**, 436–39 (1965)

93. Habel, K., and Eddy, B. E., *Proc. Soc. Exptl. Biol. Med.*, **113**, 1–4 (1963)

94. Koch, M. A., and Sabin, A. B., *Proc. Soc. Exptl. Biol. Med.*, **113**, 4–12 (1963)

95. Defendi, V., *Proc. Soc. Exptl. Biol. Med.*, **113**, 12–16 (1963)

96. Tevethia, S. S., Katz, M., and Rapp, F., *Proc. Soc. Exptl. Biol. Med.*, **119**, 896–901 (1965)

97. Girardi, A. J., *Proc. Natl. Acad. Sci. U. S.*, **54**, 445–51 (1965)

98. Todaro, G. J., Green, H., and Goldberg, B. D., *Proc. Natl. Acad. Sci. U. S.*, **51**, 66–73 (1964)

99. Nilhausen, K., and Green, H., *Exptl. Cell Res.*, **40**, 166–68 (1965)

100. Todaro, G. J., and Green, H., *Science*, **147**, 513–14 (1965)

101. Todaro, G. J., Habel, K., and Green, H., *Virology*, **27**, 179–85 (1965)

102. Todaro, G. J., and Green, H., *Virology*, **24**, 393–400 (1964)

103. Todaro, G. J., and Green, H., *Proc. Natl. Acad. Sci. U. S.*, **55**, 302–7 (1966)

104. Huebner, R. J., Chanock, R. M., Rubin, B. A., and Casey, M. J., *Proc. Natl. Acad. Sci. U. S.*, **52**, 1333–40 (1964)

105. Rowe, W. P., and Baum, S. G., *Proc. Natl. Acad. Sci. U. S.*, **52**, 1340–47 (1964)

106. Rapp, F., Melnick, J. L., Butel, J. S., and Kitahara, T., *Proc. Natl. Acad. Sci. U. S.*, **52**, 1348–52 (1964)

107. Rowe, W. P., Baum, S. G., Pugh, W. E., and Hoggan, M. D., *J. Exptl. Med.*, **122**, 943–54 (1965)

108. Rowe, W. P., and Baum, S. G., *J. Exptl. Med.*, **122**, 955–66 (1965)

109. Boeye, A., Melnick, J. L., and Rapp, F., *Virology*, **28**, 56–70 (1966)

110. Rapp, F., Butel, J. S., and Melnick, J. L., *Proc. Natl. Acad. Sci. U. S.*, **54**, 717–24 (1965)

111. Rowe, W. P., *Proc. Natl. Acad. Sci. U. S.*, **54**, 711–17 (1965)

112. Piña, M., and Green, M., *Proc. Natl. Acad. Sci. U. S.*, **54**, 547–51 (1965)

113. Black, P. H., and Todaro, G. J., *Proc. Natl. Acad. Sci. U. S.*, **54**, 374–81 (1965)

114. Huebner, R. J. (Personal communication)

115. Rabson, A. S., O'Conor, G. T., Berezesky, I. K., and Paul, F. J., *Proc. Soc. Exptl. Biol. Med.*, **116**, 187–90 (1964)

116. Easton, J. M., and Hiatt, C. W., *Proc. Natl. Acad. Sci. U. S.*, **54**, 1100–4 (1965)

117. Schell, K., Lane, W. T., Casey, M. J., and Huebner, R. J., *Proc. Natl. Acad. Sci. U. S.* **55**, 81–87 (1966)

118. Ginsberg, H. S., and Dingle, J. H., in *Viral and Rickettsial Infections of Man*, Chap. 40, 860–891. (Horsfall, F. L., Jr., and Tamm, I., Eds., J. B. Lippincott, Philadelphia, 1282 pp., 1965)

119. Green, M., and Piña, M., *Virology*, **20**, 199–207 (1963)

120. Green, M., and Piña, M. (Unpublished data)

121. Trentin, J. J., Yabe, Y., and Taylor, G., *Science*, **137**, 835–41 (1962)

122. Huebner, R. J., Rowe, W. P., and Lane, W. T., *Proc. Natl. Acad. Sci. U. S.*, **48**, 2051–58 (1962)

123. Huebner, R. J., Casey, M. J., Chanock, R. M., and Schell, K., *Proc. Natl. Acad. Sci. U. S.*, **54**, 381–88 (1965)

124. Girardi, A. J., Hilleman, M. R., and Zwickey, R. E., *Proc. Soc. Exptl. Biol. Med.*, **115**, 1141–50 (1964)

125. Green, M., and Piña, M., *Proc. Natl. Acad. Sci. U. S.*, **51**, 1251–59 (1964)

126. Lacy, S., Sr., and Green, M. (Unpublished data)

127. Green, M., Piña, M., and Kimes, R. (Unpublished data)

128. Smith, K. O., *Science*, **148**, 100–2 (1965)

129. Dales, S., *J. Cell Biol.*, **13**, 303–21 (1962)

130. Lawrence, W. C., and Ginsberg, H. S., *Federation Proc.*, **24**, 379 (1965)

131. Thomas, D. C., and Green, M. (Manuscript in preparation)

132. Flanagan, J. F., and Ginsberg, H. S., *J. Exptl. Med.*, **116**, 141–57 (1962)

133. Wilcox, W. C., and Ginsberg, H. S., *Virology*, **20**, 269–80 (1963)

134. Green, M., *Virology*, **18**, 601–13 (1962)

135. Polasa, H., and Green, M., *Virology*, **25**, 68–79 (1965)

136. Flanagan, J. F., and Ginsberg, H. S., *J. Bacteriol.*, **87**, 977–87 (1964)

137. Kohler, K., and Odaka, T., Z. Natur-forsch., 19b, 331–36 (1964)
138. Rose, J. A., Reich, R. R., and Weissman, S. M., Virology, 27, 571–79 (1965)
139. Kjellen, L., Virology, 18, 64–70 (1962)
140. Piña, M., and Green, M. (Unpublished data)
141. Green, M., and Daesch, G. E., Virology, 13, 169–76 (1961)
142. Ginsberg, H. S., and Dixon, M. K., J. Exptl. Med., 109, 407–22 (1959)
143. Levine, A. J., and Ginsberg, H. S., Federation Proc., 24, 597 (1965)
144. Green, M., Cold Spring Harbor Symp. Quant. Biol., 27, 219–35 (1962)
145. Bello, L. J., and Ginsberg, H. S., Federation Proc., 23, 245 (1964)
146. McAuslan, B. R., Herde, P., Pett, D., and Ross, J., Biochem. Biophys. Res. Commun., 20, 586–91 (1965)
147. Consigli, R. A., and Ginsberg, H. S., J. Bacteriol., 87, 1034–43 (1964)
148. Consigli, R. A., and Ginsberg, H. S., J. Bacteriol., 87, 1027–33 (1964)
149. MacBride, W. D., and Wiener, A., Proc. Soc. Exptl. Biol. Med., 115, 870–74 (1964)
150. Pope, J. H., and Rowe, W. P., J. Exptl. Med., 120, 577–88 (1964)
151. Levinthal, J. D., and Peterson, W. (In press)
152. Larson, V. M., Girardi, A. J., Hilleman, M. R., and Zwickey, R. E., Proc. Soc. Exptl. Biol. Med., 118, 15–24 (1965)
153. Huebner, R. J., Rowe, W. P., Turner, H. C., and Lane, W. T., Proc. Natl. Acad. Sci. U. S., 50, 379–89 (1963)
154. Hoggan, M. D., Rowe, W. P., Black, P. H., and Huebner, R. J., Proc. Natl. Acad. Sci. U. S., 53, 12–19 (1965)
155. Gilead, Z., and Ginsberg, H. S., J. Bacteriol., 90, 120–26 (1965)
156. Fujinaga, K., and Green, M., Proc. Natl. Acad. Sci. U. S. (In press)
157. Green, M., Piña, M., and Fujinaga, K. (Unpublished data)
158. Morgan, C., Rose, H. M., Holden, M., and Jones, E. P., J. Exptl. Med., 110, 643–56 (1959)
159. Munk, V., and Sauer, G., Z. Natur-forsch., 18b, 211–15 (1963)
160. Kaplan, A. S., and Ben-Porat, T., Virology, 19, 205–14 (1963)
161. Hamada, C., and Kaplan, A. S., J. Bacteriol., 89, 1328–34 (1965)
162. Hamada, C., Kamiya, T., and Kaplan, A. S., Virology, 28, 271–81 (1966)
163. Ben-Porat, T., and Kaplan, A. S., Virology, 20, 310–17 (1963)
164. Ben-Porat, T., and Kaplan, A. S., Virology, 25, 22–29 (1965)
165. Kaplan, A. S., and Ben-Porat, T., Virology, 23, 90–95 (1964)
166. Kaplan, A. S., Virology, 24, 19–25 (1964)
167. Coto, C., Ben-Porat, T., and Kaplan, A. S., Bacteriol. Proc., 111 (1966)
168. Kamiya, T., Ben-Porat, T., and Kaplan, A. S., Virology, 26, 577–89 (1965)
169. Roizman, B., Aurelian, L., and Roane, P., Virology, 21, 482–98 (1963)
170. Roizman, B., and Roane, P., Virology, 22, 262–69 (1964)
171. Roizman, B., Borman, G. S., and Rousta, M., Nature, 206, 1374–75 (1965)
172. Russell, W. C., Gold, E., Keir, H. M., Omura, H., Watson, D. H., and Wildy, P., Virology, 22, 103–10 (1964)
173. Keir, H. M., and Gold, E., Biochim. Biophys. Acta, 72, 263–76 (1963)
174. Kit, S., and Dubbs, D. R., Biochem. Biophys. Res. Commun., 11, 55–59 (1963)
175. Kit, S., and Dubbs, D. R., Biochem. Biophys. Res. Commun., 13, 500–4 (1963)
176. Cairns, J., Virology, 11, 603–23 (1960)
177. Joklik, W. K., J. Mol. Biol., 8, 263–76 (1964)
178. Joklik, W. K., J. Mol. Biol., 8, 277–88 (1964)
179. Dales, S., J. Cell Biol., 18, 51 (1963)
180. Salzman, N. P., Shatkin, A. J., and Sebring, E. D., Virology, 19, 542–50 (1963)
181. Shatkin, A. J., and Salzman, N. P., Virology, 19, 551–60 (1963)
182. Shatkin, A. J., Virology, 20, 292–301 (1963)
183. Easterbrook, K. B., Virology, 21, 508–10 (1963)
184. Loh, P. C., and Payne, F. E., Virology, 25, 575–84 (1965)
185. Joklik, W. K., and Becker, Y., J. Mol. Biol., 10, 452–74 (1964)
186. Penman, S., Becker, Y., and Darnell, J. E., J. Mol. Biol., 8, 541–55 (1964)
187. Kit, S., and Dubbs, D. R., Virology, 18, 286–93 (1962)
188. Becker, Y., and Joklik, W. K., Proc. Natl. Acad. Sci. U. S., 51, 577–85 (1964)
189. Salzman, N. P., Shatkin, A. J., and Sebring, E. D., J. Mol. Biol., 8, 405–16 (1964)
190. Joklik, W. K., and Becker, Y., J. Mol. Biol., 13, 511–20 (1965)

191. Scharff, M. D., Shatkin, A. J., and
     Levintow, L., *Proc. Natl. Acad.
     Sci. U. S.*, **50**, 686–94 (1963)
192. Weiss, S. W., *Proc. Natl. Acad. Sci.
     U. S.*, **46**, 1020–30 (1960)
193. Goldberg, I., *Biochim. Biophys. Acta*,
     51, 201–4 (1961)
194. Shatkin, A. J., *Nature*, **199**, 357–58
     (1963)
195. Shatkin, A. J., Sebring, E. D., and
     Salzman, N. P., *Science*, **148**, 87–90
     (1965)
196. McAuslan, B. R., *Virology*, **21**, 383–89
     (1963)
197. Jungwirth, C., and Joklik, W. K.,
     Virology, **27**, 80–93 (1965)
198. Green, M., and Piña, M., *Virology*, **18**,
     601–13 (1962)
199. Magee, W. E., *Virology*, **17**, 604–7

200. Kit, S., Dubbs, D. R., and Piekarski,
     L. J., *Biochem. Biophys. Res.
     Commun.*, **8**, 72–74 (1962)
201. Joklik, W. K., *Cold Spring Harbor
     Symp. Quant. Biol.*, **27**, 199–208
     (1962)
202. McAuslan, B. R., and Joklik, W. K.,
     Biochem. Biophys. Res. Commun.,
     8, 486–91 (1962)
203. Hanafusa, T., *Biken J.*, **4**, 97–110
     (1961)
204. McAuslan, B. R., *Biochem. Biophys.
     Res. Commun.*, **19**, 15–20 (1965)
205. Kit, S., Dubbs, D. R., and Piekarski,
     L. J., *Biochem. Biophys. Res.
     Commun.*, **11**, 176–81 (1963)
206. Kit, S., and Dubbs, D. R., *Virology*,
     26, 16–27 (1965)

TUMOR ANTIGENS[1,2]

By George Klein

Institute for Tumor Biology, Karolinska Institute Medical School, Stockholm, Sweden

Contents

THE CELLULAR LOCALIZATION, NATURE, OCCURRENCE, AND DETERMINATION MECHANISM OF TUMOR-SPECIFIC TRANSPLANTATION ANTIGENS.................................. 226
    Localization of antigens..................................... 226
    Nature of antigens.. 227
    Occurrence of antigens..................................... 228
    Mechanisms determining antigens............................ 229
WHAT HOST DEFENSE MECHANISMS ARE OF IMPORTANCE FOR THE REJECTION OF ANTIGENIC TUMOR CELLS?.......... 233
WHY DOES REJECTION FAIL IN THE CASE OF "SUCCESSFUL" TUMORS?... 243
    Escape from Immunological Surveillance.................. 243
        Tolerance and "sneaking through"........................... 244
        Enhancement... 246
        Antigenic loss.. 247
    Escape from Nonimmunological Surveillance............... 247
WHAT IS THE SIGNIFICANCE OF TUMOR-SPECIFIC TRANSPLANTATION ANTIGENS FOR STUDIES ON THE ETIOLOGY, PREVENTION, AND THERAPY OF NEOPLASMS?............ 248

Considerable experimental evidence has accumulated during recent years to show that neoplastic cells of many types can be antigenic for the host in which they have arisen. While little is known about the behavior of human tumors as yet, in experimental systems it can be clearly shown that, under certain conditions at least, the host is capable of mobilizing immunological defense mechanisms of varying strength and efficiency, depending on the system. The most unequivocal demonstration of such defense mechanisms has been the rejection of small numbers of grafted tumor cells by untreated or preimmunized, genetically compatible (syngeneic) hosts, and in the cases where this could be tested, by the autochthonous, primary host as well.

The immunological nature of such rejection mechanisms has been proved by different lines of independent evidence. In tumor-host systems where they occur, preirradiation of untreated, genetically compatible hosts reduces the

---

[1] The survey of the literature pertaining to this review was concluded in December 1965.

[2] The following abbreviations will be used: TSTA (tumor-specific transplantation antigen); PHA (phytohemagglutinin).

223

threshold cell dose required for successful takes by one or several log units, as a rule. Preimmunization with irradiated tumor cells or, if feasible, with viable tumor cells, prevented progressive growth by subthreshold dosage, excision of tumor or, in the case of cross-reacting antigens, homografting, increases the threshold dose for take by one or several log units. When the resistance of such preimmunized animals is broken down by an overwhelming tumor cell dose, tumor outgrowth is often delayed. The lymph node cells of preimmunized animals are capable of damaging or neutralizing the target cells against which they have been sensitized when the two are mixed *in vitro*, and survival of the latter is tested by inoculation of susceptible animal hosts. In certain instances, particularly as far as target cells of the lymphoma or leukemia type are concerned, humoral antibodies can be demonstrated as well, e.g., by cytotoxicity or immunofluorescence tests. In other systems, these methods give negative results but the presence of humoral antibodies nevertheless can be demonstrated, e.g., by immunological enhancement.

These findings have clearly established that, in contrast to what has been previously believed, neoplastic cells are not necessarily accepted as "self" by the host organism. In the many different experimental tumor systems that have been studied in this respect so far, this seems to be the rule rather than the exception, even though considerable differences in detail have been shown to exist among different systems. One conspicuous exception is represented by those systems in which tolerance prevails, due to the vertical transmission of a causative oncogenic virus to fetal or newborn animals. In such cases immunological reactivity may be entirely absent, not because tumor-specific antigens are lacking but because of a state of unresponsiveness against the antigens of the virus and the virus-induced neoplastic cells as well. In cases where it is possible to break the vertical transmission cycle, responsiveness to the virus and the cellular antigens of the virus-induced neoplastic cells is re-established.

With the exception of such tolerant systems, immunological reactivity against genetically compatible tumors has been regularly present in most experimental tumors studied so far. Although some important details of this reactivity, particularly its strength and mediation, are quite different in the different systems, common general patterns have begun to emerge. As a rule, chemically induced tumors are individually distinct with regard to antigenic specificity, even if induced by the same dose of the same chemical agent in the same animal genotype and, in cases where multiple primary tumors have been tested, even if induced in the same individual animal. In contrast, neoplasms induced by the same virus show extensive and possibly complete antigenic cross-reactivity. Both among chemical and viral inducers of neoplasms, some characteristically give rise to weakly and others to strongly antigenic tumors. Antigenic "strength" is a purely operational concept, judged by some such criterion as the logarithmic units by which the cell doses required for growth in untreated and preimmunized animals differ. Other related but more indirect criteria are the threshold cell dose required for progressive growth in untreated syngeneic animals, or the highest resistance levels that can be achieved by preimmunization, judged by the cell numbers required to break them down. Antigenic strength of tumors varies not only with different groups of etiological agents, but also within a group. A relationship has been found between the time of appearance of a given tumor during oncogenesis and its antigenic strength; tumors with stronger antigenicity appear after a shorter latent period.

Although the study of tumor antigens is of comparatively recent origin, a number of comprehensive review articles are already available (1–6). It would serve little purpose to add another review to this already impressive list. Rather than summarizing the available factual information in detail, the purpose of this article will be to discuss some specific questions that arise from the collected data. A limitation in such an effort is imposed by the wide variations in methodology used for the demonstration of tumor-specific antigens. There is no reason to assume that antigens detected by such different methods as, e.g., complement fixation and graft rejection are necessarily identical; on the contrary, there is some indication that they are probably different, since they show different patterns of cross-reactivity, different kinetics of appearance and, in some cases, probably different cellular localization as well. A convenient limitation of the subject matter can be achieved by concentrating the discussion around antigens that have been shown to be capable of inducing rejection responses in genetically compatible hosts. As a rule, these are demonstrated by transplantation tests and can be referred to as tumor-specific transplantation antigens. They can be discussed in relation to postulated surveillance mechanisms of the normal organism, capable of eliminating potential neoplastic cells, and to the prospects for the utilization of tumor-specific antigens for prevention and therapy. Antigens detected by methods other than graft rejection will be discussed only to the extent that they are of particular relevance to the problems considered. No attempt will be made to review the field of tumor antigens detected by the use of immune sera produced in foreign animal species. Here, the immunological discrimination of the reacting animal may yield a certain "profile analysis" of the neoplastic tissue in comparison with certain normal tissues, similar to biochemical analysis, but no information can be obtained about the crucial question of "self" versus "nonself" components. Identification of a constituent as tumor-specific will then entirely depend on the nature and composition of the normal tissue used for comparison. Any tissue component may appear as tumor-specific, provided that the normal tissue does not contain it or contains it in a concentration insufficient for recognition by the antibody-producing foreign species. Unquestionably, interesting information may be obtained from such analyses, but the same questions of representativeness and normal tissue homology hamper interpretation as in the field of tumor biochemistry. Tumor-specific transplantation antigens are not subject to this difficulty, provided that consideration is limited to reactions occurring in the strain of origin and adequate care is taken to distinguish between the ordinary transplantation antigens determined by genetic differences between donor and host, and tumor-specific antigens proper, i.e., cases in which new antigenic specificities arise in parallel with the neoplastic transformation. In these situations, the reacting animal automatically eliminates all specificities to which it is tolerant, i.e., the antigens of its own normal tissues, unless compartmentalization enters into the picture, as in the case of organ-specific antigens.

Because of these considerations, the present review will be concentrated on the following problems:

1. What is known about the cellular localization, nature, occurrence, and genetic determination mechanism of tumor-specific transplantation antigens?

2. What host defense mechanisms are of importance for the rejection of antigenic tumor cells?

3. Why does rejection fail in the case of the "successful" tumors?

4. What is the significance of tumor-specific transplantation antigens for studies on the etiology, prevention, and therapy of neoplasms?

THE CELLULAR LOCALIZATION, NATURE, OCCURRENCE, AND DETERMINATION MECHANISM OF TUMOR-SPECIFIC TRANSPLANTATION ANTIGENS

Localization of antigens.—Graft rejection reactions are initiated by an interaction between antigenic sites on the surface of the target cell and either humoral antibodies or sensitized host cells. One may therefore expect that most, if not all, antigens capable of inducing graft rejection responses must be expressed on the cell surface. Although ordinary transplantation antigens must be regarded as indirect models of the tumor-specific systems at best, this view has been, nevertheless, reinforced by recent experimental findings concerning the best known transplantation antigen system, the histocompatibility-2 (H-2) system in the mouse (7–10). Previous cell fractionation studies gave rather contradictory results, and opinions were long divided about intracellular versus surface localization [cp., e.g. (11–14)]. However, cell fractionation has the drawback that one fraction can be easily contaminated with another, and the dangers of artefacts are numerous. Cell membrane fragments particularly may easily contaminate all other isolated fractions. A different approach was made by Haughton (7). Using inhibition of the rather precise cytotoxic test (15) based on the release of Cr^{51} from labeled cells after exposure to antiserum and complement as a measure of antigenicity, he compared the total H-2 antigen content of a known number of intact living tumor cells with sonicated homogenates derived from the same cell number. Control experiments showed that the sonication treatment did not destroy more than a small fraction of the H-2 antigens involved in the reaction. Making corrections for this, he could show that at least 80 per cent of the total H-2 antigen content of the ascites tumor cells studied was expressed on the surface of the intact living cell. The remaining 20 per cent may be intracellular, or may be accounted for by the conditions of the test, which may understate the inhibiting effect of the homogenates (cp. 10); it is quite possible that the proportion of H-2 antigens expressed on the cell surface is even higher. This agrees with the cellular localization indicated by the indirect fluorescent antibody test, applied to living and fixed cells as well (8), and showing a membrane reaction exclusively. The localization of the tumor-specific transplantation antigens is less well known. The indirect fluorescence method applied to living cells indicated that such antigens must also be expressed on the cell surface, at least in methylcholanthrene-induced sarcomas (16, 17), Moloney virus-induced lymphomas (18), and leukemias induced by the Graffi agent (19). It is highly probable, furthermore, that the cytotoxic reaction occurring when living tumor cell suspensions are incubated with the sera of resistant, syngeneic animals, in the presence of complement *in vitro*, is also due to the combination of antigenic sites on the cell surface with antibody. Intact living tumor cell suspensions can completely absorb the activity of such antisera. Cytotoxic tests of this type extend the list of tumor-specific antigens with a cell membrane localization to leukemias induced by the Gross (20), Friend and Rauscher (21, 22) and Rich (23) agents. In the Moloney system, there is evidence to indicate that the concentration of the tumor-specific antigens on the cell surface is different for individual lymphomas, and this is correlated with cytotoxic sensitivity and absorbing ability (24).

Nature of antigens.—This can be dealt with very briefly since the chemical nature of TSTA is completely unknown at present. This is not surprising in view of the fact that ordinary transplantation antigens of the H-2 type have now been known for several decades and their immunological and genetic aspects have been studied in very great detail, but knowledge about their molecular composition is still in the most rudimentary stage. Recent experimental evidence indicates that they are most probably lipoproteins but even this conclusion is quite tentative; other possibilities have not been completely excluded (12–14). As far as TSTA are concerned, one important question is whether they represent modified transplantation antigens or entirely new cellular structures or, alternatively, slight changes in previously nonantigenic structures, unrelated to transplantation antigens, that render them foreign to the immune system of the host. There is probably no uniform answer to these questions; the situation may be different for different systems. In chemically induced tumors with individually different antigenic specificities, a modification of pre-existing transplantation antigens or other cell surface structures appears most likely. Randomly occurring genetic changes, perhaps of the deletion type, at any among a large number of relevant loci, may lead to such a picture. In the case of virus-induced tumors on the other hand, with common group-specific cellular antigens appearing independently of virus release, the appearance of entirely new specificities induced and controlled by genetic material derived from the virus appears to be quite probable. But even in this case it cannot be excluded that the virus may act in a more indirect fashion, inducing some change in the synthesis of an already existing cellular antigen as in lysogenic conversion in bacteria (25).

The future feasibility of chemical studies of tumor-specific transplantation antigens will depend on the availability of suitable methods. Obviously, the transplantation method itself is much too cumbersome and not sufficiently quantitative for such purposes. *In vitro* reaction systems, preferably based on humoral antibody reactions, are necessary to permit precise large-scale quantitative testing of fractionated material for specific inhibitory activity. One such test, the inhibition of Cr^{51} release from labeled cells exposed to antiserum and complement, has been found useful not only for H-2 antigens, but for tumor-specific antigens of Moloney lymphomas as well (26). Inhibition techniques can be used in conjunction with the membrane immunofluorescence test, although this involves much more labor. While both approaches are feasible for lymphomas and leukemias, they appear to be less promising with large carcinoma and sarcoma cells as a rule (see below). The polyoma system is a case in point; although this was the first virus-induced neoplasm to yield evidence of a group-specific transplantation antigen (27, 28) it has still resisted most attempts to demonstrate this antigen by a direct humoral antibody reaction *in vitro*. This may be due to a relative scarcity of antigenic receptors per surface unit in these large cells. As a possible way out of this dilemma, Sjögren and Hellström have induced the polyoma antigen in Moloney lymphoma cells by superinfection with polyoma virus (29, 30). The superimposed polyoma TSTA became demonstrable by the transplantation test and by an *in vitro* cytotoxic (colony inhibition) method as well. Similar approaches, based on the selection of the most suitable target cell for *in vitro* reactions by superimposing the required antigenic specificity, may become important for developing appropriate reaction systems for the assay of isolated cell fractions by inhibition tests.

Occurrence of Antigens.—Table I presents a schematic summary of the tumor systems in which antigen(s) capable of inducing tumor-specific rejection responses have been demonstrated by transplantation to genetically compatible (syngeneic) or authochthonous hosts, or both. Detailed references to the individual papers are to be found in previous review articles (1, 2). Such antigens have been shown to occur in all chemically and virally induced tumors so far studied. As a rule, different individual tumors induced by the same virus cross-react antigenically, while chemically induced tumors tend to have individually distinct, non- or only occasionally cross-reacting transplantation antigens.

All antigens of the TSTA type are comparable to weak histocompatibility antigens. The strength of TSTA is different for different etiological groups. As an example, methylcholanthrene-induced sarcomas in mice are more "strongly" antigenic than are morphologically similar sarcomas induced by dibenzanthracene, and sarcomas induced by the implantation of cellophane or Millipore films are only very weakly antigenic (1, 4, 31, 32). Among the virus tumors, Moloney-induced mouse lymphomas are strongly antigenic (18), whereas the Gross agent induces morphologically similar but only very weakly antigenic lymphomas (33). Many other examples could be quoted. There is a variation regarding the strength of TSTA even within one

TABLE I

Systems With Demonstrated Occurrence of Tumor-Specific Antigens Capable of Inducing Rejection Responses in Isologous Hosts

Chemical carcinogens			
	3-Methylcholanthrene	no cross-reactivity	
	1,2,5,6-Dibenzanthracene		
	9,10-Dimethylbenzanthracene		
	3,4,9,10-Dibenzpyrene		
	3,4-Benzpyrene		
	p-Dimethylaminoazobenzene		
Physical agents			
	Films: Millipore filter		
	Cellophane film		
	Radiation: Ultraviolet		
	Sr^{90}		
Virus			
DNA	Polyoma	cross-reaction within each group	
	SV40		
	Adenovirus 12, 18		
	Shope papilloma		
RNA	Mammary tumor agent		cross-reaction within each group
	Leukemia		
	Gross		
	Moloney	cross-reaction between groups	
	Rauscher		
	Friend		
	Graffi		
	Rich		
	Rous (Schmidt-Ruppin)		

group of tumors induced by the same chemical carcinogen, e.g., methylcholanthrene, or the same virus, e.g., polyoma. On the whole, tumors appearing after a short latent period of induction in their primary hosts tend to be more strongly antigenic in subsequent transplantation tests than are similar tumors that appear after a long latent period (2, 4).

Mechanisms determining antigens.—As already mentioned, the mechanisms which determine alterations in antigenicity are entirely unknown, but several alternative possibilities have been considered. Antigens of the TSTA type may represent ordinary transplantation antigens altered in specificity by the interaction of the cell genome or other cellular systems with chemical carcinogens or oncogenic viruses, or both. Alternatively, they may represent new specificities that are not built on the structural basis of pre-existing transplantation antigens. This question does not seem to be open to experimental study as yet because of insufficient knowledge of the chemical natures of the transplantation and TSTA antigens. In relation to this question, the common antigenicity of the virus-induced tumors poses the problem whether TSTA specificity is controlled by the viral genome which would be maintained and carried in some integrated form by the transformed neoplastic cells or, alternatively, whether their appearance is due to a "hit and run" type of mechanism, which implies that the entry of the virus leads to a permanent modification of some synthetic process in the cell and thereby to the expression of new specificities. While both alternatives are conceivable, several facts speak for the first.

Neoplasms of closely similar morphology induced by different viruses in the same target tissue, show distinctly different antigenic specificities. The lymphomas evoked by the Gross and Moloney viruses are cases in point (18, 33). Hamster sarcomas induced by the closely related SV40 and polyoma viruses, respectively, are also antigenically distinct (34). In contrast, tumors of completely different morphological types but induced by the same agent have the same antigenic specificity, even in cases where they do not continue to release infectious virus. One instance is represented by the many different polyoma tumors induced in mice, originating partly from epithelial and partly from mesenchymal tissues, but characterized nevertheless by the same TSTA specificity. Another illustrative case is the absence of cross-reactivity between lymphatic leukemias induced by the Gross and Graffi viruses, as contrasted to the cross-reactivity of histogenetically quite different lymphoid and myeloid leukemias, provided that both are induced by the Graffi virus (19). Furthermore, in those TSTA systems tested, antigenicity was highly stable (35) and resistant to secondary modifications even after prolonged exposure to negative selection in preimmunized hosts, as will be discussed below. It cannot be excluded that a virus may act momentarily or through a limited time period, to bring about a permanent repression or modification of cellular syntheses that no longer depends upon the continued presence of any genetic information derived from the virus. But this seems rather improbable and requires the further assumption that this temporary virus-cell interaction leads to an identical result (i.e., the same antigenic specificity) without regard to the previous differentiation or histogenetic derivation of the target cell. Furthermore, it would follow that once it had occurred, the change would be resistant to secondary modifications by selection in preimmunized hosts, in which such variants would be at a distinct advantage. It is impossible to exclude this so-called "hit and run" hypothesis, but it appears less likely to the reviewer than the simpler alternative which postulates the continued presence of virus-derived genetic information in the transformed neoplastic cell. At the present rudimentary state of our knowledge of moderate (nonlytic) interactions between viruses and cells of higher organisms, it appears unwise and unnecessarily restrictive to burden this hypothesis with further and more specific assumptions borrowed from microbial genetics, which may not be applicable in detail. In the non-releasing system at least, the virus must be present in a form that precludes its vegetative multiplication because of a defective state of the virus genome, or of a repressor produced by the target cell or, as seems to be the case in the Shope papilloma (36) and polyoma systems (37), because of the inability of certain cells to synthesize mature virus particles, depending on their state of differentiation. Regarding the nature of the virus-cell association, all intermediates between full integration with the cell genome and looser forms of association with more subordinated cellular systems can be visualized, provided that it is postulated that either the replication of the virus genome is somehow synchronized with and regulated by cellular replication, or that cells which accidentally lose the virus-derived information become nonneoplastic and are eliminated from the growing tumor cell population. Evidence for the occurrence of reversion that may correspond to the latter possibility has been actually obtained in hamster cell cultures transformed by the Schmidt-Ruppin strain of the Rous virus (38).

If it is assumed that virus-derived genetic information is present in virus-transformed neoplastic cells, it may be surmised that it controls both neoplastic behavior and antigenicity. This would explain the common antigenic specificity of all tumors induced by the same virus, irrespective of type, as contrasted with the differences in antigenicity among neoplasms of the same type induced by different viruses, or with the individually distinct antigenic specificities of chemically induced tumors.

It would be outside the scope of this article to review all experiments carried out for the purpose of obtaining information on the question of possible viral integration. The evidence has been inconclusive in most experiments. It has been claimed that a type-specific CF antigen of virion specificity can be found in transformed, nonvirus-releasing tumor cells in the adenovirus type 12 system, but this was not found regularly. It is not quite clear at present whether this irregularity is due to quantitative variations combined with a relative insensitivity of the method used for detection (complement fixation), or to a merely fortuitous association between this antigen and the neoplastic transformation (39, 40). It has also been reported (41) that nonvirus-releasing SV40-induced hamster tumor cells could be induced to release small amounts of infectious virus by *in vitro* exposure to proflavine, H_2O_2, or mitomycin C, but it is not quite clear whether this owed to the amplification of pre-existing, subliminal virus production caused by a carrier state, or by true induction of nonproducing "virogenic" cells.

The most conclusive evidence for the presence of viral genome in transformed, neoplastic cells has been obtained in the Rous and the Shope papilloma systems. The Bryan strain of the Rous virus is defective, i.e., incapable of building up the apparatus required for its own transmission from cell to cell, unless a helper virus is present. Neoplastic cells transformed by high dilutions of virus may remain uninfected with helper and therefore unable to release the Rous virus or the helper. They can be induced to release both by superinfection with pure helper (42). This is definite proof of an association between the virus genome and the transformed neoplastic cell of the type postulated. Unfortunately, because of the difficulties in obtaining suitably inbred fowl strains, tumor-specific transplantation antigens have not been studied in the Rous-Bryan system. The closest approximation is the corresponding study of the antigenicity of the Schmidt-Ruppin-Rous system in mice (43, 44). Although this strain of the virus does not seem to be defective in its natural host, the fowl, it behaves as a defective virus in mammals such as mice or rats, since it induces tumors that release no infectious virus unless brought into close contact with chicken cells (45, 46) that act either by providing a suitable soil for virus maturation ("production by association") or by supplying essential elements required for virus reproduction but missing from mammalian cells ("induction by association"). Quite apart from the unclarified state of this latter phenomenon, the fact remains that mouse tumors induced by this agent contain strong transplantation antigens in the absence of detectable virus production in this species, but with maintained ability to produce virus in association with chick cells. Although not critically decisive, this evidence again favors the assumption of a direct relationship between maintenance of virus-derived genetic information and the presence of the TSTA antigen.

Another quite similar case in point is represented by the Shope papilloma-carcinoma system. In contrast to papillomas arising in the natural host of this virus, the cottontail rabbit, papillomas induced in domestic rabbits tend to become nonvirus releasers, and the same is true for the carcinomas that can be derived from them. In recent years, evidence has been accumulating to show that like other virus-induced tumors, Shope papillomas and carcinomas contain a specific transplantation antigen capable of inducing not only graft rejection but an increased regression rate of the primary virus-induced papillomas as well (47, 48). The presence of this antigen is not dependent on virus release but infectious DNA can be isolated from nonreleasing domestic rabbit papillomas and carcinomas as well (49, 50), which is definite proof for the presence of virus-derived genetic material in these tissues.

Turning now to the chemically induced tumors, a discussion of the genetic mechanisms determining the TSTA systems is even more difficult. In the first place; one may assign an active or a passive role to the chemical carcinogen. According to the "active" hypothesis, the carcinogen induces the neoplastic change by acting directly on the target cells. On this assumption, the individually distinct antigenicity of chemically induced sarcomas suggests that the details of the interaction between chemical carcinogen and target cell are slightly different for each tumor. If the change is at the genetic level, this would imply that different genetic rearrangements occur, identical only with regard to their effect on cell behavior, but different with regard to the exact details of the underlying mechanism. Differences in genetic structure are also suggested by two different investigations, carried out with methyl-cholanthrene-induced mouse sarcomas. Studies of the chromosome constitution of primary sarcomas have shown considerable individual variations among different tumors with regard to the karyotype of the predominating "stem-cell" (51). Another case in point is the finding that phenotypic cell variation, traced through antigenic markers (H-2) with known genetic de-terminative mechanisms has shown individual patterns for different sarco-mas induced by the same dose of methylcholanthrene in the same tissue of the same mouse genotype (52).

The alternative possibility, the assignment of a more indirect role to the chemical carcinogen, leads to a different interpretation of the same picture (53). According to this view, the action of methylcholanthrene and other aromatic hydrocarbons is owing to their immunodepressive effect, leading to the inhibition of local graft rejection mechanisms which would normally eliminate antigenic, potentially neoplastic cells. The evidence for such a "surveillance" function of graft rejecting reactions will be discussed in the next section. In particular, the effects of thymectomy on newborn animals, indicates that such factors do play a certain role in chemically induced onco-genesis.

Chemical carcinogens have been found earlier to exert a certain immuno-depressive effect on humoral antibody formation and the rejection of weakly antigenic tissue grafts as well (53, 54, 55). More recently, Stjernswärd has shown that methylcholanthrene (56) and two other carcinogenic aromatic hydrocarbons (57) markedly depress the number of antibody-forming spleen cells, as estimated by the Jerne plaque assay. The number of plaque-forming cells remains low during several months, in comparison with untreated con-trols or controls treated with noncarcinogenic hydrocarbons of a similar structure (56, 57). BCG[3] vaccine increases the number of antibody-forming cells when given alone, and counteracts the depressive effect of methyl-cholanthrene in the Jerne assay. Perhaps even more significantly, methylcho-lanthrene facilitates acceptance of small grafts of methylcholanthrene-in-duced sarcoma cells by syngeneic hosts, approximately to the same extent as does whole body X irradiation (57, 58). This is so far the most seriously sug-gestive evidence for a possible indirect effect of methylcholanthrene. Viewed from this basis, methylcholanthrene-induced tumors would be caused by the proliferation of spontaneously arising neoplastic cell clones that would be otherwise eliminated by the graft rejection response. The above argument concerning genetic differences among individual methylcholanthrene-induced sarcomas would remain essentially the same, but the differences would now be attributed to spontaneous variability of the genetic material rather than to its reaction with the chemical carcinogen.

WHAT HOST DEFENSE MECHANISMS ARE OF IMPORTANCE FOR THE REJECTION OF ANTIGENIC TUMOR CELLS?

As soon as it was realized that tumors induced by chemical carcinogens or viruses contain specific antigens capable of stimulating host rejection responses, the question arose whether many antigenic and potentially neo-plastic cells are normally eliminated by the host before they give rise to a tumor and if so, why this mechanism breaks down in the case of the antigenic tumors that do develop. Burnet (59) has postulated that the physiological function of the homograft reaction is this elimination of spontaneously arising neoplastic cells and other types of "forbidden clones" that do not fall into the established pattern and represent potential threats against the organism. Burnet's postulate of such an "immunological surveillance mechanism" is based on the deductive reasoning that the need for such a mechanism must have arisen at a very early stage of evolution, at the time when multicellular organisms started to develop, and might therefore represent the most ancient form of immunological reaction.

Immunological surveillance no doubt exists. A number of workers have shown recently (60–66) that the incidence of various tumors induced by chemical carcinogens and viruses is higher in animals thymectomized at birth than in intact or sham-thymectomized controls. Virus-induced lymphomas represent an exception, but here the thymus is an important part of the target cell system itself. The increased incidence of, e.g., polyoma, or methylcholanthrene-induced sarcomas can hardly be explained in any other way than by assuming that immunologically competent cells, capable of normal development in the presence of the thymus only, are normally instrumental in eliminating potentially neoplastic cells that arise through spontaneous cellular changes or by chemical or viral induction. The existence of antigenic tumors then implies that in these cases the neoplastic cells have escaped the immunological surveillance mechanisms in one way or another.

While immunological surveillance thus no doubt exists, it does not appear to be a particularly efficient mechanism. The increase in tumor incidence after thymectomy is significant but not very impressive. If, as has been postulated by Habel (67) for the case of polyoma in mice, immunological mechanisms are mainly, if not exclusively, responsible for keeping transformed neoplastic cells under control, one would expect that thymectomy of newborn polyoma-infected mice would lead to an early outburst of multiple tumors in high frequency, in view of the high oncogenic efficiency of this virus. Actually, a slight-to-moderate increase has been observed. This suggests the existence of other surveillance mechanisms in addition to the immunological one. The efficiency of the latter is further hampered by a number of demonstrated escape mechanisms, to be discussed in more detail in the next section, such as weak or missing cellular antigenicity and immunological tolerance, paralysis, or enhancement. Furthermore, the race between tumor growth and the mobilization of host defense forces may often lead to the defeat of the host, because of differences in timing ("sneaking through"). If immune mechanisms were the only means of protecting the organism against the outgrowth of its potentially neoplastic cells, it would have to be concluded that neoplastic transformation must be a rather rare event. This is hardly in line with the pronounced tendency of normal cells to change into neoplastic ones in tissue culture. Also, since neoplasia can be induced by a wide variety of agents and, in all probability, through a large number of different cellular mechanisms, the concept of very infrequent neoplastic change seems improbable. It may be recalled in this connection that some of the most rapidly dividing mammalian cells, e.g., the epithelium of the small intestine which has a proliferation rate far exceeding that of most neoplastic tissues, show a notoriously low incidence of malignant change.

If the notion of frequent spontaneous or induced cellular change to potential malignancy is accepted, and immunological surveillance is postulated as the main elimination mechanism, it has to be assumed that most of the changed cells are highly antigenic and manage to release enough antigen to immunize an often distant immunologically competent tissue in time. Furthermore, since humoral antibodies are only rarely efficient, it has to be postulated that a sufficient number of sensitized host cells must reach the target cells in time, even if these are located in the deep shelters of compact, differentiated tissues, and must destroy them before their number has exceeded what the defense resources can cope with. While all this may happen occasionally, it appears rather unlikely that this is the whole explanation and that no more efficient mechanisms exist.

From the evolutionary point of view, it is easy to see that the need to deal with cells which do not subordinate themselves to the growth control mechanisms of the organism must have arisen very early, as soon as multicellular organisms of the most primitive types appeared, and thus much earlier than any immune system in the ordinary sense of the term had become established. An immune system would be required only after the problems of inner regulation are so settled that the menace to survival from without exceeds that from within. Accordingly, it will be postulated that prior to the evolution of the immune system, mechanisms must have developed which were able to deal with variant cells of the primitive organism that represented reversions to a still more primitive, unicellular form of life, or, in vertebrate language, potentially neoplastic cells. Such revertants must be assumed to occur at an early stage of evolution, as in the case of reverse mutations in bacteria, for example. Due to the paucity of differentiated tissues at this stage, such mechanisms are best visualized as contactual, operating between neighboring cells and with universal competence for all cells to react against an unacceptably changed neighbor.

After a certain inner stability has been established in the primitive multicellular organism, outside microbiological menaces would become more important than before. It is then that the evolution of immune mechanisms can be expected to start. As a further speculative step, it seems reasonable to expect that these evolve on the basis of the mechanisms already existing, since the same principles that allow the recognition and rejection of the organism's own unacceptable cell variants may be useful, after suitable modifications, such as for example the development of mobile vehicles, for the rejection of foreign intruders.

Deductive as it seems, this concept has been actually formulated by an inductive process, based on the interpretation of recent experimental evidence. Before proceeding to a discussion of this, it may be added, in support of the theoretical argument, that the homograft reaction shows surprising parallelisms with many forms of antiparasitic immunity. Thus, immunity against many types of parasites is mediated by sensitized host cells rather than by humoral antibody, and the interplay of humoral antibodies and cell-bound reactions may occasionally lead to enhancement-like phenomena. The state of sensitization can be transferred with immune lymph node cells but not with humoral antibodies, as a rule. Stable host-parasite relationships usually develop through the establishment of weakly antigenic strains, in which the adult forms induce an immunity sufficient for the rejection of reinfecting eggs or larval forms of the same parasite ("premonition"), but not sufficient for the destruction of the already established adult. The parallelism with the immune status of mice bearing large, transplanted, weakly isoantigenic (nonspecific) tumors which they cannot reject in spite of the fact that they readily inhibit the growth of a small second inoculum, is striking. Experimental evidence concerning the immunological aspects of parasitism and the parallelisms with transplantation immunity have been recently surveyed by Dineen, who also formulated an interesting theory concerning the immunological forces influencing the evolution of the parasite and the host in relation to each other (68, 69).

An immune mechanism that is mediated by a mobile cell such as the lymphocyte, can thus be more reasonably assumed to have developed in order to seek out parasites localized in tissue spaces, body cavities, or seated within tissues but surrounded by a capsule, than to destroy mutant tissue cells. It seems therefore a reasonable assumption that transplantation immunity, and its obvious corollary, immunity against cells carrying tumor-specific antigens, is based on the evolution of an immune mechanism originally directed against exogenous parasites. As in the case of parasites, immune rejection of antigenic grafts is practicable as long as the grafts are sufficiently antigenic, and are accessible and vulnerable to the host response.

It follows from this reasoning that one should look for "contactual" tissue surveillance mechanisms. These would be local functions expected to exist in all differentiated tissues, uniform in principle but not necessarily identical in detail. In higher organisms, the system may be rather complex. One may postulate essentially two kinds of receptors or "feelers" on the cell surface: genetically determined components, specific for the whole individual, present on all cells, and capable of interacting with cell variants whose corresponding surface structure has been altered. This interaction would lead to inhibition of cell division or to cell death, or both. As will be discussed below, there is experimental evidence to indicate that transplantation antigens of the H-2 type in mice may function in this fashion. They fulfill the requirement of expression on all cells, surface localization, a high degree of complexity to allow the establishment of many different patterns, and broad variation in nature, proving the changeability of the pattern by mutation. Other genetically determined components such as other (non-H-2) types of transplantation antigens may function in the same way, thus increasing the uniqueness of the individual pattern. In addition to these genetically determined patterns there are obviously other organ or tissue-specific components, varying for each differentiated tissue. The work of Moscona (70), e.g., and the Wolffs (71) indicates that organ-specific receptors of this type do exist and may be changed in connection with neoplastic development. The relationship between genetically determined, individually specific, and developmentally regulated organ-specific receptors, respectively, and their possible bearing on contact inhibition relationships between cells is quite unknown and can only be speculated upon, but because of lack of information, such speculations do not appear to be particularly fruitful at this time.

Experimental evidence has been recently forthcoming to support the above concept. Hellström (72–74) has found that tumor cells carrying a certain genetically determined complex of H-2 antigens are inhibited in hosts that carry other H-2 complexes. This happens even in situations in which the hosts are not immunologically competent to react against the tumor cells because they are F_1 hybrids with the tumor donor strain as one parent, and have been irradiated prior to inoculation in order to eliminate possible tumor-specific reactions. Small numbers of grafted tumor cells grow better in their own homozygous strain of origin that in such F_1 hybrids. Hellström called this phenomenon "syngeneic preference" and termed the corresponding inhibition in the F_1 hybrid "allogeneic inhibition." Hellström et al. (75, 76) could also reproduce allogeneic inhibition *in vitro*. Tumor cells carrying certain H-2 antigens were grown in monolayer cultures and exposed to homogenates or cell extracts containing syngeneic and allogeneic H-2 components, respectively. Allogeneic extracts inhibited growth considerably in comparison with the syngeneic extracts.

Meanwhile, Möller (77), working on a different problem, has encountered a very similar, if not identical phenomenon. Her primary purpose was to demonstrate cell-bound immunity in an *in vitro* system in essentially the same way as was done previously by other investigators who worked with the H-2 and other systems (78–83). In earlier studies, immune lymph node cells were added, as a rule, to target cells, and cytotoxic effects were registered by microscopic examination for monolayer damage, by cell counting, by measurement of isotope incorporation, etc. Using the first two methods. Möller (77) has obtained clear-cut effects when adding H-2-immune lymph node cells to tumor cell monolayers of different types, but in addition, she also observed a certain inhibiting effect when adding nonimmune allogeneic, as compared to syngeneic lymph node cells, even though this inhibition was much less pronounced than with the immune cells. Replacement of the routinely used calf serum with fetal calf serum in the culture medium decreased the cytotoxic effect of the nonimmune allogeneic lymphoid cells markedly. The ordinary calf serum contained agglutinins in high titers against mouse red cells, whereas such antibodies were not found in the fetal serum. It was assumed that the heterologous antibodies of the calf serum induced mixed agglutination between the nonimmune lymph node cells and the target sarcoma cells, and that this resulted in death of the latter. Direct experiments were performed to test this possibility by artificial aggregation of the two cell types. Immune rabbit antimouse serum or phytohemagglutinin was added to the culture medium to induce cellular aggregation. Normal allogeneic or syngeneic cells were aggregated to target tumor cells *in vitro*. Treatment of the target tumor cells with heterologous antiserum or phyto-hemagglutinin alone had no significant effect on the number of living cells after 48 hours, whereas the addition of allogeneic lymphoid cells resulted in a marked cytotoxic effect. The nonimmune allogeneic lymph node cells had no effect in the absence of an aggregating agent. Syngeneic lymphoid cells had no cytotoxic effect in the presence of heterologous antiserum or phytohemag-glutinin. Microscopically there was pronounced aggregation of both the allogeneic and the syngeneic cells around the target cells. Since the syngeneic cells were not cytotoxically active, aggregation as such could not be regarded as sufficient for cytotoxicity. One possible explanation was that a primary immune response was induced in the aggregated allogeneic lymphoid cells *in vitro*. To investigate this possibility, semisyngeneic F_1 hybrid cells were tested for their ability to kill coaggregated, parental-type target cells. It is known that F_1 hybrids are genetically incompetent to respond immunologi-cally against target cells of parental types. When aggregated with PHA or heterologous antibody onto parental target cells, F_1 hybrid cells nevertheless induced pronounced cytotoxicity, similar to allogeneic cells, whereas syngeneic lymph node cells showed no such effect (77). This made quite untenable the assumption that aggregation between the allogeneic lymph node cells and the target cells induced a primary immune response in the classical sense. It appeared that close contact between target tumor cells and lymph node cells containing foreign histocompatibility factors was a neces-sary and sufficient requirement for the cytotoxic effect. The only difference between immune and nonimmune allogeneic cells was the ability of the former to adhere spontaneously to the target cell. Once adherence has been brought about, either by the mechanism available to the immune lymph node cells (possibly antibody), or artificially, by the addition of PHA or hetero-logous immune serum, killing was the result of the intimate contact between two cell types that were incompatible with regard to their genetically deter-mined (surface?) structures. This sequence of events was in agreement with the concept previously advanced by Granger & Weiser (84), and was also in line with the finding of Holm et al. (85, 86), who showed that *in vitro* aggrega-tion of normal, allogeneic rat lymphoid cells and rat kidney cells by phyto-hemagglutinin resulted in target cell destruction, whereas aggregation with syngeneic cells was not damaging to target cells. As an extension of this work, the Möllers (87) have studied the effect of aggregated lymph node cells on normal embryonic target cells *in vitro*. The test was based on the method de-veloped by Granger & Weiser to demonstrate the cytotoxic activity of im-mune macrophages (84). Syngeneic and allogeneic lymphoid cells were ag-gregated onto different sites of the same embryo monolayer culture by PHA.

In some experiments, lymphoid cells of semisyngeneic (F_1 hybrid) origin were added as well. Syngeneic lymphoid cells had no detectable effect. Allogeneic or semisyngeneic F_1 hybrid cells produced clear plaques in the monolayer, characterized by the absence of target fibroblasts and lymphoid cells as well. In the absence of PHA, nonimmune allogeneic lymphoid cells had no detectable effect. In this test system, they also studied the effect of X irradiation (1500 to 3000 r) on the lymphoid cells. The plaque-inducing ability of allogeneic or semisyngeneic lymphoid cells was not affected; plaques appeared after one and one half to six days. Analogous experiments were performed with immune lymphoid cells. Irradiation with 3000 r did not abolish their ability to induce plaques in the absence of PHA. Much lower X-ray doses are known to inhibit various primary immunological reactions *in vivo*, including the homograft reaction and humoral antibody responses.

The PHA-aggregation principle was recently adopted by Hellström and his colleagues and extended to *in vivo* systems as well (76, 88). Target lymphoma cells were exposed *in vitro* either to normal spleen cells or to other lymphoma cells. The two reactant cell types were brought into close contact by adding PHA to the mixture. They were either syngeneic or allogeneic in relation to each other, and, if allogeneic, they differed in regard to the H-2 locus. The viability and reproductive integrity of the target cells were assayed by measuring tumor outgrowth after inoculation of the mixture into animal hosts syngeneic with the target cells and irradiated with 350 r prior to inoculation. In part of the experiments the cell component tested for reactivity was irradiated with doses up to 10,000 r. Allogeneic, but not syngeneic spleen or lymphoma cells were strongly inhibitory, even if preirradiated. The inhibitory effect was not dependent on cell integrity: sonicated allogeneic homogenates were efficient as well. Later, it was found (88, 89) that allogeneic, PHA-exposed liver cells were also inhibitory. The inhibitory effect of added allogeneic cells was abolished by adding anti-H-2 antibodies, specifically directed against their foreign antigenic sites.

The mechanism by which cells, differing in their H-2-antigenic surface structure, inhibit or kill each other, or both, is completely unknown, and can only be the subject of speculation. One possibility is that genetically determined, individual-specific, cell surface receptors of this type interact normally by forming mutually complementary structures. Such "bridges" may be essential for the structural organization of at least some compact tissues and they may also play a role for either contact inhibition of cell division or cell movement, or both. It may be mentioned in this connection that the incorporation of C^{14}-thymidine into the DNA of tumor target cell monolayers was inhibited by the addition of syngeneic as well as allogeneic lymph node cells, but inhibition by the latter was stronger (90). If this finding is relevant in the present context, it may mean that contact between syngeneic receptors normally leads to inhibition of cell division while allogeneic contact has a similar, but more serious, cytopathogenic effect. The misfitting of only partially complementary structures may be particularly harmful in connection with cell division. It is known that cells, such as fibroblasts, which are normally in close contact with their neighbors by adherence, free themselves and round up prior to division. If their contact structures are maladjusted, they may become entangled with deleterious results. From this concept it would follow that an otherwise tolerable cell-neighbor incompatibility may become lethal in connection with cell division.

Another piece of evidence that may be of relevance in this connection is the finding of Beisson & Sonneborn (91) that normal reproduction of the cell cortex in paramecium is dependent on the integrity of the pre-existing cortex structure in the parent cell; unless this is maintained, the genetic information available to the cell will not be sufficient to reproduce the normal cortical structure. On this model, modifications of the surface may therefore lead to faulty replication, with subsequent cellular dysfunction and death.

There is, of course, no reason to assume that all cells react in the same way upon interaction with allogeneic cells. One cell in which the situation may be different is the lymphocyte itself. According to Möller (92), lymph node cells and lymphoma cells may respond with stimulated rather than inhibited growth when encountering foreign H-2 antigens, at least when they are exposed to relatively small quantities, whereas larger quantities may become inhibitory for these targets as well. It may be part of the specifically differentiated function of the lymphocyte, itself a free cell and therefore probably not dependent on contactual growth regulation, to respond in this way when exposed to a "misfit" between its own surface receptor and a foreign, only partially complementary structure. At this point, immunological and non-immunological surveillance meet at a crossroad and the question arises whether the former may not represent a special case of the latter, as expressed and modified through the specific function of a differentiated cell, the lymphocyte.

Attractive as this picture is, many facts remain to be explained. It has to be postulated that organ-specific antigenic differences must not lead to reactions of this kind or serious calamities would result. In principle, the same type of developmental sequence has to be postulated to explain self-acceptance and nonself-rejection on this basis as has been suggested for immunological mechanisms. During an early period in development when the normal pattern is being established, everything entering the system must be accepted as self. Later, this has to be replaced by a nonself recognition and rejection mechanism. Of course, the real picture may be more variegated, with special differences of detail in each individual tissue. It follows from this general picture however, that tolerance should be inducible in this system as well as in the immunologic one. Recent experiments of Hellström (93) lend direct experimental support to this concept, as will be discussed in the final section.

Another requirement that must be imposed on a nonimmunological, contactual surveillance mechanism of the postulated type is that it must perceive alterations to new, nontolerated cell surface structures in a highly sensitive way, and one may raise the question whether the proposed mechanism, based so far on a single known transplantation antigen complex, may be sufficiently versatile to do this. However, the H-2 is only one among a large number of different transplantation antigen systems in mice. At least fifteen independent loci determining histocompatibility antigens in the mouse have been postulated to exist, and the true figure may be much higher (95). In this one system at least 18 different alleles are known within the relatively limited number of mouse strains that have been studied. Each alternative (pseudoallelic) form determines a different mosaic of individual antigens, with 5 to 14 different specificities having been identified. Taken together, the systems of histocompatibility antigens would thus provide a highly individualistic fingerprint, characterizing each cell in the organism.

Until recently little work has been directed specifically toward the study of histocompatibility mutations, even though the fairly rapid differentiation of independently maintained sublines of the same inbred strain into skin-incompatible strains and the high degree of natural polymorphism indicates frequent mutations. Recently, Bailey & Cohn have demonstrated (95) that "gain" mutations, leading to the appearance of new specificities, can be readily shown to occur spontaneously in mice, and to increase in frequency after X irradiation.

While all transplantation antigens may conceivably function in a surveillance capacity provided that they are expressed on the cell surface, the reverse proposition that all surface receptors that have this function must be capable of serving as transplantation antigens when introduced into hosts carrying a different pattern is probably not true. It has been postulated above that the lymphocyte uses the same mechanism for cell killing as originally evolved for the direct, contactual elimination of variants within compact tissues. If this is so, it will follow that many surface receptors will be able to function in both capacities. In hosts lacking the same receptor, grafted receptor-carrying cells will induce an ordinary immune response, i.e., antibodies. These will facilitate the adherence of lymphocytes to the target. The destruction of the target will occur because of the incompatibility of co-aggregated cells with different receptors. The antibodies may either facilitate this process, as in the case of antibody-sensitive cells, or counteract it, as is true of antibody-resistant cells that may respond with enhancement. One case where a surface difference is not reflected by graft immunity is represented by the grafting of cells derived from a parental strain to an F_1 hybrid host. In this situation, large skin or tumor grafts survive as well as in the parental strains themselves. The F_1 host cannot mobilize an ordinary homograft response against antigenic components which it shares with the graft. As a result, the lymphocyte, although different in surface structure from the target, will not attach and does not kill. As demonstrated by the tissue culture experiments in which coaggregation was induced artificially, it is fully competent to kill, however, and the same may be true for other tissue cells of the F_1 host, provided that they can come into close, three-dimensional contact with the target. In agreement with this picture, implantation of small numbers of dissociated, free tumor cells from parental to F_1 hosts does result in marked inhibition. This was, in fact, the way in which allogeneic inhibition was discovered by Hellström (72).

If this reasoning is correct, it follows that the nonimmunological, contactual surveillance mechanism is more versatile than immune elimination, and a larger number of surface structure differences (including losses) may be efficient in the former than in the latter system in which antibody formation is an additional requirement. All transplantation antigens should function in both capacities, unless graft destruction involves other mechanisms in addition to those already considered.

So far, we have been dwelling on the theoretical aspects of surveillance mechanisms in a rather speculative fashion, rather than reviewing in detail those immune mechanisms that have been demonstrated to act in the rejection of established neoplastic cells. Most experimental work has been done in transplantation systems, involving the grafting of viable tumor cells across more or less well-defined histocompatibility barriers or, more recently, tumor-specific antigenic barriers. This subject matter is more classical and has been often reviewed before, also by the present author (95). For these reasons, and also because relevant aspects are discussed in other sections of this article, only a brief summary of some more important points is given here.

There is abundant evidence that humoral as well as cell-mediated host reactions are directed against tumor cells containing transplantation or tumor-specific antigens foreign to the host organism. Humoral antibodies have been demonstrated in all leukemia systems studied, but in other systems they have not been as regularly demonstrable; there is considerable variation depending on the system used for detection and the tumor-host combination. The rather exclusive position of the leukemias is not necessarily due to the fact that humoral antibodies are more readily formed against leukemic cells than against other tumors, but depends more probably on a relatively high susceptibility of such cells to humoral antibodies. Such a difference is quite apparent if leukemic cells are compared with other tumors with regard to their sensitivity to anti-H-2 antibodies (96, 97). This variation in immunosensitivity has been shown to depend on a difference in concentration of antigenic surface receptors (98). Leukemia cells are usually smaller than carcinoma and sarcoma cells and, at least as far as H-2 receptors are concerned, these are more densely concentrated on the former. A similar variation in concentration of antigenic receptors has been shown to be critical in hemolytic systems (99). In the tumor-H-2 system, it has been found that increasing the concentration of reacting receptors upon the cell surface by combining several immune sera directed against different antigens results in cytotoxicity, so that cells which were resistant to the action of any one serum became sensitive when two or three were combined (98).

Whether a similar relationship is responsible for the more regular demonstrability of tumor-specific humoral antibodies in the leukemia systems than in other specifically antigenic tumors is not known, but there are good reasons to assume that this may be the case. At least in one virus-induced leukemia system, the Moloney mouse lymphoma, considerable variation was demonstrated in the immunosensitivity of different individual lymphomas *in vivo* and *in vitro* (24). Immunosensitive lymphoma cells were characterized by a higher specific antigen concentration on their surface, as shown by absorption and immunofluorescence tests. Only cells with a high relative antigen concentration were susceptible to the *in vitro* cytotoxic action of the specific antibody formed in immunized syngeneic hosts, whereas leukemic cells with a lower antigen concentration were partially or completely resistant *in vitro* and also less sensitive to *in vivo* rejection than the others.

With respect to the cell-mediated rejection reaction, its possible mechanisms have been dealt with elsewhere in this review. Concerning its occurrence, it may be stated that host cell-mediated rejection has been demonstrated in all tumor-specific and transplantation antigen systems where it has been looked for, ever since Algire et al. conclusively showed its importance by mixing sensitized host lymphoid cells with target tumor cells in cell-impermeable diffusion chambers (100). One convenient way to demonstrate this effect is by mixing sensitized lymph node or other immunologically competent cells with target tumor cells *in vitro* and inoculating the mixture into compatible and preferably preirradiated recipient hosts (101–103). Inhibition of tumor growth is revealed by a reduced incidence of takes or by a delayed latency period, sometimes both. The tumor-specific antigen systems in which this method was successful in showing cell-bound immunity include chemically induced sarcomas (103, 104) and hepatomas (1), sarcomas induced by the implantation of cellophane films (32) and tumors induced by oncogenic viruses, such as polyoma (105) or the Gross leukemia agent (20). In the case of virus-induced tumors that contain common antigenic specificities, sensitized lymph node cells tend to inhibit or neutralize all syngeneic tumors of the same viral etiology, whereas in chemically induced tumors with individually distinct antigenic specificities there is no evidence for such "cross-neutralization," and the inhibitory action of sensitized lymph node cells appears to be as specific as transplantation immunity itself (106).

Quite generally it can be said that an inhibiting effect of sensitized, immunologically competent host cells has been demonstrable in every system studied in which transplantation methods showed the existence of tumor-specific transplantation antigens even though the minimum efficient ratio of host to target cells has been very variable, depending on the system and the experimental conditions.

WHY DOES REJECTION FAIL IN THE CASE OF "SUCCESSFUL" TUMORS?

Escape from Immunological Surveillance

This problem can obviously be discussed only in relation to antigenic tumor cells that have managed to grow out and have thus escaped immunological surveillance.

It has been shown in virus as well as chemically induced tumor systems (2, 4) that primary neoplasms arising after a short latent period tend to be more strongly antigenic than tumors which appear after a longer time. This indicates that immunological surveillance requires a certain amount of time before it can become effective. More rapidly growing tumors are therefore permitted to reach irreversible size even if strongly antigenic, whereas the slowly growing neoplasms have to face an efficient host reaction which would be capable of eliminating the more antigenic tumors. This dynamic nature of the tumor-host balance makes the outcome of the race between tumor growth and promptness of the host reaction rather uncertain and, in the individual case, quite unpredictable. Nevertheless, certain conditions are known that can favor the tumor in a decisive way. Some experimentally documented mechanisms will be considered briefly.

Tolerance and "sneaking through".—Tolerance has been conclusively demonstrated in the case of several tumors induced by vertically trans-mitted viruses: fowl lymphomatosis transmitted through the eggs of viremic hens (107); mouse mammary carcinomas induced by the milk agent (108); mouse lymphomas induced by transmitted Gross virus (109–111), or by inoculation of the Moloney leukemia agent into newborn mice (112). With the exception of fowl lymphomatosis in which no such studies could be made due to the absence of inbred strains, in all other systems mentioned the tumors were shown to contain the tumor-specific transplantation antigen, but the host was incapable of reacting against it. In the case of the mammary tumor agent and the Moloney virus, it was possible to compare the resis-tance of syngeneic hosts lacking the agent with animals that had received the virus neonatally or as adults. These comparisons have clearly shown that tolerance to the specific transplantation antigen is causally related to neona-tal virus infection.

When mice are infected with the same agents for the first time as adults, they develop resistance to the tumors and promptly reject small inocula derived from established neoplasms induced by the same agent in syngeneic hosts (18, 33, 108). In spite of this relative resistance, they are not always able to prevent the development of their own primary tumors. Mice inocu-lated with the milk agent as adults can develop mammary carcinoma, but at a lower frequency than neonatally infected mice. The same is true for the Moloney lymphoma virus. In other virus systems, e.g., Gross or polyoma, neonatal infection is more a requisite for establishment of the tumor; the adult-infected host is more successful in preventing its development. In the case of polyoma, full tolerance has not been demonstrated (2) but partial tolerance may nevertheless prevail (67) and may explain the sensitivity of newborn mice to the oncogenic effect of the agent, and the complete re-sistance of older animals. Alternatively, the less responding immune system of the newborn host may never catch up with the growth of the antigenic tumor cells.

Another interesting case is the SV40-hamster sarcoma system. Several workers have shown that hamsters inoculated with SV40 virus as newborns can be protected at least partially from virus-induced tumors if given a second inoculation of X-irradiated SV40-induced sarcoma cells (113), or live SV40 virus (114, 115), or human cells transformed by the SV40 virus (116). It follows that the virus-inoculated newborn hamsters do not become tolerant to the SV40 tumor-specific antigen but are nevertheless unable to prevent their outgrowth. A second inoculation of irradiated cells is then capable of immunizing against the developing antigenic tumor cells that would otherwise escape immune rejection, probably because of insufficient release of antigen. This, rather than specific tolerance, may be the reason for the outgrowth of antigenic tumors in other systems as well. The situation appears to be quite similar to the "sneaking through" of small numbers of cells from chemically induced antigenic tumors in syngeneic hosts that are capable of inhibiting the growth of medium-sized but not of large inocula, as shown by Old et al. (117).

Relevant findings of still another type and of a mutually complementary nature have been recently obtained with mouse sarcomas induced by methylcholanthrene (118) and with the Schmidt-Ruppin-variant of the Rous virus (119). With the former, we have shown (104) that the primary autochthonous host can be immunized against its own tumor cells, after the tumor has been removed by operation and the host rechallenged with irradiated cells of its own tumor. Haddow & Alexander (120) found that autografting with irradiated autochthonous tumor cells may induce regression or increase the radiosensitivity of primary, benzopyrene-induced rat sarcomas. Thus, in these cases the host defense was insufficient to prevent the outgrowth of the tumor *in situ* when unaided, but it could be made to function by autoimmunization. Recently, Stjernswärd (118) has examined the immune status of the primary MC-sarcoma host immediately after operative removal of the tumor, by regrafting it with small numbers of autochthonous tumor cells. He has found no evidence that these animals had a heightened resistance against their own tumor cells; on the contrary, they were more susceptible to small inocula than were untreated isologous controls. Their response was not irreversibly paralyzed, however, since they could be immunized by inoculating irradiated tumor cells repeatedly, subsequent to the operation. Closely analogous findings were obtained by Jonsson & Sjögren (119) with the Schmidt-Ruppin-Rous virus-induced mouse sarcoma. The primary autochthonous host in this case gave no evidence of resistance when tested immediately after tumor removal, but it could be made to react if treated with irradiated tumor cells. In both systems, the tumor hosts thus failed to show evidence of sensitization. It appears probable that the amount of antigen released by the large tumors had paralyzed the host response in a reversible way. Whether this is akin to immunological tolerance or not must be left open at present; preliminary evidence of Stjernswärd (118) favors tolerance, since the operated primary host showed increased susceptibility to small implants of its own tumor only, but not to similar implants of presumably noncrossreacting methylcholanthrene sarcomas obtained from other individuals of the same strain.

In the above two systems, "tolerance" could be broken after operative removal of the tumor, i.e., the bulk of the antigenic material. With vertically transmitted viruses, such as the milk agent or the leukemia viruses, this is not possible since the viruses multiply in normal cells and there is often viremia. It is noteworthy, however, that Old et al. (121) found that treatment with the mycobacterial vaccine BCG delays the appearance of primary Gross virus-induced lymphomas in AKR mice and of mammary carcinomas in an agent-bearing strain. Although there is no direct evidence that this effect of BCG is immunological in nature, the same type of treatment was found to stimulate the homograft response and the reaction against tumor-specific antigens of chemically induced sarcomas as well (121). This lead seems to be an interesting one to follow up, since it is possible that BCG may break the tolerant status of the host.

Enhancement.—The paradoxical phenomenon of immunological enhancement has been the subject of much recent study. Its occurrence has been clearly documented in a variety of host-tumor systems, including isoantigenic and tumor-specific antigen systems as well (122, 123). As far as tumor-specific antigens are concerned, it has been demonstrated in the case of chemically induced sarcomas (16, 124) of mammary carcinomas induced by the milk agent (125), and of Moloney virus-induced lymphomas (126). In all cases the test for enhancement was based on isografting and can only be regarded as a model of what may happen during oncogenesis. No experiments have been reported so far dealing directly with the possible role of enhancement during the oncogenic process itself.

If the transplantation systems are regarded as models of what may happen under spontaneous circumstances, an analysis of the mechanisms of the so-called nonspecific tumor growth, i.e., the progressive growth of transplanted neoplasms across strong histoincompatibility barriers, appears to be particularly relevant (127–129). Tumor lines selected for nonspecific growth capacities by serial passage through genetically incompatible animals were characterized by a decreased concentration of the relevant antigens, in comparison with the original, more specific line. Because of this decrease, they become more resistant to the cytotoxic action of isoantibody in the presence of complement. When such antigenic but resistant cells are exposed to isoantibodies, the foreign sites on their surface become covered and this appears to protect them from destruction by the cell-mediated response. The weak antigenicity of the tumor cells is thus actually to their advantage since it protects tham from direct contact with the host lymphocyte. Admittedly, this model is artificial since it is based on cell lines established by prolonged selection, but the weak antigenicity of several TSTA systems is suggestive and urges further and more direct studies.

If enhancement does operate during oncogenesis, it ought to be possible to increase the yield of tumors by the repeated injection of tumor-specific antiserum during the latent period. We have performed some experiments of this type with the Moloney system but the yield of tumors decreased rather than increased (94). This indicates that enhancement does not play a major positive role in this system but obviously this is not the best material for such experiments, since lymphoma cells are often sensitive to the cytotoxic action of isoantibodies. Chemical or viral induction of sarcomas may provide more appropriate model systems.

Antigenic loss.—Complete loss of antigenicity with selective overgrowth of nonantigenic variants is a possible mechanism of escape from immunological surveillance. Again, only model systems are available and these are all of the same general type. Heterozygous tumor cells of F_1 hybrid origin, containing two different H-2 complexes, may lose one but not both complexes through negative selection, as has already been discussed in the section dealing with mechanisms determining antigens. With tumor-specific antigens, quantitative changes but no losses have been encountered and, as discussed, this has been taken to indicate that such antigens represent cellular characteristics essential for the neoplastic behavior of the tumor cell.

ESCAPE FROM NONIMMUNOLOGICAL SURVEILLANCE

It has been postulated above that allogeneic inhibition may represent a contactual, nonimmunological surveillance mechanism. One may therefore briefly consider the experimentally demonstrated ways in which cells can be shown to escape allogeneic inhibition. These are twofold: breakthrough due to a large colony size, and specific adaptation upon selective passage. With regard to the first, allogeneic inhibition was found to operate only when the number of homozygous, parental-type tumor cells inoculated into the F_1 hybrid host was very small (10^3–10^5 cells), but it failed with larger numbers of cells, (72–74). This means that the inhibition can be overcome if a critical colony size is reached. A similar threshold effect has been postulated to explain two-phase carcinogenesis (130). Another possibly relevant situation has been encountered in studies on a mammary carcinoma which was hormone-dependent when inoculated in a small dose but independent when large inocula were tested (131). This can be understood if it is assumed that tumor growth depends on the outcome of an interplay between stimulating and inhibiting forces, and it is possible to overcome the local inhibition imposed on small inocula by an adequate hormonal stimulus. After critical tumor size has been reached, local inhibition would no longer be efficient.

Hellström has also shown (93) that it is possible to escape allogeneic inhibition by a more specific adaptation. He has passaged tumors of homozygous origin (symbolized as strain A) through different types of F_1 hybrids (symbolized as $A \times B$, $A \times C$, $A \times D$, etc.). After a number of passages, each line was compared with the original line that had been maintained in strain A. A certain adaptation could be demonstrated: the A B line was less inhibited in A B than was the A line, but was still inhibited in A C and A D, etc., and approximately to the same extent as before. The same was true with the other sublines in relation to their passage hosts. This adaptive change shows a striking resemblance to the Barrett-Deringer phenomenon (131, 132), interpreted as the induced adaptation of tumor cells to the inhibitory effect of foreign transplantation antigens (133). The mechanism of this adaptation is unknown, but at least one specific hypothesis is testable. As already discussed, H-2 is a complex locus, determining a number of distinct antigenic specificities. The H-2 complex responsible for a given case of allogeneic H-2 inhibition is partially cross-reactive with the target cells' own H-2 complex and partially distinct. Adaptation to allogeneic inhibition could be due to an increase in the concentration of the cross-reacting sites and a decrease in the concentration of the nonidentical sites. This hypothesis can be tested readily with cells of appropriate antigenic constitution.

WHAT IS THE SIGNIFICANCE OF TUMOR-SPECIFIC TRANSPLANTATION ANTIGENS FOR STUDIES ON THE ETIOLOGY, PREVENTION, AND THERAPY OF NEOPLASMS?

Most of the material that can serve as the basis for this discussion has already been mentioned in previous sections. It may be sufficient to summarize briefly some points of more general significance.

Immunological methods may be of a certain value when looking for common etiological factors in tumors of unknown origin. The existence of common tumor-specific transplantation antigens in groups of tumors induced by the same virus is particularly relevant in this context, with the important reservation that passenger viruses may induce new transplantation antigens as well (134–136). Even oncogenic viruses may appear as passengers in tumors which they have not caused and can impose new antigenic specificities on them. In this context it may be worth noting that many known tumor viruses have been actually isolated as passengers from other tumors for which they could not have causative significance. The isolation of the Friend, Graffi, and Moloney agents, three leukemia viruses, from long transplanted anaplastic sarcomas and carcinomas, and the isolation of polyoma virus from lymphatic leukemias induced by the Gross agent, are cases in point. This is not surprising, since tumors often proliferate in immunologically depressed hosts, and long transplanted lines pass, in addition, through many different laboratories and the hands of many investigators. It is possible that the danger is less with spontaneous tumors. Nevertheless, the possibility of accidental contamination and identification of the "wrong" TSTA must be kept in mind. A possible way out of this dilemma is in the comparison of the antigenicity of similar tumors collected from very different geographical areas.

Even with this reservation, the search for common tumor-specific transplantation antigens in human tumors is of potential value, particularly since no better approach is available. Direct virus isolation has to face the problem of passenger contamination and is further hampered by the fact that many tumors induced by known oncogenic viruses do not release the inducing virus. The group-specific TSTA is nevertheless present and the immunological approach has therefore a wider applicability from the etiological point of view than has the isolation of infectious virus.

No studies are yet available on human tumors that would conclusively prove the presence of a TSTA specific for a certain group of neoplasms. However, strongly suggestive evidence has been obtained in the case of the Burkitt lymphoma by the membrane immunofluorescence reaction (137).

Concerning the possible value of immunological aproaches to tumor prevention and therapy, the potential usefulness of immunological prevention will depend on the existence of tumor-specific antigens which can be expected to vary for different systems, the cross-reactive versus the individually distinct natures of the antigens involved, and the probability of favoring cell-bound rejection mechanisms rather than enhancement. Specific immunization appears to be a rational approach only in cases of extensive cross-reactivity as is found in virus-induced experimental tumors. An immunizing procedure must be chosen so that it favors rejection and counteracts enhancement. It is not known which factors are of critical importance in this respect, but the successful application of irradiated cell vaccines in reducing the frequency of primary SV40- and polyoma-induced tumors seems to represent a hopeful start (113). If the antigens are individually distinct for different neoplasms induced by the same agent, as is the situation with chemically induced tumors in mice, attempts to increase the host's own response by nonspecific means would seem to be more appropriate (117).

Immunological prevention of viral neoplasms seems to depend, *inter alia.* on the horizontal versus vertical transmission of the virus. Vaccination seems theoretically feasible in cases of horizontal transmission, although the danger of enhancement enters here as well. If transmission is vertical, tolerance to the tumor-specific antigens may be involved (107–112), dooming specific immunization to failure. Breaking the transmission cycle or tolerance, or both, have to be envisaged in that case.

As to the potential significance of immunological responses in therapy, it is known that experimental tumors growing in genetically slightly incompatible hosts are more easily curable by chemotherapy or radiotherapy than are the same tumors when growing in genetically compatible hosts in which the antigenic barrier is slight or nonexistent (138, 139). The curability of choriocarcinoma by chemotherapy is also often attributed to the presumed antigenicity of neoplastic cells of foetal origin. Another example of how therapy and host response may act synergistically in bringing about tumor regression is represented by the finding (5, 6, 120) that inoculation of X-irradiated tumor autografts increased the radiosensitivity of primary, benzpyrene-induced rat sarcomas, known to carry tumor-specific antigens. Furthermore, preliminary evidence indicates (140) that an immunosensitive Moloney virus-induced mouse lymphoma is more easily influenced by methotrexate than an immunoresistant lymphoma of the same origin. In patients with Burkitt lymphoma, a correlation was found between the reactivity of the patient's serum against the tumor cells as judged by the membrane immunofluorescence test, and the durability of tumor regression obtained by chemotherapy.

All this suggests that immunological approaches, although probably not useful for the treatment of established tumors when applied alone, may play an important role in an adjuvant capacity, together with other forms of therapy. A rational approach will require adequate assessment of the immune status of the host versus its own tumor, followed by specific or nonspecific stimulation of reactivity, with adequate care taken to avoid preferential stimulation of humoral antibody formation and the risk of enhancement. At the same time, other therapy should be employed designed to decrease the number of tumor cells with which the host must cope.

LITERATURE CITED

1. Old, L. J., and Boyse, E. A., *Ann. Rev. Med.*, **15**, 167–86 (1964)
2. Sjögren, H. O., *Progr. Exptl. Tumor Res.*, **6**, 289–322 (1965)
3. Sjögren, H. O., *Progr. Med. Virol.* (In press)
4. Prehn, R. T., *Can. Cancer Conf.*, **5**, 387–95 (1963)
5. Haddow, A., *Brit. Med. Bull.*, **21**, 133–39 (1965)
6. Alexander, P., Immunological Reactions of the Host against Primary Tumors, 478–95. In *Scientific Basis of Surgery*, Irvine, (W. T., Ed., Churchill Publ., 1965)
7. Haughton, G., *Transplantation* (In press)
8. Möller, G., *J. Exptl. Med.*, **114**, 415–34 (1961)
9. Klein, G., *Symp. Soc. Gen. Physiol.*, *Woods Hole, Mass.*, *1965.* (In press)
10. Wallach, D., *Symp. Soc. Gen. Physiol.*, *Woods Hole, Mass.*, *1965.* (In press)
11. Medawar, P. B., *Ann. N.Y. Acad. Sci.*, **68**, 2655–67 (1957)
12. Davies, D. A. L., *Nature*, **193**, 34–36 (1962)
13. Palm, J., and Manson, L. A., *Wistar Inst. Symp. Monographs*, **3**, 21–33 (1965)
14. Herzenberg, L. A., and Herzenberg, L. A., *Proc. Natl. Acad. Sci., U.S.* **47**, 762 (1961)
15. Wigzell, H., *Transplantation*, **3**, 423–31 (1965)
16. Möller, G., *Nature*, **207**, 846–47 (1964)
17. Lejneva, O. M., Zilber, L. A., and Ievleva, E. S., *Nature*, **206**, 1163 (1965)
18. Klein, E., and Klein, G., *J. Natl. Cancer Inst.*, **32**, 547–68 (1964)
19. Pasternak, G., *J. Natl. Cancer Inst.*, **34**, 71–83 (1965)
20. Slettenmark, B., and Klein, E., *Cancer Res.*, **22**, 947–54 (1962)
21. Old, L. J., Boyse, E. A., and Stockert, E., *J. Natl. Cancer Inst.*, **31**, 977–86 (1963)
22. Wahren, B., *J. Natl. Cancer Inst.*, **31**, 411–23 (1963)
23. Rich, M., in Viruses Inducing Cancer, Implications for Therapy. (Burdette, W. J., Ed., Univ. of Utah Press, Salt Lake City. In press, 1966)
24. Klein, G., Klein, E., and Haughton, G., *J. Natl. Cancer Inst.* (In press)
25. Luria, S. E., *Science*, **136**, 685–92 (1962)
26. Haughton, G., *Science*, **147**, 506–7 (1965)
27. Sjögren, H. O., Hellström, I., and Klein, G., *Exptl. Cell. Res.*, **23**, 204–8 (1961)
28. Habel, K., *Proc. Soc. Exptl. Biol. Med.*, **106**, 722–25 (1961)
29. Hellström, I., and Sjögren, H. O., *Exptl. Cell. Res.*, **40**, 212–15 (1965)
30. Sjögren, H. O., and Hellström, I., *Exptl. Cell Res.*, **40**, 208–11 (1965)
31. Klein, E., *Intern. Symp. Immunopathology, 4th, Monte Carlo, Monacco, 1965.* (Grabar. P., Ed., Schwabe Publ., Basel/Stuttgart, in press)
32. Klein, G., Sjögren, H. O., and Klein, E., *Cancer Res.*, **23**, 84–92 (1963)
33. Klein, G., Sjögren, H. O., and Klein, E., *Cancer Res.*, **22**, 955–61 (1962)
34. Habel, K., and Eddy, B. E., *Proc. Soc. Exptl. Biol. Med.*, **113**, 1–4 (1963)
35. Sjögren, H. O., *J. Natl. Cancer Inst.*, **32**, 645–49 (1964)
36. Shope, R. E., *J. Gen. Physiol.*, **45**, 143 (1962)
37. Saxén, L., Vainio, T., and Toivonen,

S., *J. Natl. Cancer Inst.*, **29,** 597–631 (1962)
38. Macpherson, I., *Science,* **148,** 1731–33 (1965)
39. Huebner, R. J., Pareira, H. G., Allison, A. C., Hollinshead, A. C., and Turner, H. C., *Proc. Natl. Acad. Sci., U.S.,* **51,** 432–39 (1964)
40. Huebner, R. J., Complement-fixing neoantigens. *Proc. Symp. Unio Intern. Contra Cancrum, Sukhumi, 1965.* (Symp. on Tumor-Specific Antigens, in press)
41. Gerber, P., *Science,* **145,** 833 (1964)
42. Hanafusa, H., Hanafusa, T., and Rubin, H., *Proc. Natl. Acad. Sci. U.S.,* **49,** 572–80 (1963)
43. Sjögren, H. O., and Jonsson, N., *Exptl. Cell. Res.,* **32,** 618–21 (1963)
44. Jonsson, N., and Sjögren, H. O., *J. Exptl. Med.,* **122,** 403–21 (1965)
45. Ahlström, C. G., and Forsby, N., *J. Exptl. Med.,* **115,** 839–52 (1962)
46. Svoboda, J., Chyle, P., Simkovic, D., and Hilgert, I., *Folia Biol.,* **9,** 77 (1963)
47. Evans, C. A., Gorman, L. R., Ito, Y., and Weiser, R. S., *J. Natl. Cancer Inst.,* **29,** 277–85 (1962)
48. Evans. C. A., Weiser, R. S., and Ito, Y., *Cold Spring Harbor Symp. Quant. Biol.,* **27,** 453–62 (1962)
49. Ito, Y., *Cold Spring Harbor Symp. Quant. Biol.,* **27,** 387–94 (1962)
50. Ito, Y., *Proc. Am. Assoc. Cancer Res.,* **4,** 31 (1963)
51. Hellström, K. E., *J. Natl. Cancer Inst.,* **23,** 1019–33 (1959)
52. Klein, G., and Klein, E., *J. Cell. Comp. Physiol.,* **52,** Suppl. 1, 125–68 (1958)
53. Prehn, R. T., *J. Natl. Cancer Inst.,* **32,** 1–17 (1964)
54. Malmgren, R. A., Bennison, B. E., and McKinley, T. W., *Proc. Soc. Exptl. Biol. Med.,* **79,** 484–88 (1952)
55. Linder, O. E. A., *Cancer Res.,* **22,** 380–83 (1962)
56. Stjernswärd, J., *J. Natl. Cancer Inst.,* **35,** 885–92 (1965)
57. Stjernswärd, J. (To be published)
58. Prehn, R. T., *J. Natl. Cancer Inst.,* **31,** 791–805 (1963)
59. Burnet, F. M., *Brit. Med. Bull.,* **20,** 154–58 (1964)
60. Defendi, V., and Roosa, R. A., *Wistar Inst., Monographs,* **2,** 121–36 (1964)
61. Ting, R. C., and Law, L. W., *J. Natl. Cancer Inst.,* **34,** 521–27 (1965)
62. Miller, J. F. A. P., *Science,* **144,** 1544–51 (1964)
63. Vandeputte, M., and De Somer, P., *Nature,* **206,** 520–21 (1965)

64. Kirschstein, R. L., Rabson, A. S., and Peters, E. A., *Proc. Soc. Exptl. Biol. Med.,* **117,** 198–200 (1964)
65. Grant, G. A., and Miller, J. F. A. P., *Nature,* **205,** 1124–25 (1965)
66. Mishizuka, Y., Nakakuki, K., and Usui, M., *Nature,* **205,** 1236–38 (1965)
67. Habel, K., *J. Exptl. Med.,* **115,** 181–93 (1962)
68. Dineen, J. K., *Nature,* **197,** 268–69 (1963)
69. Dineen, J. K., *Nature,* **197,** 471–72 (1963)
70. Moscona, A., *Proc. Natl. Acad. Sci. U.S.,* **43,** 184–94 (1957)
71. Wolff, E., and Wolff, E., *Compt. Rend.,* **258,** 2439–41 (1964)
72. Hellström, K. E., *Nature,* **199,** 614–15 (1963)
73. Hellström, K. E., *Science,* **143,** 477–78 (1964)
74. Hellström, K. E., *Nature,* **201,** 893–95 (1964)
75. Hellström, K. E., Hellström, I., and Haughton, G., *Nature,* **204,** 661–64 (1964)
76. Hellström, K. E., Hellström, I., and Bergheden, C., *Nature,* **208,** 458–60 (1965)
77. Möller, E., *Science,* **147,** 873–79 (1965)
78. Rosenau, W., and Moon, H. D., *J. Natl. Cancer Inst.,* **27,** 471–83 (1961)
79. Wilson, D. B., *J. Cell. Comp. Physiol.,* **62,** 273 (1963)
80. Brondz, B. D., *Folia Biol.,* **10,** 164 (1964)
81. Koprowski, H., and Fernandes, M. V., *J. Exptl. Med.,* **116,** 467 (1962)
82. Vainio, T., Koskimies, O., Perlmann, P., Perlmann, H., and Klein, G., *Nature,* **204,** 453 (1964)
83. Wilson, D. B., *J. Exptl. Med.,* **122,** 167 (1965)
84. Granger, G. A., and Weiser, R. S., *Science,* **145,** 1427 (1964)
85. Holm, G., Perlmann, P., and Werner, B., *Nature,* **203,** 841 (1964)
86. Holm, G., and Perlmann, P., *Nature,* **207,** 818 (1965)
87. Möller, G., and Möller, E., *Nature,* **208,** 260–63 (1965)
88. Bergheden, C., and Hellström, K. E. (Submitted for publication to *Intern. J. Cancer*)
89. Hellström, I., and Hellström, K. E., *Ann. N.Y. Acad. Sci.* (In press)
90. Ming, S. C., Klein, E., and Klein, G. (To be published)
91. Beisson, J., and Sonneborn, T. M., *Proc. Natl. Acad. Sci.,* **53,** 275–82 (1965)
92. Möller, G. (Personal communication)

93. Hellström, K. E., *Exptl. Cell Res.* (In press)

94. Klein, G., in Viruses Inducing Cancer, Implications for Therapy. (Burdette, W. J., Ed., Univ. of Utah Press, Salt Lake City. In press, 1966)

95. Bailey, D. W., and Cohn, J., *Genet. Res.*, **6**, 330–40 (1965)

96. Gorer, P. A., *Advan. Cancer Res.*, **4**, 149–86 (1956)

97. Hellström, K. E., *Transplant. Bull.*, **6**, 411–16 (1959)

98. Möller, E., and Möller, G., *J. Exptl. Med.*, **115**, 527–53 (1962)

99. Mayer, M. M., Complement and complement fixation, in *Experimental Immunochemistry*, 2nd ed. (Kabat, E. A., and Mayer, M. M., Charles C Thomas, Springfield, Ill., (1961)

100. Prehn, R. T., Weaver, J. M., and Algire, G. H., *J. Natl. Cancer Inst.*, **15**, 509–18 (1954)

101. Klein, E., and Sjögren, H. O., *Cancer Res.*, **20**, 452–61 (1960)

102. Winn, H. J., *Natl. Cancer Inst., Monograph*, **2**, 113–38 (1959)

103. Old, L. J., Boyse, E. A., Bennett, B., and Lilly, F., in: *Cell Bound Antibodies*, 89–99. (Amos, B., and Koprowski, H., Eds., Wistar Inst. Press, Philadelphia, 1963)

104. Klein, G., Sjögren, H. O., Klein, E., and Hellström, K. E., *Cancer Res.*, **20**, 1561–72 (1960)

105. Sjögren, H. O., Hellström, I., and Klein, G., *Cancer Res.*, **21**, 329–37 (1961)

106. Klein, G., and Klein, E., *Cold Spring Harbor Symp. Quant. Biol.*, **27**, 463–70 (1962)

107. Rubin, H., Fanshier, L., Cornelius, A., and Hughes, W. F., *Virology*, **17**, 143–56 (1962)

108. Attia, M. A., DeOme, K. B., and Weiss, D. W., *Cancer Res.*, **25**, 451–57, (1965)

109. Axelrad, A. A., *Nature*, **199**, 80–83, (1963)

110. Wahren, B., *Intern. J. Cancer*, **1**, 41–50 (1966)

111. Bubenik, J., Adamcova, B., and Koldovsky, P., *Folia Biol.*, **10**, 293–300 (1964)

112. Klein, E., and Klein, G., *Cancer Res.*, **25**, 851–54, (1965)

113. Goldner, H., Girardi, A. J., Larson, V. M., and Hilleman, M. R., *Proc. Soc. Exptl. Biol. Med.*, **117**, 851 (1964)

114. Eddy, B. E., Grubbs, G. E., and Young R. D., *Proc. Soc. Exptl. Biol. Med.*, **117**, 575 (1964)

115. Deichman, G. J., and Kluchareva, T. E., *Virology*, **24**, 131–37, (1964)

116. Girardi, A. J., *Proc. Natl. Acad. Sci. U. S.*, **54**, 445–51 (1965)

117. Old, L. J., Boyse, E. A., Clarke, D. A., and Carswell, E. A., *Ann. N. Y. Acad. Sci.*, **101**, 80–106 (1962)

118. Stjernswärd, J. (Submitted for publication to the *J. Natl. Cancer Inst.*)

119. Jonsson, N., and Sjögren, H. O., *J. Exptl. Med.*, **123**, 487–504 (1966)

120. Haddow, A., and Alexander, P., *Lancet*, **1**, 452–55, (1964)

121. Old, L. J., Benacerraf, H., Clarke, D. A., Carswell, E. A., and Stockert, E., *Cancer Res.*, **21**, 1281–1301 (1961)

122. Hellström, K. E., and Möller, G., *Progr. Allergy*, **9**, 158–245 (1965)

123. Moller, G., *J. Nat. Cancer Inst.*, **30**, 1205–26 (1963)

124. Bubenik, J., and Koldovsky, P., *Folia Biol.*, **11**, 258–65 (1965)

125. Weiss, D. W., Faulkin, L. J., and DeOme, K. B., *Cancer Res.*, **24**, 732–41 (1964)

126. Glynn, J. P., Bianco, A. R., and Goldin, A., *Cancer Res.*, **24**, 502–8 (1964)

127. Klein, E., and Möller, E., *J. Natl. Cancer Inst.*, **31**, 347–64 (1963)

128. Möller, E., *J. Natl. Cancer Inst.*, **33**, 979–89 (1964)

129. Möller, E., *J. Natl. Cancer Inst.*, **35**, 1053–59 (1965)

130. Berenblum, I., *Cancer Res.*, **14**, 471–77, (1954)

131. Klein, G., and Klein, E., *Symp. Soc. Exptl. Biol.*, **11**, 305–28 (1957)

132. Barrett, M. K., and Deringer, M. K., *J. Natl. Cancer Inst.*, **11**, 51–59 (1952)

133. Klein, G., *Ann. Rev. Physiol.*, **18**, 13–34 (1956)

134. Hamburg, V. P., and Svet-Moldavsky, G. J., *Nature*, **203**, 772 (1964)

135. Sjögren, H. O., *J. Natl. Cancer Inst.*, **32**, 361–74 (1964)

136. Stück, B., Old, L. J., and Boyse, E. A., *Nature*, **202**, 106–18 (1964)

137. Klein, G., Clifford, P., Klein, E., and Stjernswärd, J., *Proc. Natl. Acad. Sci. U. S.* (In press)

138. Cohen, A., and Cohen, L., *Brit. J. Cancer*, **8**, 303–12 (1964)

139. Dunning, W. F., and Curtis, M. R., *Proc. Intern. Cancer Congr., 7th, London, 1958*, 128.

140. Klein, G., (Unpublished observations)

THE BIOSYNTHESIS OF BACTERIAL POLYSACCHARIDES[1,2,3]

By B. L. Horecker

Department of Molecular Biology, Albert Einstein College of Medicine, Bronx, New York

Contents

Introduction... 254
Cellulose and Capsular Polysaccharides........................... 254
  Bacterial cellulose... 254
  Capsular polysaccharides...................................... 255
Lipopolysaccharide of Gram-Negative Organisms.................... 256
  Isolation and characterization................................ 256
  Polysaccharides of "rough" and "smooth" strains............... 256
  Structure of lipid A.. 258
  Structure of the KDO-heptose-phosphate backbone and the incorporation of KDO... 258
  Biosynthesis of the core portion of lipopolysaccharide........ 259
  The role of phospholipid in the biosynthesis of the lipopolysaccharide core....... 260
  Structure of the lipopolysaccharide core...................... 262
  Biosynthesis of the antigenic side chains in Salmonellae...... 264
  Biosynthesis of the antigenic side chains in E. coli.......... 267
  Semirough strains and their possible biochemical origin....... 268
  Biochemistry of phage conversion of lipopolysaccharide structures........... 268
  Control mechanisms in lipopolysaccharide biosynthesis......... 269
Glycopeptide... 270
  Incorporation of N-acetylmuramic acid and N-acetylglucosamine........... 270
  Function of membrane-bound lipid intermediates................ 270
  Formation of the cross-linked structure and the action of penicillin.......... 273
  The mechanism of action of cycloserine....................... 274
Teichoic Acids... 274
  Biosynthesis of polyribitolphosphate and polyglycerophosphate............... 275
  Addition of side chain sugars................................. 275
  Biosynthesis of polymers of glucosyl-glycerophosphate and galactosyl-glycerophosphate....... 275
  Linkage of teichoic acids to glycopeptide and control of synthesis............ 276

[1] The survey of literature pertaining to this review was concluded in December 1965.

[2] The following abbreviations are used: CDP (cytidine diphosphate); CMP (cytidine monophosphate); GDP (guanine diphosphate); KDO (3-deoxyoctulosonate); LPS (lipopolysaccharide); TDP (thimidine diphosphate); UDP (uridine diphosphate); UDPG (uridine diphosphoglucose).

[3] Work from this laboratory was supported by grants from the National Institutes of Health (GM 11301) and the National Science Foundation (GB 1465). This is Communication No. 61 from the Joan and Lester Avnet Institute of Molecular Biology.

253

Intracellular "Storage" Polysaccharides........................... 276
　　Biosynthesis of glycogen from ADP-glucose............................ 277
　　Other homopolysaccharides... 278
Glycolipids.. 278
　　Occurrence of glycolipids.. 278
　　Biosynthesis of glycolipids... 278
Biosynthesis of Sugar Nucleotides and Control of Polysaccharide
　　Synthesis.. 279
　　Sugar nucleotides containing glucose and galactose.................... 279
　　The formation of 6-deoxy and 3,6-dideoxy sugars..................... 280
　　Sugar nucleotides derived from GDP-mannose........................ 281
　　Nucleotide precursors of teichoic acids.............................. 282
　　Feedback control mechanisms....................................... 282
　　Genetic control of the biosynthesis of sugar nucleotides................ 284

Introduction

Earlier studies of the biosynthesis of bacterial polysaccharides were largely restricted to a few special cases where the precursors were either disaccharides, such as sucrose or maltose, or phosphate esters, such as glucose 1-phosphate. [For a review see (1).] Studies of the biosynthesis of other bacterial polysaccharides, particularly the more complex heteropolysaccharides, were hampered by a complete ignorance of their biological precursors. It is only during the past ten years that the important role of the nucleoside diphosphate sugars in the biosynthesis of polysaccharides has become apparent. It is now clear that these compounds serve not only as the precursors for the majority of bacterial polysaccharides, but also are directly involved in the interconversion of monosaccharides and thus in the biosynthesis of the monosaccharide building blocks themselves. An important factor which has made possible the recent advances in our knowledge of the biosynthesis of bacterial polysaccharides has been the increased availability of these nucleoside diphosphate sugar derivatives, through the development of both chemical and enzymatic methods for their preparation.

Since a considerable number of reviews have appeared recently dealing with one or another aspect of bacterial polysaccharide biosynthesis, this author will not attempt a comprehensive review of the entire field. However, in many cases understanding of the structure and of the mechanism of biosynthesis have gone hand in hand, and it will therefore be necessary to refer frequently to structural studies in discussing the biosynthetic mechanisms. In the bacteria, polysaccharides appear to have their primary function as structural components, rather than as energy reserves, and we will be concerned primarily with capsular and cell wall polysaccharides. Although little information is yet available, one of the most interesting problems for future exploration is the regulation of polysaccharide biosynthesis. Attention will be drawn to work in this area wherever possible.

Cellulose and Capsular Polysaccharides

Bacterial cellulose.—Although cellulose is one of the most abundant of all polysaccharides in nature, until very recently attempts to demonstrate its biosynthesis by *in vitro* systems have been unsuccessful. In the bacteria, cellulose occurs in the genus *Acetobacter*, in which it appears in the extracellular phase in the form of a tough pellicle. The occurrence and biosynthesis of bacterial cellulose have been reviewed by Hestrin (1) and by Neufeld & Ginsburg (2). Glaser has obtained evidence for UDP-glucose as the precursor of cellulose with particulate preparations from *Acetobacter xylinum* (3, 4). Recently, cellulose synthesis has been accomplished in a cell-free system from mung bean seedlings (5); in this case the reaction was specific for GDP-glucose and the possibility remains that in bacterial systems as well, GDP-glucose or some sugar nucleotide other than UDP-glucose is the true precursor. On the other hand, Brummond (6) has obtained evidence for cellulose synthesis from UDP-glucose. The suggestion by Colvin (7) that the precursor of cellulose is a glucolipid is interesting in view of the role of glycolipids in the biosynthesis of bacterial cell wall structures (see below).

Capsular polysaccharides.—Recent work on the structure of pneumococcal polysaccharides and some aspects of their biosynthesis has been covered in a review by How, Bimacombe & Stacey (8). Cell-free extracts which catalyze the synthesis of Type III and Type I polysaccharides have been obtained. The former, a polymer of cellobiuronic acid (β-1,4-glucuronosidyl-glucose)[4] is synthesized by a particulate enzyme fraction which utilizes UDP-glucose and UDP-glucuronic acids. The sugar residues from these nucleotides are incorporated in equal amounts into a product which is precipitable by specific antiserum and hydrolyzed by a specific depolymerase (9, 10). The biosynthesis of Type I *Pneumococcus* polysaccharide appears to involve two steps: first, the polymerization of D-galacturonic acid, with UDP-galacturonic acid as the substrate, followed by the addition of N-acetylglucosamine residues from UDP-N-acetylglucosamine (11). More recently, a particulate preparation of *Diplococcus pneumoniae* Type XIV has been shown to catalyze the synthesis of Type XIV polysaccharide from UDP-glucose, UDP-galactose, and UDP-N-acetyl-D-glucosamine (12). The same preparation catalyzed the synthesis of two glycolipids, a 1-[α-D-glucopyranosyl] (2,3)-diglyceride, and a 1-[α-D-galacto-pyranosyl-(1$\rightarrow$2)-α-D-glucopyranosyl] (2, 3)-diglyceride, although a possible role of these lipids as intermediates in polysaccharide biosynthesis remains to be established (12, 13). Evidence for the widespread occurrence of such glycolipids in Gram-positive microorganisms has been obtained (14–16). The biosynthesis of type-specific *Pneumococcus* polysaccharides appears to be controlled by the presence or absence of enzymes involved in the interconversion of the nucleoside diphosphate sugars (17, 18).

Although considerable work has been done on the structure of polysaccharides elaborated by mucoid strains of *Escherichia coli* (19-21), their formation in cell-free systems has not yet been accomplished. Recently, however, Markovitz has obtained evidence for a specific regulator gene controlling the formation of capsular polysaccharide in *E. coli* K12 (22). On the basis of the

---

[4] Unless otherwise specified, all sugars mentioned are the common D-forms.

fact that partial heterozygotes were nonmucoid under normal conditions of growth, it was concluded that the nonmucoid state was dominant. The regulatory gene appeared to control the activity of several enzymes involved in the biosynthesis of GDP-fucose, which is a component of the capsular polysaccharide in this strain. There is increasing evidence that genetic regulatory mechanisms for the synthesis of polysaccharides may frequently operate at the level of biosynthesis of sugar nucleotides (see below).

LIPOPOLYSACCHARIDE OF GRAM-NEGATIVE ORGANISMS

Among the more interesting of the complex heteropolysaccharides are the lipopolysaccharides found in the cell envelopes of the Gram-negative bacteria, particularly the Enterobacteriaceae. These complex macromolecules are responsible for many of the biological properties of the cell surface. They contain the O antigen determinants and bacteriophage receptor sites, and they are responsible for the toxic properties (so-called endotoxin) of heat-killed bacteria or isolated cell wall preparations. A number of excellent reviews covering the biological, chemical, and immunological properties of these structures are available (23–33). The present review will emphasize the biosynthetic work, although it will be necessary to make frequent reference to recent and earlier work on the biological and chemical properties.

Isolation and characterization.—On the basis of a limited number of flagellar (H) antigens and about 60 different lipopolysaccharide (O) specificities, the *Salmonellae* are classified into a number of groups and approximately 1000 different serotypes (27, 33), each determined by the genetic composition of the strain. Additional, and frequently overlapping, serotypes are recognized in *E. coli*, *Shigellae*, and *Citrobacter* strains, as well as in other Gram-negative species. Lipopolysaccharide, which carries the O-specific antigens, may be isolated from whole cells or from purified cell envelope by extraction with warm phenol, according to the procedure of Westphal et al. (34). These preparations contain little, or no, protein. However, an earlier procedure introduced by Boivin et al. (35) yields a product containing protein as well as polysaccharide and lipid, and the possibility that protein is present in covalent linkage to lipopolysaccharide has not been excluded. Following phenol extraction, the lipopolysaccharide can be further purified by centrifugation at $105,000 \times g$ (36) or, in the case of certain incomplete mutant lipopolysaccharides, by precipitation with $0.02 \ M \ MgCl_2$ (37). As isolated, the polysaccharide is linked covalently to a glucosamine-containing lipid, lipid A (38), from which it can be split by very mild acid hydrolysis. This procedure yields a flocculent precipitate of lipid A and a water-soluble polysaccharide.

Polysaccharides of "rough" and "smooth" strains.—In *Salmonella, Escherichia*, and related organisms, two distinct types of polysaccharides are recognized (33, 36, 39–43). The simplest forms, isolated from "rough" strains, contain the neutral sugars, L-glycero-D-mannoheptose, glucose, galactose, and in many cases N-acetylglucosamine. The polysaccharides isolated from the "smooth" pathogenic strains contain these common sugars, and in addition, may also contain mannose, L-fucose, or L-rhamnose, and one of the 3,6-dideoxyhexoses, abequose, colitose, paratose, or tyvelose. A fifth dideoxyhexose ascarylose, has been reported to occur in a strain of *Pasteurella pseudotuberculosis* (26). Mutation to the "rough" state results in loss of these additional components, as well as of the O-specific antigens, indicating that these sugars are components of antigenic side chains attached to a basal core structure. In addition to the neutral sugars, the core also contains substantial quantities of organic phosphate, ethanolamine (44), and 3-deoxyoctulosonate [KDO, 3-deoxy-D-manno-octulosonate (45)]. Besides mannose and the deoxy sugars, the antigenic side chains frequently contain additional galactose and glucose. Galactosamine is also a common constituent of smooth forms of *Salmonella* (33), and neuraminic acid has been identified in smooth strains of *Salmonella*, *Arizona*, and *Citrobacter* (27, 33). Ribose has been detected in certain smooth forms and may also be associated with the core structure (33, 46, 47). Only colitose, among the 3,6-dideoxyhexoses, is found in *E. coli*, and three strains of *Escherichia* are exceptional in that they are reported to be devoid of galactose (48).

A single lipopolysaccharide may contain as many as fourteen different structural components and carry several different antigenic determinants. It has been established (49) that when several O antigens are present in a single strain, these are all part of a single lipopolysaccharide molecule.

Recent biosynthetic work has been concerned with the incorporation of sugars into the core portion of the polysaccharide, and with the formation of the highly polymerized antigenic side chains. Nothing is known of the biosynthetic mechanism for lipid A, and only fragmentary evidence is available for the biosynthesis of that portion of the core polysaccharide which contains heptose and KDO, and which is frequently referred to as the backbone portion. Heptose was first identified in *E. coli* by Weidel (50), and has since been shown to be a component of all lipopolysaccharides, including those isolated from "rough" and "super-rough" mutants (33, 36, 37, 51). It has been identified as L-glycero-D-mannoheptose (51) and in the lipopolysaccharide is linked to phosphate (33). In *Chromobacter violaceum*, a heptose is present which has been identified as D-glycero-D-galactoheptose (26, 52). A component giving the colorimetric test for ketodeoxy sugars (46) has been identified as 3-deoxyoctulosonate (KDO) (45), and shown to be the component of lipopolysaccharide involved in the covalent linkage between polysaccharide and lipid A (53). The latest component discovered to be part of the backbone structure of the lipopolysaccharide was ethanolamine phosphate, which was isolated from mutant strains of *Salmonella typhimurium* (44) and has since been shown to be present in lipopolysaccharide of *E. coli* and *Shigella*.

An important development, which made it possible to undertake studies of the biosynthesis of lipopolysaccharide, was the discovery by Fukasawa & Nikaido (54, 55) that certain galactose-negative strains of *E. coli* and *Salmonella* produced a lipopolysaccharide which was deficient not only in galactose, but also in several other sugars which were present in the wild-type lipopolysaccharide. These mutants were lacking in the enzyme UDP-galactose-4-epimerase and were, therefore, unable to convert UDP-glucose to UDP-glactose. They exhibited two properties which proved useful in the selection of similar mutants from other strains of *Salmonella:* (*a*) They were resistant to phage PLT 22 and (*b*) they would undergo lysis if placed in a medium containing galactose (56, 57). They also accumulated certain sugar nucleotides which were the precursors of the wild-type lipopolysaccharide (58, 59). Recently, a number of other mutants have been isolated and employed for biosynthetic studies (see below); their composition is shown in Table I, compared with that of the two previously isolated "rough" strains.

TABLE I

SUGAR COMPONENTS OF LIPOPOLYSACCHARIDE IN MUTANTS
EMPLOYED IN BIOSYNTHETIC STUDIES

Lipid A	Polysaccharide							Biochemical Defect	References
GlcNAc	KDO	Heptose	Glc	Gal	GlcNAc	Man	Deoxy and Dideoxy-hexoses		
+	+	+	0	0	0	0	0	Synthesis of UDPG[a]	65, 67
+	+	+	0	0	0	0	0	UDPG transferase I	68
+	+	+	+	0	0	0	0	Synthesis of UDPGal[b]	37, 54, 58, 86
+	+	+	+	+	0	0	0	Unknown[c]	77, 80, 81
+	+	+	+	+	+	0	0	Unknown[d], synthesis of TDPRha	77, 80, 81
+	+	+	+	+	+	0	0	Synthesis of GDP-Man[e]	82

[a] Lacking phosphoglucose isomerase or UDPG-pyrophosphorylase.
[b] Lacking UDP-galactose-4-epimerase.
[c] R$_I$ (*rouA*). The biochemical defect is not yet established.
[d] R$_{II}$ (*rouB*). The biochemical defect is not yet established.
[e] Lacking phosphomannose isomerase.

Structure of lipid A.—Lipid A contains N-acetylglucosamine, phosphate, and fatty acid residues, including acetyl and β-hydroxymyristyl groups. A structure for lipid A has been proposed by Burton & Carter (60) and more recent work confirms their suggestion that β-hydroxymyristic acid is linked to the amino group of glucosamine. From alkali degraded lipid A Mayer et al. (61) have isolated an oligosaccharide containing three moles of glucosamine (including one reducing terminal group), three of β-hydroxymyristic acid, and slightly less than one equivalent of phosphate. This degraded lipid A has been used in studies of the incorporation of deoxyoctulosonic acid.

Structure of the KDO-heptose phosphate backbone and the incorporation of KDO.—Mutants lacking KDO are thus far unknown, but Heath and his coworkers have demonstrated the enzymatic incorporation of this substance by employing as acceptor alkali-degraded lipopolysaccharide, from which KDO residues have been removed by mild acid hydrolysis (61, 62). In the presence of enzyme preparations obtained from extracts of *E. coli* J5 (UDP-galactose-4-epimerase-negative), KDO was transferred from CMP-KDO to the acceptor. The degraded lipid A acceptor contains the available hydroxyl groups of glucosamine, as well as of β-hydroxymyristic acid; however, the site of attachment of KDO remains unknown. Osborn (53) had previously obtained evidence that KDO provided the link between the heptose phosphate backbone and lipid A, and recently Cherniak & Osborn (63) have employed hydrofluoric acid to obtain oligosaccharides containing KDO, heptose, and glucose. Their results suggest that the polysaccharide backbone of *S. typhimurium* contains trisaccharide-repeating units composed of two heptoses

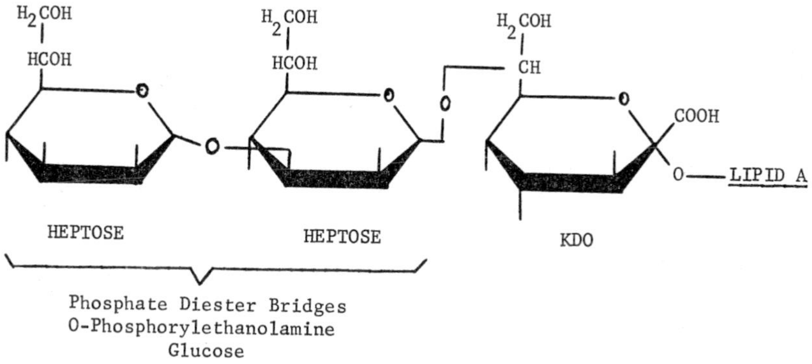

FIG. 1. Tentative formulation of the backbone repeating unit [from Cherniak & Osborn (63)].

linked to a terminal KDO group, with a single glucosyl residue attached to each repeating unit (Fig. 1). A somewhat different structure was proposed by Kuriki & Kurahashi (64) for the backbone units of *E. coli;* they obtained evidence for larger chains of nine to ten mannoheptose residues linked through 1,2-glycosidic linkages and terminating in KDO.

The source of heptose in the backbone and the mechanism of its incorporation remain unknown, but recently new strains of *Salmonella*, lacking heptose, have been isolated by Schlosshardt [quoted in (33)], and these should greatly facilitate work on this problem.

Biosynthesis of the core portion of lipopolysaccharide.—Mutant strains blocked in the production of UDP-glucose or UDP-galactose have been particularly useful for studies of biosynthesis of the lipopolysaccharide core. In the absence of exogenous glucose, strains of *S. typhimurium* lacking phosphoglucose isomerase produce a lipopolysaccharide which contains heptose, KDO, and glucosamine (the last in lipid A) (65, 66), as the only sugars. Fukasawa et al. (67) had earlier made similar observations with a mutant strain of *E. coli* deficient in UDP-glucose pyrophosphorylase. Cell-free preparations of the *S. typhimurium* isomerase-less mutant were shown to catalyze the transfer of glucose from UDP-glucose into lipopolysaccharide (66). The bulk of the transferase activity was associated with the 12,000 g cell wall fraction, but a significant amount was detected in the soluble fraction. Recently, a mutant strain of *S. typhimurium* has been studied which is lacking in this UDP-glucose transferase (68); this mutant is more stable than the phosphoglucose isomerase-less and better suited for biosynthetic studies. The site of attachment of glucose to the backbone structure is still unknown, but the use of hydrofluoric acid for the isolation of oligosaccharides containing glucose as well as heptose promises to provide a solution to this problem.

More extensive studies have been carried out on the incorporation of galactose into the polysaccharide core structure. The transfer of this sugar from UDP-galactose to lipopolysaccharide was first demonstrated by Nikaido (58) with UDP-galactose-4-epimerase-less strains of *Salmonella enteritidis*. A similar UDP-galactose-4-epimerase-less mutant was isolated from *S. typhimurium*, using resistance to bacteriophage PLT 22 as a selection method, and lysis in the presence of galactose for secondary screening (37). Cell envelope preparations obtained from this mutant catalyzed the incorporation of galactose from UDP-galactose into endogenous lipopolysaccharide. The new galactosyl linkage was very labile, and oligosaccharides containing the new group could not be isolated. However, when the soluble polysaccharide was prepared by hydrolysis at pH 3.5 and treated with galactose oxidase, it was possible by mild acid hydrolysis to isolate the disaccharide α-galacturonosyl1-(1→3)-glucose, thus establishing the linkage of the galactose residue in the lipopolysaccharide (69).

With the same UDP-galactose-4-epimerase-less mutant, Osborn & D'Ari (70) were able to demonstrate the sequential addition of galactose, glucose, and N-acetylglucosamine, suggesting that the core portion of the lipopolysaccharide contains the sequence N-acetylglucosaminosyl→glucosyl→galactosyl→glucose. The enzymes which catalyze these reactions have been designated UDP-galactose-LPS transferase I, UDP-glucose-LPS transferase II, and UDP-N-acetylglucosamine-LPS transferase, respectively. Incorporation of the first glucose residue is catalyzed by the enzyme UDP-glucose-LPS transferase I. Similar results have subsequently been obtained by Elbein & Heath (71) with *E. coli* J5, the UDP-galactose-4-epimerase-less mutant of *E. coli* 0111, although here the sugars may have been incorporated into the antigenic side chains, rather than the "core." This mutant, like other epimerase-less mutants, lacked the smooth antigenic lipopolysaccharide and contained little galactose or colitose; it also contained smaller quantities of N-acetylglucosamine and glucose than did the wild-type lipopolysaccharide. Particulate preparations from this strain catalyzed the sequential incorporation of galactose, glucose, N-acetylglucosamine, and finally, of colitose into endogenous lipopolysaccharide (62).

The role of phospholipid in the biosynthesis of the lipopolysaccharide core.— Two enzymes in the biosynthesis of lipopolysaccharide in *S. typhimurium* have now been obtained in soluble form. These are UDP-glucose-LPS transferase I, and UDP-galactose-LPS transferase I (51, 66). These soluble enzyme preparations made it possible to examine the specificity of the lipopolysaccharide acceptors. The soluble UDP-glucose-LPS transferase catalyzed the incorporation of glucose only into cell envelope fractions prepared from the glucose-deficient strains; in these strains the core polysaccharide contained only heptose and KDO, but no glucose, galactose, or N-acetylglucosamine. Cell envelope fractions prepared from the galactose-deficient strain, whose lipopolysaccharide already contained glucose, or from the wild-type *S. typhimurium* were inactive. Similarly, the soluble UDP-galactose-LPS transferase I catalyzed the incorporation of galactose only into cell envelope fractions prepared from the galactose-deficient strain; in this strain the polysaccharide contained glucose, heptose, and KDO, but neither galactose nor glucosamine. Cell envelope preparations from the glucose-deficient strain, which lacked the glucosyl acceptor sites, were completely inactive (51, 66). In these experiments the purified lipopolysaccharide isolated from the active cell envelope fraction by phenol extraction was completely inactive, regardless of the source of lipopolysaccharide, nor was any activity observed with the soluble polysaccharide obtained by mild acid hydrolysis of lipopolysaccharide.

The lack of activity of purified lipopolysaccharide in the transferase reactions suggested that the active cell envelope fractions contained an additional factor which was essential for activity. This factor has now been identified by Rothfield and his co-workers (72, 73) as phospholipid. The active acceptor has been characterized as a lipopolysaccharide-phospholipid complex which can be generated from the separated components by subjecting them to an annealing procedure in which lipopolysaccharide and phospholipid are mixed at 60° C and allowed to cool slowly. Under these conditions, lipopolysaccharide purified by phenol extraction shows full activity. A number of phospholipids have been shown to be active; the essential structures are unsaturated or cyclopropane fatty acids, and a relatively negative charge in the phosphatidyl group. Phosphatidyl ethanolamine and phosphatidic acid were fully active, but phosphatidyl choline showed no activity.

Rothfield & Takeshita (74, 75) have obtained evidence for a specific binding of the soluble enzymes to the lipopolysaccharide-phospholipid complex, with the specificity determined by the nature of the acceptor groups in the lipopolysaccharide. A complex prepared from the galactose-deficient lipopolysaccharide and phospholipid was shown to bind only the galactose transferase and not that required for the incorporation of glucose. The results suggest that the mechanism of biosynthesis of the core portion of the lipopolysaccharide may involve selective adsoprtion of the specific transferases to the unfilled acceptor sites in the lipopolysaccharide-phospholipid complex; the enzyme would be released when the reaction is completed and the new lipopolysaccharide, containing the additional sugar, would be ready to absorb the next transferase enzyme. The core would thus be constructed by the stepwise addition of individual sugars, as illustrated in Figure 2. All of the transferase activities represented in this figure have been demonstrated in cell-free systems. The presence of an additional enzyme (not shown) is inferred from the fact that the complete core structure contains a second galactose residue linked in 1,6-glycosidic linkage to the innermost glucosyl residue (see below).

Structure of the lipopolysaccharide core.—The biosynthetic studies, in conjunction with chemical analyses of rough and mutant strains, have led to a tentative structure for the core and backbone portions of *Salmonella* lipopolysaccharide (33, 47, 51, 61, 63, 68, 76, 77). Much of the information upon which this structure is based has been derived from analyses of rough mutants which contain only the core sugars, glucose, galactose, glucosamine, and heptose (39, 40, 42). There appears to be one side chain containing two glucose residues, two galactose residues, and one N-acetylglucosamine for every other heptose residue in the backbone. The biosynthetic studies had established the location of one galactose residue (see Fig. 2), but quantitative analysis of

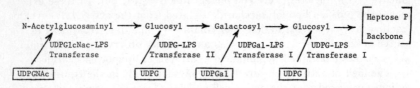

Fig. 2. Scheme for stepwise synthesis of core (rough) portion of *Salmonella* and *E. coli* lipopolysaccharide.

the proportions of sugars in the rough lipopolysaccharide suggested the presence of an additional galactose residue, and recent studies have confirmed this and established its location (47, 68, 76, 77). Although all rough strains belong to chemotype I (containing heptose, glucose, galactose, and glucosamine), two distinct serological groups, R_I and R_{II}, have been recognized (78), as well as two genetic loci *rouA* and *rouB* (79). One genetic class of rough mutations, designated *rouB*, is located close to the *his* locus on the *Salmonella* genetic map, and the other, designated *rouA*, lies close to the *ile* locus. Immunochemical studies have shown that mutants in the *rouA* locus are serologically of type R_I, and those in the *rouB* locus are serologically of type R_{II} (47, 80). An important and stimulating observation was the discovery by Beckmann and her collaborators (80) that mutants of type *rouA* (R_I) contain a water-soluble hapten which reacts with O-specific antibody and contains all of the O-specific sugars of the antigen. It was suggested that this haptenic material was possibly a precursor of the O-specific lipopolysaccharide side chains.

With only one exception, the nature of the biochemical defects which lead to *rouB*-type mutations remains unknown. One *rouB* mutant (*S. typhimurium* TV 208) was shown to be blocked in the biosynthesis of TDP-rhamnose (81).

Recently, both types of rough mutants have been isolated from a single smooth strain of *Salmonella minnesota*, and a study of their composition and structure was undertaken (47, 76). These results, together with analyses of an R_{II} strain from *S. typhimurium*, are shown in Table II. The composition of the R_{II} strains conforms to the biosynthetic sequence (Fig. 2), except for the presence of two equivalents of galactose (76, 82). This extra galactose is also present in strains of R_I, which contain no N-acetylglucosamine and only a single glucose (76). R_I mutants appear to be blocked in the incorporation of N-acetylglucosamine and usually of the second glucosyl residue as well, and may be deficient in UDP-glucose-LPS transferase II. Recently, mutant strains of *S. typhimurium* isolated in Stocker's laboratory, have been shown by Osborn (68) to be deficient in UDP-galactose-LPS transferase I. The core polysaccharide of these strains contains one galactose and one glucose, and from partial acid hydrolysates Osborn has isolated melibiose, indicating that

TABLE II

MOLAR RATIOS OF CORE SUGARS IN R_I AND R_{II} MUTANTS

Type	Heptose[a]	Galactose	Glucose	Glucosamine
R_{II} (*Salmonella minnesota*)[b]	2	2	2	0.7
R_{II} (*Salmonella typhimurium*)[c]	2	2	2	1
R_I (*Salmonella minnesota*)[b]	2	2	1	0

[a] The ratios are based on heptose content, since there appears to be one side chain for every other heptose in the backbone.
[b] Reference (76).
[c] References (51) and (82).

the 1,6-linkage is present (68). On the basis of the biosynthetic and structural studies, the structure of core polysaccharide would therefore be:

$$\alpha GlcNAc \rightarrow Glu \rightarrow \alpha Gal\text{-}(1 \rightarrow 3)$$
$$\searrow$$
$$Glu \rightarrow (Backbone)$$
$$\nearrow$$
$$\alpha Gal\text{-}(1 \rightarrow 6)$$

Melibiose has also been isolated from R_I and R_{II} type mutants by Lüderitz and Sutherland and their co-workers (47, 77). In addition to melibiose, a number of other oligosaccharides predicted from this structure have been isolated from R_I and R_{II} mutants (47, 68, 77), including the pentasaccharide

$$(GlcNAc \rightarrow Glu \rightarrow Gal \rightarrow Glc).$$
$$\uparrow$$
$$Gal$$

There is some indication, however, that this may not be the complete structure of the lipopolysaccharide core. Thus, the isolated pentasaccharide is not a good inhibitor of R_{II} antigen precipitation by anti-R_{II} antibody (47), and mild hydrolysis has yielded several oligosaccharides containing ribose in addition to galactose and, in one case, glucose, which are considerably more active as inhibitors of the antigen-antibody reaction (47). Lüderitz and his co-workers (47) report that ribose is a common component of R_{II} mutants, amounting to 1 to 4 percent of the total sugar, and that this ribose cannot be attributed to contaminating RNA, since it is not accompanied by ultraviolet absorption. In an earlier study of lipopolysaccharide isolated from a UDP-glucose-pyrophosphorylase-less mutant, Kalckar and his co-workers had also reported the presence of ribose (46). However, in these experiments, ribose was detected in a single mutant strain deficient in glucose or galactose.

Biosynthesis of the antigenic side chains in Salmonellae.— The biosynthesis of the O-specific antigenic side chains has been studied with strains of *S. typhimurium* (83–88), *S. anatum* (89–92), and *E. coli* 0111 (61, 62). In *S. typhimurium* and *S. anatum*, chemical and serological evidence had shown that these antigenic side chains were composed of repeating units with the prob-

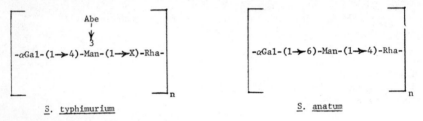

FIG. 3. Repeating units in O-specific antigens of *Salmonella*.

able structures shown in Figure 3 (28, 33, 83, 89, 90, 93, 94), and hexasaccharides corresponding to two repeating units have been isolated from mild acid hydrolysates of lipopolysaccharide of *S. anatum* (91).

Recent studies of the biosynthesis of the antigenic side chains have proved to be consistent with these structures. A useful tool in these studies was the mannose-negative mutant of *S. typhimurium* (82), although similar results have been obtained with wild-type *S. anatum* (92). The mannose-negative strain produced a lipopolysaccharide similar in composition to the R_{II} strains (see Table I), lacking mannose, rhamnose, and abequose, Cell envelope preparations from this mutant catalyzed the incorporation of ^{14}C-galactose, ^{14}C-mannose, and ^{14}C-rhamnose into a macromolecular product (83). Maximum incorporation of any one of the three sugars from the ^{14}C-labeled sugar nucleotide precursor required the presence of all three sugar nucleotides (UDP-galactose, TDP-rhamnose and GDP-mannose), and the trisaccharide α-galactosyl-mannosyl-rhamnose was obtained from the reaction product by mild acid hydrolysis. In these experiments, the linear sequence of the trisaccharide product was established by oxidation with galactose oxidase, which converted it to a galacturonosyl derivative from which galacturonosyl-mannose could be isolated and characterized (83). The α-galactosyl-(1→4)-linkage in the lipopolysaccharide of *S. typhimurium* may be more acid-labile than the corresponding α-galactosyl-(1→6)-linkage in *S. anatum* (89).

The nature of the product formed in the *S. typhimurium* system has been clarified by the recent studies of Weiner et al. (84, 85) with *S. typhimurium* and Wright et al. (92) with *S. anatum*. The first group employed the galactose-negative mutant which forms an incomplete core; this strain would not be expected to incorporate the antigenic side chains into lipopolysaccharide. In the presence of all three nucleotide sugar precursors, UDP-galactose, TDP-rhamnose, and GDP-mannose, an insoluble macromolecular product was formed which contained the galactosyl-mannosyl-rhamnose repeating unit. On treatment with warm phenol, the product was degraded to yield a water-soluble polysaccharide terminating in galactose 1-phosphate.

Smaller intermediates could be obtained with the *S. typhimurium* or *S. anatum* systems by carrying out the reaction in the absence of GDP-mannose

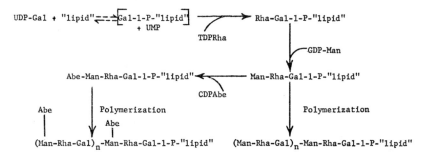

FIG. 4. Biosynthesis of O antigen side chains in *S. typhimurium*.

(84, 85, 92). Incubation of the particulate cell envelope preparation with UDP-galactose and TDP-rhamnose yielded a lipid-soluble intermediate which decomposed in warm phenol, or in hydrolysis with dilute acid, to yield a product identified as rhamnosyl-galactose-1-phosphate. The addition of GDP-mannose to cell envelope preparations which had previously been treated with UDP-galactose and TDP-rhamnose led to the transient formation of a trisaccharide phospholipid intermediate followed by rapid polymerization. Incorporation of abequose in this system required the presence of all three of the other sugar nucleotides, and a transient tetrasaccharide-phospholipid was detected (85). Polymerization of the tetrasaccharide proved to be more rapid than that of the trisaccharide. According to Tinelli & Staub (93, 94) the tetrasaccharide containing abequose is the normal component of the *S. typhimurium* O-specific antigen. In the *in vitro* cell-free system, abequose incorporation is only about one half that of mannose and in this system the polysaccharide chains are likely to be composed of mixtures of trisaccharide and tetrasaccharide. The pathway of biosynthesis of the antigenic side chains in *S. typhimurium* is summarized in Figure 4.

All of the phospholipid intermediates are unstable to acid and alkali and to warm phenol, and are converted by such treatment to the corresponding

1-phospho derivatives. In the case of the polymerized intermediate, approximately one-sixteenth of the galactose residues can be shown to be present as terminal galactose-1-phosphate. The chain formed in the biosynthetic system, therefore, contains approximately 48 sugars.

It should be noted that biosynthesis of the O antigenic side chains begins with galactose, and that the lipid-linked intermediate contains the sequence mannosyl-rhamnose-galactose. This is different from the repeating unit usually isolated by partial acid hydrolysis. However, the difference is only operational, since in the mild acid treatment used to obtain the repeating unit from the *S. typhimurium* cell wall the sensitive abequosyl and rhamnosyl linkages are the first to be hydrolyzed, yielding galactosyl-mannosyl-rhamnose. These results serve to confirm the earlier conclusion (87, 94) that the mannosyl-rhamnosyl-galactosyl units are present in the side chain as a linear polysaccharide with abequosyl branch points. *Salmonella* group B, to which *S. typhimurium* belongs, also may contain a glucosyl residue attached to galactose. This glucosyl linkage accounts for serological Factors 1_{12} and 12_2 in the B group, and its presence is attributed to conversion by bacteriophages PLT 22 or iota. This group is not present in *S. typhimurium* LT 2 and its biosynthesis has not yet been investigated. With respect to the abequosyl linkage, Tinelli & Staub (93, 94) have obtained convincing evidence that this involves the 3-position of mannose, since mannose in the intact lipopolysaccharide is resistant to periodate oxidation, but becomes sensitive when the abequosyl groups are removed by mild acid hydrolysis.

The polysaccharide phospholipid intermediate formed in the cell-free system may be related to the water-soluble hapten which has been isolated from warm phenol extracts of R_I strains of *Salmonella* (80). Osborn[5] has obtained evidence that the hapten contains a terminal reducing galactose residue, and efforts are now underway in several laboratories to determine whether this product is derived from the lipid-linked intermediate in lipopolysaccharide biosynthesis. Its presence in the R_I strains indicates that the mechanism for formation of the phospholipid intermediate is intact in these strains, but that the final attachment to lipopolysaccharide is not made because of the incomplete core structure. This also applies to the *in vitro* studies by Weiner et al. (84, 85), in which incorporation into lipopolysaccharide has not been detected.

Similar lipid-linked intermediates in the biosynthesis of the O antigen side chains were obtained by Wright et al. (92) with cell-free preparations of wild-type *S. anatum*, but in these experiments the side chains appeared to become partially attached to endogenous lipopolysaccharide. When GDP-mannose was added together with UDP-galactose and TDP-rhamnose, polymerization and incorporation into lipopolysaccharide was observed.

Incorporation of O antigen-specific sugars into lipopolysaccharide *in vitro* has also been reported by Nikaido and his co-workers with a TDP-

[5] M. J. Osborn, unpublished experiments.

rhamnose-negative strain of *S. typhimurium* (87, 88, 95) and with cell-free extracts from *E. coli* (see below). Nikaido employed Stocker's *S. typhimurium* strain TV 208, which has been shown to lack one of the enzymes in the biosynthesis of rhamnose (95). The lipopolysaccharide in this strain is of the R_{II} type, lacking mannose, rhamnose, and abequose. In contrast to the results obtained by Weiner and Wright and their co-workers, Nikaido observed some incorporation of rhamnose when ^{14}C-TDP-rhamnose alone was added to a particulate fraction isolated from *S. typhimurium* TV 208, although this was strongly stimulated by the addition of UDP-galactose. Strains which already possessed rhamnose in the O antigen were inactive. The radioactive product isolated by phenol extraction showed all the properties of typical lipopolysaccharide, including sedimentation at $104,000 \times g$ and precipitation with anti-R_{II} serum. Galactose was poorly incorporated in the absence of TDP-rhamnose, but when both sugar nucleotides were added, there was increased incorporation and acid hydrolysates yielded the disaccharide rhamnosyl-galactose. Later, Nikaido and his co-workers (87, 88) demonstrated the incorporation of mannose and abequose, in addition to galactose and rhamnose, from the appropriate sugar nucleotides into lipopolysaccharide. Hydrolysis of the product yielded oligosaccharides which were identified as mannosyl-rhamnose and galactosyl-mannosyl-rhamnose. The presence of galactose linked to mannose suggests that some polymerization must have occurred.

Failure to observe incorporation into lipopolysaccharide may, as suggested by Nikaido et al. (88), be related to the type of "enzyme" employed. In those cases in which accumulation of the polymerized phospholipid intermediate was not detected (88, 92, 95), the endogenous lipopolysaccharide contained the complete core structure. Where this is lacking, accumulation of the polymerized phospholipid intermediate (and possibly also of hapten in the R_I forms) may be a side reaction resulting from the inability to transfer the individual repeating units to lipopolysaccharide. In this connection, Nikaido et al. (88) have pointed out that the first repeating unit of the antigenic side chain is probably linked to glucosamine, whereas subsequent units are attached to mannose, a difference which requires different enzyme systems.

No definitive information is available concerning the nature of the lipid carrier. Partial degradation of the radioactive intermediates has yielded fractions containing two phosphate groups per disaccharide,[6] suggesting that a phosphate group of the lipid is the point of attachment. This would be similar to the mucopeptide disaccharide intermediate recently isolated in Strominger's laboratory (96) (see below).

Biosynthesis of the antigenic side chains in E. coli.—Incorporation of the O antigenic sugars in a mutant strain of *E. coli* 0111 (*E. coli* J5) has been reported by Heath and his co-workers (61, 62). This mutant strain lacks UDP-galactose-4-epimerase and produces a lipopolysaccharide which is lacking in

---

[6] I. Weiner and M. J. Osborn, unpublished experiments.

galactose, glucosamine, and colitose. It also was shown to accumulate GDP-colitose. Particulate fractions isolated from cell-free extracts catalyzed the incorporation of colitose from GDP-colitose, provided that UDP-galactose, UDP-glucose, and UDP-N-acetylglucosamine were all present. Since the colitose linkage is extremely acid-labile, colitosyl oligosaccharides could not be isolated, but characterization of the structure of the antigenic side chains in this organism was accomplished by the ingenious use of periodate (97). Lipopolysaccharide, converted to a soluble form by degradation with alkali at 60° C, was oxidized with sodium periodate and reduced with sodium borohydride. This treatment resulted in complete destruction of galactose and yielded the following oligosaccharides:

$$\text{Col} \rightarrow \text{GlcNAc} \rightarrow \text{Glc} \rightarrow \text{threitol} \quad \text{and} \quad \text{GlcNAc-Glc-threitol}$$
$$\qquad\qquad\quad \uparrow \qquad\qquad\qquad\qquad\qquad\quad | $$
$$\qquad\qquad\quad \text{Col} \qquad\qquad\qquad\qquad\qquad\; \text{Col}$$

It was concluded that the repeating unit in the *E. coli* 0111 antigen is:

$$\text{Col} \rightarrow \text{GlcNAc} \rightarrow \text{Glc} \rightarrow \text{Gal}$$
$$\qquad\qquad\qquad\quad \uparrow$$
$$\qquad\qquad\qquad\;\; \text{Col}$$

Semirough strains and their possible biochemical origin.—A novel serological type, designated "semirough," may provide some clues to the mechanism of attachment of the O-specific antigenic side chains. Two classes of "semirough" mutants were encountered, both of which contained relatively small amounts of the O-specific antigen sugars (86). One type of semirough mutants failed to react with anti-R_{II} serum; in this type, glucosamine in the R_{II} core structure is completely covered by many short chains, suggesting that no free terminal N-acetylglucosamine residues are present. These may be covered by single repeating units of the O antigen polysaccharide. This would be consistent with the suggestion that the first repeating unit is incorporated by a different mechanism from that which is involved in the addition of subsequent repeating units, a conclusion which is supported by the observation that these semirough mutants do not accumulate soluble hapten. Lack of polymerization was confirmed by the failure to isolate oligosaccharides containing the galactosyl-mannose linkage. The second class of semirough mutants (Class D) appeared to contain fewer than the usual number of antigenic side chains and many exposed terminal groups of the R_{II} core. Lipopolysaccharide from these strains reacted strongly with anti-R_{II} serum. The Class C and Class D mutants map in different loci.

Biochemistry of phage conversion of lipopolysaccharide structures.—Lysogenic conversion of O antigen by temperate phages was first discovered by Iseki & Sakai (98) in 1953. Since then, a large number of temperate phages have been shown to produce similar effects [for a review and listing of many of the known bacteriophage conversions see reference (33)].

Conversion by temperate phages may cause some new factors to appear and others to be replaced. The biochemical studies of Robbins and his co-workers (28, 91, 99) with *Salmonella* species of serotype E, which contains the repeating unit: 6-O-acetyl-α-galactosyl-(1→6)-mannosyl-(1→4)-rhamnose, have shown that phage ϵ^{15} represses the enzymes responsible for O acetylation of the α-galactosyl residues, as well as for the formation of the α-galactosyl linkage itself. A new enzyme is produced which catalyzes the formation of β-galactosyl linkages. Subsequent infection with ϵ^{34} introduces an enzyme which catalyzes attachment of α-glucosyl residues to the β-galactosyl structure (28, 91, 99a). These brilliant studies by Robbins and Uchida and their co-workers have clearly established that the O antigen structures are under genetic control and that the presence or absence of specific enzymes, rather than a template mechanism, accounts for the structural specificity. They have also demonstrated the O acetylation reaction with an *in vitro* system, using a flavazole derivative of hexasaccharide (Gal-Man-Rha-Gal-Man-Rha-flavazole). With this artificial substrate a particulate fraction catalyzed the acetylation of α-galactosyl residues by acetyl CoA.

Conversion by phage 27 has been studied by Staub & Girard (100) and by Bagdian et al. (101). In this case, the change is in the linkage of galactose to mannose, hence phage infection must affect the polymerases.

Control mechanisms in lipopolysaccharide biosynthesis.—One of the more important problems yet to be considered is the mechanism of control of lipopolysaccharide synthesis. Evidence for control at the level of sugar nucleotide synthesis will be discussed in detail later. Some interesting observations pertaining to this problem have been made with L forms of *Proteus mirabilis*. Nesbitt & Lennarz (102) examined L forms of this organism and found them to contain much more phospholipid and less lipopolysaccharide than bacillary forms. Since naturally occurring L forms were used in these studies, it was difficult to determine which bacillary form was to be taken as the control. Westphal's group (103) have recently compared penicillin L forms with the bacillary forms of *P. mirabilis* from which they were derived, and concluded that less lipopolysaccharide was present in the former and that the endotoxin was considerably less toxic. Galactose could not be detected in the lipopolysaccharide, but this may be a property of the normal *Proteus* lipopolysaccharide, which has not been extensively investigated.

A recent observation by Work and her collaborators (104–106) suggests a structural or biosynthetic relation between lipopolysaccharide and glycopeptide in the bacterial cell envelope. A lysine-dependent mutant of *E. coli* was observed to produce large quantities of extracellular lipopolysaccharide when grown under conditions of limiting lysine. The release of lipopolysaccharide correlated with release of phage particles has been observed by Falaschi & Kornberg (107) in cells infected with bacteriophage M13. Although phage M13 does not produce visible lysis, release of lipopolysaccharide may be due to disorganization of the cell envelope structure. On the other hand, no such accumulation and release of lipopolysaccharide has been detected in cells treated with penicillin.

Glycopeptide

This subject has been thoroughly covered in excellent recent reviews by Martin (108)[7] and Strominger (109), and the present discussion will be limited to a consideration of some interesting developments which have occurred since these reviews were written. The recent discovery of *in vitro* systems for the incorporation of N-acetylmuramic acid has led to the discovery of lipid-linked intermediates and the proposal that penicillin acts at a final stage in the formation of cross-linkages in the biosynthesis of cell wall glycopeptide.

Incorporation of N-acetylmuramic acid and N-acetylglucosamine.—Cell-free preparations from *Staphylococcus aureus* which catalyze the biosynthesis of glycopeptide have been described by Chatterjee & Park (110), and by Meadow, Anderson & Strominger (111). The enzyme activity was associated with the small particle fraction prepared by centrifugation at $105,000 \times g$. Incorporation of muramyl pentapeptide from UDP-N-acetylmuramyl pentapeptide was stimulated by the addition of UDP-N-acetylglucosamine. In one case (111), the product was rendered soluble by digestion with lysozyme.

Meadow et al. (111) suggested that UMP rather than UDP was the other product formed on incorporation of UDP-muramyl peptide, and this was confirmed by Struve & Neuhaus (112). The results reported by Meadow et al. (111) and Struve & Neuhaus (112) suggested that the first step leading to incorporation of the sugar derivative was transfer to an acceptor:

UDP-MurNAc pentapeptide + acceptor ⇌ MurNAc-pentapeptide-P-acceptor + UMP

The antibiotics, ristocetin and vancomycin, inhibited the incorporation of N-acetylmuramic acid pentapeptide (111, 112); penicillin and other antibiotics known to affect glycopeptide biosynthesis were inhibitory only at very high concentrations.

Function of membrane-bound lipid intermediates.—An important development in our understanding of the mechanism of biosynthesis of bacterial cell wall components was the recent discovery by Strominger and his co-workers that membrane-bound lipid intermediates are involved in the biosynthesis of the glycopeptide chains (96). The formation of such lipid-linked intermediates may provide a mechanism for the transport of N-acetylglucosamine and muramyl-N-acetyl-pentapeptide from within the cell membrane, where they are synthesized as nucleotide derivatives, to the outer surface of the cell where they are presumably utilized for cell wall synthesis. The suggestion that other cell wall heteropolysaccharides might be synthesized by a similar mechanism has since been confirmed by the studies of the biosynthesis of O antigen and its incorporation into lipopolysaccharide described in the previous section. The scheme for biosynthesis of glycopeptide proposed by Anderson et al. (96) is illustrated in Figure 5. In the first step, N-acetyl-

---

[7] The name, murein, is employed by Martin (108) to describe the polymer previously designated as mucopeptide, glycosaminopeptide, glycopeptide, etc.

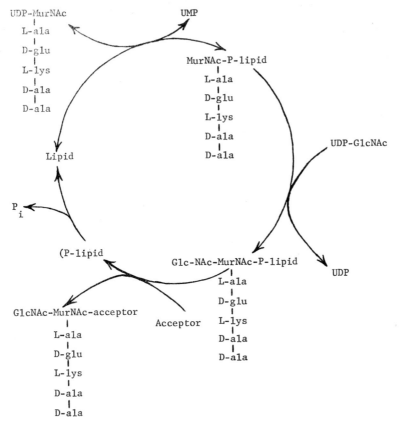

FIG. 5. Role of lipid-linked intermediate in formation of glycopeptide polymer
[from Anderson et al. (96)].

muramyl-pentapeptide is transferred to the lipid acceptor with the formation
of UMP. This is followed by the transfer of N-acetylglucosamine from UDP-
N-acetylglucosamine to the lipid-linked N-acetylmuramyl peptide. The
disaccharide peptide is then transferred from the lipid carrier to cell wall
acceptor, which is presumably the growing glycopeptide chain. In this last
step the lipid carrier is regenerated and inorganic phosphate is formed. Both
the monosaccharide and disaccharide lipid intermediates have been obtained
as components of the particulate membrane fraction, the former from an incubation mixture containing only UDP-N-acetylmuramyl peptide, and the
other from an incubation mixture containing both sugar nucleotide precursors. The first intermediate, N-acetylmuramyl pentapeptide-P-lipid, was
incorporated into polymer only in the presence of UDP-N-acetylglucosamine.
It could be converted back to UDP-N-acetylmuramic acid by the addition

of UMP, since the first step was reversible (112, 113). The disaccharide intermediate was converted to polymer simply by further incubation with the isolated membrane fraction, without the further addition of nucleotide precursors. In confirmation of the proposed mechanism, $^{32}P_i$ was shown to derive specifically from $UD^{32}P$-N-acetylmuramyl peptide and not from $UD^{32}P$-N-acetylglucosamine. Furthermore, the lipid intermediate could not be formed from ^{14}C-labeled UDP-N-acetylglucosamine in the absence of UDP-N-acetylmuramyl peptide. All of the products isolated were shown to contain the pentapeptide with two D-alanine residues. The formation of glycopeptide in this system was not blocked by penicillin, but ristocetin, vancomycin, and bacitracin were effective inhibitors of polymerization.

Recent reports from Strominger's laboratory have shed some light on the nature of the lipid acceptor. The lipid intermediates were extracted from membrane fractions of *Micrococcus lysodeikticus* and *S. aureus* with mixtures of isobutanol and isobutyric acid; preparations were obtained and purified by fractionation on DEAE cellulose and silicic acid columns (113). The purified products were found to contain, per disaccharide unit, two to three equivalents of fatty acid and glycerol, and approximately five equivalents of organic phosphorous, suggesting that they were structurally related to cardiolipin. The isolated complexes were unstable, but the intermediate derived from the *M. lysodeikticus* system was partially incorporated into polymer when incubated with the membrane fraction. No such activity was observed with the complex purified from *S. aureus* membrane, nor did the membrane fraction of *S. aureus* utilize the product obtained from *M. lysodeikticus*. Decomposition of the lipid-linked intermediate at pH 4.2 yielded a fragment

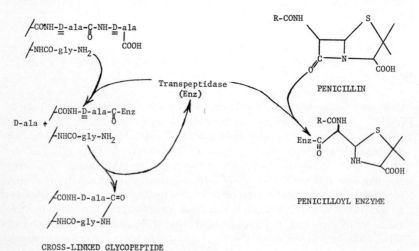

CROSS-LINKED GLYCOPEPTIDE

FIG. 6. Proposed mechanism for penicillin action in transpeptidation sequence and its inhibition by penicillin (117).

containing the disaccharide linked to glycerol through a pyrophosphate bridge (114). This clearly established that the attachment of N-acetylmuramyl peptide to lipid involved the formation of a new pyrophosphate bond.

Formation of the cross-linked structure and the action of penicillin.—It has long been suspected that the glycopeptide chains in the cell wall are cross-linked. [For a review see Martin (108)]. On the basis of studies of the composition of L forms of *P. mirabilis* and the action of lysozyme on the cell walls of L forms, Martin had proposed that penicillin acts to prevent formation of these cross-links (115). Evidence to support this hypothesis has recently been obtained for *S. aureus* by Wise & Park (116) and by Strominger and his co-workers (117, 118). The nucleotide-linked muramyl peptide contains two D-alanine residues, while only one is present in the complete cell wall polymer.

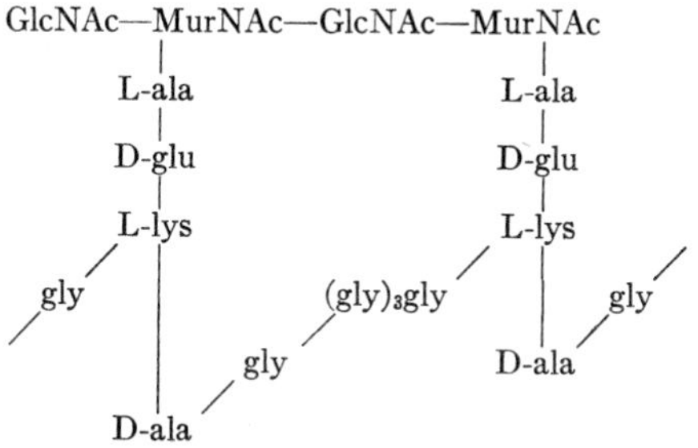

GlcNAc—MurNAc—GlcNAc—MurNAc
| |
L-ala   L-ala
| |
D-glu   D-glu
| |
L-lys   L-lys
/ | (gly)₃gly   / | gly/
gly | / | /
/ | / D-ala/
gly/
/
D-ala/

Wise & Park based their conclusions largely on the fact that in the presence of penicillin there was increased incorporation of labeled alanine into glycopeptide and that this was associated with an increase in the number of N-terminal glycine residues, as compared with the product formed in the presence of penicillin.[8]

The incorporation of glycine into glycopeptide of *S. aureus* has recently been studied by Matsuhashi and his co-workers (119, 120). It was established that formation of the polyglycine chains occurs while N-acetylmuramyl peptide is bound to lipid, the disaccharide lipid intermediate being more active as acceptor than the monosaccharide intermediate. The nucleotide-linked precursors and glycopeptide itself were completely inactive. In the case of *S. aureus*, it was demonstrated that pentaglycine units are attached to the ε-amino group of lysine, with glycine sRNA as the donor (119). With preparations from *M. lysodeikticus*, the attachment of single glycine residues to glutamic acid, with the formation of a free glycine carboxyl group, has been reported (120). Tipper & Strominger (117, 118) have proposed a mechanism (Fig. 6) for the final formation of the pentaglycine bridge in *S. aureus* and the mechanism of action of penicillin. As evidence for the formation of the cross-linked structure shown in Figure 6, they have demonstrated that the carboxyl

---

[8] However, Tipper & Strominger (117) attribute the N-terminal glycine residues in the control samples studied by Wise & Park to breakage of polyglycine cross-links by the treatment with hot trichloroacetic acid.

group of glutamine is present as isoglutamine and is not linked to glycine, and that enzymes which split the glycine bridge simultaneously expose carboxyl groups of alanine and amino groups of glycine. Most important, however, were the results found upon examination of the products obtained by treating cell walls with an endoacetylmuramidase. The low molecular weight fragments obtained by this procedure were shown to contain two D-alanine residues and one N-terminal glycine. These small fragments represented 7 per cent of the newly formed glycopeptide in control cells and 40 to 60 per cent in penicillin-treated cells. On the basis of these observations and a comparison of molecular models of the pentapeptide and penicillin, it was proposed that penicillin inhibits the final transpeptidation reaction by competing with D-alanyl-D-alanine for sites on the transpeptidase. An interesting hypothesis (118), in which penicillin binds through the lactam ring, was suggested.

Other suggestions have been made to account for the effects of penicillin. Martin (108) has not found the predicted "alanine excess" in a glycopeptide preparation from penicillin spheroplasts of *P. mirabilis* and suggests that penicillin may act to uncouple transpeptidation without preventing the release of one of the D-alanine residues. There are important differences in the nature of cross-linkages in glycopeptide polymers isolated from various organisms. While in *S. aureus* the evidence suggests that cross-linkage involves a pentaglycine bridge, in *M. lysodeikticus* and *E. coli* lysine and diaminopimelic acid appear to be directly linked to the terminal alanine carboxyl. Further work is also needed to disclose the mechanism for the introduction of new elements into the growing glycopeptide network. Martin (108) has discussed the suggestion of Schwarz & Weidel (121) for a possible need for lytic enzymes to work hand in hand with the synthetic mechanisms.

The mechanism of action of cycloserine.—Cycloserine had previously been shown to block the incorporation of D-alanine into cell wall glycopeptide (109). This agent has now been shown to operate through an effect on alanine racemase, thus preventing synthesis of D-alanine from L-alanine (122).

TEICHOIC ACIDS

In his review of the biochemistry of bacterial cell walls, Martin (108) has discussed the possible structural relations of teichoic acids to glycopeptide. The teichoic acids have recently been discussed by Ashwell (123), and the historical aspects of the subject are covered in an earlier review by Baddiley (124). Two types of teichoic acids are known, containing polyglycerophosphate and polyribitolphosphate, respectively, with a variety of sugar and amino acid substituents. These compounds were discovered by Baddiley and his co-workers nearly ten years ago, and they have since been shown to be responsible for some of the immunological properties of Gram-positive species (125, 126). They are present in the cell wall and exist in an "intracellular" form, Polyglycerophosphate was originally thought to be confined to the second category, but has since been shown to occur in the cell wall as well. These compounds appear to be confined to the Gram-positive bacteria; their presence in Gram-negative forms has not been definitely established.

Biosynthesis of polyribitolphosphate and polyglycerophosphate.—Since the discovery of CDP-ribitol and CDP-glycerol by Baddiley and his co-workers [see (124)], it had been assumed that these compounds were the precursors of the teichoic acids. The biosynthesis of polyribitolphosphate from CDP-ribitol was first reported by Glaser (127), with particulate fractions from *Lactobacillus plantarum.* More recently (128), fractions from *Bacillus lichenoformis* and *Bacillus subtilis* were found to catalyze the synthesis of polyglycerophosphate chains containing about 30 units. Similar preparations from *L. plantarum* catalyzed the biosynthesis of polyribitolphosphate. Both systems were sensitive to vancomycin, novobiocin, and crystal violet. Electron microphotographs of the enzyme preparation, which was isolated from intact cells following digestion with lysozyme and treatment of the membrane fraction with DNase and RNase, indicated that activity was associated with a cell wall (membrane) fraction. The mechanism of polymerization has not been elucidated, nor has a function for primers or acceptors in the particulate fractions been established.

Addition of side chain sugars.—The natural teichoic acid polymers contain a variety of substituents including sugars and amino acids. Nathenson & Strominger (129, 130) demonstrated the incorporation of one of these, N- acetylglucosamine, into polyribitolphosphate using UDP-N-acetylglucosamine and a particulate fraction isolated from *S. aureus.* The acceptor was teichoic acid which had been treated with β-N-acetylglucosaminidase to remove some of the endogenous glucosamine residues. Teichoic acid itself, with a full complement of α- and β-N-acetylglucosamine residues, was not active. The enzyme fraction employed catalyzed the formation of both α- and β-glycosidic linkages, although evidence was obtained to suggest that two different enzymes were present in the particulate fraction, and that the amount of each product was determined by their relative activity.

A similar incorporation of glucosyl residues into teichoic acids has been described by Glaser & Burger (131). A particulate enzyme preparation from *B. subtilis,* which contains a simple teichoic acid glucosylated at each α-position of polyglycerophosphate, was employed. Cell wall teichoic acid, which was fully glucosylated, was inactive as acceptor. "Intracellular" teichoic acid, which was characterized as a mixture of fully glucosylated and nonglucosylated forms, was active. Since fully glucosylated teichoic acid is resistant to both phosphodiesterase and alkaline hydrolysis, it was necessary to use cleavage of the phosphate esters by hydrofluoric acid (132) to obtain fragments for analysis. This permitted the identification of glucosyl-glycerol in the enzymatic reaction product.

Biosynthesis of polymers of glucosyl-glycerophosphate and galactosyl-glycerophosphate.—Recently, Burger & Glaser (133) have described the biosynthesis of a novel polymer catalyzed by the same membrane fractions of *B. lichenoformis* which catalyzed the synthesis of polyglycerophosphate. In this system, the incorporation of glucose or galactose from UDP-glucose or UDP-galactose was enhanced by the presence of CDP-glycerol and vice versa, unlike the biosynthesis of polyglycerophosphate which proceeded in the absence of other nucleotide sugars. The product was shown to contain the repeating unit glycerol-P-glucosyl-, formed according to the following sequence:

1. Glucosyl-X + CDP-glycerol → CMP + glycerol-P-glucosyl-X

2. Glycerol-P-glucosyl-X + UDPG → UDP + glucosyl-glycerol-P-glucosyl-X

A similar, but apparently completely independent, system was detected for the formation of a glycerol-P-galactosyl polymer. The nature of the acceptor, X, remains unknown, although different acceptor sites appear to function in the formation of the galactosyl and glucosyl polymers. An examination of the cell wall fraction in *B. lichenoformis* showed that structures of this type were present. Similar polymers of N-acetylglucosamine phosphate and glycerophosphate had previously been isolated from *Staphylococcus lactis* by Archibald et al. (134). Their relation to teichoic acids, or to the polymers which occur in *Pneumococcus* type VI capsule (8), is not known.

Linkage of teichoic acids to glycopeptide and control of synthesis.—Although teichoic acids appear to be covalently linked to glycopeptide, previous suggestions as to the nature of this linkage have failed to find support. Now, Ghuysen et al. (135) have skillfully used a combination of hydrolytic enzymes to obtain native teichoic acid attached to disaccharide components of glycopeptide. They have suggested that the glycopeptide polymer is linked through phosphodiester groups to the end of the teichoic acid chains. These phosphodiester groups may be very labile to acid.

The existence of covalent linkages between teichoic acid and glycopeptide raises the question of the reciprocal control of the biosynthesis of these polymers. In this connection, Glaser (136) has pointed out that although teichoic acid synthesis continues in the absence of glycopeptide synthesis, the product formed is more readily extracted from the cell wall, as in penicillin-treated cells (137). In the presence of crystal violet or novobiocin, CDP-ribitol and CDP-glycerol are accumulated by *L. plantarum*, along with UDP-glucose, UDP-galactose, and UDP-N-acetylglucosamine (136).

A different mechanism for control is suggested by the discovery in *B. subtilis* of a specific CDP-glycero-pyrophosphatase which catalyzes the cleavage of CDP-glycerol when this substance is present in high concentrations (138).

Intracellular "Storage" Polysaccharides

The synthesis of "storage" polysaccharides, such as glycogen, amylose, and amylopectin, has been shown to occur in bacteria by a variety of pathways (1), but the true metabolic function of these glycogen- and starch-like substances remains unknown. In some species they appear to accumulate when growth ceases (139). Biosynthesis of polysaccharides by glycosyl transfer from disaccharides has been reviewed by Hestrin (1). Our present concern is with a few recent developments which establish the existence of true glycogen synthesis in bacteria. These developments have also been reviewed by Sharon (140).

Biosynthesis of glycogen from ADP-glucose.—The first clue to the existence of a novel pathway of polysaccharide synthesis in bacteria came from the work of Sigal et al. (141), who found that mutant strains of *E. coli* blocked in the synthesis of UDP-glucose were still able to synthesize glycogen. Mayer and his co-workers (142) have also studied the polysaccharides formed in such UDP-glucose-deficient strains. They found that although these mutants would not incorporate glucose into cell wall lipopolysaccharide, they were able to synthesize a soluble acidic polymer containing glucose, and it was suggested that glucosyl donors other than UDP-glucose might be involved.

Some years earlier, Recondo & Leloir (143) had synthesized ADP-glucose and demonstrated that this sugar nucleotide could serve as a precursor of starch in plant systems (144). A similar role for ADP-glucose in the biosynthesis of glycogen-like polymers in bacterial systems has now been established by the elegant studies of Preiss and his co-workers (145–148). They have demonstrated the wide-spread occurrence in bacterial systems of enzymes which catalyze the following reactions:

$$\text{ATP} + \text{glucose 1-P} \rightleftharpoons \text{ADP-glucose} + \text{PP}_i$$

$$\text{ADP-glucose} + \alpha\text{-(1, 4)-glucan} \rightarrow \alpha\text{-(1, 4)-glucosyl-glucan} + \text{ADP}$$

Other nucleotides, such as UDP-glucose, TDP-glucose, or GDP-glucose, were completely inactive (145) in the second reaction, catalyzed by the enzyme adenosine diphosphate glucose:glycogen transglucosylase. The enzyme may be largely in the soluble fraction, as in *Agrobacterium tumefaciens* (145), or particulate, as in *Aerobacter aerogenes* and *E. coli*. The soluble *Arthrobacter* enzyme (149) and the particulate *E. coli* enzyme (148) have been purified and found to be very similar in their properties. Both were highly specific for ADP-glucose (or dADP-glucose), and showed an absolute requirement for glycogen or oligosaccharides of the maltodextrin series as primers. They differed from other glycogen transglucosylases in they that were not activated by glucose 6-P. The bacterial systems appear to differ from those found in animal tissues in that control of polysaccharide synthesis is not exerted at the level of transglycosylase. This will be discussed later.

The products of the enzymatic reaction were characterized as polymers containing α-glucosyl-(1→4)-linkages. However, 1,6-linkages must also be produced, since glycogen isolated from *Arthrobacter* was shown to resemble closely animal glycogens in its chemical structure and in the products formed on hydrolysis with α- and β-amylases. The formation of α-1,6- branch points would presumably be catalyzed by a branching enzyme which has been shown by Zevenhuizen (150) to be present in another species of *Arthrobacter*. Thus, except for the fact that the bacterial systems utilize ADP-glucose instead of

UDP-glucose, and that the site of control may differ, the mechanism of biosynthesis is very similar to that of animal glycogens. The enzyme ADP-glucose:pyrophosphorylase (151, 152) has been purified from *Arthrobacter* (152). Its role in control of glycogen synthesis will be discussed later.

Other homopolysaccharides.—Although bacteria are known to contain a large variety of homopolysaccharides (1, 140), very little information is available as to their biosynthesis. Soluble mannans occur in both yeast and bacteria; in yeast they are formed from GDP-mannose by the action of a particulate enzyme (153). This system has not yet been described in bacteria.

GLYCOLIPIDS

Interest in these compounds has increased as a result of the recent indications that the biosynthesis of several classes of cell wall polysaccharides occurs by way of lipid-linked intermediates, and that these compounds may serve to transport sugars from the sugar nucleotide precursors within the cell to the polysaccharides which are present in the outermost cell structures.

Occurrence of glycolipids.—Glycolipids occur widely among bacteria (154). Rhamnosyl glycolipids are produced by *Pseudomonas aeruginosa* (155), where they are excreted into the medium during the stationary phase. A galactopyranosyl-glucopyranosyl diglyceride has been isolated from a rough strain of *Pneumococcus* type 1 (14) and from *Pneumocooccus* type XIV(13). Dimannosyl diglycerides are present in *M. lysodeikticus* (156) and a galactofuranosyl glyceride has been identified in *Bacterioides symbiosis* (157). The last is of particular interest, since galactofuranosyl sugar nucleotides which might serve as possible precursors have not yet been detected. The function of these glycolipids in polysaccharide biosynthesis remains unknown.

Biosynthesis of glycolipids.—Burger et al. (158) had obtained evidence for the following pathway for the biosynthesis of a rhamnosyl glycolipid in *P. aeruginosa*:

2-β-hydroxydecanoyl CoA $\rightleftharpoons$ β-hydroxydecanoyl-β-hydroxydecanoate
TDP-L-rhamnose + β-hydroxydecanoyl-β-hydroxydecanoate → TDP
         + L-rhamnosyl-β-hydroxydecanoyl-β-hydroxydecanoate
TDP-L-rhamnose + L-rhamnosyl-β-hydroxydecanoyl-β-hydroxydecanoate
     → TDP + L-rhamnosyl-L-rhamnosyl-β-hydroxydecanoyl-β-hydroxydecanoate

The product was insoluble in acid and extractable with ether. The enzymes were present in soluble form in extracts of the microorganism and specific fractions were obtained which catalyzed the incorporation of one or the other rhamnosyl group (158, 159). The lipopolysaccharide of this organism has been shown (158) to contain rhamnose, but no β-hydroxydecanoic acid. Recently, Barker (160) has isolated UDP-L-rhamnose, which is formed from UDP-glucose by extracts of tobacco leaves. This nucleotide sugar derivative is nine times less active than TDP-rhamnose in the formation of glycolipid in *P. aeruginosa*.

A similar sequence was shown to be responsible for the biosynthesis of mannolipid in *M. lysodeikticus* (161). Particulate enzyme preparations catalyzed the formation of mannosyl diglyceride and mannosyl-mannosyl diglyceride from GDP-mannose and a crude diglyceride preparation. Mannose was also incorporated into an unidentified acidic glycolipid by a soluble enzyme fraction from the same organism. Roseman and his co-workers (13) have studied the biosynthesis of the *Pneumococcus* glycolipid. Enzyme activity was detected in both particulate and soluble fractions and catalyzed the successive addition of glucose from UDP-glucose and galactose from UDP-galactose into a crude lipid fraction. The soluble enzyme fractions required the addition of endogenous lipid present in the boiled particle fraction. However, synthetic diglycerides, such as dipalmitin, would not serve as acceptors. The enzymic product was shown to be identical with the α-D-galactopyranosyl-(1→2)-α-D-glucopyranosyl-(1→3)-diglyceride present in Type XIV *Pneumococcus*.

BIOSYNTHESIS OF SUGAR NUCLEOTIDES AND CONTROL OF POLYSACCHARIDE SYNTHESIS

Control of polysaccharide biosynthesis may occur either through the regulation of the production of precursor sugar nucleotides, or through effects on the activity of the transferase enzymes. Although in certain mutants polysaccharide formation may be interrupted by the absence of one or another transferase enzyme, evidence is accumulating to suggest that the normal control mechanisms operate primarily in the biosynthesis of sugar nucleotides. These controls are exercised through repression at the genetic level, and by feedback inhibition of early enzymes by end products of biosynthetic pathways. The existence of different nucleotide derivatives of the same sugar in a single organism is an important factor, since it allows selective control of the formation of one polysaccharide without affecting the production of another.

In recent years, a number of excellent reviews have appeared which cover the biosynthesis of the sugar nucleotides (2, 123, 144, 162, 163). The present discussion will, therefore, be confined to recent developments, particularly those which relate to control mechanisms.

Sugar nucleotides containing glucose and galactose.—We have already considered the role of UDP-glucose and UDP-galactose in the biosynthesis of lipopolysaccharide. In *E. coli* the interconversion of these two sugar nucleotides is catalyzed by an inducible UDP-galactose-4-epimerase. This enzyme has recently been purified from extracts of *E. coli* K12 (164) and shown to contain one mole of bound DPN per molecular weight of 79,000. Mutants lacking this enzyme accumulate UDP-galactose when the sugar is present in the medium (165), suggesting that feedback control of galactokinase and UDP-glucose:galactose-1-phosphate transferase does not occur. Since UDP-galactose is an essential intermediate in galactose metabolism, absence of feedback control is not unusual. On the other hand, this enzyme does appear to be regulated at the genetic level. Markovitz (22) has recently shown that mucoid strains of *E. coli* which produce an extracellular polysacchaide containing galactose, fucose, and uronic acids, contain abnormally high levels of

UDP-galactose-4-epimerase and GDP-fucose synthetase. Since the mucoid character was found to be dominant, it was concluded that the biosynthesis of sugar nucleotides is under control of a regulatory gene which thus controls the biosynthesis of capsular polysaccharide.

The precursor of bacterial glycogen, ADP-glucose, is syntheiszed from ATP and glucose-1-phosphate. The enzyme, ADP-glucose phosphorylase, shows a rather complex pattern of activation by glycolytic intermediates (151, 166), such as fructose diphosphate, phosphoenol pyruvate, and glyceraldehyde 3-phosphate in *E. coli* and *A. aerogenes*, or fructose 6-phosphate and

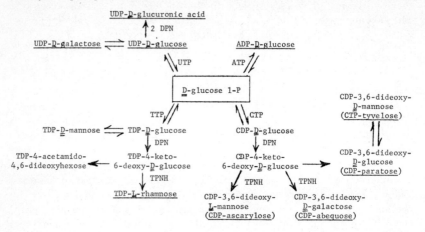

Fig. 7. Biosynthesis of sugar nucleotides from glucose 1-phosphate. Precursors of bacterial polysaccharides are underlined.

ribose 5-phosphate in *Arthrobacter* and *Rhodospirillum rubrum*. Since ADP-glycogen transglucosylase was found to be unaffected by these intermediates (146), it was suggested that control of glycogen synthesis might occur at the pyrophosphorylase level and thus at the level of sugar nucleotide synthesis. In this respect, the bacterial system was similar to that found in plants (167), but differed from that in animal tissues.

An enzyme in *Streptococcus faecalis* (168) catalyzes the direct formation of TDP-galactose from TTP and galactose-1-phosphate. This enzyme is distinct from UDP-glucose pyrophosphorylase and TDP-glucose pyrophosphorylase found in the same organism. Its role in polysaccharide biosynthesis has not yet been established.

The formation of 6-deoxy and 3,6-dideoxy sugars.—In contrast to UDP-glucose and ADP-glucose, which are utilized directly as glycosyl donors for the biosynthesis of bacterial polysaccharides, TDP-glucose and CDP-glucose serve as precursors of other sugar nucleotides (2, 123, 162, 163) (Fig. 7). During the past year, the role of these sugar nucleotides in the biosynthesis of deoxy and dideoxy hexoses has been considerably clarified. The first step in the conversion of TDP-glucose to TDP-L-rhamnose is the formation of TDP-4-keto-6-deoxy-D-glucose, catalyzed by the enzyme thymidine diphosphate D-glucose-oxidoreductase. This enzyme has been purified extensively from *E. coli* B (169) and shown to contain tightly bound DPN, which was essential for the activity of the enzyme. A similar enzyme which catalyzes the formation of CDP-4-keto-6-deoxy-D-glucose from CDP-D-glucose was purified from extracts of *P. pseudotuberculosis*, type V (170), and shown to have a similar requirement for DPN. In this case, however, the coenzyme was readily dissociated from the enzyme. Each of these enzymes was highly specific for its nucleotide substrate. In *E. coli* Y10, the intermediate TDP-4-keto-6-deoxy-D-glucose was also converted to TDP-acetamido-4,6-dideoxy-D-galactose and in *E. coli* B the same intermediate was utilized for the synthesis of TDP-acetamido-4,6-dideoxy-D-glucose (171, 172). The latter may be the precursor

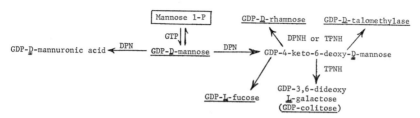

FIG. 8. Biosynthesis of sugar nucleotide from mannose 1-phosphate. Precursors of bacterial polysaccharides are underlined.

of this sugar in the lipopolysaccharide of *C. violaceum* (173). In *Xanthomanas campestris*, TDP-glucose was also converted to TDP-3-acetamido-3,6-dideoxy-D-galactose (174); the sugar component has recently been shown to be a component of the cell wall of this organism (175).

In *P. psuedotuberculosis* strain 25V, the intermediate CDP-4-keto-6-deoxy-D-glucose was utilized for the biosynthesis of CDP-ascarylose (176), in *S. typhimurium* (88) for the formation of CDP-abequose, and in *P. pseudotuberculosis* strain 43 III (177, 178) and *S. paratyphi* (179), for the synthesis of CDP-paratose and CDP-tyvelose. The enzyme which catalyzes the synthesis of CDP-glucose from CTP and glucose-1-phosphate, CDP-glucose pyrophosphorylase, has been isolated from *S. paratyphi* type A (180). CDP-glucose is thus the precursor of four of the five known 3,6-dideoxy sugars, since CDP-paratose was converted directly to CDP-tyvelose in a reaction catalyzed by an enzyme present in species of *Salmonella* and *Pasteurella* (180, 181). This last reaction, which involves epimerization at the 2-position, requires DPN (178), and thus resembles the epimerization of UDP-D-glucose to UDP-D-galactose (181).

Sugar nucleotides derived from GDP-mannose.—A more limited number of sugar nucleotides are derived from GDP-mannose (Fig. 8). The conversion of GDP-mannose to GDP-L-fucose in extracts of *A. aerogenes* was the first reaction of this type to be described (182), and this discovery was soon followed by evidence for the intermediate GDP-4-keto-6-deoxy-D-mannose (183). In other organisms this intermediate is the precursor of GDP-colitose (184–186). Formation of the intermediate required catalytic quantities of DPN, as in the case of the comparable intermediates formed from TDP-D-glucose and CDP-D-glucose, while conversion of the intermediate to GDP-colitose utilized TPNH as the reductant (186). The 4-keto intermediate was identified by reduction with $NaBH_4$, which yielded a mixture of sugar nucleotides containing 6-deoxy-D-talose and D-rhamnose. Enzymatic reduction of the sugar nucleotide intermediate to these products has been demonstrated by Markovitz (187) with extracts of a Gram-negative bacterium designated as strain GS. This organism utilized either TPNH or DPNH for the direct reduction, without epimerization, of GDP-4-keto-6-deoxy-D-mannose to a mixture of GDP-D-rhamnose and GDP-D-talomethylose. The capsular polysaccharide of this organism contains the rare sugars D-rhamnose and D-talomethylose in equal proportions.

The biosynthesis of GDP-mannose was first described in yeast (188). The synthesis of this sugar nucleotide has now been described with a purified enzyme preparation from *Arthrobacter sp.* (189) and with crude extracts of *S. typhimurium* (82). The *Arthrobacter* strain also yielded a DPN-linked enzyme which catalyzed the 2-step oxidation of GDP-D-mannose to GDP-D-mannuronate (190). Presumably, GDP-mannuronate is the precursor of mannuronic acid in the extracellular polysaccharide produced by this organism.

Thymidine diphosphate-mannose isolated from *Streptomyces griseus* may be produced by way of TDP-glucose; extracts of this organism have been reported to catalyze the interconversion of these two sugar nucleotides (191).

Nucleotide precursors of teichoic acids.—The biosynthesis of CDP-glycerol and CDP-ribitol from CTP and the polyol-1-phosphates was first described by Shaw (192) with extracts of *B. lichenoformis* and *L. plantarum*, respectively. Purified preparations of these enzymes have not yet been described, but an enzyme which catalyzes the phosphorolysis of CDP-glycerol has been found in extracts of *B. subtilis* and *B. lichenoformis* (138). A possible role of this enzyme in control of polysaccharide biosynthesis is discussed below.

Feedback control mechanisms.—In many species of bacteria, sugar nucleotides accumulate when cell wall or polysaccharide biosynthesis is blocked; in others, such accumulation does not occur and feedback control mechanisms may operate. Strominger (109) has considered feedback mechanisms as one possible explanation for the failure of many strains to accumulate uridine nucleotides containing muramyl peptides in penicillin-treated organisms. Two types of control mechanisms have been suggested by Glaser (138) to account for the lack of accumulation of teichoic acid precursors in *B. subtilis*. One is the presence of the hydrolytic enzyme described above, which converts CDP-glycerol to CMP and L-α-glycerophosphate. The other is a feedback inhibition of CDP-glycerol pyrophosphorylase by the product CDP-glycerol.

These two mechanisms would cooperate to prevent the accumulation of CDP-glycerol. In *L. plantarum*, on the other hand, both CDP-ribitol and CDP-glycerol accumulate in cells treated with crystal violet or novobiocin, together with UDP-glucose, UDP-galactose, and UDP-N-acetylglucosamine, suggesting that in this organism similar control mechanisms are absent.

In rough strains of Enterobacteriaceae blocked in the biosynthesis of the antigenic side chain, sugar nucleotide precursors might be expected to accumulate; this has been demonstrated under special conditions for UDP-galactose (193, 194), CDP-tyvelose, CDP-abequose and TDP-rhamnose (58, 195). However, a mannose-negative strain of *S. typhimurium* blocked in the conversion of mannose 6-phosphate to fructose 6-phosphate accumulated a

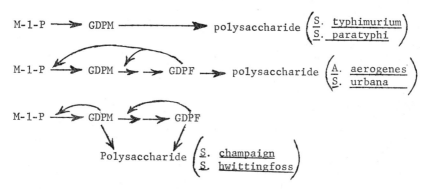

FIG. 9. Feedback inhibition of enzymes in the formation of GDP-D-mannose and GDP-L-fucose [from (199)].

mixture of mannose 1- and 6-phosphate, but very little GDP-mannose (82). Since formation of the sugar nucleotide from GTP and mannose 1-phosphate would be a relatively irreversible process, its failure to accumulate may result from feedback inhibition.

In a number of other cases, direct evidence for the control of sugar nucleotide synthesis by feedback inhibition is available. The formation of D-glucosamine-6-phosphate from D-fructose-6-phosphate and L-glutamine is inhibited by the end product of the reaction, UDP-N-acetyl-D-glucosamine (196), and the formation of TDP-glucose is inhibited by TDP-L-rhamnose, which is an end product of that pathway (197, 198). The synthesis of UDP-glucose, catalyzed by UDP-glucose pyrophosphorylase, was also inhibited by both TDP-glucose and TDP-rhamnose; the implications of these cross-inhibitory reactions have been discussed by Melo & Glaser (197). A complex pattern of inhibition has recently been reported by Kornfeld & Ginsburg (198, 199) which can be related directly to the composition of cell wall lipopolysaccharides. These results are illustrated in Figure 9. In those strains which synthesize a lipopolysaccharide containing mannose but no fucose, GDP-mannose pyrophosphorylase was found to be strongly inhibited by GDP-mannose, but only slightly by GDP-L-fucose and not at all by GDP-glucose. In other strains which contain only L-fucose in the lipopolysaccharide, GDP-mannose pyrophosphorylase was inhibited by GDP-fucose but not by GDP-mannose. In this case, GDP-fucose also inhibited GDP-mannose-oxidoreductase, which catalyzes the next step in the synthesis of GDP-fucose. In the third type of organism, whose lipopolysaccharides contain both mannose and fucose, GDP-fucose inhibited only the oxidoreductase, and GDP-mannose the pyrophosphorylase. In *S. paratyphi*, where CDP-glucose is the precursor of CDP-paratose, the activity of CDP-glucose pyrophosphorylase was controlled by CDP-paratose (180). These feedback inhibition reactions permit selective control of the synthesis of each of the sugar nucleotides, depending on their rate of utilization. In contrast to these observations, *E. coli* 44, which does not contain rhamnose in the lipopolysaccharide and appears to lack the specific transferase, accumulates TDP-rhamnose (200), suggesting that the feedback control mechanism has also been lost. Similarly, a rough strain of *S. weslaco* lacks rhamnose in the lipopolysaccharide, but accumulates the 4-keto intermediate, despite the fact that the enzyme system for the overall conversion of TDP-glucose to TDP-rhamnose is intact (200).

Genetic control of the biosynthesis of sugar nucleotides.—The structure and composition of bacterial polysaccharides is frequently determined by the presence or absence of specific structural genes which code for specific transferase enzymes. This appears to be the case in the *rouA* strains (33) and in some types of lysogenic conversion (28, 90) in *Salmonella* species. Robbins et al. (91) have obtained evidence for the elimination of specific linkages in lipopolysaccharide by the introduction of repressor genes in lysogenic conversion. In many cases, however, control of polysaccharide structure is exercised at the level of biosynthesis of nucleotide sugars. This has been demonstrated by studies of transformation in *Pneumococcus* (17, 201, 202) and in the formation of some *rouB* strains in *Salmonella* (33).

Not only the structure of polysaccharides, but also their rate of synthesis may be under direct genetic control. This has been clearly established by Markovitz (22) in his studies of mucoid and nonmucoid strains of *E. coli*. Genetic studies of rough type *Salmonella* strains are of great interest in this connection. In an elegant series of genetic and biochemical studies, Stocker, Nikaido, and Mäkelä and their co-workers have established that *rouB* (R$_{II}$) mutants of *S. typhimurium* map in a single region (the O locus) close to the *his* locus (79, 88, 203). Eight of the nine enzymes required for the biosynthesis of TDP-rhamnose, CDP-abequose, and GDP-mannose were found to be determined by genes within this locus. The only exception was the determinant for phosphomannose isomerase; however, this enzyme is also required for mannose fermentation. The determinants for abequose (partial antigen 4) and tyvelose (partial antigen 9) behaved as if they were allelic loci (204), which may explain why the two sugars are never found in a single organism. The clustering of genes which determine the *rouB* character in the O locus suggests that they may be components of a complex operon and subject to control by regulatory genes. With the clarification of the precise nature of the individual enzymes required for the biosynthesis of bacterial lipopolysac-charides, additional studies of genetic control will become possible; these should lead ultimately to an understanding of the control and coordination of biosynthetic processes for the various components of the cell wall, includ-ing the mucopeptide, the teichoic acids, lipopolysaccharide, and the capsular polysaccharides.

LITERATURE CITED

1. Hestrin, S., in *The Bacteria*, **III**, 373. (Gunsalus, I. C., and Stanier, R. Y., Eds., Academic Press, New York, 1962)
2. Neufeld, E. F., and Ginsburg, V., *Ann. Rev. Biochem.*, **34**, 297 (1965)
3. Glaser, L., *Biochim. Biophys. Acta*, **25**, 436 (1957)
4. Glaser, L., *J. Biol. Chem.*, **232**, 627 (1958)
5. Barker, G. A., Elbein, A. D., and Hassid, W. Z., *J. Biol. Chem.*, **239**, 4056 (1964)
6. Brummond, D., *Biochem. Z.*, **342**, 308 (1965)
7. Colvin, J. R., *Can. J. Biochem. Physiol.*, **39**, 1921 (1961)
8. How, M. J., Brimacombe, J. S., and Stacey, M., *Advan. Carbohydrate Chem.*, **19**, 303 (1964)
9. Smith, E. E. B., Mills, G. T., Bernheimer, H. P., and Austrian, R., *J. Biol. Chem.*, **235**, 1876 (1960)
10. Smith, E. E. B., Mills, G. T., and Bernheimer, H. P., *J. Biol. Chem.*, **236**, 2179 (1961)
11. Smith, E. E. B., and Mills, G. T., *Biochem. J.*, **82**, 42p (1962)
12. Distler, J., and Roseman, S., *Proc. Natl. Acad. Sci. U.S.*, **51**, 897 (1964)
13. Kaufman, B., Kundig, F. D., Distler, J., and Roseman, S., *Biochem. Biophys. Res. Commun.*, **18**, 312 (1965)
14. Brundish, D. E., Shaw, N., and Baddiley, J., *Biochem. Biophys. Res. Commun.*, **18**, 308 (1965)
15. Brundish, D. E., Shaw, N., and Baddiley, J., *Biochem. J.*, **95**, 21c (1965).
16. Brundish, D. E., Shaw, N., and Baddiley, J., *Biochem. J.*, **97**, 158 (1965)
17. Austrian, R., Bernheimer, H. P., Smith, E. E. B., and Mills, G. T., *Cold Spring Harbor Symp. Quant. Biol.*, **23**, 99 (1958)
18. Austrian, R., Bernheimer, H. P., Smith, E. E. B., and Mills, G. T., *J. Exptl. Med.*, **110**, 585 (1959)
19. Goebel, W. F., *Proc. Natl. Acad. Sci. U.S.*, **49**, 464 (1963)
20. Akashi, S., *Intern. Congr. Biochem.*, *6th*, **32**, VI-3 (1964)
21. Jann, K., Jann, B., Ørskov, F., Ørskov, I., and Westphal, O., *Biochem. Z.*, **342**, 1 (1965)
22. Markovitz, A., *Proc. Natl. Acad. Sci. U.S.*, **51**, 239 (1964)
23. Raistrick, H., and Tapley, W. W. C., *Brit. J. Exptl. Pathol.*, **15**, 113 (1934)
24. Boivin, A., and Mesrobeanu, L., *Rev. Immunol.*, **1**, 553 (1935)
25. Westphal, O., and Lüderitz, O., *Angew. Chem.*, **72**, 881 (1960)
26. Davies, D. A. L., *Advan. Carbohydrate Chem.*, **15**, 271 (1960)
27. Kauffmann, F., *The Bacteriology of Salmonella Species*. (Munksgaard, Copenhagen, 1961)
28. Robbins, P. W., and Uchida, T., *Federation Proc.*, **21**, 702 (1962)
29. Westphal, O., and Lüderitz, O., *Naturwissenschaften*, **12**, 413 (1963)
30. Staub, A. M., and Raynaud, M., *The World Problem of Salmonellosis*, 142. (Van Oye, E., Ed., Dr. W. Junk, Publ. Co., The Hague, 1964)
31. Staub, A. M., and Westphal, O., *Bull. Soc. Chim. Biol.*, **46**, 1647 (1964)
32. Salton, M. R. J., *The Bacterial Cell Wall*. (Elsevier, Amsterdam, 1964)
33. Lüderitz, O., Staub, A. M., and Westphal, O., *Bacteriol. Rev.* (In press)
34. Westphal, O., Lüderitz, O., and Bister, F., *Z. Naturforsch*, **7b**, 148 (1952)
35. Boivin, A., Mesrobeanu, J., and Mesrobeanu, L., *Compt. Rend. Soc. Biol.*, **113**, 490 (1933)
36. Kauffmann, F., Lüderitz, O., Stierlin, H., and Westphal, O., *Zentr. Bakteriol. Parasitenk.*, *Abt. I, Orig.*, **178**, 442 (1960)
37. Osborn, M. J., Rosen, S. M., Rothfield, L., and Horecker, B. L., *Proc. Natl. Acad. Sci. U.S.*, **48**, 1831 (1962)
38. Westphal, O., and Lüderitz, O., *Angew. Chem.*, **66**, 407 (1954)
39. Kröger, E., Lüderitz, O., and Westphal, O., *Naturwissenschaften*, **46**, 428 (1959)
40. Lüderitz, O., Kauffmann, F., Stierlin, H., and Westphal, O., *Zentr. Bakteriol. Parasitenk.*, *Abt. I, Orig.*, **179**, 180 (1960)
41. Westphal, O., Kauffmann, F., Lüderitz, O., and Stierlin, H., *Zentr. Bakteriol. Parasitenk.*, *Abt. I, Orig.*, **179**, 336 (1960)
42. Kauffmann, F., Krüger, L., Lüderitz, O., and Westphal, O., *Zentr. Bakteriol. Parasitenk. Abt. I. Orig.*, **182**, 57 (1961)
43. Kauffmann, F., Jann, B., Krüger, L.,

Lüderitz, O., and Westphal, O., Zentr. Bakteriol. Parasitenk., Abt. I, Orig., 186, 509 (1962)

44. Grollman, A. P., and Osborn, M. J., Biochemistry, 3, 1571 (1964)

45. Heath, E. C., and Ghalambor, M. A., Biochem. Biophys. Res. Commun., 10, 340 (1963)

46. Sundararajan, T. A., Rapin, A. M. C., and Kalckar, H. M., Proc. Natl. Acad. Sci. U.S., 48, 2187 (1962)

47. Lüderitz, O., Galanos, C., Risse, H. J., Ruschmann, E., Schlecht, S., Schmidt, F., Schulte-Holthausen, H., Wheat, R., Westphal, O., and Schlosshardt, J., Ann. N.Y. Acad. Sci. (In press)

48. Kauffmann, F., Braun, O. H., Lüderitz, O., Stierlin, H., and Westphal, O., Zentr. Bakteriol. Parasitenk., Abt. I, Orig., 180, 180 (1960)

49. Lüderitz, O., O'Neill, G., and Westphal, O., Biochem. Z., 333, 136 (1960)

50. Weidel, W., Z. Physiol. Chem., 299, 253 (1955)

51. Osborn, M. J., Rosen, S. M., Rothfield, L., Zeleznick, L. D., and Horecker, B. L., Science, 145, 783 (1964)

52. MacLennan, A. P., and Davies, D. A. L., Biochem. J., 66, 562 (1957)

53. Osborn, M. J., Proc. Natl. Acad. Sci. U.S., 50, 499 (1963)

54. Fukasawa, T., and Nikaido, H., Biochim. Biophys. Acta, 48, 470 (1961)

55. Nikaido, H., Proc. Natl. Acad. Sci. U.S., 48, 1337 (1962)

56. Fukasawa, T., and Nikaido, H., Virology, 11, 508 (1960)

57. Fukasawa, T., and Nikaido, H., Nature, 184, 1168 (1959)

58. Nikaido, H., Proc. Natl. Acad. Sci. U.S., 48, 1542 (1962)

59. Weismyer, H., and Jordan, E., Anal. Biochem., 2, 281 (1961)

60. Burton, A., and Carter, H. E., Biochemistry, 3, 411 (1964)

61. Mayer, R. M., Edstrom, R. D., Beaudreau, C. A., and Heath, E. C., Ann. N.Y. Acad. Sci. (In press)

62. Edstrom, R. D., and Heath, E. C., Biochem. Biophys. Res. Commun., 16, 576 (1964)

63. Cherniak, R., and Osborn, M. J., Federation Proc., 25, 410 (1966)

64. Kuriki, Y., and Kurahashi, K., J. Biochem. (Tokyo), 58, 308 (1965)

65. Fraenkel, D., Osborn, M. J., and Horecker, B. L., Biochem. Biophys. Res. Commun., 11, 423 (1963)

66. Rothfield, L., Osborn, M. J., and Horecker, B. L., J. Biol. Chem., 239, 2785 (1964)

67. Fukasawa, T., Jokura, K., and Kurahashi, K., Biochem. Biophys. Res. Commun., 7, 121 (1962)

68. Osborn, M. J., Ann. N.Y. Acad. Sci. (In press)

69. Rosen, S. M., Osborn, M. J., and Horecker, B. L., J. Biol. Chem., 239, 3196 (1964)

70. Osborn, M. J., and D'Ari, L., Biochem. Biophys. Res. Commun., 16, 568 (1964)

71. Elbein, A. D., and Heath, E. C., J. Biol. Chem., 240, 1919 (1965)

72. Rothfield, L., and Horecker, B. L., Proc. Natl. Acad. Sci. U.S., 52, 939 (1964)

73. Rothfield, L., and Pearlman, M., J. Biol. Chem., 241, 1386 (1966)

74. Rothfield, L., and Takeshita, M., Biochem. Biophys. Res. Commun., 20, 521 (1965)

75. Rothfield, L., and Takeshita, M., Ann. N.Y. Acad. Sci. (In press)

76. Lüderitz, O., Risse, H. J., Schulte-Holthausen, H., Strominger, J. L., Sutherland, I. W., and Westphal, O., J. Bacteriol., 89, 343 (1965)

77. Sutherland, I. W., Lüderitz, O., and Westphal, O., Biochem. J., 96, 439 (1965)

78. Beckmann, I., Lüderitz, O., and Westphal, O., Biochem. Z., 339, 401 (1964)

79. Subbaiah, T. V., and Stocker, B. A. D., Nature, 201, 1298 (1964)

80. Beckmann, I., Subbaiah, T. V., and Stocker, B. A. D., Nature, 201, 1299 (1964)

81. Nikaido, H., Nikaido, K., Subbaiah, T. V., and Stocker, B. A. D., Nature, 201, 1301 (1964)

82. Rosen, S. M., Zeleznick, L. D., Fraenkel, D., Weiner, I. M., Osborn, M. J., and Horecker, B. L., Biochem. Z., 342, 375 (1965)

83. Zeleznick, L. D., Rosen, S. M., Saltmarsh-Andrew, M., Osborn, M. J., and Horecker, B. L., Proc. Natl. Acad. Sci. U.S., 53, 207 (1965)

84. Weiner, I. M., Higuchi, T., Rothfield, L., Saltmarsh-Andrew, M., Osborn, M. J., and Horecker, B. L., Proc. Natl. Acad. Sci. U.S., 54, 228 (1965)

85. Weiner, I. M., Higuchi, T., Osborn,

M. J., and Horecker, B. L., *Ann. N.Y. Acad. Sci.* (In press)

86. Naide, Y., Nikaido, H., Mäkelä, P. H., Wilkinson, R. G., and Stocker, B. A. D., *Proc. Natl. Acad. Sci. U.S.*, **53**, 147 (1965)

87. Nikaido, H., and Nikaido, K., *Biochem. Biophys. Res. Commun.*, **19**, 322 (1965)

88. Nikaido, H., Naide, Y., and Mäkelä, P. H., *Ann. N.Y. Acad. Sci.* (In press)

89. Uchida, T., Robbins, P. W., and Luria, S. E., *Biochemistry*, **2**, 663 (1963)

90. Robbins, P. W., and Uchida, T., *Biochemistry*, **1**, 323 (1962)

91. Robbins, P. W., Keller, J. M., Wright, A., and Bernstein, R. L., *J. Biol. Chem.*, **240**, 834 (1965)

92. Wright, A., Dankert, M., and Robbins, P. W., *Proc. Natl. Acad. Sci. U.S.*, **54**, 235 (1965)

93. Tinelli, R., and Staub, A. M., *Bull. Soc. Chim. Biol.*, **41**, 1221 (1959)

94. Tinelli, R., and Staub, A. M., *Bull. Soc. Chim. Biol.*, **42**, 601 (1960)

95. Nikaido, H., *Biochemistry*, **4**, 1550 (1965)

96. Anderson, J. S., Matsuhashi, M., Haskin, M. A., and Strominger, J. L., *Proc. Natl. Acad. Sci. U.S.*, **53**, 881 (1965)

97. Edstrom, R. D., and Heath, E. C., *Biochem. Biophys. Res. Commun.*, **21**, 638 (1965)

98. Iseki, S., and Sakai, T., *Proc. Japan Acad.*, **29**, 127 (1953)

99. Robbins, P. W., and Uchida, T., *J. Biol. Chem.*, **240**, 375 (1965)

99a. Uchida, T., Makino, T., Kurahashi, K., and Uetake, H., *Biochem. Biophys. Res. Commun.*, **21**, 354 (1965)

100. Staub, A. M., and Girard, R., *Bull. Soc. Chim. Biol.*, **47**, 1245 (1965)

101. Bagdian, G., Lüderitz, O., and Staub, A. M., *Ann. N. Y. Acad. Sci.* (In press)

102. Nesbitt, J. A., III, and Lennarz, W. J., *J. Bacteriol.*, **89**, 1020 (1965)

103. Kotelko, K., Lüderitz, O., and Westphal, O., *Biochem. Z.* (In press)

104. Taylor, A., Knox, K. W., and Work, E., *Biochem. J.*, **99**, 53 (1966)

105. Bishop, D. G., and Work, E., *Biochem. J.*, **96**, 567 (1965)

106. Knox, E., and Work, E., *Ann. N.Y. Acad. Sci.* (In press)

107. Falaschi, A., and Kornberg, A., *Proc.*

Natl. Acad. Sci. U.S., **54**, 1713 (1965)

108. Martin, H., *Ann. Rev. Biochem.*, **35**, 457 (1966)

109. Strominger, J. L., in *The Bacteria*, III, 413. (Gunsalus, I. C., and Stanier, R. Y., Eds., Academic Press, New York, 1962)

110. Chatterjee, A. N., and Park, J. T., *Proc. Natl. Acad. Sci. U.S.*, **51**, 9 (1964)

111. Meadow, P. M., Anderson, J. S., and Strominger, J. L., *Biochem. Biophys. Res. Commun.*, **14**, 382 (1964)

112. Struve, W. G., and Neuhaus, F. C., *Biochem. Biophys. Res. Commun.*, **18**, 6 (1965)

113. Anderson, J. S., and Strominger, J. L., *Biochem. Biophys. Res. Commun.*, **21**, 516 (1965)

114. Dietrich, C. P., Matsuhashi, M., and Strominger, J. L., *Biochem. Biophys. Res. Commun.*, **31**, 619 (1965)

115. Martin, H., *Proc. Intern. Congr. Biochem., 6th*, **32**, 518 (1964) (Abstr.)

116. Wise, E. M., Jr., and Park, J. T., *Proc. Natl. Acad. Sci. U.S.*, **54**, 75 (1965)

117. Tipper, D. J., and Strominger, J. L., *Proc. Natl. Acad. Sci. U.S.*, **54**, 1133 (1965)

118. Strominger, J. L., and Tipper, D. J., *Am. J. Med.* (In press)

119. Matsuhashi, M., Dietrich, C. P., and Strominger, J. L., *Proc. Natl. Acad. Sci. U.S.*, **54**, 587 (1965)

120. Matsuhashi, M., Dietrich, C. P., and Gilbert, J. M., *Federation Proc.*, **24**, 607 (1965)

121. Schwarz, V., and Weidel, W., *Z. Naturforsch*, **20b**, 153 (1965)

122. Roze, V., and Strominger, J. L., *Mol. Pharmacol.*, **2**, 92 (1966)

123. Ashwell, G., *Ann. Rev. Biochem.*, **33**, 101 (1964)

124. Baddiley, J., *J. Roy. Inst. Chem.*, **86**, 366 (1962)

125. McCarty, M., *J. Exptl. Med.*, **109**, 361 (1959)

126. Juergens, W. E., Sanderson, A. R., and Strominger, J. L., *Bull. Soc. Chim. Biol.*, **42**, 1669 (1960)

127. Glaser, L., *Biochim. Biophys. Acta*, **71**, 237 (1963)

128. Burger, M. M., and Glaser, L., *J. Biol. Chem.*, **239**, 3168 (1964)

129. Nathenson, S. G., and Strominger, J. L. *J. Biol. Chem.*, **237**, 3839 (1962)

130. Nathenson, S. G., and Strominger,

J. L. *J. Biol. Chem.*, **238**, 3161 (1963)

131. Glaser, L., and Burger, M. M., *J. Biol. Chem.*, **239**, 3187 (1964)
132. Lipkin, D., Cook, W. H., and Markham, R., *J. Am. Chem. Soc.*, **81**, 6198 (1959)
133. Burger, M. M., and Glaser, L., *J. Biol. Chem.* (In press)
134. Archibald, A. R., Baddiley, J., and Button, D., *Biochem. J.*, **95**, 8c (1965)
135. Ghuysen, J.M., Tipper, D. J., and Strominger, J. L., *Biochemistry*, **4**, 474 (1965)
136. Glaser, L., *J. Biol. Chem.*, **239**, 3178 (1964)
137. Rogers, H. J., and Garitt, A. J., *Biochem. J.*, **88**, 6p (1963)
138. Glaser, L., *Biochim. Biophys. Acta*, **101**, 6 (1965)
139. Gunsalus, I. C., in *The Bacteria*, **II**, 48. (Gunsalus, I. C., and Stanier, R. Y., Eds., Academic Press, New York, 1962)
140. Sharon, N., *Ann. Rev. Biochem.*, **35**, 485 (1966)
141. Sigal, N. J., Cattaneo, J., and Sigal, I. H., *Arch. Biochem. Biophys.*, **108**, 440 (1964)
142. Mayer, H., Rapin, A. M. C., and Kalckar, H. M., *Proc. Natl. Acad. Sci. U.S.*, **53**, 459 (1965)
143. Recondo, E., and Leloir, L. F., *Biochem. Biophys. Res. Commun.*, **6**, 85 (1961)
144. Leloir, L. F., *Proc. Intern. Congr. Biochem., 6th*, **33**, 15 (1964)
145. Shen, L., Ghosh, H. P., Greenberg, E., and Preiss, J., *Biochim. Biophis. Acta*, **89**, 370 (1964)
146. Greenberg, E., and Preiss, J., *J. Biol. Chem.*, **239**, Pc 4314 (1964)
147. Ghosh, H. P., and Preiss, J., *Biochim. Biophys. Acta*, **104**, 274 (1965)
148. Preiss, J., and Greenberg, E., *Biochemistry*, **4**, 2328 (1965)
149. Greenberg, E., and Preiss, J., *J. Biol. Chem.*, **240**, 2341 (1965)
150. Zevenhuizen, L. P. T. M., *Biochim. Biophys. Acta*, **81**, 608 (1964)
151. Shen, L., and Preiss, J., *Biochem. Biophys. Res. Commun.*, **17**, 424 (1964)
152. Shen, L., and Preiss, J., *J. Biol. Chem.*, **240**, 2334 (1965)
153. Algranati, I. D., Carminatti, H., and Cabib, E., *Biochem. Biophys. Res. Commun.*, **12**, 504 (1963)
154. Carter, H. E., Johnson, P., and Weber, E. J., *Ann. Rev. Biochem.*, **34**, 109 (1965)
155. Houser, H. G., and Karnovsky, M. L., *J. Biol. Chem.*, **233**, 287 (1958)
156. Lennarz, W. J., *J. Biol. Chem.*, **239**, Pc 3110 (1964)
157. Reeves, R. E., Latour, N. G., and Lousteau, R. J., *Biochemistry*, **3**, 1248 (1964)
158. Burger, M., Glaser, L., and Burton, R. M., *Biochim. Biophys. Acta*, **56**, 172 (1962)
159. Burger, M., Glaser, L., and Burton, R. M., *J. Biol. Chem.*, **238**, 2595 (1963)
160. Barker, G. A., *Arch. Biochem. Biophys.*, **103**, 276 (1963)
161. Talamo, B., and Lennarz, W., *Federation Proc.*, **24**, 479 (1965)
162. Ginsburg, V., *Advan. Enzymol.*, **26**, 35 (1964)
163. Neufeld, E. F., and Hassid, W. Z., *Advan. Carbohydrate Chem.*, **18**, 309 (1963)
164. Wilson, D. B., and Hogness, D. S., *J. Biol. Chem.*, **239**, 2469 (1964)
165. Spyrides, G. J., and Kalckar, H. M., *Biochem. Biophys. Res. Commun.*, **3**, 306 (1960)
166. Preiss, J., Shen, L., and Ghosh, H. P., *Federation Proc.*, **24**, 478 (1965)
167. Ghosh, H. P., and Preiss, J., *Biochemistry*, **4**, 1354 (1965)
168. Pazur, J. H., and Anderson, J. S., *J. Biol. Chem.*, **238**, 3155 (1963)
169. Gilbert, J. M., Matsuhashi, M., and Strominger, J. L., *J. Biol. Chem.*, **240**, 1305 (1965)
170. Matsuhashi, M., Gilbert, J. M., Matsuhashi, S., Brown, J. G., and Strominger, J. L., *Biochem. Biophys. Res. Commun.*, **15**, 55 (1964)
171. Matsuhashi, M., and Strominger, J. L., *J. Biol. Chem.*, **239**, 2454 (1964)
172. Stevens, C. L., Blumbergs, P., Osterbach, D. H. O., Strominger, J. L., Matsuhashi, M., and Dietzler, D. N., *J. Am. Chem. Soc.*, **86**, 2937 (1964)
173. Wheat, R. W., Rollins, E. L., and Leatherwood, J. M., *Biochem. Biophys. Res. Commun.*, **9**, 120 (1962)
174. Volk, W. A., and Ashwell, G., *Biochem. Biophys. Res. Commun.*, **12**, 116 (1963)
175. Ashwell, G., and Volk, W. A., *J. Biol. Chem.*, **240**, 4549 (1965)
176. Matsuhashi, S., Matsuhashi, M., Brown, J. G., and Strominger, J. L.,

Biochem. Biophys. Res. Commun., **15**, 60 (1964)

177. Matsuhashi, S., *Federation Proc.*, **23**, 170 (1964)

178. Matsuhashi, S., and Strominger, J. L., *Biochem. Biophys. Res. Commun.*, **20**, 169 (1965)

179. Elbein, A. D., *Proc. Natl. Acad. Sci. U.S.*, **53**, 803 (1965)

180. Mayer, R. M., and Ginsburg, V., *J. Biol. Chem.*, **240**, 1900 (1965)

181. Kalckar, H. M., *Advan. Enzymol.*, **20**, 111 (1958)

182. Ginsburg, V., *J. Am. Chem. Soc.*, **80**, 4426 (1958)

183. Ginsburg, V., *J. Biol. Chem.*, **236**, 2389 (1961)

184. Heath, E. C., and Elbein, A. D., *Proc. Natl. Acad. Sci. U.S.*, **48**, 1209 (1962)

185. Elbein, A. D., *Federation Proc.*, **22**, 465 (1963)

186. Elbein, A. D., and Heath, E. C., *J. Biol. Chem.*, **240**, 1926 (1965)

187. Markovitz, A., *J. Biol. Chem.*, **239**, 2091 (1964)

188. Munch-Petersen, A., *Acta Chem. Scand.*, **10**, 928 (1956)

189. Preiss, J., and Wood, E., *J. Biol. Chem.*, **239**, 3119 (1964)

190. Preiss, J., *J. Biol. Chem.*, **239**, 3127 (1965)

191. Blumson, N. L., and Baddiley, J., *Biochem. J.*, **81**, 114 (1961)

192. Shaw, D. R. D., *Biochem. J.*, **82**, 297 (1962)

193. Nikaido, H., *Biochim. Biophys. Acta*, **48**, 460 (1961)

194. Nikaido, H., and Jokura, K., *Biochem. Biophys. Res. Commun.*, **6**, 304 (1961)

195. Kornfeld, S., Kornfeld, R., Neufeld, E. F., and O'Brien, P. J., *Proc. Natl. Acad. Sci. U.S.*, **52**, 371 (1964)

196. Bernstein, R. L., and Robbins, P. W., *J. Biol. Chem.*, **240**, 391 (1965)

197. Melo, A., and Glaser, L., *J. Biol. Chem.*, **240**, 398 (1965)

198. Kornfeld, R., and Ginsburg, V., *Federation Proc.*, **24**, 536 (1965)

199. Kornfeld, R., and Ginsburg, V., *Biochim. Biophys. Acta*, **117**, 79 (1966)

200. Okazaki, T., Strominger, J. L., and Okazaki, R. O., *J. Bacteriol.*, **86**, 118 (1963)

201. Smith, E. E. B., Mills, G. T., Bernheimer, H. P., and Austrian, R., *J. Gen. Microbiol.*, **20**, 654 (1959)

202. Mills, G. T., and Smith, E. E. B., *Brit. Med. Bull.*, **18**, 27 (1962)

203. Stocker, B. A. D., and Wilkinson, R. G., *Ann. N.Y. Acad. Sci.* (In press)

204. Mäkelä, P. H., *J. Gen. Microbiol.*, **41**, 57 (1965)

INTERFERON[1]

By Samuel Baron, M.D., and Hilton B. Levy, Ph.D.

National Institute of Allergy and Infectious Diseases, Laboratory of Biology
of Viruses, National Institutes of Health, Bethesda, Maryland

Contents

Introduction.. 291
Induction of Interferon... 291
   Control by host cell genome............................... 291
   Conditions needed for interferon synthesis............... 292
   Other inducers and different molecular species of interferon................. 293
Action of Interferon.. 296
   Reported effects of interferon on uninfected cells....... 296
   Induction of the antiviral state in cells exposed to interferon............... 297
   Mechanism of antiviral action............................ 300
   Nonheritable interferon resistance among viruses......... 303
   *Other aspects of pretreatment with interferon on subsequent production of
interferon*.. 303
   Antiviral effect of interferon in heterologous cells..... 305
Steroid Hormones and Interferons............................... 307
   Effect of steroid hormones on interferon production...... 307
   Effect of steroid hormones on interferon action......... 307
Phylogenetic Occurrence of the Interferon System............... 307
Interferon and Viremia... 308
   Protection of target organs by circulating interferon.... 309
   Control of viremia by circulating interferon............ 309
   Formation and eliminaton of circulating interferon...... 310
Interferon and Viral Oncogenesis............................... 311
   Prophylaxis and therapy of virus diseases............... 311
Conclusions and Summary.. 312

Introduction

Knowledge in many areas concerning interferon has markedly increased since the last review of interferon in this series (1). The major advances have occurred in the understanding of the mechanism of production of interferon, the characteristics of the interferon molecules, the mechanism of antiviral action of interferon, and the role of interferon during virus infections of animals. This review will consider these important developments with emphasis on those areas about which the authors are most familiar as outlined in the listed contents.

Induction of Interferon

Control by host cell genome.—Three observations suggest that the information for the synthesis of interferon resides in host cell DNA: (a) the high

[1] The survey of the literature pertaining to this review was concluded in April 1966.

degree of cell specificity of the antiviral action of interferon; (*b*) the similarity of the interferon produced regardless of the inducing virus; and (*c*) the lack of immunological relationship between viral proteins and interferon (2). Evidence of a more biochemical nature has been obtained through the use of actinomycin D, which is known to inhibit DNA-controlled RNA synthesis (3, 4). This inhibitor blocks the synthesis of interferon in virus-infected cells, both in tissue culture and *in vivo* (5–10) However, host DNA synthesis is not needed for interferon production (11, 12). By adding actinomycin D at varying times postinfection, it has been possible to determine the time at which interferon production is no longer sensitive to it. This has been equated with the time when messenger RNA for interferon synthesis has been made. Wagner (7), working with Newcastle disease (NDV) virus infection of mouse tumor cells has shown this to be about six hours postinfection. Levy (8), using Chikungunya virus in chick embryo tissue culture has shown that interferon messenger RNA begins to be made about 1.5 to 2 hours post infection, (just shortly before interferon can be detected in the medium), and is maximally formed by 2.5 hours after infection (6).

The finding that inhibition of cellular RNA synthesis blocks interferon production may explain why certain viruses are poor inducers of interferon production. For example, virulent poliovirus, which ordinarily inhibits cellular RNA synthesis, is a poor inducer of interferon, but the attenuated RMC strain of polio-virus leads to its production (13). Also, it has been shown that strains of herpes simplex virus that inhibit RNA synthesis are poor inducers of interferon as compared to those that do not inhibit cellular RNA synthesis (14). Vesicular stomatitis virus is also able to turn off cellular RNA synthesis (15) and interferon production. Apparently, in this case, the input virus itself contains something that inhibits cell RNA synthesis, as contrasted with other agents, such as Mengo virus or poliovirus, that require the early synthesis of a virus-coded protein for this inhibition. There are, however, cytocidal viruses that do induce interferon formation. It would be desirable to examine their effect on cell RNA synthesis before generalizing on this point. Possibly one factor that determines virulence in a virus is this ability to switch off cellular RNA synthesis, and thus prevent interferon formation. The herpes simplex strain dk$^+$, which grows in dog kidney cells, is not an interferon inducer and does cut off cellular RNA, while the dk$^-$ strain does not cut off RNA synthesis rapidly, does induce interferon, and fails to grow. Since both RNA and protein synthesis are necessary for the production of interferon and the antiviral state, comparable considerations might very well apply to cell systems in which protein synthesis is blocked by virus infection.

Conditions needed for interferon synthesis.—The need for active metabolism on the part of infected cells to produce interferon was shown long ago (16). Studies using the protein inhibitors puromycin and fluorophenylalanine showed that active synthesis of new protein was needed (17). These observations complement the need for new RNA synthesis mentioned above, and further established the idea that induction of interferon by virus infection represents a derepression of a normally repressed cell genome function. (See, however, *Other inducers and different molecular species of interferon* for exceptions to this idea.) However, maximum rates of protein synthesis are not necessary for interferon production and, under some conditions, can actually decrease the amount of interferon produced (18).

Other inducers and different molecular species of interferon.—A number of nonviral substances have been reported to lead to the appearance of interferon-like substances. These are nucleic acids (19), statolon (20), cycloheximide (9), bacterial endotoxin (9, 10, 21, 22), hellenine (23), phytohemagglutinin (24), LB-1 TRIC virus (25), mycoplasma (26), rickettsia (27), and bacteria (28).

It was suggested that interferon is induced by, and as a defense against, the intrusion of nucleic acids heterologous to the cell because it had been found that the introduction of heterologous nucleic acids led to the development of resistance of tissue culture cells to subsequent virus infection (19, 29), and small amounts of an interferon-like substance were detected in the tissue culture medium. Analogous results were obtained by Jensen et al. (30) who, in addition, showed that mice treated with yeast and other nucleic acids became resistant to infection by encephalomyocarditis and influenza viruses, and demonstrated an interferon-like material in the lungs of such animals (31). However, since other studies have not regularly yielded comparable results, and since interferon can be induced by the polysaccharide statolon, Isaacs has suggested reconsideration of the role of heterologous nucleic acids as inducers of interferon (32). Two reports have appeared dealing with the effect of purine and pyrimidine bases on virus growth and interferon production (33, 34). Both show that adenine derivatives, in particular, inhibit virus growth. One worker (33) believes that this inhibition does not involve interferon production, the other (34) thinks that it possibly may. The need for careful characterization of viral inhibitors is pertinent here. Noninterferon inhibitors of vaccinia virus have led to possible misinterpretations in the past (35). For further consideration of this point see the section on *"Antiviral effect of interferon in heterologous cells."* At the present time, the generalization that heterologous nucleic acids induce interferon formation must be regarded as not yet established.

It has been demonstrated that stimulation of cells with statolon, an impure anionic polysaccharide derived from *Penicillium stoloniferum*, results in the production of interferon (20). Within 24 hours after injection into mice, this material leads to the presence in the serum of a viral inhibitor meeting the usual characterization of interferon. This nonviral inducer can also lead to the production of interferon by chick embryo and mouse embryo tissue culture (36). However, it can also induce a strong resistance to virus infection in chick embryo cell cultures with no detectable interferon formation (37–39).

Until recently, the term interferon was applied to proteins produced by cells upon infection with viruses, and having a molecular weight of 25–30×

TABLE I

COMPARISON OF DIFFERENT STIMULI ON APPEARANCE AND PROPERTIES
OF CIRCULATING INTERFERON IN MICE

Stimulus producing circulating interferon after intravenous injection of mice	Molecular weight of interferon (Sephadex G-100)	Time maximum in plasma (hours)	Inhibited by blockade of protein synthesis	Inhibited by pre-treatment with E. coli endotoxin	Enhanced by BCG infection
Viruses					
NDV	25,000	8–12	+	+(95%)	0
Bacteria and products					
Brucella abortus	77,000; 54,000	6–12	+	+(100%)	0
Salmonella typhimurium		2	0	+(100%)	
Serratia marcescens		2	0	+(100%)	
E. coli endotoxin	89,000	2	0	+(100%)	+
B. abortus endotoxin		2	0	+(100%)	
Mold products					
Statolon (Penicillium)	90,000[a]	8	0	0	0
Cycloheximide (Streptomyces)	(41,000)[b]	12	0	+(80%)	0
Acetoxycyloheximide (Streptomyces)		12	0		

[a] Merigan and Kleinschmidt: personal communication.
[b] Preliminary results.

10^8. It was characterized by requiring cell mediation for antiviral effect by being stable between pH 2–10, by being species-specific, trypsin-sensitive, nonsedimentable at 100,000 g for several hours, and by being active against a broad group of viruses. In addition, it was considered that the material was newly synthesized (2), requiring both RNA (5–8) and protein synthesis for its formation (2, 40). With the discovery of the nonviral inducers of interferon, it was found that some of the materials meeting the above characteristics of interferon had a range of molecular weights from 20,000 to 100,000.

Table I, which was prepared by Drs. Youngner, Hallum & Stinebring (41), summarizes current information about the action and properties of the different interferon inducers as they work *in vivo* in mice. Similar information has been developed for some of these inducers in rabbits (10, 22). At first it was thought that viruses induced the 30,000 molecular weight interferon, and that nonviral inducers, exemplified by endotoxin, led to the release of a high molecular weight preformed interferon (See Table I, column 2). However, statolon leads to the synthesis of a 30,000 molecular weight interferon in tissue culture, and the release of a heavy species of interferon molecule into the circulation of animals (42). Even more confusing is the finding (42) that the spleens of mice treated with statolon contain a 30,000 molecular weight interferon. Phytohemagglutinin induces the formation, in explanted white blood cells, of an 18,000 molecular weight interferon (43). Thus, in animals, interferons of a wide range of sizes can be produced by stimulation with both viral and nonviral inducers. In tissue culture, however, only light interferons have been detected. It would appear that the distinction between viral and nonviral inducers, on the basis of molecular weight of interferon, is not a clear one, if it exists at all. Whether the interferons of different molecular weights may be related to each other as, for example, by being different sized polymers of some subunit, or by having an active structure attached to different carrier proteins, remains to be determined. Whether these different sized inhibitors should all retain the name "interferon" is not yet clear. Possibly the name should be applied to all only if they can ultimately be shown to inhibit viral growth by the same mechanism.

It will be noted in Table I, column 4, that endotoxin-induced release of high molecular weight interferon into the serum is not inhibited in mice treated with cycloheximide to inhibit protein synthesis (9). Similar results have been obtained with rabbits treated with inhibitors of RNA and protein synthesis (22). This suggests that this interferon is not produced in the same way as virus-induced interferon, i.e., the endotoxin-induced interferon does not require the synthesis of a new mRNA or protein (9). It should be noted that endotoxin leads to the presence of interferon in the serum of animals but does not induce its synthesis in tissue culture (10, 21). These results have been interpreted as indicating that the interferon released in animals upon treatment with endotoxin is not newly formed but rather was preformed, conceivably remaining from a previous infection. A less likely possibility is that a few cells *in vivo* are not affected by the metabolic inhibitors and it is these cells which synthesize the endotoxin-induced interferon.

The time of maximum appearance of interferon in the serum after inoculation of the inducer (Table I, column 3) shows that peak levels are reached earliest for those interferons which cannot be blocked by inhibitors of protein synthesis. The early appearance of these interferons is consistent with the idea that they are preformed. Postic & Ho (43a) have shown in rabbits that the appearance of endotoxin-induced interferon, as well as that induced by NDV, are both inhibited by cortisone. It is not clear what meaning this finding has with regard to the concept of preformed interferon. The demonstration that preformed interferon probably exists in the intact animal and can be rapidly released by endotoxin treatment, raised the possibility that the earliest interferon response by infected animals may be such a release. In this connection, it was observed that inhibition of protein synthesis in the mouse did not completely inhibit the early appearance of circulating interferon after intravenous injection of Newcastle disease virus (9). This finding favors the idea that at least part of the early appearing interferon which occurs during viremia is derived from preformed material. The molecular size of this early appearing interferon is 45,000. Additional studies will be necessary to determine finally whether preformed interferon is the source of the animal's first interferon response to virus infection.

There are several observations which indicate that interferon in mouse serum may originate at different sites depending upon the stimulus. Pretreatment of mice with endotoxin inhibits the subsequent appearance of interferon by all the stimuli listed, except statolon (39) (Table I, column 5). Also, preinfection of mice with Bacille Calmette Guérin (BCG) (44) enhances only that interferon which results from endotoxin stimulation (Table I, column 6). These findings indicate that the *in vivo* site of origin of interferon may vary and may depend upon the stimulus (39).

Although interferons resulting from various stimuli manifest certain differences, there are no reported differences in their gross ability to inhibit multiplication of virus. It remains to be determined whether the specific steps which lead to the antiviral state are the same following treatment with the different interferons.

The interferons discussed above generally manifest the accepted properties defining interferon, but a few exceptions have been noted (22) and require further study.

ACTION OF INTERFERON

The exact mechanism by which interferon inhibits virus growth is still not known, but evidence has accumulated to indicate that (*a*) the action affects a very early event in the course of viral replication; (*b*) the interferon molecule itself may not be the actual antiviral substance, but may be the agent leading to the synthesis of a different substance which is antiviral. Both of these points will be discussed after reconsideration of some earlier hypotheses concerning the action of interferon.

Reported effects of interferon on uninfected cells.—Experiments with unpurified preparations suggested (45) that interferon may act by uncoupling nuclear oxidative phosphorylation. However, it was subsequently observed that appropriate amounts of dinitrophenol could cause strong uncoupling of oxidative phosphorylation without affecting virus production, and that levels of interferon which strongly inhibited virus growth did not affect a variety of energy-requiring processes, both nuclear and cytoplasmic (46). Beloff-Chain et al. similarly have shown that interferon has no effect on glucose oxidation by chick embryo cells. They attributed a slight increase in aerobic glycolysis observed after treatment with interferon to an impurity in the preparation (47). Finally, partially purified interferon was found to have no effect on cell glycolysis (48). It may reasonably be concluded that a general uncoupling of cellular oxidative phosphorylation, whether nuclear or cytoplasmic, does not explain interferon action.

Several reports have indicated that interferon affects nucleic acid synthesis in uninfected cells. Cocito et al. (49) reported that crude preparations of interferon inhibit the synthesis of proteins and nucleic acids in rat cells. They re-examined (50) these observations with preparations of rat interferon that had been purified by diethylaminoethanol cellulose and carboxy-methyl cellulose columns, with similar results. However, a comparably prepared extract from uninfected cells, without antiviral action, showed as much, if not more inhibition of macromolecule synthesis than did the interferon preparation. These authors suggest that the protein from uninfected cells may be associated with normal cell regulatory properties. Sonnabend (51) found that slow labeling of RNA was inhibited in uninfected cells treated with interferon. While the published report deals with partially purified interferon, he has obtained similar results with a more purified preparation (52). Levy et al. earlier had also found a similar effect on uninfected cells, using a crude preparation of interferon (46). Recently, Levy & Merigan found no effect of high levels of purified interferon on the concentrations of RNA, DNA, or protein in growing uninfected chick embryo cells, or on the rate of incorporation of valine into protein, or of uridine into rapidly or slowly labeled RNA (53). Control experiments performed simultaneously showed that these interferon-treated cells were highly resistant to virus growth. In view of these latest results, it may be concluded that gross inhibition of cellular macromolecule synthesis is not the mechanism of action of interferon, and that reported inhibition may have been attributable to contaminating materials found in normal cell extracts (50).

The literature also contains conflicting reports concerning the effect of interferon on cell multiplication. It has been reported that interferon preparations inhibit the multiplication of mouse L cells in culture (54). However, others have shown that treatment with interferon did not decrease the number of cultured chick embryo cells in mitosis (55), and did not affect multiplication of human thyroid cells in culture (56). Partial resolution of these differences of effect of interferon preparations on cell multiplication comes from the findings that many preparations of interferon contain a noninterferon inhibitor of cell growth and multiplication (57) as well as the noninterferon inhibitor of cellular DNA and RNA synthesis mentioned above (50). Consistent with the finding of inhibition of cell multiplication by noninterferon components of certain preparations of interferon is the lack of effect of partially purified chicken interferon on cell multiplication and cell DNA and protein synthesis (53, 57). On the whole, the available evidence does not favor the view that interferon affects cell growth or multiplication.

A quantitatively small or subtle effect of interferon on uninfected cells cannot be excluded by the procedures reported. That interferon almost certainly exercises such an effect is indicated by the indirect biochemical evidence that treatment of uninfected cells with interferon leads to the synthesis of a distinct antiviral substance. (See next section).

Induction of the antiviral state in cells exposed to interferon.—It was early observed that cells treated with interferon had to be incubated at 37° C for several hours before developing full resistance to virus growth. Incubation at 4° C was only minimally effective (16, 58). It was generally agreed that this meant that metabolic activity was needed for the manifestation of interferon's antiviral action, and that, therefore, this action was intracellular.

Taylor (59) noted that actinomycin D blocked the development of anti-

viral activity in cells treated with interferon and concluded that DNA-directed RNA synthesis was needed for this. She also said, but did not document
the statement, that fluorophenylalanine (FPA), an inhibitor of protein synthesis, also prevented the antiviral action of interferon. The documentation
which was presented subsequently (60) showed that FPA inhibited the development of interferon action when the interferon was added to cells together with the FPA, but not when interferon was added 5 hours before the
FPA. These findings are in accord with those reported independently by
Lockart (61) and Levine (62).

These data are consistent with the concept that the direct effect of interferon, like that of the virus that induced its formation, is to derepress a host
genome action, leading to the formation of a new mRNA and the protein for
which this mRNA is encoded. According to this concept, this new protein
would be the effective antiviral substance. It should be pointed out that the
available data would also allow the hypothesis that the antiviral substance
could be an RNA. Using the latter interpretation, treatment of a cell with interferon would first augment the synthesis of a protein that would derepress
the host cell to make antiviral RNA. It should be noted that neither of these
hypothesized substances has been demonstrated to be the actual antiviral
substance and it is conceivable that they in turn might lead to the formation
of further substances. The advantage to an animal of an antiviral substance
distinct from the interferon molecule, would be that very little interferon
from an infected cell could induce a large quantity of an antiviral substance
in a second cell. A great amplification of the protective action of interferon
could thus be obtained. That there is a need for amplification is indicated by
the recent observations that very little, if any, interferon is taken up from the
medium when this is used to render tissue culture cells resistant to virus
growth (63, 64) (also see below).

In argument against the hypothesized antiviral substance, it has been
suggested that the new protein that is made is actually more interferon at the
intracellular site of virus inhibition. This view cannot be completely excluded
except by the actual separation of a different protein with demonstrable antiviral properties. However, the circumstantial arguments against the hypothesized new protein being more interferon are the following: 1. cells treated
with interferon do not produce detectable amounts of interferon unless
challenged by virus (2, 65); 2. this hypothesis would require either (a)
that interferon acts as a template for an RNA which would make new interferon, a requirement that goes against all current ideas of how proteins are
made, or (b) that interferon acts as its own inducer, a type of phenomenon
which, to the best of our knowledge has never been noted.

Another alternative explanation is that interferon needs, in order to
exert its action, the continued presence of an unstable protein which is always
present in the cell, and which is coded for by an unstable messenger RNA.
According to this idea, the addition of actinomycin blocks the formation of
this unstable RNA and protein, and so interferon cannot exert its antiviral

action. This possibility can be eliminated by recalling the sequence of events used to demonstrate the need for RNA synthesis to establish the antiviral state. If actinomycin is added with the interferon, the antiviral state is not developed in the treated cells. However, if interferon is allowed to interact with the cells for a few hours, then the development of the antiviral state becomes independent of subsequent addition of actinomycin, showing that the mRNA needed has already been made by the time actinomycin was added, and exhibited a reasonable degree of stability, since the antiviral state persisted for many hours even after actinomycin had been added.

As detailed above, the observations that the establishment of antiviral activity within cells exposed to interferon requires synthesis of RNA and polypeptides strongly suggests that interferon induces cells to produce a new antiviral substance. Although the biochemical data for this interpretation are indirect, the concept that interferon induces the formation of the actual antiviral material seems to be consistent with several biological findings.

It has been observed that no interferon, or at most, an undetectably small amount of it, is irreversibly taken up by cells during the period of induction of the antiviral state (63, 64). These studies have shown that there was no detectable diminution of mouse or chicken interferon in fluids surrounding cultures of homologous cells when concentrations of interferon and volumes of interferon-containing fluid in relation to the number of cells were varied, and such fluids were serially transferred through as many as eight cell cultures.

Supporting evidence that little or no interferon is irreversibly taken up by cells comes from the finding that the level of antiviral activity of cultured mouse embryo and L cells is dependent upon the concentration of interferon and independent of the total amount (63, 64). If interferon is largely absorbed and the amount taken up determines the degree of antiviral activity, then the addition of larger volumes of the same concentration of interferon would result in the availability of more total interferon which in turn would induce more antiviral activity. These observations are consistent with the concept that little or no binding of interferon occurs.

Further evidence comes from the finding that the antiviral state of cultures of mouse embryo cells remains constant as long as the applied interferon is left in contact with the cells (66, 67). If large amounts of interferon were irreversibly taken up by cells, the level of antiviral activity would fall, since experimental removal of the applied interferon is followed by gradual loss of the antiviral state (2, 67). Since the observed level of antiviral activity did not decrease during exposure to interferon, the major portion of the interferon could not have been bound to the cells as rapidly as had been previously reported (16, 68–71).

Possible explanations for most of the previous reports of a loss of interferon from cell culture fluids include its nonspecific adsorption to containers and cells, inactivation, and variability of the assay system. The finding that purified, and therefore less stable, interferon is more rapidly lost from culture fluids is thought to be consistent with these interpretations (72). The reported uptake of more than 90 per cent of applied interferon by chick embryo cells (68) is more difficult to explain. The presence of live virus in the interferon preparation used complicates the interpretation of this report.

Lack of detectable uptake of interferon suggests at least two possible ways in which interferon could react with cells to produce an antiviral effect: (a) it could act in a catalytic manner, not being consumed, but stimulating a change in the cell which leads to the antiviral state, or (b) an undetectably small amount of interferon could enter into combination with cell components to produce an antiviral effect. Available information does not permit a choice between these possibilities, nor does it indicate whether exogenous interferon enters cells. However, since relatively few molecules of interferon have been estimated to be needed for induction of antiviral activity (72), both possible mechanisms would seem to require amplification of the interferon effect on the cell. The concept that interferon induces cells to produce a new antiviral substance could satisfy the requirement for such amplification.

Implicit in the observation that little or no interferon is taken up by cells is the possibility that interferon reacts with cells to initiate a process which may not require the continued presence of interferon to produce the antiviral substance. Cells may be reacted with interferon under conditions of too short duration or too low a temperature to permit development of the antiviral state. If the interferon is removed from these treated cultures and the cells further incubated at 37° C, then there is a partial development of antiviral activity (38, 58, 64, 67, 73). These findings support the concept that reaction of cells with interferon initiates a process which precedes the steps leading to antiviral activity, and that the initiation process may continue to function for a limited time after the removal of interferon. It remains to be determined whether the persisting process is the continued action of a relatively stable messenger RNA for the proposed antiviral substance, or the continued derepression of the cistron for that messenger RNA.

Taken together these findings suggest the hypothesis that the extracellular concentration of interferon directly or indirectly exert a continuing effect on the intracellular level of the antiviral substance. Preliminary experiments indicate that the level of the antiviral material results from an equilibrium between its continued induction by interferon and its equally rapid decay (66,67). This hypothesis is under active study. The proposed antiviral material may also explain the observations that virus interference (antiviral activity of infected cells) can occur in the absence of detectable interferon (74, 75), and that interference is manifested by cells which are nevertheless resistant to exogenous interferon (76, 77). Both of these results may be due to the production of only the final antiviral substance. However, experimental test of this possibility is necessary.

Mechanism of antiviral action.—The action of interferon has been shown by several laboratories to occur at an early stage of virus replication, and during the past few years evidence has pushed this back to an event earlier and earlier in the course of viral growth. It was shown originally that interferon does not combine with virus (68,78), or with viral nucleic acid (79, 80). The recognition of the antiviral component of the interferon system now makes it desirable to determine whether the actual antiviral substance combines with viral RNA. For convenience in this article, we have referred to the action of interferon when more precise terminology would probably require reference to the action of an antiviral substance.

Interferon prevents the synthesis of new viral nucleic acid. This has been shown for several virus-cell systems (81–83). Montagnier & Sanders (84) reported that late in the development of encephalomyocarditis virus there is found an RNA that is less dense than viral RNA, resists ribonuclease action, exhibits a sharp melting temperature, and migrates in sucrose gradients as a 16S component. Comparable material has been found for RNA bacteriophage (85–90), and for poliovirus (91). This RNA has been thought to be a double-stranded replicative form, important in the reproduction of RNA viruses. A 16S, ribonuclease-resistant fraction has been found with Semliki Forest virus, as early as 2 hours after infection. Its formation is blocked by interferon (92). Gordon et al. (93) have found also that interferon blocks the formation of 16S RNA in the Mengo virus L cell system, 5 to 7 hours postinfection. An even earlier effect of interferon can be seen in cell systems where virus infection leads to an early turn-off of a high endogenous cellular RNA synthesis. Infection of exponentially growing L cells by Mengo virus has been shown by Franklin & Baltimore (94) to lead to a rapid decrease in cellular RNA synthesis. Within an hour after infection, the rate of RNA synthesis is down to 50 per cent of uninfected controls. About 3 to 4 hours postinfection, a short-lived rise in RNA synthesis is seen, which is attributable to the synthesis of viral RNA. In cells pretreated with interferon, the secondary rise in RNA synthesis is not seen, indicating that viral RNA is not made (82, 95). In addition, the cut-off of cellular RNA synthesis is delayed by an hour (82). In the infected cells, the synthesis of cellular protein is also shut off, but interferon has no effect on this shut-off even though viral replication is reduced by 99 to 99.9 per cent. It is possible that the cut-off of RNA synthesis that does eventually ensue, even in the interferon-treated cells, is merely a reflection of the fact that protein sysnthesis had been cut off an hour earlier. Comparable effects of interferon on RNA cut-off have been seen in Sindbis virus growing in suspended chick embryo cells (96). Thus, an antiviral effect of the interferon system can be detected within 1 hour after infection by certain viruses.

Another early expression of viral infection is the rise in thymidine kinase seen in cells infected with Pox viruses (97, 98). Two groups of workers (99, 100) have reported that this early manifestation of pox virus infection is prevented by interferon treatment. This can be taken as another example of the widespread inhibition of viral activities shown by interferon. Barban & Baron (101) find, in agreement with these data, that the virus-induced rise in thymidine kinase in chick cells is blocked by interferon, but they also find that the similar rise in infected mouse embryo tissue culture is not inhibited even though virus growth is inhibited. Of particular interest in this chick embryo study is the fact that when synthesis of new virus DNA was blocked by either bromdeoxyuridine or cytosine arabinoside, the persisting rise in thymidine kinase was still blocked by interferon. The apparent meaning of this observation is not only that the enzyme rise is attributable to an effect of input virus DNA as has been reported (102), but also that interferon acts upon an effect of the input virus DNA.

The early increase in cytoplasmic RNA synthesis, attributable to the input virus DNA seen in vaccinia-infected cells (103), is also reported to be prevented by pretreatment with interferon (100).

Further evidence that the antiviral action of interferon is directed against an event specified by the original input virus is that interferon inhibits SV 40 virus-induced transformation (104) and T-antigen formation (105) in mouse 3T3 cells. Both transformation and T-antigen formation can occur in this system even though virus replication does take place.

Still other experiments which indicate that interferon acts early in the course of virus infection, were done with Chikungunya virus (65). An early effect of this virus on a host cell function is the induction of the synthesis of interferon and its mRNA within less than 2 hours after infection (8). If the cells were treated with interferon prior to stimulation by virus, newly produced interferon and its mRNA were detected an hour earlier than in cells not pretreated with interferon. These observations indicate an effect of interferon on an event determined by virus less than 1 hour after infection (65).

All of the foregoing evidence indicates that, at least in the systems examined, interferon has an effect either on the input virus or on a very early manifestation of the input virus. That this may indeed be the case, is suggested by two different types of observations. Using purified Semliki Forest virus labeled with H^3 uridine in RNA, Levy & Friedman (106) found that the input virus RNA was incorporated into a so-called double-stranded RNA with sedimentation value of 18 to 22S. This occurred within 1.5 hours of infection with the labeled virus, and was prevented by interferon. Recent observations (107) indicate that two enzymes are involved in the replication of the RNA of bacteriophage f2. One is concerned with the conversion of the single-stranded parental RNA into a double-strand, and the other uses the double-strand to synthesize new viral RNA. If the replication of RNA-containing animal viruses also involves these two types of enzymatic actions then the blockage by interferon is at or precedes the action of the first enzyme. The second set of experiments indicating that the fate of the input virus is different in interferon-treated cells from control cells, was obtained with labeled Mengo virus. With this virus, the early incorporation of the parental viral RNA into a 16S form could not clearly be demonstrated. More positively, it was found that the labeled Mengo virus RNA was found associated, at 45 minutes after infection, with a 40S subribosomal particle in control cells, but not in interferon-treated cells (108). The association of rapidly labeled RNA with subribosomal particles has been seen with mRNA in liver cells (109), in HeLa cells (110), and with the mRNA generated by vaccinia virus in HeLa cells (111). In control-infected cells, the subribosomal particle plus Mengo RNA subsequently builds up a large 450–500S polysome, presumably the functional unit used to synthesize viral components, which still contains the input radioactive viral RNA. This large polysome is not seen in interferon-treated cells (108). Interferon, therefore, may inhibit the early association of the viral RNA with a subribosomal unit, and thus inhibit the subsequent synthesis of viral components. Whether this inhibition is a direct action of the interferon system, or is a reflection of a still earlier event, remains to be determined.

There has been observed an inhibition by interferon of viral-induced, RNA-primed, RNA polymerase, in a cell-free preparation. It has been reported that a crude interferon preparation inhibited the enzymatic action of a relatively crude polymerase (112). A certain amount of species specificity was demonstrated, in that interferons from species heterologous to the cells that were the source of enzyme exerted less inhibitory effect than did interferons from homologous cells. The extent of species crossing in the biochemical tests was surprisingly high for interferon, considering the high species specificity for antiviral action. It is hard to reconcile these observations with the current concepts that interferon itself is not the active antiviral material. A repetition of these experiments with more complete controls and with purified interferon would be desirable.

At the present time, the available evidence suggests that the antiviral component of the interferon system inhibits virus replication at an early stage of infection which follows uncoating of virus and precedes formation of viral polysomes. In at least certain systems, the antiviral substance may lead to a defect in the association of viral messenger RNA with a ribosomal subunit, thus inhibiting synthesis of new viral components.

Nonheritable interferon resistance among viruses.—A form of resistance to interferon which is difficult to explain with presently available information has been reported for certain virus-cell systems (113, 114). It was found that a fraction of several virus populations varying from 0.1 per cent to 15 per cent of the input virus, was capable of multiplying and producing plaques in interferon-treated cultures (113). The resistance to interferon of this "persistent fraction" was not due to a genetic property of the virus, and superficially resembled similar phenomena observed in the case of other virus-inhibiting agents. The magnitude of the "persistent fraction" depended on the virus type of cell, and cellular environment. Perhaps the underlying mechanism of this resistance will become clear when the biochemical action of the proposed antiviral component of the interferon system is determined.

Other aspects of pretreatment with interferon on subsequent production of interferon.—Pretreatment of cultured chick embryo cells with interferon has been reported by several laboratories to enhance production of interferon when the cells were subsequently induced by virus infection (38, 65, 115, 116). Not only was the final titer of interferon increased but it was produced more quickly as was its messenger RNA (38,65). In contrast, some studies have shown that pretreatment of cells with interferon decreased its production by virus-infected cells (58, 116-118). Partial resolution of these apparently conflicting findings may come from the observation that whereas pretreatment of cultured chick embryo cells with small amounts of interferon resulted in enhancement of subsequent production, pretreatment with large amounts had the reverse effect (38, 116). In contrast to this biphasic response by chick embryo cells, enhancement of interferon production was not observed when mouse L cells were pretreated with small amounts of interferon and then induced with Newcastle disease virus (118). However, pretreatment with increased amounts of interferon did decrease subsequent production. That the lack of enhancement is not a function of the mouse species comes from the finding of enhancement of a mouse cell Herpes simplex system (117). Recent studies suggest that the inhibitory effect of large amounts of interferon preparations may be attributed, at least in part, to a substance other than interferon present in the crude preparations used (216).

Further clarification of the enhancement of interferon production following pretreatment with small amounts of interferon comes from Friedman's study of the cultured chick embryo cell-Chikungunya virus system (38). Enhancement occurred when cells were pretreated with small amounts of interferon and then induced by inoculation of a suboptimal dose of heat-inactivated Chikungunya virus. The resulting amount of interferon was equal to that produced by cells induced with a larger and optimal dose of virus, but not pretreated with interferon. This finding suggests the possibility that pretreatment with a small amount of interferon may lead to enhancement by converting a suboptimal stimulation by virus into a more optimal stimulus for interferon production. These experiments deserve extension to other cell-virus systems.

An observation which may be partly explained by the findings concerning enhancement is that pretreatment of chick embryo cells with inactivated Group A arboviruses enhances subsequent interferon production when infectious virus is used as the inducer (119, 120). Inactivated virus alone does not induce the formation of detectable interferon. If the inactivated arbovirus induces the production of the antiviral component of the interferon system, then the antiviral substance may serve as the enhancer. It would therefore be important to determine whether these inactivated viruses induce the antiviral state of the interferon system without inducing production of interferon.

The underlying mechanism by which pretreatment with interferon may result in enhancement or inhibition of subsequent interferon production, may be either through an effect on cellular processes or an effect on an event specified by inducing virus. The available evidence does not permit a clear choice between these alternatives but certain experimental findings point out specific steps in the processes of enhancement or inhibition of interferon production. In the chick embryo-Chikungunya virus system, establishment of the enhancing effect of interferon requires new protein synthesis (38), as does establishment of the antiviral effect of interferon. This finding suggests that production of the proposed antiviral substance may be linked with enhancement as well as being necessary for antiviral activity.

In the mouse L cell-Newcastle disease virus system, pretreatment with interferon inhibits the subsequent production of interferon. When the polysaccharide, statolon, was substituted for virus as the inducing agent in interferon-treated cells, no inhibition of subsequent production of interferon was found (118). This indicates that the process by which statolon induces production of interferon in tissue culture differs in part from the process by which virus does this. It has been pointed out that this type of study should be carefully controlled to exclude the influence of contaminants of the crude interferon preparations (121).

There may be a similar basis for the observations that tissue cultures and animals which have yielded interferon after induction by virus and endotoxin may not yield again for a period of time following restimulation by virus, endotoxin, or bacteria (44, 122–124). The experiments *in vivo* are more difficult to interpret than those done in tissue culture because interferon in animals may come from several sources. Circulating interferon may be newly produced or it may be preformed, as indicated by studies with metabolic inhibitors (see *Other inducers and different molecular species of interferon*). Furthermore, newly produced and preformed interferon may originate from different cell populations or different subcellular sites within the intact animal (39). Thus, the presence or absence of refractoriness of animals to restimulation of interferon may reflect several independent variables, including different cell populations as well as different intracellular mechanisms. An example of another *in vivo* factor is the refractoriness of rabbits to restimulation of interferon production by endotoxin. That this inhibition may have an entirely different cause comes from the reported detection of a circulating inhibitor of endotoxin in the serum of refractory rabbits (123, 125). However, the serum inhibitor appears to be specific for the endotoxin system and would not explain refractoriness to restimulation by virus.

The enhanced or inhibited response following reaction with small or large amounts of interferon bears a superficial resemblance to the similar effects of the prior presence of small or large amounts of antibody *in vivo*. Enhancement or inhibition of interferon production may have important implications for host defences against virus infection, as does analogous enhancement or inhibition of antibody production.

Antiviral effect of interferon in heterologous cells.—The property of species specificity of interferon was first reported by Tyrrell (126) when he showed that calf and chick interferon failed to induce antiviral activity on heterologous cells. This unusual property of these antiviral proteins, that of exhibiting their strongest activity on homologous cells, has been demonstrated for interferons prepared in many different cell types (19, 68, 126–136). However, the barrier against heterologous activity has not always been reported to be absolute [reviewed by Isaacs (2)]. Some reports of heterologous activity of chick and mouse interferon (31, 137) differ with other findings of a strong barrier between these species (138, 139).

More recent studies have demonstrated that mouse serum interferon exhibits about one-twentieth of its antiviral activity on phylogenetically related rat embryo and hamster embryo cells but none on distantly related monkey testes or on chick embryo cells (35). The inducer of antiviral activity in phylogenetically related cells was shown by suitable characterization to be interferon. Antiviral activity of mouse interferon on hamster cells is in agreement with the previously reported heterologous activity between the mouse and hamster (140). That the extent of the genetic relationship between two species may determine the ability of their interferon to exhibit heterologous activity is further suggested by the consistently observed heterologous activity between human and monkey systems (130, 141–144).

One important aspect of any interferon assay is to establish that the antiviral activity observed is actually caused by interferon. Heterologous activity of mouse and chick interferon has been reported when a vaccinia interferon assay system was used (31,137 145). These observations are in contrast to the work considered above (138,139) in which, large amounts of chick or mouse interferon were found to exhibit no heterologous activity. As demonstrated in a subsequent report, vaccinia virus inhibitors other than interferon could account for the reported heterologous activity of chick and mouse interferons (35).

Similarly, several laboratories have reported that crude interferon preparations produced in calf kidney cells exert antiviral activity on human and monkey cells (131, 143). The rather common occurrence of other noninterferon inhibitors of virus (6, 146) necessitates a complete characterization of the heterologous antiviral activity before it can be accepted as interferon The same reservation would apply to the report of heterologous activity of interferons produced in several mammalian cell types (144), and the report of activity of mouse cell produced interferon on human kidney cells. (147)

The use of purified interferon preparations will eliminate many of the possible objections to studies of species specificity with crude interferon. When the most purified interferons available at this time have been utilized, a strong species specificity of action has been demonstrated (48, 71, 148, 149). A full biological characterization of heterologous antiviral activity is still necessary with such preparations to rule out undetected, noninterferon antiviral substances.

The presently available evidence favors a strong species barrier to the antiviral action of interferon. It remains to be determined whether interferon can generally exert some antiviral activity in other closely related species as it does among rodent cells.

STEROID HORMONES AND INTERFERONS

During the past several years, a number of reports have been published that deal with the effect of cortisone and other steroid hormones on interferon production and action. These will be considered in sequence.

Effect of steroid hormones on interferon production.—Certain steroid hormones have been found to have an inhibitory effect on the production of interferon in embryonated eggs infected with influenza virus (150). De Maeyer & De Maeyer (151) showed a similar effect in a continuous line of rat embryo cells infected with Sindbis virus. Reinicke (152) found that cortisone inhibits interferon production in chick embryo cells in tissue culture infected with influenza virus, without increasing the yield of virus. Mendelson & Glasgow (153) observed also that cortisone depressed interferon production with no effect on yield of vaccinia virus. Reinicke (154, 155) also showed that metandienonium and testosterone, which enhance protein synthesis *in vivo* (156), reduce interferon synthesis in tissue culture.

It should be remembered that cortisone has been shown to be able to stimulate or inhibit RNA and protein synthesis *in vivo*, depending on the organ considered; the liver is an example of a tissue in which RNA and protein are stimulated, while in the thymus they are inhibited (157–160). Recently, Kidson (161) has shown, using lymph nodes grown in tissue culture that even a one-minute exposure to cortisone inhibits the synthesis of RNA, presumably including mRNA.

Effect of steroid hormones on interferon action.—Kilbourne et al. (150) noted that interferon showed less antiviral activity in chorioallantoic membranes treated with cortisone than in membranes not so treated. However, De Maeyer & De Maeyer (151), using rat tissue and a longer pre-exposure to cortisone, found interferon to have an increased anti-Sindbis virus activity in the presence of the hormone. Reinicke (155), using pre-exposure to cortisone, found, as did Kilbourne (150), that interferon has less activity than in cells not treated with cortisone. Mendelson & Glasgow (153), to complete the picture, used mouse cells and vesicular stomatitis or encephalomyocarditis virus and found no effect of cortisone on interferon action.

Reinicke (154, 155) found that metandienonium and testosterone were stronger inhibitors of interferon production than were hydrocortisone and D-aldosterone, and were also stronger repressors of viral-induced heterologous interference in the absence of interferon, suggesting that the viral-induced interference may be attributable to interferon. However, estradiol, which inhibited interferon production as well as did aldosterone, has no effect on heterologous interference, which indicates that under some conditions the two effects can be separated.

PHYLOGENETIC OCCURRENCE OF THE INTERFERON SYSTEM

The interferon system has been demonstrated in mammals, birds, in a poikilothermic reptile (133) and fish (215). There is one report of an interferon-like substance produced by *Pseudomonas aeruginosa* after reaction with inactivated bacteriophage (162). A virus interference phenomenon of plants has been studied in detail in several laboratories. Although most of the properties of interference in plants are similar to those of the interferon system (163), there are at least two major differences. The available evidence is summarized below.

Interference among a number of plant viruses has been reported to occur in several plants during virus infection (164–171). The properties of this resistance to superinfection are: (*a*) nonspecificity for virus; (*b*) localization or distribution throughout the plant, depending on the plant-virus system; (*c*) onset several days after infection; (*d*) duration for many weeks; (*e*) continuation after infected leaf is removed, and (*f*) failure to be initiated by bacterial infections, chemical injury or by some virus infections which have been studied. Of additional interest is the report that virus protein alone can induce resistance (172). Most of these characteristics are similar to those in animal virus interference (163, 173, 174), and suggest the possibility of a chemical mediator. Extracts of infected plants were found to contain a soluble antiviral component (164, 175–183). Properties of the antiviral factor include: (*a*) nonspecificity for host plant; (*b*) nonspecificity for virus; (*c*) lack of direct inactivation of virus; (*a*) nondialyzability; (*e*) inactivation between 70 and 80° C for 10 to 15 minutes; (*f*) nonsedimentability at 93,000 *g* for one hour; and (*g*) stability at pH 2.5. Purification characteristics and reactions with various chemical reagents have suggested that the active material is a protein or nucleoprotein (179–182). However, the hypothesized protein was stable to the proteolytic agents, trypsin and papain (179). Further purification of one type of antiviral extract resulted in an active preparation containing RNA with traces of protein (183). The antiviral activity of this purified preparation was stable to trypsin and pronase but was inactivated by ribonuclease, suggesting that the active component of this particular antiviral extract is an RNA-containing molecule. A final conclusion must await similar studies of the antiviral materials from other plants.

Taken together, the evidence indicates that there are many similarities between the plant interference system and the interferon system of animals, but there are two outstanding differences. Interferon induces antiviral activity only in the same or closely related species (35), whereas several of the substances which induce antiviral activity in plants are nonspecific for plant host. Also interferon is a protein (2), whereas the most recent study of one plant substance suggests an RNA structure. A final conclusion as to the chemical nature of the antiviral material in other plant extracts must await additional information. Perhaps future studies will also determine whether a component of the interference system of plants is an induced intracellular antiviral material, as has been proposed for the interferon system in animals. (See section, *Induction of the antiviral state in cells exposed to interferon.*)

INTERFERON AND VIREMIA

Many virus infections require viremic spread to target organs during the early stages of virus infection in order to cause disease during later stages.

Antibody is not usually present in the blood during the early stages of an original virus infection in a susceptible animal (184). The detection of interferon in the bloodstream during viremia suggested that interferon may be an important host defense which may operate before antibody formation occurs (185). The studies to be cited lead to the interpretation that circulating interferon may act in two ways. It may circulate to target organs in advance of or at the same time as the virus and thereby prophylactically protect these organs. Also, circulating interferon may aid in the termination of viremia.

Protection of target organs by circulating interferon.—Following the observation that interferon appeared in the bloodstream during viremias, the possibility was considered that the smaller interferon molecule might pass from the circulation into body tissues in advance of the larger virus and thereby initiate protection of target organs before implantation of virus. Prior evidence had indicated that interferon manifests greatest antiviral effect when it is similarly applied in advance or at the same time as virus (48, 83, 128, 186, 187). Other studies, which are cited below, have provided many forms of evidence to support the theory of a natural protective role of circulating interferon.

The interferon system is recognized as a broadly acting and potent antiviral mechanism (2, 184, 188, 189). Circulating interferon has been found to occur shortly after the onset of viremia in various animal species, including man, following peripheral or intravenous inoculation (28, 124, 135, 190–198). Interferon has been detected in the bloodstream of mice as early as 1 hour after the onset of viremia, and is generally present within several hours of onset of a variety of viral infections. Interferon in the bloodstream may be disseminated into body organs within minutes (199). That the antiviral effect induced by circulating interferon can rapidly reach the brain, peritoneum, skin, and other organs is shown by protection experiments in mice (190,200), chick embryos (201), and man (197). At least some agents, such as poliovirus (202) and encephalomyocarditis virus (200), require about 24 hours in the bloodstream before seeding the target organ with a lethal dose of virus. Thus, circulating interferon, which has been shown to be produced by several viruses within hours of onset of viremia, and then reaches organs within minutes, precedes implantation of these viruses into the target organ. Transfer of interferon from infected mice to the circulation of recipients results in protection of target organs against peripheral infection by several distinct viruses (200, 203). Following the appearance of circulating interferon, the protective effect in the target organ, as would be expected, is nonspecific for challenge virus. The quantity of interferon in the circulation during viremia can be sufficient to account for protection of target organs, as shown by the effectiveness of passively transferred interferon. These lines of evidence strongly support the interpretation that circulating interferon may induce protection in target organs of animals during the viremic stage of infection.

Control of viremia by circulating interferon.—The preceding considerations emphasized the prophylactic action of circulating interferon in the protection of target organs against viremic spread. It also seems likely that serum interferon aids in the control of viremia in the same way that it aids in controlling virus growth in other infected tissues of the body. Supporting evidence comes from inhibition by actinomycin D of the production of circulating interferon in mice infected with Sindbis virus. The decreased circulating interferon was associated with an increased viremia and higher mortality (204, 205). Additional evidence which favors an effect of interferon on viremia comes from the temporary decrease of lactic dehydrogenase virus titers in the circulation of mice which were stimulated by intravenous Newcastle disease virus to produce interferon (206).

Formation and elimination of circulating interferon.—Interferon seems to be newly formed under most conditions of virus infection. However, the possibility has been considered that interferon in the circulation may, under conditions such as endotoxin stimulation, result from the release of preformed material (9, 10, 21, 22). Although the bulk of virus-induced interferon in the bloodstream seems to be newly formed, it has been suggested that the earliest interferon released into the circulation during viremia may be preformed (9) (also see section, *Other inducers and different molecular species of interferon*).

The origin of circulating interferon has not been finally determined. Since virtually any cell may produce interferon when properly stimulated by virus (2), it is possible that different viruses induce different cell types to produce interferon and release it into the bloodstream. This interpretation is consistent with the observations that virus in the circulation may be associated with various cell types and tissues, including spleen and liver macrophages (207), small vessels (208), endothelial cells (207), and smooth muscle of veined arteries (208). It has been suggested that phagocytic reticuloendothelial cells, particularly in the spleen, may be primarily responsible for the rapid production of circulating interferon in rabbits infected with Sindbis virus (arbovirus, group A) (135). The inference that other cells and tissues may also rapidly produce circulating interferon comes from the findings that circulating interferon is produced in splenectomized mice inoculated with Newcastle disease virus (209), and that chick embryo cells in culture can produce interferon as rapidly as circulating interferon is produced *in vivo* (8, 185). Also, white blood cells may not be the main source of circulating interferon, since destruction of white blood cells by X-ray treatment of mice did not significantly inhibit its production (209).

Titers of circulating interferon which accompany viremia reflect the equilibrium between the rates of interferon entering and leaving the bloodstream. The total amount of circulating interferon produced during viremia can be estimated from the titers of circulating interferon, its duration and the rate of its removal from the circulation. The rate of removal of passively administered interferon has been determined to be about 97 per cent per hour in mice (192, 203). On the assumption that this rate of removal of circulating interferon occurs during the viremia, it has been estimated that a total of 100,000 or more units of circulating interferon were produced during the viremias which followed peripheral infection of mice.

The rapid disappearance of interferon from the circulation and tissues of mice (192, 199, 203) is in contrast to the lack of detectable disappearance from tissue culture fluids (See section, *Induction of the antiviral state in cells exposed to interferon*). As yet, there is no satisfactory explanation for the rapid disappearance of interferon *in vivo*. One intriguing possibility is that the interferon that is rapidly lost from the circulation is stored and subsequently can be released rapidly as preformed material.

INTERFERON AND VIRAL ONCOGENESIS

The interferon system may act to prevent viral oncogenesis in two ways. It may inhibit multiplication of the tumor virus and thus make less virus available for transformation of cells to malignancy. Evidence that this mechanism does operate has been reviewed (188, 210). The interferon system also could prevent an essential intracellular event which leads to transformation and thereby more directly inhibit viral oncognesis. Evidence which indicates that the interferon system can act intracellularly to prevent morphologic transformation of cells comes from a study of 3T3 mouse cells infected with a high multiplicity of SV40 virus (104). Cells exposed to interferon prior to or shortly after inoculation of virus were protected against morphological transformation. However, the effect on malignant transformation could not be determined since 3T3 mouse cells were derived from a random bred mouse and both the "normal" and morphologically transformed clones are rejected by recipient mice. It is possible that the inhibition of transformation by the infected cell's endogenous interferon system may occur naturally since only small amounts of interferon were required to inhibit transformation, and since the interferon mechanism can be an early response to most virus infections. However, no firm generalizations can be made until this type of study is extended to other tumor virus-cell systems.

Prophylaxis and therapy of virus diseases.—The success of virus vaccines in preventing disease is dependent upon adapting the protective action of preformed antibody. Similarly, it may be anticipated that adaptation of the natural protective action of the interferon system may lead to additional prevention and therapy of virus disease. Two desirable properties of the interferon system are activity against a wide range of viruses and absence of detectable toxicity. Limitations on such use may be the host species barrier for interferon and the small amounts of exogenous interferon available in comparison to the large amounts produced during natural infection (192). These technical limitations may be overcome by the continually improving methods for producing interferon and by substances which induce endogenous interferon. As examples, at present 1000-fold more interferon can be produced than was first reported eight years ago (148,211); the infected animal may be additionally stimulated by avirulent viruses (185) and substances like Statolon (20) to produce large quantities of interferon and the antiviral state.

It is likely that the first practical application of the interferon system will be for prophylaxis, rather than therapy of virus infection, because of the greater protective effect of interferon applied prior to rather than subsequent to infection. Even the limited knowledge now available permits experimental prevention of a variety of virus infections in animals, and experimental vaccinia infection of man (212), by prior treatment with interferon. It is difficult to avoid considering that only the technical development of methods for increased induction of interferon or its antiviral substance are now necessary for prophylaxis of virus infections of man similar to the successful chemoprophylaxis of smallpox in man (213).

Successful treatment after onset of virus disease will be more difficult than prophylaxis because of the increased quantity of interferon needed to treat an established infection (48, 83, 128, 186, 187), and because of the difficulty of depositing interferon or an inducer within certain infected organs. Another problem is the possibility that treatment, after the development of symptoms, may be hopeless because the majority of cells within the target organ may already have been irreversibly infected. That this may not be the invariable situation is suggested by (a) the recognized ability of animals and man frequently to arrest progression of an often fatal infection, even after the development of severe symptoms; and (b) the observation that certain infections produce prodromal or early symptoms before finally infecting the target organ. Encouragement has come from recent observations that the use of increased amounts of interferon provided partial protection for infected mice even after the onset of virus infection, but before the onset of symptoms (187, 200, 203, 214). In brief, the prospects for practical application of our knowledge of the interferon system seem good for prophylaxis, and hopeful for therapy of virus infections.

CONCLUSIONS AND SUMMARY

Evidence that has accumulated over the past few years indicates that interferon production is a host genome-controlled function, and follows the usual DNA to RNA to protein sequence. This function is ordinarily repressed, but is derepressed by virus infection and by other nonviral substances. It is not known if it is the viral protein or the viral nucleic acid that initiates the events which lead to derepression. Interferon can also be released *in vivo* by at least one nonviral substance, bacterial endotoxin. Since neither RNA nor protein synthesis is needed in this latter case, it has been suggested that the interferon may exist in a preformed, possibly stored state, which can be rapidly mobilized if needed. The material released under these conditions exists predominantly in a form with a molecular weight approximating 100,000, as contrasted with the predominately 30,000 molecular weight substance induced by virus infection. Actually, the molecular weight of interferon produced *in vivo* has turned out to be heterogeneous, ranging from about 18,000 to 100,000, with several of the inducers leading to the appearance of molecules or more than one molecular weight.

In order for cells to develop resistance to virus infection upon treatment with interferon, the synthesis of RNA and protein is needed. This observation, coupled with the apparent fact that little or no interferon is absorbed by cells developing resistance to virus infection, suggests strongly that the interferon molecule per se is not the active antiviral substance, but rather that it induces the formation of a new substance which is actively antiviral. While the latter has been generally considered to be a protein, the data are equally consistent with its being an RNA. The development of an equilibrium between production and decay of this material in cells exposed to interferon may explain the steady-state antiviral condition of such cells. The available evidence indicates a near-absolute barrier to the antiviral action of interferon in cells of unrelated species. There is suggestive evidence that this species barrier is not complete in cells of related species.

The results of a variety of experiments indicate that the interferon system affects a very early event in virus infection. No new viral nucleic acid is made. The parental strand of RNA, in at least one system, is prevented from being incorporated into a ribonuclease-resistant, double-stranded form, presumably the replicative form. Also, in at least one system, interferon treatment prevents the association of the input viral genome with a 40S ribosomal subunit of the cell. This step is presumably the initial step in the development of the specific viral polysome which carries out the synthesis of virion components. The development of this specific viral polysome would then be expected to be blocked in interferon-treated cells, and it is.

Cortisone and other steroid hormones interact in a variety of ways with systems producing interferon or developing an antiviral state consequent to treatment with interferon; much more data are needed before a reliable interpretation can be given to these interesting observations.

Evidence that link the interferon system with recovery of infected tissues *in vivo* has been presented in earlier reviews (184). Recent findings indicate that circulating interferon plays an early and important role in limiting the effectiveness of virus spread through the bloodstream to target organs. The prospects for practical application of the knowledge of the interferon system in controlling virus infections seem good for prophylaxis and hopeful for therapy.

A relatively early evolutionary origin for the interferon system is indicated by its occurrence in mammals, birds, reptiles and fish. If the virus inhibitory phenomenon of plants and bacteria is demonstrated to be analogous to the interferon system of animals, then a truly primitive origin of this system will be indicated.

LITERATURE CITED

1. Wagner, R. R., *Ann. Rev. Microbiol.*, **17,** 285 (1963)
2. Isaacs, A., *Advan. Virus Res.*, **10,** 1 (1963)
3. Reich, E., Franklin, R. M., Shatkin, A. J., and Tatum, E. L., *Science*, **134,** 556 (1961)
4. Franklin, R. M., *Biochim. Biophys. Acta*, **72,** 555 (1963)
5. Heller, E., *Virology*, **21,** 652 (1963)
6. Ho, M., *Bacteriol. Rev.*, **28,** 367 (1964)
7. Wagner, R. R., *Nature*, **204,** 49 (1964)
8. Levy, H. B., Axelrod, D., and Baron, S., *Proc. Soc. Exptl. Biol. Med.*, **118,** 384 (1965)
9. Youngner, J. S., Stinebring, W. R., and Traube, E. S., *Virology*, **27,** 541 (1965)
10. Ho, M., *Science*, **146,** 1472 (1964)
11. Levy, H. B., Axelrod, D., and Baron, S., *Proc. Soc. Exptl. Biol. Med.*, **118,** 1013 (1965)
12. Burke, D. C., and Morrison, J. M., *Virology*, **28,** 108 (1966)
13. Ho, M., and Enders, J., *Proc. Natl. Acad. Sci. U. S.*, **45,** 385 (1959)
14. Aurelian, L., and Roizman, B., *J. Mol. Biol.*, **11,** 539 (1965)
15. Wagner, R. R., and Huang, A. S., *Virology*, **28,** 1 (1966)
16. Lindenmann, J., Burke, D. C., and Isaacs, A., *Brit. J. Exptl. Pathol.*, **38,** 551 (1957)
17. Buchan, A., and Burke, D. C., *Biochem. J.*, **98,** 530 (1966)
18. Friedman, R., *J. Bacteriol.*, **91,** 1224 (1966)
19. Rotem, Z., *Israel J. Exptl. Med.*, **11,** 174 (1964)
20. Kleinschmidt, W. J., Cline, J. C., and Murphy, E. B., *Proc. Natl. Acad. Sci. U. S.*, **52,** 741 (1964)
21. Stinebring, W. R., and Youngner, J. S., *Nature*, **204,** 712 (1964)
22. Ho, M., and Kono, Y., *Proc. Natl. Acad. Sci. U.S.*, **53,** 220 (1965)
23. Rytel, M., Shope, R. E., and Kilbourne, E. D., *J. Exptl. Med.*, **123,** 577 (1966)
24. Wheelock, E. F., *Science*, **149,** 310 (1965)
25. Hanna, L., Merigan, T., and Jawetz, E., *Bacteriol. Proc.*, 121 (1966)
26. Stinebring, W. R., Youngner, J. S., and Hallum, J. (Personal communication, 1965)
27. Hopps, H. E., Kohno, S., Kohno, M., and Smadel, J. E., *Bacteriol. Proc.*, 115 (1964)
28. Youngner, J. S., and Stinebring, W. R., *Science*, **144,** 1022 (1964)
29. Isaacs, A., Cox, R. A., and Rotem, Z., *Lancet*, **ii,** 113 (1963)
30. Jensen, K. E., Neal, A. L., and Owens, R. E., *Nature*, **200,** 433 (1963)
31. Takano, K., Jensen, K. E., and Warren, J., *Proc. Soc. Exptl. Biol. Med.*, **114,** 472 (1963)
32. Isaacs, A., *Australian J. Exptl. Biol. Med. Sci.*, **43,** 405 (1965)
33. Mecs, E., *Acta Virol.*, **8,** 475 (1964)
34. Gifford, G. E., *Proc. Soc. Exptl. Biol. Med.*, **119,** 9 (1965)
35. Buckler, C. E., and Baron, S., *J. Bacteriol.*, **91,** 231 (1966)
36. Kleinschmidt, W. J., and Murphy, E. B., *Virology*, **27,** 484 (1965)
37. Levy, H. B., and Baron, S. (Unpublished observations)
38. Friedman, R. M. (Personal communication, 1965)
39. Youngner, J. S., Stinebring, W. R., and Hallum, J., *Bacteriol. Rev.* (In press, 1966)
40. Buchan, A., and Burke, D. C., *Biochem. J.* (In press, 1966)
41. Youngner, J.S., Hallum, J., and Stinebring, W. R., *Bacteriol. Rev.* (In press, 1966)
42. Merigan, T., and Ke, Y. (Personal communication, 1965)
43. Merigan, T., and Wheelock, F. (Personal communication)
43a. Postic, B., and Ho, M. (Personal communication)
44. Youngner, J. S., and Stinebring, W. R., *Nature*, **208,** 456 (1965)
45. Isaacs, A., Klemperer, H. S., and Hitchcock, S., *Virology*, **13,** 191 (1961)
46. Levy, H. B., Snellbaker, L. F., and Baron, S., *Virology*, **21,** 48 (1963)
47. Beloff-Chain, A., Catanzaro, R., Pocchiari, F., Balducci, M., and Balducci, D., *Biochim. Biophys. Acta*, **90,** 228 (1964)
48. Lampson, G. P., Tytell, A. A., Nemes, M. M., and Hilleman, M. R., *Proc. Soc. Exptl. Biol. Med.*, **112,** 468 (1963)
49. Cocito, C., De Maeyer, E., and De Somer, P., *Life Sci.*, **1,** 753 (1962)
50. Cocito, C., Schonne, E., and De Somer, P. (Personal communication)
51. Sonnabend, J. A., *Nature*, **203,** 496 (1964)

52. Sonnabend, J. A. (Personal communication)
53. Levy, H. B., and Merigan, T. C., *Proc. Soc. Exptl. Biol. Med.*, **121**, 53 (1966)
54. Paucker, K., Cantell, K., and Henle, W., *Virology*, **17**, 324 (1962)
55. Wagner, R. R., and Levy, A. H., *Ann. N. Y. Acad. Sci.*, **88**, 1308 (1960)
56. Baron, S., and Isaacs, A., *Brit. Med. J.*, **1**, 18 (1962)
57. Baron, S., Merigan, T. C., and McKerlie, M. L., *Proc. Soc. Exptl. Biol. Med.*, **121**, 50 (1966)
58. Vilcek, J., and Rada, B., *Acta Virol.*, **6, 9** (1962)
59. Taylor, J., *Biochem. Biophys. Res. Commun.*, **14**, 447 (1964)
60. Friedman, R. M., and Sonnabend, J. A., *Nature*, **203**, 366 (1964)
61. Lockart, R. Z., Jr., *Biochem. Biophys. Res. Commun.*, **15**, 513 (1964)
62. Levine, S., *Virology*, **24**, 229 (1964)
63. Buckler, C. E., Baron, S., and Levy, H. B., *Science*, **152**, 80 (1966)
64. Youngner, J. S., and Stinebring, W. R. (Personal communication)
65. Levy, H. B., Buckler, C. E., and Baron, S., *Science* (In press, 1966)
66. Baron, S., Buckler, C. E., and Levy, H. B., *Bacteriol. Proc.* (In press, 1966)
67. Baron, S., Buckler, C. E., Levy, H. B., and Friedman, R. M., *Bacteriol. Rev.* (In press, 1966)
68. Wagner, R. R., *Virology*, **13**, 323 (1961)
69. Sellers, R. F., and Fitzpatrick, M., *Brit. J. Exptl. Pathol.*, **43**, 674 (1962)
70. Gifford, G. E., *J. Gen. Microbiol.*, **33**, 437 (1963)
71. Merigan, T. C., *Science*, **145**, 811 (1964)
72. Merigan, T. C., Winget, C., and Dixon, C., *J. Mol. Biol.*, **13**, 679 (1965)
73. Levine, S. (Personal communication, 1965)
74. Henderson, J. R., and Taylor, R. M., *Virology*, **13**, 477 (1961)
75. Hermodsson, S., *Acta Pathol. Microbiol. Scand.*, **62**, 224 (1964)
76. Mayer, V., *Acta Virol.*, **6**, 326 (1962)
77. Stancek, D., *Acta Virol.*, **9**, 298 (1965)
78. Isaacs, A., *Cold Spring Harbor Symp. Quant. Biol.* **27**, 343 (1962)
79. Ho, M., *Proc. Soc. Exptl. Biol. Med.*, **107**, 639 (1961)
80. Grossberg, S. E., and Holland, J. J., *J. Immunol.*, **88**, 708 (1962)

81. Ho, M., *Proc. Soc. Exptl. Biol. Med.*, **112**, 511 (1963)
82. Levy, H. B., *Virology*, **22**, 575 (1964)
83. DeSomer, P., Prinzie, A., Denys, P., Jr., and Schonne, E., *Virology*, **16**, 63 (1962)
84. Montagnier, L., and Sanders, K., *Nature*, **199**, 664 (1963)
85. Weissmann, C., Borst, P., Burdon, R. H., Billeter, M. A., and Ochoa, S., *Proc. Natl. Acad. Sci., U. S.*, **51**, 682 (1964)
86. Kelly, R. B., and Sinsheimer, R. L., *J. Mol. Biol.*, **8**, 602 (1964)
87. Fenwick, M. L., Erikson, R. L., and Franklin, R. M., *Science*, **146**, 527 (1964)
88. Kaerner, H. G., and Hoffmann-Berling, H., *Nature*, **202**, 1012 (1964)
89. Nonoyama, M., and Ikeda, Y., *J. Mol. Biol.*, **9**, 763 (1964)
90. Ammann, J., Delius, H., and Hofschneider, P. H., *J. Mol. Biol.*, **10**, 557 (1964)
91. Pons, M., *Virology*, **24**, 467 (1964)
92. Friedman, R. M., and Sonnabend, J., *Nature*, **206**, 532 (1965)
93. Gordon, I., Chenault, S., Stevenson, D., and Acton, J., *J. Bacteriol.*, **91**, 1230 (1966)
94. Franklin, R., and Baltimore, D., in *Viruses, Nucleic Acids and Cancer*, 310. (Univ. of Texas M. D. Anderson Hosp. & Tumor Inst., Williams & Wilkins, Baltimore, Md., 1964)
95. Taylor, J., *Virology*, **25**, 340 (1965)
96. Levy, H. B., Snellbaker, L. F., and Baron, S., *Proc. Soc. Exptl. Biol. Med.* (In press, 1966)
97. Kit, S., Dubbs, D. R., and Piekarski, L. J., *Biochem. Biophys. Res. Commun.*, **8**, 72 (1962)
98. McAuslan, B. R., and Joklik, W. K., *Biochem. Biophys. Res. Commun.*, **8**, 486 (1962)
99. Gosh, S. N., and Gifford, G. E., *Virology*, **27**, 186 (1965)
100. Ohno, S., and Nozima, T. (Personal communication, 1964)
101. Barban, S., and Baron, S. (Unpublished observations)
102. Kit, S., Dubbs, D. R., Piekarski, L. J., and Hsu, T. C., *Exptl. Cell Res.*, **31**, 297 (1963)
103. Salzman, N. P., Shatkin, A. J., and Sebring, E. D., *J. Mol. Biol.*, **8**, 405 (1964)
104. Todaro, G., and Baron, S., *Proc. Natl. Acad. Sci. U. S.*, **54**, 752 (1965)
105. Oxman, M. M., and Black, P. H.,

Proc. Natl. Acad. Sci. U. S. (In press, 1966)

106. Levy, H. B., Carter, W. A., and Friedman, R. M. (Unpublished observations)

107. Lodish, H., and Zinder, M. (Personal communication, 1965)

108. Levy, H. B., and Carter, W. A., *Bacteriol. Proc.*, 119 (1966)

109. Henshaw, E., Revel, M., and Hyatt, H., *J. Mol. Biol.*, **14**, 241 (1965)

110. Girard, M., Latham, H., Penman, S., and Darnell, J. E., *J. Mol. Biol.*, **11**, 187 (1965)

111. Joklik, W. K., and Becker, Y., *J. Mol. Biol.*, **13**, 511 (1965)

112. Glasky, A. V., Simon, L., and Holper, J. C., *Science*, **144**, 1581 (1964)

113. Takemoto, K. K., and Baron, S., *Proc. Soc. Exptl. Biol. Med.* (In press, 1966)

114. Gauntt, C., and Lockart, R. (Personal communication)

115. Isaacs, A., and Burke, D. C., *Nature*, **182**, 1073 (1958)

116. Lockart, R. Z., Jr., *J. Bacteriol.*, **85**, 556 (1963)

117. Glasgow, L., and Habel, K., *Virology*, **19**, 328 (1963)

118. Youngner, S. S., Stinebring, W. R., and Hallum, J. (Personal communication, 1965)

119. Ho, M., and Breinig, M., *J. Immunol.*, **89**, 177 (1962)

120. Mahdy, M. S., and Ho, M., *Proc. Soc. Exptl. Biol. Med.*, **116**, 174 (1964)

121. Paucker, K., *Bacteriol. Rev.* (In press)

122. Cantell, K., and Paucker, K., *Virology*, **21**, 11 (1963)

123. Ho, M., Kono, Y., and Breinig, M., *Proc. Soc. Exptl. Biol. Med.*, **119**, 1227 (1965)

124. Van Rossum, W. (Personal communication, 1965)

125. Ho, M., and Kono, Y., *J. Clin. Invest.*, **44**, 1059 (1965)

126. Tyrrell, D. A. J., *Nature*, **184**, 452 (1959)

127. Ho, M., and Enders, J. F., *Virology*, **9**, 446 (1959)

128. Isaacs, A., and Westwood, M. A., *Lancet*, **ii**, 324 (1959)

129. Wagner, R. R., *Bacteriol. Rev.*, **24**, 151 (1960)

130. Gresser, I., *Proc. Soc. Exptl. Biol. Med.*, **108**, 303 (1961)

131. Sellers, R. F., and Fitzpatrick, M., *Brit. J. Exptl. Pathol.*, **43**, 674 (1962)

132. Rotem, Z., Cox, R. A., and Isaacs, A., *Nature*, **197**, 564 (1963)

133. Falcoff, E., and Fauconnier, B., *Proc. Soc. Exptl. Biol. Med.*, **118**, 609 (1965)

134. Force, E. E., Stewart, R. C., and Haff, R. F., *Virology*, **25**, 322 (1965)

135. Kono, Y., and Ho, M., *Virology*, **25**, 162 (1965)

136. Paucker, K., *J. Immunol.*, **94**, 371 (1965)

137. Gifford, G. E., *J. Gen. Microbiol.*, **33**, 437 (1963)

138. Merigan, T. C., *Science*, **145**, 811 (1964)

139. Baron, S., Barban, S., and Buckler, C. E., *Science*, **145**, 814 (1964)

140. Henle, G., and Henle, W., *J. Natl. Cancer Inst.*, **31**, 143 (1963)

141. Chany, C., *Virology*, **13**, 485 (1961)

142. Isaacs, A., Porterfield, J. S., and Baron, S., *Virology*, **14**, 450 (1961)

143. Sutton, R. N. P., and Tyrrell, D. A. J., *Brit. J. Exptl. Pathol.*, **42**, 99 (1961)

144. Pollikoff, R., Donikian, M. A., Padron, A., and Liu, O. C., *Proc. Soc. Exptl. Biol. Med.*, **110**, 232 (1962)

145. Andrews, R. D., *Brit. Med. J.*, **1**, 1728 (1961)

146. Ginsberg, H. S., *Bacteriol. Rev.*, **24**, 141 (1960)

147. Henle, W., Henle, G., Deinhardt, F., and Bergs, V., *J. Exptl. Med.*, **110**, 525 (1959)

148. Finter, N. B., *Nature*, **204**, 1114 (1964)

149. Lampson, G. P., Tytell, A. A., Nemes, M. M., and Hilleman, M. R., *Proc. Soc. Exptl. Biol. Med.*, **118**, 441 (1965)

150. Kilbourne, E. D., Smart, K. M., and Pokorny, B. A., *Nature*, **190**, 650 (1961)

151. De Maeyer, E., and De Maeyer, J., *Nature*, **197**, 724 (1963)

152. Reinicke, V., *Acta Pathol. Microbiol. Scand.*, **64**, 338 (1965)

153. Mendelson, V., and Glasgow, L., *J. Immunol.*, **96**, 345 (1966)

154. Reinicke, V., *Acta Pathol. Microbiol. Scand.* (In press)

155. Reinicke, V. (Personal communication, 1965)

156. Desaulles, P. A., and Krähenbühl, C., *Ciba Found. Symp., Protein Metabolism, 1962* (F. Gross, Ed., Springer-Verlag, Berlin, 1962)

157. Tremolieres, J., Derache, R., and Griffatin, G., *Ann. Endocrinol.*, **15**, 694 (1954)

158. Feigelson, M., Gross, P., and Feigelson, P., *Biochim. Biophys. Acta*, **55**, 495 (1962)

159. Feigelson, P., and Feigelson, M., *J. Biol. Chem.*, **238**, 1073 (1963)
160. Pena, A., Dvorkin, B., and White, A., *Biochem. Biophys. Res. Commun.*, **16**, 449 (1964)
161. Kidson, C. (Personal communication)
162. Mercer, C., and Mills, R., *J. Gen. Microbiol.*, **23**, 253 (1960)
163. Fantes, K., and O'Neill, C., *Nature*, **203**, 1048 (1964)
164. Van der Want, J., *Tijdschr. Plantenziekten*, **57**, 72 (1951)
165. Gilpatrick, J., and Weintraub, M., *Science*, **115**, 701 (1952)
166. Yarwood, C., *Phytopathology*, **43**, 490 (1953)
167. Yarwood, C., *Phytopathology*, **50**, 741 (1960)
168. Ross, A., and Bozarth, R., *Phytopathology*, **50**, 652 (1960)
169. Ross, A. F., *Virology*, **14**, 329 (1961)
170. Ross, A. F., *Virology*, **14**, 340 (1961)
171. Bozarth, R., and Ross, A., *Virology*, **24**, 446 (1964)
172. Loebenstein, G., *Virology*, **17**, 574 (1962)
173. Henle, W., *J. Immunol.*, **64**, 203 (1950)
174. Schlesinger, R. W., in *The Viruses: Biochemical, Biological and Biophysical Properties*, **3**, 157. (Burnet, F. M., and Stanley, W. M., Eds., Academic Press, New York, 1959)
175. Weintraub, M., and Gilpatrick, J., *Can. J. Botany*, **30**, 549 (1952)
176. Ragetli, H., *Tijdschr. Plantenziekten*, **61**, 245 (1957)
177. Sela, I., and Applebaum, S., *Virology*, **17**, 543 (1962)
178. Ragetli, H., and Weintraub, M., *Virology*, **18**, 232 (1962)
179. Ragetli, H., and Weintraub, M., *Virology*, **18**, 241 (1962)
180. Loebenstein, G., and Ross, A. F., *Virology*, **20**, 507 (1963)
181. Sela, I., Harpaz, I., and Birk, Y., *Virology*, **22**, 446 (1964)
182. Loebenstein, G., and Von Praagh, T. (Personal communication, 1965)
183. Sela, I., Harpaz, I., and Birk, Y., *Virology*, **28**, 71 (1966)
184. Baron, S., *Advan. Virus Res.*, **10**, 39 (1963)
185. Baron, S., and Buckler, C. E., *Science*, **141**, 1061 (1963)
186. Hitchcock, G., and Isaacs, A., *Brit. Med. J.*, **ii**, 1268 (1960)
187. Finter, N. B., *Brit. Med. J.*, **ii**, 981 (1964)
188. Baron, S., in *Interferon*. (N. Finter, Ed., in press, 1966)
189. Baron, S., in *Modern Trends in Medical Virology*. (Waterson, A., and Heath, R., Eds., Butterworths, London, 1966, in press)
190. Baron, S., Buckler, C. E., Friedman, R. M., and McCloskey, R. V., *Bacteriol. Proc.*, 116 (1964)
191. Baron, S., du Buy, H. G., Buckler, C. E., and Johnson, M. L., *Proc. Soc. Exptl. Biol. Med.*, **117**, 338 (1964)
192. Baron, S., Buckler, C. E., McCloskey, R. V., and Krischstein, R. L., *J. Immunol.*, **96**, 12 (1966)
193. Gresser, I. (Personal communication, 1964)
194. Wheelock, E. F., and Sibley, W. A., *Lancet*, **ii**, 382 (1964)
195. Wheelock, E. F., and Sibley, W. A., *New Engl. J. Med.*, **273**, 194 (1965)
196. Larke, R. *Proc. Soc. Exptl. Biol. Med.*, **119**, 1234 (1965)
197. Merigan, T. C., Petralli, J. K., and Wilbur, J., *Clin. Res.*, **13**, 297 (1965)
198. Torlone, V., Titoli, F., and Gialletti, L., *Life Sci.*, **4**, 1707 (1965)
199. Subrahmanyan, T., and Mims, C. (Personal communication, 1965)
200. Baron, S., Buckler, C. E., Friedman, R. M., and McCloskey, R. V., *J. Immunol.*, **96**, 17 (1966)
201. Grossberg, S. E., *Bacteriol. Proc.*, 116 (1964)
202. Nathanson, N., and Bodian, D., *Bull. Johns Hopkins Hosp.*, **111**, 198 (1962)
203. Finter, N. B., *Brit. J. Exptl. Pathol.*, **47**, (In press)
204. Postic, B., Singer, S. H., and Ho, M., *Federation Proc.*, **23**, 193 (1964)
205. Postic, B., Singer, S., and Ho, M., *Federation Proc.*, **24**, 318 (1964)
206. du Buy, H. G., and Johnson, M. L., *J. Exptl. Med.*, **122**, 587 (1965)
207. Mims, C. A., *Bacteriol. Rev.*, **28**, 30 (1964)
208. Kundin, W. D., Liu, C., Hysell, P., and Hamachige, S., *Arch. Ges. Virusforsch.*, **12**, 514 (1962)
209. Baron, S., and Buckler, C. E. (Unpublished observation, 1964)
210. Allison, A., in *Viruses, Nucleic Acids, and Cancer*, 462. (Univ. of Texas M. D. Anderson Hosp. & Tumor Inst., Eds., Williams & Wilkins, Baltimore, Md., 1965)
211. Isaacs, A., and Lindenmann, J., *Proc. Roy. Soc. B.*, **147**, 258 (1957)
212. Scientific Committee on Interferon,

Report to the Medical Research Council, *Lancet*, **1**, 873 (1962)

213. Bauer, D. J., St. Vincent, L., Kempe, C. H., and Downie, A. W., *Lancet*, ii, 494 (1963)

214. Baron, S., Friedman, R. M., Kirkam, W. R., and Buckler, C. E., *Intern.*

Congr. for Microbiol. Abstr., Montreal, 96 (1962)

215. Beasley, A., Sigel, M., and Clem, L., *Proc. Soc. Exptl. Biol. Med.*, **121**, 1169 (1966)

216. Isaacs, A., Rotem, Z., and Fantes, K. (Personal communication)

MICROBIOLOGY OF WASTE WATERS[1,2]

By Anthony F. Gaudy, Jr., and Elizabeth T. Gaudy

Oklahoma State University, Stillwater, Oklahoma

Contents

Kinetics of Substrate Removal and Growth.................. 320
   Activated sludge... 320
   Exertion of biochemical oxygen demand...................... 322
Mechanisms of Substrate Removal and Growth................ 324
   Sequential substrate removal............................... 324
   Products of partial oxidation................................ 326
   Oxidative assimilation...................................... 326
Constants for Design and Operation....................... 327
   Relation between biological solids and oxygen uptake............. 327
   Relation between biological solids and purification rate........... 328
   Relation between biological solids production and substrate concentration.. 328
Anaerobic Digestion...................................... 332
Summary and Conclusions................................. 333

In many respects, the microbiology of waste waters could aptly be termed the "microbiology of heterogeneous populations." While much microbiological interest has traditionally been centered on removing, killing, or controlling specific species or groups of organisms in waste waters, a more challenging area of endeavor is embodied in the quantitative description of the mechanisms and kinetics of growth of natural (heterogeneous) microbial populations and of the concomitant substrate removal (waste water purification) which they bring about. The challenging aspect to researchers in this field is the necessity of uncovering facts of predictive value for natural populations rather than for a single pure culture.

Ideally, pure culture studies may form useful tools for the investigation of heterogeneous populations. In addition, it is often the case that the presence of a specific species in waste water comprises the problem, and work of a basic nature on the particular organism finds direct application toward solution of the pollution problem. Recent work on the growth of *Sphaerotilus natans* (1–3) may be cited as one example of such basic work which is directly applicable to the slime problem in many receiving streams. Also, investigations into the mechanisms of species predomination can ideally be made with mixtures of known species as, for example, the recently reported

---

[1] The survey of the literature pertaining to this review was concluded in December 1965.

[2] The following abbreviations will be used: BOD (biochemical oxygen demand); COD (chemical oxygen demand).

research of Shindala et al. (4). Nevertheless, studies using heterogeneous populations offer the shortest route to attainment of the requisite knowledge for engineering control over the regeneration of polluted waters.

Since the most fruitful approach toward solution of the nation's water problem lies in the re-use of the water resource, research aimed toward understanding and improvement of biological treatment of waste waters is urgently needed. The review which follows will cover critical areas of aerobic metabolism, with only brief mention of anaerobic processes. Space will not permit discussion of all of the work which has contributed to recent progress in the microbiology of waste water treatment; therefore, we have chosen to confine ourselves primarily to discussion of areas which have been of particular interest in our own laboratories.

KINETICS OF SUBSTRATE REMOVAL AND GROWTH

Activated sludge.—It seems obvious that studies on the kinetic description of biological processes should be accompanied by concomitant study of the mechanisms which cause the observed kinetic behavior. However, this seemingly logical approach has not always been taken, partially because of a tendency to oversimplify the mechanistic aspects, and partially because of the urgency of the need for adequate kinetic description of waste water treatment processes.

One of the most prominent areas of kinetic research at present is the determination of the applicability of steady-state reaction models to description of biological treatment processes. Most of the work is directly related to the activated sludge process, and research has accelerated as the use of newer aeration equipment and changes in the geometric design of aeration tanks have fostered intimate or complete mixing of the cells and substrate in the reactor rather than hydraulic systems approaching plug flow conditions.

Mathematical and experimental treatments of steady-state systems were introduced into the microbiological field by Monod (5) and Novick & Szilard (6), and into the field of biological waste water treatment by Garrett & Sawyer (7). Most microbiologists accept, at least as a starting point, the empirical expression developed by Monod (8) relating logarithmic growth rate to substrate concentration. Using data from batch experiments, the equation yields a rectangular hyperbola if growth rate is plotted against initial substrate concentration, and the curve becomes asymptotic to the maximum nonsubstrate-limited exponential growth rate attainable by the particular system under the environmental conditions employed. The saturation constant, maximum growth rate, and cell yield are used as system constants (obtainable from either batch or continuous flow steady-state experiments) and may be used in deriving the equations for steady-state levels of substrate and cells. Some of the objections, on a theoretical basis, to the Monod equation are given in the excellent review of James (9) and the writings of Moser (10). Much useful information concerning theoretical development and applications of steady-state models can be found in two recent symposia (11, 12).

In the waste water treatment field there are presently two major schools of thought concerning the quantitative description of the dependence of growth rate upon substrate concentration. One school of thought states that the Monod equation is applicable, or can be adapted, to waste water treatment kinetics. The work of Garrett & Sawyer (7) laid the foundation for the use of another type of relationship between substrate concentration and growth rate. It will be recalled that the Monod relationship predicts that the logarithmic growth rate is a continuous function of substrate concentration up to the concentration of substrate at which growth rate becomes a maximum (8). If, for various dilution rates in completely mixed reactors, one plots dilution rate (or the reciprocal of detention time, which is equal to the logarithmic growth rate in a completely mixed steady-state reactor) against substrate remaining in solution or appearing in the effluent, the resulting curve is relatively flat at low dilution rates and becomes increasingly concave upward as dilution rate is increased up to the point of total dilute-out of cells. Garrett & Sawyer (7) plotted soluble BOD (biochemical oxygen demand) remaining against dilution rate for continuous flow experiments, using three different detention times. Although there was some scatter in the data for replicate experiments, they could be fitted to a straight line, yielding a linear relationship between remaining substrate and growth rate. It seems probable that the three dilution rates used by Garrett & Sawyer were actually on a flattened part of the curve predicted using the Monod relationship and, if additional higher dilution rates had been examined, these researchers might have reproduced the Monod type of substrate curve. Indeed, data obtained in our laboratory with the use of glucose rather than peptone at both higher and lower concentrations than employed by Garrett & Sawyer indicate that their dilution rates would fall on the flattened portion of the substrate curve (13). This conclusion is supported by the fact that the highest effluent BOD Garrett & Sawyer observed was 83 mg/l for a feed concentration of 1150 mg/l. Based upon their work, they concluded that "for practical purposes the relation between the rate of growth and the remaining soluble BOD is well represented by a discontinuous function." Above a critical concentration of BOD the rate of growth was considered to be constant, and below this level the rate of growth was concluded to be directly proportional to the remaining soluble BOD. While the authors felt that such a discontinuous function could be used for practical purposes, their concept was adopted as theory by other workers. Eckenfelder (14) used this concept with some modifications in design procedures for biological waste treatment systems, and McKinney (15) adopted this concept in his treatment of the mathematics of complete mixing activated sludge processes.

Grieves, Milbury & Pipes (16) have compared the two concepts, using constants selected from the literature, and they have shown that different steady-state performance curves with respect to cell concentration and substrate remaining are obtained, depending upon the model used. However, they felt that fairly comparable results were obtained with both models if cell feedback was included. Wilson (17) compared substrate removal and growth curves, using arbitrarily selected constants from the data of Garrett & Sawyer, and concluded that the two models yielded fairly comparable results. However, when Wilson applied the mathematics of either model to his own data, obtained in "rolling-tube filter" studies, the data fitted in accordance with the Monod concept rather than with the discontinuous relationship. Many other studies, both theoretical and experimental, have supported or suggested modifications of one or the other kinetic model (18–21). Complicating factors, such as the possible need to consider the decrease of sludge mass due to endogenous metabolism in the presence of exogenous substrate and the use of some exogenous substrate for cell maintenance (18, 22), represent refinements which as yet cannot be adequately treated for heterogeneous populations. From data obtained in a three-year study in our laboratory (13), we have tentatively concluded that the continuous growth function is, in general, valid for heterogeneous populations. However, it must be forcefully pointed out that the maximum growth rate, the saturation constant, and the yield constant are by no means true constants for such populations. While it would be ideal if these parameters, and others which might be devised to describe kinetic behavior, were simple functions of the type of substrate or waste, it appears to us on an experimental and theoretical basis that such is not the case for heterogeneous populations and that we must be content with a usable range of values. When one considers that the value for maximum growth rate for the same substrate differs for various species, and when one contemplates the changes in bacterial predominance which can occur in mixed or heterogeneous populations, it seems obvious that precise values of kinetic constants for specific substrates or waste waters will not be forthcoming. While it can be said that the rash of recent work on growth kinetics has complicated rather than simplified the kinetic picture, it must be concluded that the true advance within the past decade has been a necessary disenchantment with the empirical methods formerly employed, and that the increasing volume of research in this area should find ultimate fruition in more theoretically correct kinetic descriptions of heterogeneous microbial systems.

Exertion of biochemical oxygen demand.—The kinetic course of the BOD test, which has for many years been used as a means of assessing the pollutional strength of waste water, has been treated as a continuous curve of first-order decreasing rate (23). It has also been described as discontinuous, consisting of two or more first-order curves (24) or as S-shaped, following the pattern of bacterial growth (25). More recently, Busch (26) has shown that oxygen uptake during the exertion of BOD can consist of two main phases with a distinct pause or plateau between the phases. The existence of this type of BOD, or oxygen uptake, curve has been verified by the work of

Wilson & Harrison (27), McWhorter & Heukelekian (28), and Gaudy et al. (29). While it is now generally accepted that the plateau occurs, there has been a considerable amount of doubt concerning its causative mechanisms and the significance of its occurrence. Busch (26) has stated that oxygen utilization beyond the plateau represents the sum of endogenous uptake by bacteria and uptake by protozoa. However, no explanation for the plateau itself, i.e., the distinct pause in oxygen uptake, was advanced, although it was stated that large numbers of protozoa could mask the plateau. The time required to reach the plateau was considered to be that which was needed for removal of the soluble carbon source. Busch & Myrick (30) also concluded that the oxygen used prior to the plateau was a constant percentage of the theoretical oxygen demand of the carbon source (41.1 per cent for glucose).

Using heterogeneous populations, it is doubtful that the plateau value could be expected to be so precisely reproducible and, in our hands at least, it was not. In 51 long-term experiments using a variety of compounds (28 such experiments were conducted using glucose as sole source of carbon) the plateau was apparent in 43 (29). Usually 30 to 40 per cent of the theoretical oxygen demand of the substrate had been exerted at the time of the occurrence of the plateau, but values below and above this range were recorded.

A further complication was introduced when the plateau was observed to occur in studies using a pure culture of bacteria (29). Wilson & Harrison (27) had also observed a plateau in oxygen uptake with the use of a pure bacterial culture and phthalic acid as substrate, and a plateau was apparent in the data for oxidation of various substrates by *Alcaligenes faecalis* in the studies of Marion & Malaney (31). Such observations, of course, created some doubt as to the role played by the protozoa. Wilson & Harrison felt that the plateau might be caused by the delayed onset of endogenous respiration, but no explanation was offered as to the cause of such a delay. Bhatla & Gaudy (32) showed that a plateau in oxygen uptake for a pure culture system, using glucose as the sole source of exogenous carbon, was caused by the release of volatile acids during the removal of glucose in the first stage of oyxgen uptake. After an acclimation period (plateau), volatile acids were removed in a second stage of O_2 uptake. The need for enzyme induction before the second stage of oxygen utilization was demonstrated by introducing chloramphenicol into the system during the first stage of oxygen uptake. It is also interesting to note that Halvorson and his co-workers, using *Bacillus cereus*, have observed two stages of oxygen uptake, separated by a period of low uptake (33) during which acetate-utilizing enzymes were induced (34). Using heterogeneous populations, Bhatla & Gaudy (35) have also demonstrated that a plateau can occur in the BOD bottle as a result of the sequential removal of originally exogenous substrates.

In extended studies with heterogeneous populations designed to determine experimentally the actual role played by the protozoa in exertion of BOD, Bhatla & Gaudy (36) found that oxygen uptake beyond the plateau was due largely to the respiration of protozoa feeding on the bacteria. This experimental proof was in opposition to concepts first put forth by Butterfield, Purdy & Theriault (37) and presently held by many in the field, which stated that protozoa contribute little to oxygen uptake and function merely to keep the bacterial population at a level where replication can continue. There is now experimental proof, based on population counts and other data, that the protozoa play an autonomous role in the exertion of BOD (36), thus substantiating the original suggestion of Busch (26). The plateau in oxygen uptake actually represents the endogenous respiration phase of bacterial metabolism which, if no protozoa were present, would be manifested as a second stage of very low magnitude. The secondary rise in O_2 uptake is actually a third stage, caused by an increase in the predator population. The occurrence of the plateau and its duration depend upon the relative time lag between the peaks in bacterial and protozoan populations. Since the plateau has been shown to occur in three different situations, only one of which involves exhaustion of soluble exogenous substrate, it is rather difficult to place complete reliance in the proposed use of the plateau value (30) as a quantitative measure of waste water purification or substrate removal. However, as a result of our studies (29, 36) it can be concluded that, in populations which are heterogeneous with respect to the cells and substrates they contain, the most probable cause for a substantial second stage of oxygen uptake is the metabolism of bacteria by protozoa.

MECHANISMS OF SUBSTRATE REMOVAL AND GROWTH

Sequential substrate removal.—Much information is now becoming available concerning the mechanisms of substrate removal and the interactions that occur in systems which are heterogeneous with respect to substrate as well as organisms. It was formerly thought that, under these circumstances, the various species present would attack those carbon sources to which they were best suited; thus, the various substrates would come under concurrent attack. However, some years ago Monod (8) showed with pure cultures that diphasic growth could occur in media containing two carbon sources, one of which blocked removal of the other. This work led to intensive investigation of the mechanism of the repression, and to discovery and elucidation of other mechanisms of control of metabolic reactions (38, 39).

Since control mechanisms are of significance in the economy of the cell, they might be expected to apply not only to a few bacterial species but to the majority of organisms and thus possibly to heterogeneous populations. Such an occurrence would have significant ramifications to biological treatment processes, which are subject to both qualitative and quantitative changes in waste composition. The possibility of *en masse* repression and induction of enzyme systems in heterogeneous populations was examined by Gaudy (40) in a mixed substrate consisting of glucose and sorbitol (using cells acclimated to sorbitol), and it was found that sorbitol was not utilized until the glucose had been metabolized. This work was later verified by Prakasam & Dondero

(41). Interest in metabolic control mechanisms in heterogeneous populations has led to continuing research in our laboratory. Briefly, Gaudy and co-workers (42–45) have found that sequential substrate removal occurs with a number of combinations of compounds. It is significant to note that sequential removal was found to depend somewhat upon the age of the cells (45). Young heterogeneous populations which exhibited sequential removal of glucose and sorbitol yielded concomitant removal of these substrates when the cells were aged. The effect could not be attributed simply to changes in predominance during the aging process, since a small inoculum of old cells placed in new medium and harvested near the end of the log growth phase again exhibited sequential substrate removal. The occurrence of sequential removal in systems containing large initial inocula suggested that the blockage mechanism did not necessarily involve repression of enzyme synthesis, since ample quantities of the requisite enzyme system were already present in the acclimated population. With both heterogeneous populations and a prototrophic strain of *Escherichia coli*, Gaudy, Gaudy & Komolrit (43) found that sequential removal of glucose and sorbitol occurred also under non-proliferating conditions, i.e., in the absence of an exogenous source of nitrogen. Furthermore, Komolrit & Gaudy (42) found that even when cells were actively metabolizing various sugar alcohols to which they were acclimated, such as sorbitol, dulcitol, mannitol, or glycerol, additions of glucose caused an immediate metabolism of glucose and a cessation of metabolism of the alcohols. These were not again utilized until all of the glucose had been metabolized. From such studies it seems reasonable to postulate the existence of a metabolic control mechanism which operates in catabolic pathways in a manner analogous to the mechanism of feedback inhibition which is known to exist in biosynthetic pathways.

From the standpoint of operation of biological treatment processes, changes in the chemical structure of the carbon source have been termed "qualitative" shock loadings (46), as distinguished from "quantitative" shock loads which indicate an increase or a decrease in the total amount of carbon source in the incoming waste stream. Komolrit & Gaudy (47) have found that qualitative shock loading can cause serious disruption of completely mixed continuous flow activated sludge units whether the shock loading is administered by rapid injection of a new carbon source or by a change in the inflowing composition without a change in the rate of liquid flow to the aerator. Studies of this type have been extremely useful from an engineering standpoint, since biological waste water treatment facilities are unit operations which, from time to time, are subjected to severe environmental changes. Unlike many other bioengineering operations, selection of the raw materials (the waste water) and precise control of operational conditions are not practical, nor is it possible to control the species of organisms producing the product (purified waste water). It is therefore extremely important to determine, in highly controlled laboratory research, the types of environmental changes which cause severe disruption of treatment efficiency. The ultimate aim must be to seek economical remedial measures for unavoidable changes in environment, and to seek economical ways to control the environment where possible.

Products of partial oxidation.—In the waste water treatment field, organic matter (substrate) has traditionally been measured as the total organic matter subject to biological oxidation (BOD) or to chemical oxidation (COD). In our laboratory, as in others, more specific analyses are now being used in conjunction with the use of defined media. The use of both nonspecific (COD) and specific tests for the removal of substrate in waste water treatment studies has revealed a problem of possibly major significance in biological treatment. In many of the studies of sequential substrate removal described above (43, 45), the total COD could not be accounted for as substrate, measured by specific tests, and it was concluded that portions of one or both substrates were excreted into the medium after partial oxidation. Krishnan & Gaudy (48), and Krishnan (49), have found that in many systems utilizing a single substrate such as glucose, considerable amounts of COD remain after glucose, as measured by anthrone or glucose oxidase, has been removed. Further analysis has shown that volatile acids (primarily acetic) may constitute a large fraction of the COD (49). Intermediates (or end products) may accumulate during active growth or under nonproliferating conditions (48). If adequate nitrogen is available, they are metabolized after the original carbon source has been removed. Clifton has reported similar partial oxidations of glucose by *Bacillus megaterium* (50) and *E. coli* (51). The release of metabolic intermediates during biological treatment could convert an industrial waste containing only a few carbon sources to a much more heterogeneous mixture of compounds, and could seriously affect the overall purification rate and efficiency. These findings also indicate a need for caution in interpreting data from studies in which analyses for specific substrates are used as the only measure of purification rate.

Oxidative assimilation.—It has been known for some time that substrates may be totally removed from solution under nonproliferating conditions. It was shown by Gaudy & Engelbrecht (52) that glucose could be assimilated by heterogeneous populations with almost equal efficiency in the presence or absence of nitrogen. Similar findings were later reported for phenol and acetate by Rao, Speece & Engelbrecht (53). The possibility of oxidative assimilation of waste has suggested two modifications in the design of activated sludge plants for treatment of nitrogen-deficient waste. Rao et al. (53) proposed a flow sheet, using duplicate aerators and settling tanks with nitrogen added to only one aerator. The sludge from this aerator was used as return sludge for both aerators. A somewhat different modification proposed by Komolrit, Goel & Gaudy (54) would also effect savings in nitrogen supplementation, would prevent nitrogen enrichment of the receiving stream and would require less aeration volume. Our studies on a laboratory scale have shown that glucose can be assimilated as carbohydrate in the absence of exogenous nitrogen and converted to protein under endogenous conditions when ammonium ion is added. The sludge is thus regenerated and can be recycled to the aeration tank where it again removes glucose efficiently without the addition of a nitrogen source. Therefore, the effluent would be essentially devoid of nitrogen since nitrogen is added only to the separated sludge which is to be recycled; no nitrogen would be required for the portion of sludge which is to be wasted.

CONSTANTS FOR DESIGN AND OPERATION

In the design of facilities for the biological treatment of wastes, values for design factors such as oxygen requirement, biological solids level, rate of solids production, purification rate, etc., must be estimated from past experience or from pilot plant experiments. The establishment of constant relationships between any of the factors involved in design or in operation would be of considerable value, and several such relationships have been proposed.

Relation between biological solids and oxygen uptake.—Recently, the effect of initial biological solids concentration on the percentage of the theoretical oxygen demand of the substrate exerted at the time of substrate removal has been investigated. Using glucose as the carbon source, McWhorter & Heukelekian (28) ran experiments at three initial biological solids concentrations varying from 0.5 per cent sewage seed up to 1010 mg/l activated sludge. They found that, at the lower initial solids level, 30 per cent of the theoretical oxygen demand of glucose had been exerted at the time of COD removal, whereas for the highest solids level only 21 per cent had been exerted. When glucose (anthrone), rather than COD, was measured, it was found that the removal of glucose approached completion at 18 per cent of the theoretical oxygen demand regardless of the initial biological solids concentration. In a series of 44 experiments, Rao & Gaudy (55) found that, whether COD or anthrone was used as a measure of substrate removal, the percentage of the theoretical oxygen demand of the substrate exerted at the time of substrate removal followed a decreasing trend as initial biological solids concentration was increased. Our results were consistent with the following hypothesis: Cells removed from the stationary phase of a batch culture and placed in a new medium normally require a period of adjustment to the new environment before replication can begin. During this lag period the cells increase in weight as carbon stores and metabolic pools are replenished and enzymes necessary for balanced synthesis are formed. The behavior of sludge removed from a batch-activated sludge unit at some time after the substrate has been exhausted or the sludge returned to the aerator in the activated sludge process is comparable to cells which have existed in the stationary phase for some period of time. These cells, placed in fresh medium, remove substrate initially without replication, and it seems apparent that the larger the initial cell concentration the greater the percentage of the available substrate which may be utilized during the early lag phase. The relation of the percentage theoretical oxygen demand exerted at substrate removal to initial solids can be explained by assuming some degree of respiratory control in bacteria, i.e., if there is obligatory coupling between phosphorylation and O_2 uptake (56). It has been shown in a number of experiments in our laboratory (52, 55) and by van Gils (57) that when sludge is placed in a fresh medium the initial product of synthesis is predominantly carbohydrate, particularly when the substrate is a carbohydrate. A possible function of glycogen synthesis as an overflow outlet for excess ATP has been proposed (58, 59). Since the energy requirement for such synthesis would be considerably lower than that for balanced synthesis and growth (59), the ratio of ATP utilization to substrate utilization would be low. If some degree of respiratory control exists in bacteria, oxygen uptake during the initial portion of the lag period would also be proportionately low. Although studies with bacterial particles have failed to demonstrate respiratory control (60), these experiments are not conclusive because of the technical difficulties involved in preparation of phosphorylating systems from bacteria (61). However, it would seem to us that the occurrence of oxidative assimilation, with the usual fairly high efficiency of conversion of substrate to storage products, is indicative of respiratory control and of coupling of ATP production to synthesis. While the nature of the synthetic products is different in proliferating and nonproliferating cells, and ATP production is uncoupled from the synthetic reactions involved in growth, as pointed out by Senez (62), the mechanism of obligatory coupling to synthesis (products unspecified) is retained. The occurrence of a lag period, during which large amounts of substrate can be removed without appreciable replication of cells, also accounts for the approximately linear uptake of oxygen and substrate often observed with relatively large initial concentrations of sludge (14, 55). Such a system is functionally analogous to a nonproliferating system, i.e., one in which there is no exogenous nitrogen supply and it would be expected to exhibit approximately zero-order kinetics until cell replication begins, or at least until an appreciable amount of enzyme synthesis has occurred.

Relation between biological solids and purification rate.—The relationship between the rate of waste water purification and biological solids concentration has been of long-standing interest in the water pollution control field. It has been generally held that this relationship is linear and that the slope of the line of correlation is dependent upon the nature of the carbon source or type of waste (14, 63). Recently, Rao & Gaudy (55) have shown that, while there is a linear relationship between substrate removal rate and initial biological solids concentration for portions of the same sample of activated sludge, the relationship is not constant for random sludge samples taken from a system operated over a long period of time. Therefore, the relationship is not solely dependent upon the given substrate or type of waste. It was found that changes in the slope of the line could be correlated with gross changes in predominance, detectible by macroscopic and microscopic observation (55).

Relation between biological solids production and substrate concentration.— Both microbiologists and water pollution control engineers have been concerned for a number of years with the problem of predicting the proportion of substrate which will be assimilated into cell material. Studies by Placak & Ruchhoft (64) with a number of pure organic compounds showed that the proportion of substrate converted to cells varied within classes of compounds, but that variation was even greater between classes of compounds. The highest yields (maximum, 85 per cent) were found with carbohydrates and the lowest (minimum, 10 per cent) with organic acids. They concluded that yield depends upon the specific substrate being utilized. A number of other investigators (15, 65–68), using domestic and industrial wastes and pure compounds, have concluded that sludge production is related by a constant factor to the BOD or COD of the waste. Although ranges of yields have been reported, the yield constants generally accepted are approximately 0.5 and 0.67, expressed as fraction of BOD and COD loading, respectively.

Reports in the microbiological literature over a longer period of time indicate that no generalized statement can be made concerning yields in aerobic systems. Bauchop & Elsden (69) were able to generalize concerning the relation between yield and ATP production in several anaerobic cultures in which the substrate was used almost exclusively for energy production and cell material was synthesized from preformed monomers supplied in the medium. The problem of yield prediction in aerobic cultures is complicated by uncertainties as to the ATP yield from specific substrates in specific microorganisms and the extent of coupling between ATP production and synthetic reactions. Gunsalus & Shuster (70) and Senez (62) have discussed the data available for aerobic bacteria and the problems inherent in their interpretation. Kluyver [see (71)] and Clifton (71) concluded that growth in an aerobic system is limited by the nature of the substrate (ease of conversion to necessary building blocks) rather than by the free energy available from the substrate, and experiments by Siegel & Clifton (72, 73) supported this concept. Hadjipetrou et al. (74) have attempted to relate yield to oxygen uptake for *Aerobacter aerogenes* with a large number of substrates, using the Y^O (yield per oxygen atom consumed) and the Y^{ATP} (determined under anaerobic conditions) to calculate the P/O for aerobic growth. Ratios of approximately three were found for maltose, sucrose, sorbitol, glucose, fructose, and gluconate, but for other compounds much lower ratios were found (e.g., 0.6 for lactate and malate, and 0.5 for acetate). These results would seem to support the Kluyver hypothesis, i.e., although *A. aerogenes* is capable of obtaining the maximum ATP yield (three per oxygen atom), ATP production is not the limiting factor for aerobic growth except possibly on substrates readily converted to cell material.

It is quite probable that the extent of uncoupling of ATP production and utilization varies both with the conditions of growth and with the organism. An even more important source of variation in hypothetical energy-limited yield, however, would be the efficiency of ATP production. Differences in catabolic pathways, differences in electron transport systems, and in efficiency of coupling electron transport to phosphorylation would be expected to produce different yields of ATP from the same substrate in different organisms. Recent studies by Stouthamer (75) have shown that *Gluconobacter liquefaciens* achieves a P/O ratio of only 0.40 with glucose-6-phosphate and 0.09 with NADH. The molar growth yield, however, corresponds to a Y^{ATP} of 10, equal to that found in other organisms.

In summary, work with pure cultures has not yet clarified the factors which affect growth yield, but it can be stated with a considerable degree of certainty that yield in aerobic systems is not a constant percentage of the available substrate, regardless of its nature, nor is it directly proportional to the available free energy of the substrate, regardless of growth conditions or the organism involved.

In applying these findings to waste treatment processes, the problem is complicated by the heterogeneity of both the biological population and the medium. Four recent studies have arrived at different conclusions. Servizi & Bogan (68, 76) have attempted to revive the concept of constant proportionality between yield and the free energy of oxidation of the substrate. Based on yields with heterogeneous cultures for several compounds, they found a correlation between sludge production and ΔF_{ox}. Recalculation of data published by Siegel & Clifton (72, 73) and McKinney, Tomlinson & Wilcox (77) as molar growth yields also showed a correlation with ΔF_{ox}, although the constants obtained from the different sets of data were in serious disagreement, as pointed out by McCarty (78). The difference between Servizi & Bogan's and Siegel & Clifton's interpretation of the same data would seem to lie in the amount of variation one is willing to accept in a "constant." If Servizi & Bogan's equation for yield as a function of COD, $Y = 0.37$ COD, is applied to Hadjipetrou's data for *A. aerogenes*, the predictive value of the equation is slight. Those substrates, in particular, which require considerable manipulation to bring them into biosynthetic pathways, produce much lower amounts of cell material than the equation predicts.

Hetling, Washington & Rao (18) criticized the conclusions of Servizi & Bogan on the basis of theoretical considerations and also because a factor for endogenous metabolism was not included. Hetling et al. determined growth yields in continuous flow with several pure cultures and mixtures of pure cultures, using as substrates glucose, acetate, glutamate, an industrial waste, and a synthetic sewage. A mixture of monomers was also added in one experiment. By operating at a series of dilution rates and plotting yield vs. dilution rate, the intercept of the plot could be used to determine the "heterogeneous metabolism rate" which includes both the "basal metabolism rate and the death rate." Hetling et al. concluded that the heterogeneous metabolism rate was not constant for all organisms or all substrates, but even after correction for this factor, yield varied with the substrate and with the organism. Higher yields were obtained on complex than on simple media, and with mixtures of organisms than with single organisms.

McCarty (79) recognized the necessity of considering both the coupling of oxidation to phosphorylation and the coupling of ATP production to synthetic reactions. He proposed a formula relating yield to free energy, which contained proportionality constants involving coupling of both types as well as the maintenance requirement, and attempted to evaluate these constants on the basis of large numbers of yield determinations reported in the literature. He concluded that transfer efficiencies (efficiency of utilization of free energy in cellular synthesis) for aerobic heterotrophs are generally in the range of 20 to 40 per cent, although a number of reported yields fall considerably outside this range. His conclusion that reasonable predictions of yield can be based on free energy, energy transfer efficiency, and energy requirements for synthesis and maintenance would seem to be somewhat optimistic at the present time since, of these factors, only free energy can be approximated with any degree of accuracy. However, when more data obtained under standardized experimental conditions are available, this approach may prove to be quite useful.

It seems reasonable that both the agreement among yield factors reported by some investigators and the wide divergence of yields reported by others can be explained on the basis of selection in heterogeneous populations. Different pure cultures are known to produce different amounts of cellular material from the same substrate. It is to be expected that, if the carbon source constitutes the only limiting factor, those organisms which can grow most efficiently on the substrate will predominate. However, not all investigations, particularly those in the waste water treatment field and those using complex wastes, have been conducted under identical conditions or even under conditions in which the carbon source was known to be the yield-determining factor. Some investigators (28, 80) have used nitrate as a nitrogen source, and Senez (62) has reported that yields with nitrate are considerably lower than those with ammonia using the same carbon source. It is possible that some such factor limited the yields reported by Servizi & Bogan (68, 76), since they were of the same magnitude as those reported using nitrate (28), but their data connot be evaluated on this basis since they did not report the constituents of the medium used. A second important factor is the failure of many investigators to determine the amount of carbon source actually used. It has been assumed that the carbon source is either oxidized completely to CO_2 and H_2O or converted to cell material. Several recent studies have shown that even during active aerobic metabolism intermediates may accumulate in both heterogeneous populations (48, 49) and in pure cultures (50, 51). McCarty's (78) suggestion that "there seems to be more difference between investigators than between substrates" may be quite correct, since the conditions of the experiment may affect not only the yields of individual organisms, but may affect also the predominance of organisms. The importance of the latter factor was demonstrated in an extensive investigation by Rao & Gaudy (55). Using a minimal medium with glucose as sole carbon source, three laboratory scale batch-activated sludge systems were operated for prolonged periods of time, 90, 90, and 65 days, respectively. Sludge yields were determined in 44 separate experiments, using in each experiment, several different initial concentrations of sludge from each population. The average yield constant, expressed as percentage of COD removed, was 65 which agrees well with that reported by a number of other investigators. However, the coefficient of variation for yields obtained in different experiments was 17 per cent, corresponding to a range of yields of 48 to 82 per cent for populations grown on a single carbon source. The different yields were correlated with macroscopically and microscopically detectible changes in predominance. It therefore seems evident that factors other than efficiency of conversion of carbon to cell material may govern selection in a mixed population, and that yields measured in short-term experiments may not be applicable in practice to activated sludges. The degree of environmental selection may be expected to vary with the particular treatment process employed and also with characteristics of the waste other than amount of oxidizable carbon sources.

ANAEROBIC DIGESTION

The work of Buswell and Barker and their co-workers [see (81) for review] with pure and enriched cultures of methane-forming bacteria, furnished the major outlines of the consecutive fermentations involved in the conversion of CO_2, fatty acids, and alcohols to methane. Barker proposed a general scheme for methane formation involving a hypothetical one-carbon carrier, X. However, the details of the reactions involved in methane formation have remained completely unexplored until recently when Wolfe & co-workers (82, 83) and Blaylock & Stadtman (84) succeeded in preparing cell-free extracts of methane bacteria which were capable of forming methane. Studies using these extracts now indicate that tetrahydrofolate may function at least partially as the X of Barker's scheme. Formation of $^{14}CH_4$ from 3-^{14}C-serine, 5,10-^{14}C-methylenetetrahydrofolate, and 5-^{14}C-methyltetrahydrofolate has been obtained by Wood et al. (83). Formation of $^{14}CH_4$ from methylcobalamin ($^{14}CH_3$-B_{12}) had previously been observed by both Wolin, Wolin & Wolfe (82), and by Blaylock & Stadtman (84). All of these reactions are completely dependent upon ATP. Neither the function of ATP nor the position of CH_3-B_{12} in the overall scheme is understood. However, Wood et al. (83) have shown that *Methanobacterium omelianskii* forms formic acid from 5,10-methylenetetrahydrofolate in the absence of ATP, and have suggested that the availability of ATP may therefore regulate the route of C_1 metabolism in this organism.

Much research in the waste water treatment field has been concerned with the cause and the prevention of digester failure, i.e., accumulation of volatile acids and a decrease or cessation of methane formation. Pohland & Bloodgood (85) have recommended analyses which may be used to detect impending digester failures. The inhibition of methane formation has been variously attributed to the lowered pH (86), toxicity of the acids (87), or associated salt toxicity (88). Buzzell & Sawyer (89) have suggested that the initial event in digester failure must involve the inhibition of methane formation to account for the accumulation of acids which is usually considered to be the cause, not the effect, of a decrease in methane formation. Jeris & McCarty

(90) suggested that digester upsets may occur because of a change in predominance of acid-forming bacteria, resulting in the accumulation of different substrates for which the appropriate species of methane bacteria are not present in sufficient numbers. This explanation appears reasonable in view of the narrow substrate specificities of methane bacteria (81).

Jeris & McCarty (90) have applied the ^{14}C tracer technique used by Barker and Buswell (81) to studies with heterogeneous populations and have demonstrated that the labeling of methane is the same as that found in pure culture studies for ethanol and acetaldehyde. Octanoic and palmitic acid also produced methane labeled as predicted on the basis of complete conversion to acetate via β-oxidation. However, fermentation of other substrates such as glucose, leucine, and nutrient broth, from which a number of possible fermentation products may be formed, yielded inconclusive results with labeling studies. It would seem that tracer studies with heterogeneous populations are likely to contribute little useful information regarding pathways of fermentation. Most of the pathways for fermentation of single substrates by various pure cultures are known and it is the interactions of these organisms and their consecutive fermentations which lead to the final conversion of the waste to CO_2 and CH_4.

McCarty (91) has attempted to define the rate-limiting step in sludge digestion by the application of steady-state kinetics. His derivation of kinetic equations for these studies must be considered irrelevant, since steady-state kinetics cannot be applied to systems fed once in 24 hours using a waste of unknown and possibly varying complexity and having a population composed of many interdependent subpopulations. However, his conclusions, which did not depend upon the use of the model, are of interest. Based upon analysis of compounds accumulating, as solids retention time was reduced, it was concluded that the fermentation of free fatty acids represents the slowest step in the overall process. Studies with formate, methanol, propionate, and acetate showed that the minimum solids retention time for fermentation of these compounds increased in the order given.

Summary and Conclusions

From this brief review, it should be apparent that the microbiology of waste waters is basically not unlike other areas of microbiology. However, there are major points of difference and these lie primarily in the heterogeneity of the population, the high ratios of organisms to available substrate, and the physiological condition of the cells. While these aspects add difficulty to the already perplexing problems of understanding biological processes, they also increase the challenge to the researcher in this field. Information obtained with pure cultures may be useful to the engineer, but application to waste treatment systems must always be made with these basic differences in mind, and many problems must be solved by new approaches dictated by the specific characteristics of biological treatment systems. It seems apparent that while we may expect improved understanding and more satisfying mathematical expressions for bioengineering processes, we must be content with "constants" which represent a usable range of values rather than a precise numerical value. While there is increasing need for mathematical formulations of predictive value, there is an even greater need for accumulation of sufficient data, obtained under controlled conditions, to test the validity of models, equations, and theories which are often proposed and accepted with a minimum of experimental verification. However, the overall picture which emerges from a review of recent work in this field is one of rapidly developing effort to understand the specialized ecological systems involved in the microbial purification of waste waters.

LITERATURE CITED

1. Gaudy, E., and Wolfe, R. S., *Appl. Microbiol.*, **9**, 580–84 (1961)
2. Mulder, E. G., and van Veen, W. L., *Antonie van Leeuwenhoek J. Microbiol. Serol.*, **29**, 121–53 (1963)
3. Ordal, E. J., and Palmer, F. E., in *Continuous Cultivation of Microorganisms*, 133–39 (Malek, I., Beran, K., and Hospodka, J., Eds., Academic Press, Inc., New York, 382 pp., 1962)
4. Shindala, A., Bungay, H. R., III, Krieg, N. R., and Culbert, K., *J. Bacteriol.*, **89**, 693–96 (1965)
5. Monod, J., *Ann. Inst. Pasteur*, **79**, 390–410 (1950)
6. Novick, A., and Szilard, L., *Science*, **112**, 715–16 (1950)
7. Garrett, M. T., Jr., and Sawyer, C. N., *Proc. Ind. Waste Conf., 7th, Purdue Univ., 1952.* (Purdue Eng. Extension Ser. No. 79, **36**, No. 6, 51–77, 1952)
8. Monod, J., *Ann. Rev. Microbiol.*, **3**, 371–94 (1949)
9. James, T. W., *Ann. Rev. Microbiol.*, **15**, 27–46 (1961)
10. Moser, H., The Dynamics of Bacterial Populations Maintained in the Chemostat, *Carnegie Inst. Wash. Publ. 614* (1958)
11. Continuous Culture of Micro-organisms, *Soc. Chem. Ind. London, Monograph*, 12 (Macmillan Co., New York, 1961)
12. Malek, I., Beran, K., and Hospodka, J., Eds., *Continuous Cultivation of Microorganisms* (Academic Press, Inc., New York, 382 pp., 1962)
13. Ramanathan, M., *Kinetics of completely mixed activated sludge* (Doctoral thesis, Oklahoma State University, Stillwater, Oklahoma, 1966)
14. Eckenfelder, W. W., in *Advances in Biological Waste Treatment*, 277–89 (Eckenfelder, W. W., and McCabe, J., Eds., Pergamon Press, New York, 1963)
15. McKinney, R. E., *J. Sanit. Eng. Div., Am. Soc. Civil Engrs.*, **88**, SA3, 87–113 (1962)
16. Grieves, R. B., Milbury, W. F., and Pipes, W. O., Jr., *J. Water Pollution Control Federation*, **36**, 619–35 (1964)
17. Wilson, I. S., *Proc. Intern. Congr. Water Pollution Res., 1st, London, 1962.* (Preprint, Sect. 2, Paper 32, 1962)
18. Hetling, L. J., Washington, D. R., and Rao, S. S., *Proc. Ind. Waste Conf., 19th, Purdue Univ., 1964* (Purdue Eng. Extension Ser. No. 117, **49**, No. 2, 687–715, 1965)
19. Schultze, K. L., *Water Sewage Works*, **11**, 526–38 (1964)
20. Fugimoto, Y., *J. Theoret. Biol.*, **5**, 171–91 (1963)
21. Downing, A. L., and Wheatland, A. B., *Trans. Inst. Chem. Eng. London*, **40**, 91–103 (1962)
22. Marr, A. G., Nilson, E. H., and Clark, D. J., *Ann. N. Y. Acad. Sci.*, **102**, 536–48 (1963)
23. Theriault, E. J., The oxygen demand of polluted waters, *U. S. Public Health Serv., Bull.*, 173 (1927)
24. Greenfield, R. E., and Elder, A. L., *Ind. Eng. Chem.*, **18**, 291–94 (1926)
25. Greenfield, R. E., Elder, A. L., and McMurray, R. E., *Ind. Eng. Chem.*, **18**, 1276–79 (1926)
26. Busch, A. W., *Sewage Ind. Wastes*, **30**, 1336–49 (1958)
27. Wilson, I. S., and Harrison, M. E., *J. Inst. Sewage Purif.*, **3**, 261–75 (1960)
28. McWhorter, T. R., and Heukelekian, H., *Proc. Intern. Congr. Water Pollution Res. 1st, London,*

1962. (Preprint, Sect. 2, Paper 23, 1962)

29. Gaudy, A. F., Jr., Bhatla, M. N., Follett, R. H., and Abu-Niaaj, F., *J. Water Pollution Control Federation,* **37,** 444–59 (1965)

30. Busch, A. W., and Myrick, N., *J. Water Pollution Control Federation,* **33,** 897–905 (1961)

31. Marion, C. V., and Malaney, G. W., *J. Water Pollution Control Federation,* **35,** 1269–84 (1963)

32. Bhatla, M. N., and Gaudy, A. F., Jr., *Biotech. Bioeng.,* **7,** 387–404 (1965)

33. Halvorson, H. O., *J. Appl. Bacteriol.,* **20,** 305–14 (1957)

34. Hanson, R. S., Srinivasan, V. R., and Halvorson, H. O., *J. Bacteriol.,* **85,** 451–60 (1963)

35. Bhatla, M. N., and Gaudy, A. F., Jr., *Appl. Microbiol.,* **13,** 345–47 (1965)

36. Bhatla, M. N., and Gaudy, A. F., Jr., *J. Sanit. Eng. Div., Am. Soc. Civil Engrs.,* **91,** SA3, 63–87 (1965)

37. Butterfield, C. T., Purdy, W. C., and Theriault, E. J., *Public Health Rept. U. S.,* **46,** 393–426 (1931)

38. Cohen, G. N., *Ann. Rev. Microbiol.,* **19,** 105–26 (1965)

39. Maas, W. K., and McFall, E., *Ann. Rev. Microbiol.,* **18,** 264–71 (1964)

40. Gaudy, A. F., Jr., *Appl. Microbiol.,* **10,** 264–71 (1962)

41. Prakasam, T. B. S., and Dondero, N. C., *Proc. Ind. Waste Conf., 19th, Purdue Univ., 1964.* (Purdue Eng. Extension Ser. No. 117, **49,** No. 2, 835–45, 1965)

42. Komolrit, K., and Gaudy, A. F., Jr. *Proc. Ind. Waste Conf., 19th, Purdue Univ., 1964* (Purdue Eng. Extension Ser. No. 117, **49,** No. 2, 796–810, 1965)

43. Gaudy, A. F., Jr., Gaudy, E. T., and Komolrit, K., *Appl. Microbiol.,* **11,** 157–62 (1963)

44. Gaudy, A. F., Jr., Komolrit, K., and Gaudy, E. T., *Appl. Microbiol.,* **12,** 280–86 (1964)

45. Gaudy, A. F., Jr., Komolrit, K., and Bhatla, M. N., *J. Water Pollution Control Federation,* **35,** 903–22 (1963)

46. Gaudy, A. F., Jr., and Engelbrecht, R. S., *J. Water Pollution Control Federation,* **33,** 800–16 (1961)

47. Komolrit, K., and Gaudy, A. F., Jr., *J. Water Pollution Control Federation.,* **38,** 85–101 (1966)

48. Krishnan, P., and Gaudy, A. F., Jr., *Biotech. Bioeng.,* **7,** 455–70 (1965)

49. Krishnan, P., *Biochemical response of activated sludge to quantitative shock loading.* (Doctoral thesis, Oklahoma State University, Stillwater, 1966)

50. Clifton, C. E., *J. Bacteriol.,* **85,** 1365–70 (1963)

51. Clifton, C. E., *J. Bacteriol.,* **85,** 1371–77 (1963)

52. Gaudy, A. F., Jr., and Engelbrecht, R. S., in *Advances in Biological Waste Treatment,* 11–26. (Eckenfelder, W. W., and McCabe, J., Eds., Pergamon Press, New York, 431 pp., 1963)

53. Rao, C. V. R., Speece, R. E., and Engelbrecht, R. S., *Proc. Ind. Waste Conf., 18th, Purdue Univ., 1963.* (Purdue Eng. Extension Ser. No. 115, **48,** No. 3, 427–46, 1964)

54. Komolrit, K., Goel, K. C., and Gaudy, A. F., Jr., *Regulation of exogenous nitrogen supply and its possible applications to the activated sludge process.* (Paper presented at 38th Ann. Conf., Water Pollution Control Federation, Atlantic City, N. J., October, 1965) (To be published)

55. Rao, B. S., and Gaudy, A. F., Jr., *J. Water Pollution Control Federation.* (In press, 1966)

56. Newsholme, E. A., *Sci. Progr.,* **53,** 237–55 (1965)

57. van Gils, H. W., *Bacteriology of activated sludge,* Rept. No. 32, Res. Inst. Public Health Engr., Netherlands (1964)

58. Bovell, C. R., and Helgerson, R., *Bacteriol. Proc.,* 192 (1961)

59. Duguid, J. P., and Wilkinson, J. F., *Symp. Soc. Gen. Microbiol.,* **11,** 69–99 (1961)

60. Smith, L., in *The Bacteria,* **II,** 365–96. (Gunsalus, I. C., and Stanier, R. Y., Eds., Academic Press, Inc., New York, 508 pp., 1961)

61. Lascelles, J., *Symp. Soc. Gen. Microbiol.,* **15,** 32–56 (1965)

62. Senez, J. C., *Bacteriol. Rev.,* **26,** 95–107 (1962)

63. Eckenfelder, W. W., and O'Connor, D. J., *Biological Waste Treatment.* (Pergamon Press, New York, 289 pp., 1961)

64. Placak, O. R., and Ruchhoft, C. C., *Sewage Works J.,* **19,** 423–40 (1947)

65. Hoover, S. R., Jasewicz, L., Pepinsky, J. B., and Porges, N., *Sewage Ind. Wastes,* **23,** 167–73 (1951)

66. Helmers, E. N., Frame, J. D., Greenberg, A. E., and Sawyer, C. N.,

Sewage Ind. Wastes, **23**, 884–99 (1951)

67. Heukelekian, H., Orford, H. E., and Manganelli, R., *Sewage Ind. Wastes*, **23**, 945–58 (1951)

68. Servizi, J. A., and Bogan, R. H., *J. Sanit. Eng. Div., Am. Soc. Civil Engrs.*, **89**, SA3, 17–40 (1963)

69. Bauchop, T., and Elsden, S., *J. Gen. Microbiol.*, **23**, 457–69 (1960)

70. Gunsalus, I. C., and Shuster, C. W., in *The Bacteria*, **II**, 1–58. (Gunsalus, I. C., and Stanier, R. Y., Eds., Academic Press, Inc., New York, 508 pp., 1961)

71. Clifton, C. E., *Advan. Enzymol.*, **6**, 269–308 (1946)

72. Siegel, B. V., and Clifton, C. E., *J. Bacteriol.*, **60**, 573–83 (1950)

73. Siegel, B. V., and Clifton, C. E., *J. Bacteriol.*, **60**, 585–93 (1950)

74. Hadjipetrou, L. P., Gerrits, J. P., Teulings, F. A. G., and Stouthamer, A. H., *J. Gen. Microbiol.*, **36**, 139–50 (1964)

75. Stouthamer, A. H., *Biochim. Biophys. Acta*, **56**, 19–32 (1962)

76. Servizi, J. A., and Bogan, R. H., *J. Water Pollution Control Federation*, **36**, 607–18 (1964)

77. McKinney, R. E., Tomlinson, H. D., and Wilcox, R. L., *Sewage Ind. Wastes*, **28**, 547–57 (1956)

78. McCarty, P. L., *J. Sanit. Eng. Div., Am. Soc. Civil Engrs.*, **89**, SA2, 65–68 (1963)

79. McCarty, P. L., *Proc. Intern. Congr. Water Pollution Res., 2nd, Tokyo, 1964*. (Preprint, Sect. 11, Paper 9, 1964)

80. Pipes, W. O., Jr., Miholits, E. M., and Boyle, O. W., *Proc. Ind. Waste Conf., 18th, Purdue Univ., 1963*. (Purdue Eng. Extension Ser. No. 115, **48**, No. 3, 418–26, 1964)

81. Barker, H. A., *Bacterial Fermentations.* (John Wiley & Sons, Inc., New York, 90 pp., 1956)

82. Wolin, M. J., Wolin, E. A., and Wolfe, R. S., *Biochem. Biophys. Res. Commun.*, **12**, 464–68 (1963)

83. Wood, J. M., Allam, A. M., Brill, W. J., and Wolfe, R. S., *J. Biol. Chem.*, **240**, 4564–69 (1965)

84. Blaylock, B. A., and Stadtman, T. C., *Biochem. Biophys. Res. Commun.*, **11**, 34–38 (1963)

85. Pohland, F. G., and Bloodgood, D. E., *J. Water Pollution Control Federation*, **35**, 11–42 (1963)

86. Cassell, E. A., and Sawyer, C. N., *Sewage Ind. Wastes*, **31**, 123–32 (1959)

87. Buswell, A. M., and Hatfield, W. D., Anaerobic Fermentation, Illinois State Water Surv. Bull. 32 (1936)

88. McCarty, P. L., and McKinney, R. E., *J. Water Pollution Control Federation*, **33**, 399–415 (1961)

89. Buzzell, J. C., Jr., and Sawyer, C. M., *J. Water Pollution Control Federation*, **35**, 205–21 (1963)

90. Jeris, J. S., and McCarty, P. L., *J. Water Pollution Control Federation*, **37**, 178–92 (1965)

91. McCarty, P. L. *Kinetics of waste assimilation in anaerobic treatment* (Paper presented at annual meeting Society for Industrial Microbiology, Urbana, Ill., August, 1965)

RESISTANCE OF PLANTS TO INFECTIOUS AGENTS[1]

By Joseph Kuć

Departments of Biochemistry, Botany and Plant Pathology,
Purdue University, Lafayette, Indiana

Contents

PENETRATION INTO HOST............................... 338
PRODUCTION OF INHIBITORS........................... 342
DETOXICATION... 348
SUSCEPTIBILITY....................................... 352
SHIFTS IN METABOLISM................................ 354
   Respiration, Enzyme Activity, and Proteins................ 355
   Biosynthetic Pathways................................... 360
SUMMARY... 364

Multifarious forms of plant and animal life exist in a common environment, but the parasitism of one form by another is rare. All plants have resistance to some pathogens under certain conditions (1). It is the unique combination of host, pathogen, environment, and their interaction that results in susceptibility.

Many terms have been used to describe and interpret aspects of disease resistance. The terms, disease resistance and immunity, describe different degrees of the same thing (2). Various degrees of resistance are possible, with immunity being the ultimate in resistance. Immunity is absolute; therefore, an immune plant would not be attacked by an infectious agent. Resistance is the extent to which a plant can withstand, oppose, lessen, or overcome the attack of a pathogen. Susceptibility is the extent to which it cannot. Field or practical resistance refers to a degree of resistance great enough to prevent serious crop loss though there may be considerable invasion of the host by the pathogen, and expression of limited symptoms typical of susceptibility. Hypersensitivity is a violent and rapid reaction of a plant to the presence of an infectious agent resulting in the death of a limited number of host cells and containment of the agent. Hypersensitivity can be considered extreme metabolic susceptibility, but its practical effect is extreme resistance. Similarly, an organism with high metabolic resistance may be susceptible. Thus, an extreme allergic response in animals can lead to death, though the antibody-antigen reaction is a vital part of an animal's disease resistance mechanism, and the hypersensitive reaction of a leaf to mass inoculum can cause abscission. Occasionally, immunity is considered a zero relationship between a plant and a pathogen, and susceptibility and resistance are based on the interaction of the two systems (3). A zero relationship would imply that the patho-

---

[1] The survey of the literature pertaining to this review was concluded in November 1965.

gen does not influence the metabolism of the plant and the plant does not influence the metabolism of the pathogen. Accordingly, a plant would be immune only if the pathogen could not penetrate its tissues or influence the plant by its presence. Such a phenomenon would be rare. Menke et al. (4), in their thorough investigation, indicated that even ungerminated spores of *Rhizopus stolonifer* on a carrot disk stimulated the production of an inhibitory substance.

Plants are considered diseased if they have become altered in their physiology, morphology, or development to such a degree that signs of such alterations are obvious (5). Disease can be considered a departure from normal; however, the normal condition is a matter of definition. It is apparent that the terms, susceptibility and resistance, as commonly used are largely based on economic or aesthetic considerations rather than on metabolic function. Resistance is not a static condition, either present or absent in a plant, but rather one that, under a given set of conditions, is adequate to prevent a deleterious effect on the plant as judged by man. Temperature, light, nutrition, moisture, oxygen tension, and age all effect the metabolism of the plant and microorganism and, hence, their resistance. The metabolism of host and pathogen are distinct and it is not surprising that both may be affected differently by environmental conditions. Resistance is often a result of an interaction of the metabolism of host and pathogen, which gives rise to a distinctive metabolism—that of the diseased tissue. Thus, it is not surprising that its expression is not always predictable from the effect of environment on the metabolism of host or pathogen alone. For a clear understanding of the defense mechanisms of plants to invasion and proliferation of infectious agents, it is important to differentiate between economic and metabolic definitions of susceptibility and resistance.

This review will be concerned primarily with fungal and bacterial diseases of plants. Comparatively little has been published concerning the biochemical basis for the disease resistance of plants to viruses.

PENETRATION INTO HOST

The penetration of host tissues by microorganisms is a complex process that is not well understood. Why do some microorganisms penetrate only wounded tissue, others stomata, and still others through the intact cuticle? The mode of transmission of a microorganism to the site of penetration can also be highly specific. Thus, a plant might be resistant to a disease because of its resistance to an insect vector. Not all spores germinate on all plant tissues (4, 6). The ritual of penetration and establishment of physiological contact with the host can be highly specific with the formation of structures such as germ tubes, stroma, appresoria, infection cushions, infection pegs, haustoria, and primary and secondary mycelia. Specificity is exhibited in parasitism with regard to tissue attacked, mechanism of entrance, ritual of penetration, and, at times, mode of pathogen transmission. Studies using artificial membranes and foils (7) at best consider only the mechanical phase of penetration.

The outermost walls of epidermal cells of foliage, and the roots of some plants, are coated with a thin layer of cutin and waxes (8–11) composed of a mixture of esters, hydrocarbons, carbonyl derivatives, alcohols, and acids (12–18). Often the cutin extends in the form of a very thin membrane via stomata into intercellular spaces (19–22). Beneath the cutin is the cuticular layer which contains progressively less cutin and waxes and more pectin, hemicellulose, and cellulose. In this review the cuticle will refer to the outer layer of cutin and waxes, whereas the cuticular layer will refer to the layers beneath containing polysaccharides.

Openings through the cuticle to the tissue surface have been observed in some tissues (8, 23–25) and not in others (10, 26). Wax patterns on growing leaves suggest that the upper walls of epidermal cells enlarge at the cell margins (26). Thus, the greater susceptibility of growing leaves to herbicides and some microorganisms might be related to a permeable immature zone in the cuticle through which chemicals can enter or leave readily and through which microorganisms can penetrate (27–29). The leaching of nutrients from plant tissue, however, has also been reported to increase greatly just before maturity and death (30). Loss of differential membrane permeability with age may account for this phenomenon. The fire blight bacterium has been shown to penetrate through foliar trichomes and hydathodes on the upper surface of apple leaves, which are free of stomata, as well as through lenticels of the stem (31). The ions, ^{45}Ca, ^{86}Rb, $^{35}SO_4$, and ^{36}Cl, moved through the isolated cuticle of tomato fruit, having no stomata, and green onion leaves with stomata (21, 32). Ion penetration occurred preferentially inward from the outside. The cuticle is not continuous or uniform in thickness or structure (10), and the existence of stomata, trichomes, and hydathodes suggests the presence of active or infectible sites which are required by some microorganisms for penetration. These sites may either be openings through the cuticle or areas adapted for penetration because of thinness of the intact cuticle or the presence of anatomical features necessary for the establishment of a host-parasite interaction. Access to such sites may also be very important in disease resistance. Rich (33), in his review of the role of stomata in disease resistance, emphasizes their importance not only as portals of entry for microorganisms but also as exits permitting their dissemination. Infectible or active sites might explain cuticular penetration of foliar-applied nutrients (34), the appearance of small necrotic pits below drops of salt solutions on the upper surface of apple leaves (35), and the observation that only 50 per cent of the spores of *Venturia inaequalis* germinated on the upper surface of rapidly expanding apple leaves as compared to 90 per cent in a nutrient solution. Only 50 per cent of the germinated spores formed appresoria and approximately 50 per cent of these appeared to establish physiological contact with the host (36). Grijseels (37), however, did not report necrotic pits beneath organic solvents supplied to the upper surface of apple leaves. He observed browning and cell collapse which started at the leaf veins. Perhaps this could be explained by the increased number of glandular trichomes along leaf veins and the lipophilic nature of the solvents. Root cells are seldom cutinized, and have walls made of pectins including polyuronides that are polar and possess base-exchange properties (38). These are highly permeable to water and salts in their primary region.

It is not necessary, however, for a microorganism to penetrate into a cell to establish physiological contact with it (4, 6, 39). In order to reach host cells physically, the movement of a microorganism on the plant surface and through the cuticular layer would be as important as pentration through the cuticle. The thickness or hardness of the cuticle, therefore, can, at best, be only one of the factors influencing physiological and physical contact of host and pathogen. Indeed, the cuticle of tomato fruit not only covers the surface of epidermal cells but apparently completely surrounds them (32). If thickness of the cuticle were determining resistance by denying nutrients to a microorganism, an external supply of nutrients might reverse resistance. This was not observed when mature apple leaves were sprayed with nutrients and then inoculated with *V. inaequalis* (40). Older leaves, stems, and fruits generally have a thicker cuticle than younger tissues, yet thickness of cuticle and completeness of coverage are not always correlated with disease resistance. Some microorganisms parasitize only older tissues (41–43). The parasitism of older tissues, however, seems to occur primarily by pathogens that enter through natural openings or wounds or that penetrate younger tissues and remain dormant until the tissue reaches an appropriate stage of development. Flentje (29) speculates that cuticular development plays an important role in resistance where plant tissues are susceptible in the early stages of development but are resistant later. This author suggests that the binding of calcium and other polyvalent ions in the cuticular layer (42, 44) also contributes to resistance associated with the age of tissue. It appears as logical, however, to argue that the association of susceptibility with young, rapidly expanding cells, e.g., apple scab, is as much a consequence of the physiology of such tissue as of the thickness of the cuticle.

How thick or hard can the cuticle be before a pathogen can no longer penetrate? Measurements of the cuticle as milligrams of ether-soluble substances per area of leaf (13, 14, 45), though informative, do not indicate its hardness, the thoroughness of leaf coverage, or the existence of infectible sites. Flentje, Martin, and Dickinson in their excellent work and reviews (29, 46, 47), emphasized the importance of considering the cuticle not merely as a physical barrier to infection. Kerr & Flentje (28) found that the cuticle surface and a diffusible material from underlying cells were important for attachment and penetration of *Pellicularia filamentosa* into radish seedlings. Hyphae became attached to the cuticle above the junction of the epidermal cells, grew along the lines of junction of these cells, formed infection cushions, and then penetrated the cuticle. They suggested that the specificity of different fungal strains for different hosts may be due to variations from host to host in the nature of the cuticle surface and of the diffusate. In addition to growth stimulants, diffusates may also be responsible for the inhibition of microbial development (48, 49). The high resistance of *Ginko biloba* to disease may reside in the wax components of the leaf cuticle (50). Fatty acids, hydroxy fatty acids and their oxidation products, which are liberated by the action of cutin esterase, may also inhibit the growth of certain fungi (51, 52). This author has observed, however, that many fungi will germinate on nonhost as well as on host tissues; but such generalization may be dangerous since it does not include all or even most fungi.

Light intensity, humidity, temperature, and water stress influence cuticle thickness (10, 53) and the same environmental factors can influence disease resistance. Changes in cuticle thickness, however, do not always result in changes in disease resistance. Thus, it has not been possible to reverse the resistance of bean seedlings to *Colletotrichum lindemuthianum* (54) or *Helminthosporium carbonum* (35) or cucumber seedlings to *Cladosporium cucumerinum* (55) by growing them in the dark and in an atmosphere saturated with water. Not only does high temperature and low humidity induce a thick cuticle but also it causes the cuticle to contract and makes it a more formidable barrier to penetration and the movement of diffusates (38, 46). The hydration of the cuticle and carbohydrates making up the cuticular layer can open up the surface of the cuticle and disrupt the waxy layer. Thus, the number or size of active or infectible sites is increased (38). In this manner the cuticle could influence the degree of susceptibility or severity of attack. The infection process in viral diseases of plants is reviewed by Siegel & Zaitlin (56). With mechanically transmitted viruses, some type of wounding is necessary in order to create infectible sites.

In summation, Martin (46) states "In assessing the role of the cuticle in the protection of plants in general, it must be concluded that its contribution is not great. In some infections the cuticle itself is bypassed by the stomata or other natural openings; where penetration occurs, and excluding the possibility of pathways through it, the cuticle is often feebly developed (cutin <0.1 mg/cm^2 of surface) and is of such composition that it cannot be thought to provide a serious barrier to invasion." The author agrees with Martin that the thickness and hardness of cuticle are not the sole criteria in determining all cases of resistance. It may be important in some cases, e.g., the resistance of lime leaves with age to *Gloeosporium limetticola* (57) and resistance of cucumber to *Colletotrichum lagenarium* (58). The composition of the cuticle and its ability to serve as an appropriate physical surface for penetration or allow the passage of diffusates demands more attention. This author is intrigued by the small size of infection pegs, relative to the size of fungal spores and mycelia, and the expansion of the fungus from the peg once within the host, either inter or intracellularly. Does the pathogen follow thin pectin channels through the cuticle? How does a nonobligate intracellular parasite penetrate a host cell without completely disrupting cell membranes? Perhaps this occurs through existing openings in cell walls and membranes which are of molecular dimension, or the parasite is engulfed by the cytoplasm without penetrating the membrane. The charge on the cuticle surface influences the absorption of cations and anions (38) and may be important in the establishment of parasitism. Certainly, the cuticle serves as a highly efficient barrier to fungi, bacteria, and viruses that can invade the plant tissue only through stomata or wounds in the cuticle. One could compare the cuticle of a plant to an animal skin. Skin serves as an effective barrier to infection but is only part of the complex mechanism of disease resistance. Indeed, this author does not know of any attempt to correlate resistance of animals to pathogens and nonpathogens with skin thickness. It is important to differentiate general mechanisms for resistance to most microorganimss from mechanisms for resistance to a specific pathogen or strain of a pathogen.

PRODUCTION OF INHIBITORS

The concept that plants produce compounds that are inhibitory to the growth of microorganisms in response to infection or injury, was supported early by Müller and co-workers (59–62). They proposed that these compounds were part of a mechanism for disease resistance. Subsequent investigations have clearly established the validity of this concept (63–99). Whether the production of a single compound can explain a host's resistance to all nonpathogens and varietal susceptibility and resistance is doubtful.

Pisatin, 3-hydroxy-7-methoxy-4′,5′-methylenedioxy chormanocoumarin, was identified as a compound produced by the exposed endocarp of detached pods of the garden pea in response to inoculation with fungi or injury, and it was assigned a role in disease resistance (82–91). Working with more than fifty species of fungi, including pathogens and nonpathogens of the garden pea, Cruickshank clearly established a relationship between the ability of a fungus to induce the production of pisatin at levels inhibitory to its growth and its ability to parasitize the detached pea pod. Fungi, nonpathogenic to peas, induced the formation of pisatin at moderate to high concentrations, and the concentration varied with the fungus tested. Nonpathogens of peas induced the formation of pisatin at concentrations in excess of their ED_{50} values. The pathogens of pea, *Ascochyta pisi* and *Fusarium solani* var. *martii* f. *pisi*, induced the formation of high concentrations of pisatin and the rate of formation compared favorably with that of any of the nonpathogens. The pathogen *Septoria pisi* induced the formation of a very low concentration, and the wound pathogen *Botrytis cinerea* an intermediate concentration. Pea pathogens, if they induced the formation of pisatin, induced it at concentrations less than that of their ED_{50} values. None of the bacteria tested were able to induce the formation of significant amounts of pisatin, implying that a mechanism other than pisatin production is responisble for resistance or that conditions for infection were not suitable, e.g., the techniques of inoculation did not permit physiological contact between host and pathogen. Pisatin is produced by 58 named cultivars, nine numbered lines of *Pisum sativum* and *Pisum arvense*, and three other species of *Pisum* inoculated with *Monilinia fructicola* (90). Reduced or delayed production of pisatin by pea pods, induced by high temperature or anaerobic storage, made them susceptible to *M. fructicola* (89). Storage of pods at normal temperatures and aerobic conditions prior to inoculation resulted in the accumulation of a high level of pisatin and resistance. Thus, it would seem that pisatin is not an artifact, but is indeed a key substance in the disease resistance mechanism of the garden pea. Phaseollin, a chromanocoumarin resembling pisatin, was isolated from detached pods of the French bean (88, 92), and it may function as pisatin does in the pea.

Kuć and co-workers presented evidence for the role of 3-methyl-6-methoxy-8-hydroxy-3,4-dihydroisocoumarin in the disease resistance mechanism of carrot root (72, 73, 74), and steroid glycoalkaloids in the resistance of Irish potato tubers (98, 99). These authors, unlike Cruickshank, do not limit their consideration to a single compound within a host. They include chlorogenic and caffeic acids and other fungitoxic compounds produced by plants as possibly having a role in disease resistance (66–70). The production of several inhibitors by the plant in response to infection is an added measure of protection for the plant. A microorganism might overcome the inhibitory activity of one compound, but the difficulty of overcoming multiple inhibitors is greatly increased. The multiple inhibitor concept may help to explain why resistance is the rule and not the exception in nature. Certainly, the microorganism in or on a plant tissue is under the influence of a multitude of compounds in its environment.

The isocoumarin and chlorogenic acid in carrot root reach fungitoxic levels at the site of fungus penetration within 24 hours after inoculation with *Ceratocystis fimbriata*, a nonpathogen of carrot root (6, 71). Histological studies indicate that the cessation of fungal growth in the carrot coincides with the production of isocoumarin at fungitoxic levels in the environment of the fungus (72, 74). Isocoumarin strongly inhibits the growth of *C. fimbriata*, whereas chlorogenic acid does not. Chlorogenic acid, however, is inhibitory to other nonpathogens of carrot, e.g., *H. carbonum* (67), *V. inaequalis* (100), *Dothidella ulei* (101), and a weak pathogen *Thielaviopsis basicola* (102). Herndon et al. (6) reported that two to three times as much isocoumarin accumulated in the top 2 mm of tissue inoculated with *C. fimbriata* as that inoculated with *T. basicola*. This was true at 16°, 20°, 28°, and 32° C, after all periods of incubation tested, for all varieties of carrot tested (Red Cored Chanteney, Long Imperator, Imperator, Danver's Half Long, and Nantes Coreless), for both freshly pulled carrots and commercially obtained carrots, and for all isolates of *C. fimbriata* and *T. basicola* tested. The isocoumarin did not accumulate in response to inoculation with *Ceratocystis fagacearum*, *C. pilifera* or *C. coerulescens*, and spores of these fungi did not germinate on the surface of carrot slices. Approximately 3×10^{-3} molal isocoumarin accumulated in the peel three days after inoculating the outer intact carrot root surface with *C. fimbriata* or *T. basicola*. The rate of germination of *C. fimbriata* and *T. basicola* conidia was only slightly decreased at 1×10^{-3} molal isocoumarin, and the growth of *C. fimbriata* was slightly more inhibited by isocoumarin than that of *T. basicola*. Asexual sporulation of *C. fimbriata* was completely inhibited at a concentration of 5×10^{-4} *M* isocoumarin, whereas sporulation of *T. basicola* was only slightly inhibited at 1×10^{-3} *M* isocoumarin. The data for isocoumarin production, growth, and asexual development of the fungi are consistent with the observation that *C. fimbriata* is a nonpathogen and *T. basicola* is a weak pathogen of carrot root. The growth of a microorganism in host tissue appears to be a primary factor in disease resistance; however, the effect of post-infectional compounds on the reproduction of a microorganism might also influence resistance.

The increase in chlorogenic acid and isocoumarin in the top millimeters of inoculated carrot root is quite remarkable. The chlorogenic acid level increases from less than 2.5×10^{-5} molal at 0 time to 5×10^{-3} molal 72 hours after inoculation. Isocoumarin level increases from 0 to 250×10^{-4} molal 120 hours after inoculation. Crystals of isocoumarin are often apparent on the surface of the infected carrot slices 72 hours after inoculation (71). The quantitative influence of different microorganisms upon plant response is equally pronounced. Cruickshank (83) reported that, depending upon the microorganism used for inoculation, the concentration of pisatin which diffused into a droplet of water on the pea pod endocarp varied from a trace to 116 μg/ml of diffusate 72 hours after inoculation. The concentration of isocoumarin varied from 5 to 342 μg/g of carrot, depending upon the organism used for inoculation (74).

The importance of post-infectional inhibitors is further substantiated by the work of Gaumann and co-workers who isolated orchinol, 9,10-dihydro-2, 4-dimethoxy-6-hydroxyphenanthrene, as one of the fungitoxic compounds produced following interaction between *Orchis militaris* and various microorganisms (75–78). More recently, Gaumann reported (79, 103) hircinol, a derivative of orchinol, is produced by *Loroglossum hircinum* and, to a lesser degree, by *O. militaris*. Other inhibitors are produced by *Ophrys araneifera* and *Ophrys arachnitiformis*. Uritani (39) suggested a primary role for ipomeamarone, 2-methyl-2-(4-methyl-2-oxpentyl)-5-(3-furyl)-tetrahydrofuran, in the resistance of sweet potatoes to the pathogen *C. fimbriata*. The quantity of furanoterpenes, including ipomeamarone, was generally higher in resistant than in susceptible varieties following inoculation. The compounds are present at the site of infection at concentrations which exceed that required to markedly inhibit the fungus in culture (80). Umbelliferone and scopoletin also increased more rapidly in resistant varieties though their concentration at the site of infection apparently was not sufficient to inhibit the fungus (81) Sakai & Tomiyama (104) reported that varieties of potato resistant to an incompatible race of *Phytophetora infestans* exhibited higher levels of peroxidase and polyphenoloxidase activity and higher concentrations of *o*-diphenols, but those having lower concentrations of *o*-diphenols were not necessarily susceptible. These correlations were not apparent for field resistance.

Uehara (95, 96), working with pea pods inoculated with *A. pisi*, *Glomerella cingulata*, and *Gibberella zea;* pods of rape and common vetch, and leaves of broad bean (epidermis peeled off) inoculated with *G. cingulata;* concluded, as had Cruickshank, that the nature of the inhibitor produced was specific to the host plant species and not specific to the fungi that were introduced to the hosts. Pathogens of a host were only weakly inhibited by the levels of compounds produced by the host, whereas nonpathogens were strongly inhibited. The inhibitor(s) appeared detoxicated *in vitro* by *A. pisi* and *Fusarium oxysporium*, two pea pathogens. Klement & Lovrekovich (94) suggested that the multiplication of the phytopathogenic bacteria, *Pseudomonas syringae*, *Xanthomonas juglandis*, and *X. malvacearum*, which are nonpathogenic to bean, was inhibited in bean by a post-infectional defense mechanism. *P. phaseolicola*, *X. phaseoli*, *X. phaseoli* var. *fuscans*, bean pathogens, were not inhibited. The saprophytic bacterium, *P. aeruginosa*, was inhibited by a pre-infectional factor in bean. The bulk of the work dealing with the synthesis of antibiotic compounds by plants in response to injury or infection has been done with storage organs or seed pods. Comparatively little data are available concerning the response of foliage to infection or injury. The apparent avoidance of foliage is difficult to understand since disease resistance or susceptibility is often determined by changes occurring in the foliage. Klarman & Gerdemann (93) have shown that the foliage of resistant but not susceptible varieties of soybean produced a fungitoxic substance when inoculated with *Phytophthora sojae*. Nonpathogens induced the production of a fungitoxic substance by soybeans regardless of the soybean's susceptibility to *P. sojae*. Susceptibility of barley coleoptiles to *Helminthosporium sativum* is associated with tissue senescence. Ludwig et al. (105) found that extracts of young coleoptiles showed high antifungal activity. This activity disappeared rapidly with age owing to the appearance of an inhibitor of the antifungal factor(s). Inhibition of activity was caused by various divalent cations. A role for calcium and magnesium, other than in the formation of resistant pectate complexes, was offered as a disease-resistance mechanism. The appearance of phloretin (106, 107) in apple leaves following injury or inoculation with the pathogen *Venturia inaequalis* illustrates the liberation of a phenol from its nonfungitoxic glycoside. Phloridzin, the glucoside of phloretin, is found in leaves of apple varieties susceptible or resistant to attack by *V. inaequalis*. There is no correlation between phloridzin content and disease resistance to the pathogen. When the pathogen penetrates the leaf of a highly resistant variety, the plant cells around the point of penetration immediately collapse, phloridzin is hydrolyzed by liberated β-glycosidase to yield phloretin and glucose, and the phloretin is oxidized by phenoloxidases to yield highly fungitoxic compounds. The fungus penetrates the leaves of susceptible varieties and makes extensive growth beneath the cuticle for 10 to 14 days without initiating collapse of plant cells. Thus, phloridzin is not hydrolyzed and the pathogen is not contained. After 10 to 14 days, sporulating lesions appear on the leaves and shortly thereafter the affected tissue collapses. As in resistance of soybeans to *P. sojae,* the potential for resistance appears to be present in all apple varieties, and resistance may be determined by the ability of the fungus to trigger the synthesis or liberation of an inhibitor in the host. A similar series of reactions involving arbutin and hydroquinone may be important in determining the resistance of pear to fire blight (108).

Some of the compounds that accumulate around sites of infection or injury, e.g., chlorogenic and caffeic acid, are widely distributed throughout the plant kingdom. The synthesis of others appears limited to a narrow host range, e.g., the isocoumarin in carrot, phaseollin in French bean, pisatin in the garden pea, and ipomeamarone in sweet potato. Apparently the host has the potential for the synthesis of the compounds and the microorganism used for inoculation determines the quantitative response of the host (6, 90). Where two or more compounds are produced in response to infection, the microorganism controls the relative concentration of each. This is true even when the compounds are synthesized by two different pathways, e.g., chlorogenic acid and isocoumarin in the carrot. As might be expected, the interaction of compounds produced at the site of injury or infection may influence the fungitoxicity of the environment. Thus, chlorogenic and caffeic acids appear to reduce the fungitoxicity of α-solanine and α-chaconine found in Irish potato tubers (98, 99). Tomiyama (109) points out that the interrelation among the factors of resistance should not be overlooked, especially when considering field resistance. Toughness of the cell wall may delay penetration by a microorganism and thereby give sufficient time for the host to develop its defense mechanism. In his most interesting hypothesis concerning resistance to the *Verticillium* wilt disease, Talboys (110) brings into focus the need for considering many factors contributing to the expression of the varying degrees of disease. The threshold of the fungus and its metabolites in the host, the rate of host response, the effect of environment on attaining the threshold and rate of host response, and the concentration of pathogen in the soil are all considered. He does not postulate specific wilt resistance factors in the host. The mechanisms described are structural or biochemical features common to a wide range of vascular plants or else nonspecific responses that can be induced in many plants by many fungi. The concept of low resistance zones even in roots of highly resistant varieties is introduced.

Resistance in some host pathogen combinations is reported not to be dependent upon post-infectional inhibitors. Thus, Nishimura & Scheffer (111) reported that a post-infectional inhibitor of spore germination arose from the interaction of *Helminthosporium victoriae* with susceptible and resistant oat leaves. Spores of pathogenic and nonpathogenic strains of the fungus were affected equally by the inhibitor. It was suggested that the pathogen germinated, invaded susceptible tissue, and moved out of range of the inhibitor even though levels inhibitory to spore germination were soon present. The fungus made very limited growth in the resistant host. It is apparent that susceptibility and resistance are not determined by an inhibitor of spore germination, but it is not clear that a post-infectional inhibitor of growth is not important. Resistance is characterized not only by the lack of symptons. The fungus apparently is inhibited and then killed in the resistant tissue even before symptoms become apparent in the susceptible host. Post-infectional inhibitors of growth might explain resistance to the nonpathogenic strain but their presence may not be sufficient to explain resistance to the pathogenic strain which produces toxin. It is not unreasonable to assume that more of a post-infectional compound can accumulate in a susceptible host than in a resistant host. Our white blood cell count is highest when we have a severe infection, and yet the white blood cells are very much part of our mechanism for disease resistance. A balance of offensive and defensive weapons may be important. Two questions remain unanswered: is toxin formation necessary for growth of the fungus in the host or for symptom expression, or both; does the pathogenic strain produce toxin in the resistant host? The inability of the microorganism to multiply also appears to be important in the resistance of plants to bacteria (112).

Wound healing is often associated with the production of fungitoxic substances around sites of injury (66–68, 97–99, 103). This mechanism includes the formation of a protective layer of tissue forming a barrier between the wound and the environment. Wound healing certainly is not a specific mechanism for disease resistance but it can very be important. Potato tuber sections are often allowed to suberize prior to planting to minimize rotting. Gaumann (103) emphasized the importance of the wound mechanism in the disease resistance of orchid bulbs. Orchid bulbs have little mechanical protection, but are covered only with thin skin layer. Therefore, they are easily injured in soil and the traumatic induction of inhibitor production in the injured tissue prevents the nonspecific microorganisms in the soil from entering into the bulb through the open wound. It has often been reported that chlorogenic and caffeic acids inhibit indole acetic acid (IAA) oxidase. Their quinones participate in IAA synthesis and the acids enhance the growth-stimulatory effect of IAA on *Avena*. It may be more than coincidence that chlorogenic acid is associated with growth response in many plants, including the proliferation and increased metabolic activity of cells adjacent to the injury as well as in gall formation (113). Thus, chlorogenic acid and related compounds may function as general plant stress compounds. Physiology of virus symptomatology is essentially stress physiology since many of the metabolic alterations in infected plants occur as well in starving or senescent tissues (114).

The similarity of reactions of plant and animal tissues to pathogenic invasion is emphasized by Kalyanasundram (115). This is not surprising in light of the basic similarities of their metabolic processes. In their review of the role of phenolic compounds in the disease resistance of plants, Farkas & Kiraly (116) emphasized the need for caution in assigning a role to post-infectional compounds in disease resistance and also the need for analytical work in the field. Though many reports have appeared in the literature concerning the production of antibiotic materials in plant tissues, more work is needed on their chemical characterization. It is this author's opinion that the critical investigations of Müeller, Cruickshank, Uritani, Tomiyama, the late Prof. Gaumann, and their co-workers, among others exemplify the approach in research necessary in this phase of the disease resistance problem.

DETOXICATION

The ability of a host to resist factors arising from host-microbial interactions that lead to tissue disintegration or impaired metabolic activity, may be part of a disease resistance mechanism. This resistance mechanism may include: the presence of resistant structural components and metabolic pathways, mechanisms for detoxication, and the presence of alternate pathways in the host. The detoxication of microbial toxins may proceed via mechanisms outlined in the excellent works on the metabolism by plants and microorganisms of fungicides (117, 118).

Wallace et al. (42, 119) correlated the resistance of green immature apple fruit to *Botryosphaeria ribis*, *G. cingulata*, *Physalospora obtusa*, and *Physalospora* Sp. with the delayed production of pectin methylesterase and polygalacturonases and reduced growth in media containing a water-insoluble fraction (cell wall material) from immature vs. ripe apples. During the 1960 and 1961 growing seasons, they demonstrated that the amount of water-insoluble fraction decreased as the fruit matured. A major drop in the content of polyvalent cations occurred at about the time the fruit became susceptible. Conversely, the potassium content of the fraction was higher in susceptible than resistant fruit with a major increase occurring with the onset of susceptibility. The authors suggested that a pectin-protein-polyvalent cation complex, resistant to hydrolysis by fungal hydrolytic enzymes, plays an important role in the resistance of immature apple fruit. The effect of age on the susceptibility of cucumber hypocotyl tissue to extracellular enzymes produced by *C. cucumerinum* at first seems directly opposed to the results reported for apple fruit (120). Cucumber hypocotyl slices taken 0.5 to 1 cm or more below the cotyledons were intact even after 24 hours of immersion in a mixture of proteolytic, pectinolytic, and cellulolytic enzymes; whereas, slices taken immediately below the cotyledons were completely disorganized within 30 to 60 minutes. Symptoms are most severe on intact inoculated hypocotyls in the zone immediately below the cotyledons. The physiological effects of aging, however, in apple fruit and cucumber hypocotyls are also opposed. Apples soften as they ripen and cucumber hypocotyls harden as they age. The hardening and softening of these tissues may reflect, in part, changes in the pectic complexes of the cell walls. The importance of a protein-pectin complex in resistance is supported by the observation that proteolytic, but not cellulolytic enzymes, enhanced the separation and disorganization of cucumber hypocotyl slices by pectinolytic enzymes but could not substitute for the latter (120).

Thomas & Orellana (121) reported that crude enzyme preparations containing pectinmethylesterase, polygalacturonases, and cellulases cause browning and maceration of caster bean pods susceptible to *Botrytis ricini* but do not affect resistant pods. The fungus was shown to produce enzymes with macerating activity. The authors suggested that resistance was due to the inability of extracellular fungal enzymes to degrade the capsule. In subsequent studies (122) they showed that resistant capsule tissue contains less water-soluble pectin than does susceptible tissue. Calcium and magnesium levels were higher and sodium and potassium levels were lower in the alcohol-insoluble fraction obtained from boiling water extracts of the pericarp of resistant as compared to susceptible capsules. They reported no significant varietal difference in polyphenoloxidase or peroxidase activities and phenols appeared to be more concentrated in the susceptible tissue than in the resistant tissue.

Recent evidence for the role of polyvalent cations in an induced mechanism of resistance is provided in the critical work of Bateman (123). Calcium ions accumulated in and immediately around developing *Rhizoctonia* lesions. Barium, Ca, and Mg ions inhibited tissue meceration by polygalacturonase, whereas K and Na ions did not significantly influence the process. The hydrolysis of sodium polypectate by polygalacturonase was prevented by Ba and Ca but not by Mg ions and monovalent cations. The inhibitory affect of Ba and Ca was reversed, however, by adding oxalate ions to the reaction mixture. Bean tissue bearing *Rhizoctonia* lesions was more difficult to macerate with polygalacturonase than was comparable healthy tissue. Histological examination revealed that the middle lamella of cells adjoining one-week-old lesions were intact and more difficult to hydrolyze than the middle lamella of cells more distant from lesion. It was proposed that the accumulation of cations in and immediately around developing lesions resulted in the liberation and activation of pectinmethylesterase in host cell walls. The pectic substances near and in advance of the pathogen were demethylated, formed pectate salts with polyvalent cations, particularly calcium, and were rendered resistant to hydrolysis by fungal polygalacturonase. This mechanism was considered to play a major role in confining *Rhizoctonia* to lesions of limited size in infected hypocotyl tissue. Thus, economic susceptibility and a metabolic mechansim for resistance exist in the same plant. In subsequent studies, Bateman & Beer (124) indicated a synergistic action between oxalic acid and polygalacturonase produced by *Sclerotium rolfsii* in infected red kidney bean hypocotyl. The oxalic acid apparently creates an acid environment favorable for polygalacturonase activity and binds calcium, previously occurring in the pectates of cell walls, permitting rapid destruction of the host. The hypocotyl tissue of red kidney bean is highly susceptible to *Rhizoctonia solani* during the first two weeks of plant growth and resistant thereafter. Bateman & Lumsden (125) found higher calcium and lower methoxyl content in cell wall and noncell wall components in the hypocotyl as tissue aged. These results suggested that the increased resistance of bean hypocotyl tissue to *R. solani* during aging is associated with the conversion of pectin to calcium pectate which renders the pectic materials resistant to polygalacturonase. The authors did not differentiate between the changes occurring in cell wall structure from cytoplasmic changes, but their work certainly is supported by that of Wallace et al. (42, 119), Thomas & Orellana (121, 122), Edgington & Walker (126), and Corden & Edgington (127), which also suggested that high calcium content is associated with disease resistance.

The formation of polyvalent cation-pectate complexes in resistant tissue offers an explanation for the role of growth regulators in inducing resistance (128, 129). Corden & Edgington (127) indicated that growth regulator treatment allowed demethylation of the plant's pectic substances. Without sufficient calcium present, however, rigid cross-linkage failed to form and the pectic materials remained susceptible to fungal enzymes. With sufficient calcium present, there was increased calcium bonding of the pectic substances. Subsequently, Corden (130) reported that tomato wilt caused by *Fusarium oxysporum f. lycopersici* was most severe when the calcium content in the vascular sap was low, and was suppressed when the calcium content was high. Calcium in the sap from inoculated and noninoculated plants receiving the same calcium nutrition was similar. Therefore, low calcium in the vascular sap of severely diseased plants could not be due to reduced calcium uptake in the diseased plants. Calcium in the vascular sap apparently interferes with the growth of *Fusarium*, possibly by inhibiting the activity of its polygalacturonase which can function to provide an increased supply of carbohydrates for the fungus. This suggested role for calcium in the wilt syndrome is not incompatible with the hypothesis that calcium affects the susceptibility of pectic substances to enzymatic hydrolysis and that calcium inhibition of fungal polygalacturonase is an effect on the substrate and not the enzyme. The chemical and physical interactions of host and pathogen which result in the wilt syndrome are well reviewed by Dimond (131).

Phenols and phenolic oxidation products inhibit a broad spectrum of enzymes including extracellular fungal pectinolytic enzymes (132–140). The resistance of cider apples to wound infection by *Sclerotinia fructigena* was reported to be due to the ability of phenolic oxidation products in these apples to inactivate extracellular pectinolytic enzymes produced by the fungus (132). No variety of apple is immune to attack by this organism but there are differences in varietal susceptibility. An examination of twenty apple varieties revealed a relationship between the rate of browning of injured tissue and resistance; moreover, the more resistant cider varieties had a high polyphenol content. Cole & Wood (137) studied the biochemical changes associated with the firm rot of apples incited by *S. fructigena* and the soft rots incited by *Botrytis cinerea* and *Penicillium expansum*. They demonstrated that oxidized phenols, probably leucoanthocyanins, inactivated the polygalacturonase produced by *S. fructigena*. Kuć et al. (140) reported that juice from resistant green apples markedly inhibited the endopolygalacturonase activity of commercial pectinase as well as endopolygalacturonase in culture filtrates of *Botryosphaeria ribis*. The juice did not inhibit the growth of the fungus. The inhibition of endopolygalacturonase decreased with age, and juice from ripe apples, which were completely susceptible to the fungus, did not inhibit. The polymerization of tannins which occurs during ripening of fruit (141) may account for the loss of inhibitory activity. Indeed, polymers arising as end products from phenol and tannin oxidation did not inhibit polygalacturonase or growth of B. ribis (140). The concentration of enzymes relative to inhibitors and length of their contact influenced inhibition, and the break in field resistance to B. ribis occurred while apples still possessed inhibitory juice as measured in the assay. The inhibitory activity of the juice could be prevented but not reversed by sodium bisulfite, cysteine, 4-chlororesorcinol, phenylthiourea, and polyvinylpyrrolidone. Lyr (139), however, reported inhibition of pectinase by oxidized phenols was partially reversed by glutathione, cysteine, and hydroxylamine. Kuć et al. (140) did not assign to enzyme inhibitors a primary role in the resistance of apples to B. ribis. They offered evidence supporting the hypothesis that resistance of the cell walls of immature apples to hydrolysis by extracellular fungal enzymes was the primary mechanism for resistance.

The accumulation of more ascorbic acid in rust-susceptible than in rust-resistant wheat varieties (142), suggests the presence of a mechanism for detoxication based on the reduction of phenol oxidation products. An inhibitor of commercial pectinase and endopolygalacturonase produced by C. cucumerinum was found in higher concentrations in seedlings of three resistant varieties of cucumber following inoculation, as opposed to three susceptible varieties (55). Susceptibility to Verticillium wilt was correlated with the formation of abundant polygalacturonase on stems from susceptible tomato plants; the inhibition or suppression of this enzyme appeared to be associated with a high oxidizing power found in stems of resistant varieties (143). The lack of a suitable substrate necessary for the induction of extracellular microbial enzymes may be a mechanism in disease resistance.

The apparent absolute specificity of the toxins produced by Helminthosporium victoriae for susceptible varieties of oats has been reported (144–147). Physiological changes appearing within susceptible hosts treated with toxin follow the patterns of inoculated tissue (147–151). Romanko (144) presented evidence that resistance in plants depends upon their ability to rapidly inactivate the toxin produced by the fungus. Scheffer & Pringle (151) disagreed with this hypothesis on the basis of their observation that toxin could not be demonstrated in the cuttings of either susceptible or resistant plants. They believe the only reasonable explanation is that resistance to toxin depends upon the lack of receptor sites which are present in susceptible tissue. Their data, however, did not prove that a difference in toxin uptake between susceptible and resistant plants does not exist, and they have not demonstrated that detoxication or binding or both, proceed at equal rates in susceptible and resistant plants. Wheeler & Doupnik (152) reported that victorin is absorbed by two resistant varieties of oats, ryegrass and sorghum. These plants, as well as an oat variety intermediate in susceptibility, all gave similar respiratory responses to the toxin. It seems logical to argue the presence of a mechanism for detoxication in all resistant plants (resistance is common and susceptibility is the exception), and its reduced activity in susceptible plants. Resistance or susceptibility to toxin does not explain the limited growth of the pathogen in resistant hosts unless one assumes that growth of the fungus in the host depends upon action of the toxin. The mechanism for symptom expression, i.e., the toxin, and the mechanism for resistance to the fungus, i.e., the inhibition of fungal growth within the host, may not be related. Keyworth (153, 154) has reported that scions of resistant tomato varieties on susceptible Bonny Best root stocks showed symptoms of *Fusarium* wilt before susceptible varieties and the symptoms occurred considerably in advance of fungal invasion. In this host-parasite interaction, the resistance of the monogenic resistant varieties appears to reside in the suppression of fungal growth within them and not in the resistance of the varieties to the toxin. Indeed, the resistant tomato varieties are more susceptible to certain *Fusarium* toxins than are the susceptible varieties. Tomato and cotton plants rapidly metabolize toxins produced by *Fusaria* wilt pathogens, with the production of nontoxic products including N-methyl fusaric acid (115, 155–157). The wilt-resistant tomato variety, Red Current, inactivated fusaric acid by N-methylation more rapidly than did two susceptible varieties (156). An antagonist of fusaric acid is also produced by *Fusarium lycopersici* and its level in the host relative to fusaric acid may be important in symptom expression (158). Resistant plants and nonhosts are not affected by specific toxins produced by *Periconia circinata* (159, 160), *Alternaria kikuchiana* (146), and *Helminthosporium carbonum* (161). Whether the selective action of these toxins is dependent upon the presence of receptor sites or stability in resistant plants has not been reported.

Recently, Kern & Naef-Roth (162) reported four phytotoxic pigments produced by *F. martii*, *F. solani* var. *minus* and *F. javanicum*. The pigments were identified as fusarubin, javanicin, marticin, and isomarticin. The last two are highly toxic to green plants. A highly pathogenic strain of *F. martii* var. *pisi* produced high toxin (mostly isomarticin), whereas the weakly pathogenic strain did not. Toxin formation and pathogenicity appeared closely related. Marticin, isomarticin, and fusarubin were identified in diseased tissue of infected plants and may, therefore, be considered vivotoxins. These toxins differ from others, e.g., the toxin of *H. victoriae* which cannot be recovered from susceptible or resistant hosts.

The ability to break the resistance of nonhosts to *Fusaria* by growing them contiguous to diseased host tissues suggests that broad spectrum phytoirritants are a factor in selective pathogenicity (163).

SUSCEPTIBILITY

The growth of a microorganism in a host does not *a priori* constitute disease or host susceptibility. Since susceptibility is often based on economic or aesthetic considerations, a plant is susceptible only when the presence of the microorganism results in reduced crop yield, quality, or asethetic value. Symptom expression need not be concomitant with the growth of the microorganism in the plant, e.g., *Colletotrichum lindemuthianum* grows in susceptible bean varieties for approximately five days, and *Venturia inaequalis* in apple leaves for ten to fourteen days before symptoms appear. Symptoms often appear very shortly after inoculation, however, with microorganisms which have low host specificity and produce gross disintegration of tissues. Aside from the obvious gross disintegration of tissues as evidenced in the various rots, symptoms may be quite varied in a given host-pathogen interaction, and dependent for expression on the nature of the host tissue. Thus, the symptoms of bean anthracnose on foliage include wilting, vein coloration, epinastic curvatures, and occasional lesions. Symptoms are not visible on roots and are limited to dark lesions on the pods. Susceptible plants, therefore, may contain resistant tissues. The interaction of two metabolites, gibberellin and fusaric acid, produced by *F. moniliforme* at various levels of inoculum is probably the cause of the distinctly different symptoms on rice (164); elongation of seedlings known as Bakanae and wilting known as foot rot.

Known mechanisms for susceptibility include the production by microorganism of extracellular hydrolytic enzymes and toxins which affect host structure or metabolism, or both. Extracellular microbial pectinolytic, cellulolytic, proteolytic, and, recently, hemicellulolytic enzymes (165) have all been implicated in disease. The scope of this review cannot include a detailed discussion of the role of these enzymes and the reader is directed to recent reviews including Sadasivan & Subramanian (166), Wood (167), and Husain & Kelman (168). The action of extracellular hydrolases is most readily evident with various rots. Most organisms, however, produce some hydrolytic extracellular enzymes in culture filtrate, and yet susceptibility is the exception and resistance is the rule. As emphasized by Sadasivan & Subramanian (166), there is no correlation between the ability of microorganisms to produce extracellular pectinolytic enzymes and their ability to attack higher plants or their parasitic vigor. Indeed, many nonpathogenic organisms secrete powerful pectinolytic enzymes. The potential for host tissue degradation is not realized if the microorganism does not grow. Highly host-specific and nonspecific toxins have been reported as offensive weapons of fungi. (See Detoxication section, pp. 348–52.)

In many considerations of host-pathogen interaction, compounds arising in a susceptible host are often discounted as functioning in a resistance mechanism especially if they are found in higher concentrations in the susceptible as compared to the resistant host. Once again, this author cautions against the limitation of resistance to a single mechanism, i.e., post-infectional compounds or resistance to toxin. The interaction of host and pathogen is the sum total of microbial offense and host defense. Compounds accumulating in high concentration in a susceptible host may be part of a resistance mechanism, unsuccessful for the moment; a mechanism that is overcome by an offensive microbial factor or a factor arising from the interaction of host and pathogen.

The presence in a host of a factor necessary for microbial growth may also be important in determining susceptibility. Garber (169, 170) found the virulence of specific bacterial mutants related to the availability of nutrients at the tissue surface. Lukezic & DeVay (171) reported that an invasion of plum tree bark by *Rhodosticta quercina*, a fungus requiring myoinositol, was related to the myoinositol content of the bark. A susceptible variety contained 10 to 30 times the amount of myoinositol contained in two resistant varieties. Boone and co-workers (172–174) found that nutritional mutants of *V. inaequalis* which required choline or riboflavin were nonpathogenic, but they did parasitize leaves that were supplemented with the needed factors. They concluded, however, that resistance to the wild-type isolates did not indicate a direct nutritional control of pathogenicity.

SHIFTS IN METABOLISM

It is not surprising that the inoculation of plant tissues with microorganisms induces changes in the chemical composition and metabolism of both. It is hoped that somewhere in the mass of changes it is possible to discern those that are involved in the mechanisms responsible for resistance or susceptibility and are not merely artifacts arising because of injury or the influence of two living systems upon each other. The critical question still remains, why doesn't the microorganism grow or at best makes limited growth in the resistant host? This author does not know of any report in the literature where a change in respiratory rate or pathway could directly account for resistance. Similarly, this author has not found a report where a change in protein content, enzyme content, or enzyme activity was directly responsible for disease resistance. The critical assay for resistance appears to be the inhibition of microbial growth. The lack of a nutrient does not appear to be a major mechanism for resistance since many plant pathogens are not obligate parasites but can be cultured in the laboratory in a simple synthetic medium. However, since susceptibility is the exception in nature perhaps it should be considered as specific and demanding as obligate parasitism—a unique adaptation of host and microorganisms at the moment. Changes in respiration, proteins, and enzymes seem to be primarily important in disease resistance because they reflect fundamental changes in metabolism which provide for a chemical or physical environment, or both, that is either inhibitory or conducive to the growth of a microorganism. Post-infectional inhibitors arise as a result of profound shifts in metabolism, and the control of metabolism via nucleic acid, protein, and enzyme synthesis or activation is a critical metabolic feature of susceptibility or resistance. Though it is possible that a peroxidase, which increases in a resistant host after infection, could inhibit a microorganism directly by oxidizing selective sites on a microbial surface, microbial enzymes or toxins, this author does not know of any such report.

Respiration, Enzyme Activity, and Proteins

Many researchers have reported an increase in oxygen uptake following the interaction of plant tissue and microorganisms, including obligate and nonobligate parasites (80, 175–181). The list of hosts and microorganisms studies is long and it appears that infection results in an increase in oxygen uptake in either tissue penetrated by the microorganism or that adjacent to it. With ectoparasites and with storage organ slices it has been possible to differentiate between increased oxygen uptake of the host as influenced by the microorganism, and the oxygen uptake of the microorganism. Injury also appears to cause an increase in oxygen uptake, but often this is discounted by investigators as unimportant. The cutting of tissues, however, is a transitory upset of metabolism, but the presence of a microorganism results in a more continuous metabolic upset. Of greater significance than merely an increase in oxygen uptake is a differential increase between a susceptible and resistant host, especially if the increase is due to a microbial toxin or occurs in a resistant host in which the microorganism has made minimal growth.

In the black rot of sweet potato, a model host-parasite system often studied, the root tissue located near the infected area showed a marked increase in oxygen uptake and the rate increased for one to two days after infection (39). Cutting induced a comparatively small increase in oxygen uptake which attained a constant level within one day after cutting. In resistant varieties of sweet potato, the initial increase in oxygen uptake was greater than in susceptible varieties; however, the resistant varieties showed a decline in oxygen uptake three or four days after infection, whereas the susceptible varieties did not. The tissue affected was not penetrated by the fungus, hence, the fungus influenced host metabolism in advance of its growth. Oxygen uptake was increased in uninvaded leaf tissue of the ground nut infected by *Cercospora personata* (182). This increase occurred earlier and was more pronounced in a less susceptible variety. Similarly, oxygen uptake of potato tuber tissue increased after infection by *Phytophthora infestans*. The increase in oxygen uptake was most rapid in the infected resistant varieties (183, 184); it gradually extended more deeply in susceptible tissue. Inoculation of cut surfaces of potato tubers with *P. infestans*, or treatment with pectinase, resulted in increased polyphenoloxidase activity in the host. The increase extended deeper into the host following inoculation with an incompatible race of the fungus than it did following cutting or inoculation with a compatible race (185). An increase in oxygen uptake of potato leaves treated with culture filtrates from *P. infestans* was also observed (186). Again, oxygen uptake tended to be greater in the resistant leaves than in susceptible leaves following infection. Cotton plants susceptible to *Fusarium vasinfectum* showed a decrease followed by a marked increased in oxygen uptake following infection and the increase could be induced by fungal toxins (187). Oxygen uptake of susceptible but not resistant oats is initially markedly increased following infection by *H. victoriae*, and a similar pattern of increase is evident after treatment of susceptible plants with toxin produced by the fungus. (See Detoxification section, p. 348).

Marked increases in oxygen uptake have been reported for hypersensitive reactions (116, 188). Indeed, the increased oxygen uptake associated with hypersensitive reactions supports the hypothesis that the increase merely reflects injury to the host. In the hypersensitive reaction, injury occurs very soon after penetration and is of short duration; in susceptible hosts it may be delayed but is often greater in magnitude and longer in duration. Rubin & Aksenova (189) reported that the dehydrogenases in potatoes resistant to *P. infestans* were inhibited, but in susceptible varieties they were activated near the infection site. Held et al. (190), working with the same fungus, found that with compatible combinations of host and fungus there was an increase in the dehydrogenase activity which persisted until copious aerial mycelia were produced. In a more resistant variety, a smaller increase in the dehydrogenase activity occurred. In a hypersensitive reaction, there was a relatively early decrease in the dehydrogenase activity. This followed an initial increase in the dehydrogenase activity similar to, or slightly greater than, that in the susceptible reaction. No relationship was found between the dehydrogenase activity of healthy tuber tissue of a given variety and its potential reaction to late blight infection. The initial rate of the dehydrogenase activity increase was proportional to the concentration of inoculum and to host susceptibility.

The works of Akazawa et al. (191), Heitefuss et al. (192), Uritani & Stahmann (193, 194), Staples & Stahmann (195, 196), Rudolph (197), Rudolph & Stahmann (198), and Weber & Stahmann (199) have clearly established the concept that infection results not only in an increase in enzyme activity but also in the appearance of enzyme forms and compounds with antigenic properties previously not detected in the healthy host or pathogen. Akazawa, Umemura & Uritani (191) demonstrated a qualitative and quantitative difference in the protein fraction obtained from sweet potato tissue inoculated with *C. fimbriata*. The difference was apparent in tissue adjacent to the site of infection. Heitefuss et al. (192) found that immunological analyses with rabbit antisera revealed at least seven components in extracts of susceptible cabbage infected with *F. oxysporum, f. conglutinans*, only four of which were detected in extracts of uninfected susceptible or resistant tissue, or resistant tissue inoculated with the fungus. Electrophoresis revealed no significant qualitative differences in the protein in extracts of healthy and infected cabbage, but immunological analyses showed an increase in components in extracts of infected susceptible plants. Two races of *Xanthomonas malvacearum* were found to share several antigens in common with cotton, but the resistant varieties shared fewer antigens than did susceptible varieties (200). Antigenic compatibility may play a role in governing the resistance or susceptibility of certain host varieties as well as specificity of pathogens for a given host species. The tissue of sweet potato is also reported to synthesize antigenic compounds following infection by *C. fimbriata*

(194). Four components showed precipitation lines on agar gel. Two of the components were found in healthy tissue and did not change upon infection. Two components were specific to or greatly increased in diseased tissue. One of the latter components was a perioxidase. Kawashima & Uritani (201) continued the studies of peroxidase activity in infected tissue. They found that little change occurred in peroxidase activity during the first day following infection. This was followed by a rapid increase in activity which continued until approximately the third day after infection. The first millimeter of diseased tissue showed less activity than the second and third millimeter. Cutting increased peroxidase activity but to a much smaller extent than infection. Four major peroxidases were found in extracts of healthy, diseased, and cut tissue. Polyphenoloxidase also increased in infected sweet potato (39), and three polyphenoloxidase fractions were separated. One of the fractions was common to healthy, diseased, or cut tissue and another was produced in response to both cutting and infection. A third fraction was found only in diseased tissue, and this fraction had antigenic properties. In addition to peroxidase and phenoloxidase activity, cytochrome oxidase and ascorbic acid increased in diseased tissue. Some of the antigenic compounds mentioned appeared to be related to the degree of resistance (194). Thus, an antigenic compound, component B, increased to a much greater extent upon infection in resistant than in susceptible varieties. It was suggested (39) that the change in certain peroxidases and phenoloxidases may parallel the magnitude of resistance of sweet potato tissue to black rot.

Staples & Stahmann (195, 196) reported that changes in leaf proteins occurred after infection of susceptible bean leaves by the rust, *Uromyces phaseoli*. Electrophoresis of extracts showed that one new protein was formed and one host protein had decreased after rust infection. An increased number of isozymes of acid and alkaline phosphatase, succinate dehydrogenase, and malate dehydrogenase were also reported. The activity of acid phosphatase decreased after infection. A small increase in peroxidase activity was detected after infection but its isozymic complexity was not changed. The protein content of rust-infected susceptible beans was not grossly different from healthy leaves even after extensive growth of the fungus. The authors suggested that the host alters the number and form of the rust isozymes, while the fungus alters the rate of synthesis of enzymes by the host, enhancing some while depressing others. Infection of bean leaves with the bacterium, *Pseudomonas phaseolicola*, also caused changes in the protein patterns (197). These changes were different for susceptible and resistant varieties. New bacterial dehydrogenases, oxidases, acid phosphatases, and esterases were detected. A catalase, also of bacterial origin, was found one day after infection. Within two days after infection, the peroxidase activity of susceptible bean leaves decreased or remained unchanged; in contrast, it increased in the resistant variety. The author suggested that the resistant hypersensitive reaction is related to host peroxidases which are suppressed by bacterial catalase in the susceptible reaction. The concept of protein-protein detoxication by competition for a common substrate is intriguing. Weber & Stahmann (199), working with sweet potato tissue, showed a stimulation of peroxidase in the first layer of tissue adjacent to a cut surface but little peroxidase activity in the second and third layers. In contrast, inoculation with a nonpathogenic or pathogenic isolate of *C. fimbriata* induced high peroxidase activity in both underlying layers. A resistant host appeared to be more responsive to the pathogenic isolate. An increase in polyphenoloxidase activity was also observed in the underlying tissues of resistant and susceptible hosts after inoculation with the nonpathogenic or pathogenic isolate. Acid phosphatases decreased following inoculation with either isolate; activity decreased proportionately from the surface, but the decrease was more pronounced with the pathogenic isolate. An acid phosphatase of fungal origin was also detected in tissue inoculated with the pathogenic isolate; activity of this enzyme was highest in the first layer. It was concluded that the acid phosphatase of the host was inactivated in the first layer, whereas the fungal acid phosphatase retained its activity. Malic dehydrogenase activity decreased proportionately from the surface following inoculation with nonpathogenic or pathogenic isolates. Similar patterns in esterase activity were observed in the susceptible hosts; in the resistant host, esterase activity was very low and difficult to detect. The increases and decreases in enzyme activity suggest that the fungus induced changes in the host's protein metabolism, affecting enzyme activities several millimeters away from the site of infection. The inoculation of a susceptible variety of sweet potato with a nonpathogenic isolate induced, in a thin layer of tissue around the site of inoculation, an acquired immunity to subsequent inoculation with the pathogenic isolate. Ipomeamarone formation did not seem to account for the induced immunity. Ipomeamarone could not be detected with Ehrlich reagent in the tissue inoculated with the nonpathogenic isolate, whereas it was readily detected during the same period in the tissue inoculated with the pathogenic isolate. The acquired immunity to *C. fimbriata* in sweet potato was not associated with a hypersensitive necrotic reaction. Evidence from this investigation associates resistance with altered protein synthesis and enzyme activity, but the factor(s) responsible for limiting the growth of the fungus is not reported.

Respiration and the activities of glucose 6-phosphate dehydrogenase, 6-phosphogluconate dehydrogenase, phosphohexoisomerase, phosphofructokinase, phenolase, aconitase, isocitratedehydrogenase, and malate dehydrogenase were measured in susceptible barley leaves infected with *Erysiphe graminis* var. *hordei* and in leaves from which the pathogens had been removed (202). The respiratory increase in infected leaves was the result of an increase in host tissue as well as a contribution to total respiration by the pathogen. Glucose 6-phosphate dehydrogenase and 6-phosphogluconate dehydrogenase activities were two- to threefold higher in infected leaves and the enhancement resulted from increased activities in the host tissue as well as the pathogen. The haustoria contributed slightly to the total activity of these enzymes in the fungus. In contrast, phosphohexoisomerase and malate dehydrogenase activities were not increased in infected leaves. Small increases were observed in the activities of phosphofructokinase, enolase, aconitase, and isocitrate dehydrogenase. These increases were due to the pathogen rather than the host tissue. It was concluded that not only is the pentose pathway enhanced in the host tissue after infection, but also that it is the major respiratory pathway of the pathogen. Fric & Majernik (203) reported that infection of a susceptible variety of barley with *E. graminis* resulted in respiration which was more inhibited by substances forming solid complexes with copper, whereas respiration of healthy leaves was more inhibited by substances forming solid complexes with iron. Respiration was markedly stimulated by ascorbic acid in infected but not healthy plants. This author is puzzled by the inability of the investigators to detect polyphenoloxidase in homogenates of control or infected plants. Malca et al. (204) reported that the activities of glucose 6-phosphate and 6-phosphogluconate dehydrogenases increased in leaves mildewed by *E. graminis* at the time of or shortly after the appearance of symptoms and continued to increase as the disease developed. Part of the increased activity was due to enzymes contributed by the fungus, since washing the mildew off the leaves resulted in a decrease of activity. The activity of ribulose 1,5-diphosphate carboxylase decreased considerably in infected leaves soon after the appearance of symptoms. The activities of phosphoribose isomerase and phosphoribulokinase decreased in extracts of mildewed plants only when the fungus was not removed; washing off the mildew resulted in levels of activity in leaves similar to those present in healthy leaves. Effects similar to those with powdery mildew were observed with susceptible leaves of maize infected with *Helminthosporum carbonum*. The activity of ribulose 1,5-diphosphate carboxylase decreased after symptom expression, and that of phosphoriboisomerase or phosphoribulokinase, or both, decreased after an initial stimulation (205). Glucose 6-phosphate and 6-phosphogluconate dehydrogenase activity increased after infection (206). Strobel & Sharp (207) worked with two wheat varieties, Rego and Nord Desprez, which are susceptible to *Puccinia striiformis* when grown at a temperature profile of 15° night 24° day and resistant when grown at 2° night 18° day. They found at least two protein bands to be present in both varieties grown at the higher temperature profile that were not found in the plants grown at the lower profile. They suggested that the two bands arose as a result of the activation of certain genes by the specific temperature profile in which the plants were grown. They further speculated that the two protein bands might be necessary for the production of compounds vital to the growth and development of the fungus or that they destroyed compounds otherwise inhibitory to the fungus. Their speculations are strengthened by the observation that two wheat varieties which did not change infection types in the two environmental conditions, likewise did not show intravarietal qualitative protein changes. It is unclear, however, which of the two varieties was susceptible or resistant and whether either contained the two protein bands. The fact that the fungus itself need not necessarily be in host tissue in order to cause profound changes in enzyme or protein content and activity is supported by the work of Farkas & Lovrekovich (208). They found that tobacco half leaves injected with toxin from culture filtrates of *P. tabaci* induced typical chlorotic symptoms, a marked breakdown of proteins, and simultaneous change in the activity of a number of enzymes. As measured in tissue extracts, 14 of 25 enzymes tested were shown to increase in activity upon treatment of tissue with the toxin. The activity of four enzymes was reduced in the toxin-treated half leaves. The activity of the other seven enzymes remained more or less unchanged in spite of the toxin-induced protein breakdown. Peroxidase activity increased in tobacco leaves following infection by *Colletotrichum destructivum* (209, 210). Part of the increased activity apparently resulted from an increase in the activity of peroxidase that is normally present in the tissue and part from the synthesis or activation of at least one peroxidase not detected in healthy tissue.

The effect of viral infection on host metabolism is admirably reviewed by Farkas & Solymosy (114). Virus-induced lesion development was associated with a marked increase in polyphenoloxidase activity within and around the lesions, and the formation of toxic phenol oxidation products may be responsible for lesion development. This hypothesis is supported by the close association of lesion formation with polyphenoloxidase activation and the ability of reducing agents to inhibit lesion formation. The virus-induced activation of polyphenoloxidase, however, did not precede the appearance of lesions. Increased activity of glucose 6-P and 6-P gluconate dehydrogenases were also reported, as was a shift in respiration in favor of the pentose pathway. Bell (211) observed a marked increase in the activity of the pentose pathway following virus infection in local lesion but not in systemic hosts. The increased enzyme activity and appearance of new proteins and enzymes following infection may be due in part to the liberation of enzymes from inactive forms by the action of proteolytic or pectinolytic enzymes since the activations characteristic of microbial infections and local lesion virus reactions are also characteristic for detached leaves (212). The review by Farkas et al. (212) contains a table summarizing metabolic alterations of leaves following detachment, and following fungal, bacterial, or viral infection. Protein breakdown and enzyme activation are retarded by kinetin in detached leaves (213). Surprisingly, the process of photosynthesis is highly resistant to virus-induced damage except in very late stages of disease development (114).

BIOSYNTHETIC PATHWAYS

Increased biosynthesis of compounds by the acetate-malonate, acetate-mevalonate, and shikimic acid pathways is often associated with wounding or infection in plants. Ipomeamarone, 3-methyl-6-methoxy-8-hydroxy-3,4-dihydroisocoumarin, steroid glycoalkaloids, pisatin, phaseollin, chlorogenic and caffeic acid are end products of such syntheses. The three pathways are functional in the biosynthesis of compounds vital in the metabolism of healthy plants. What, then, loosens the brake, directs synthesis toward one, the other, or all three and results in the accumulation of compounds often not found in the healthy plant?

Increased biosynthesis requires an increased utilization of carbon skeletons and energy, and is often associated with an increase in the amount or activity of necessary enzymes and cofactors. A lack of any could serve as a brake. Increased utilization of glucose is often associated with wounding or infection (39, 181, 214), as is the operation of the pentose pathway (180, 181, 202, 214, 215).

The respiratory pattern in sweet potato tissue inoculated with *C.fimbriata* is more complex, however, than that arising merely as a result of wounding (214). The $^{14}CO_2$ recovery from G-1-^{14}C and G-6-^{14}C was greater in diseased than from cut tissue. The recovery was very large 24 to 48 hours after inoculation when recovery from G-1-^{14}C was at its maximum, and the C-6/C-1 ratio was similar to that of cut tissue. Subsequently, the pattern of glucose breakdown profoundly changed in diseased tissue; the C-1 contribution markedly decreased and the C-6 decreased only slightly. The transition period occurred 48 to 72 hours after inoculation. Decreased participation of the pentose pathway appeared to occur during this transition. It may be more than coincidence that the accumulation of chlorogenic acid reaches a peak in sweet potato and carrot 72 hours after inoculation with *C. fimbriata* and then remains constant or slowly declines. The synthesis of ipomeamarone in sweet potato and isocoumarin in carrot, however, increases gradually for 24 to 48 hours and markedly for as long as 120 hours after inoculation. The decrease in chlorogenic acid accumulation could be explained by the decrease in erythrose 4-phosphate as a result of decreased activity of the pentose pathway. Similarly, the increase in ipomeamarone and isocoumarin could be explained by acetate arising from participation of the Embden Meyerhof pathway. Wounding and inoculation of Norin 1 sweet potato roots, which are resistant to black rot, with *C. fimbriata* caused a marked increase in the activity of phenylalanine deaminase and tyrosine deaminase (216). These deaminases may play an important role in the increased synthesis of polyphenols, including chlorogenic acid via cinnamic acid derivatives. Imaseki & Uritani with Takei (217, 218) presented evidence that the accumulation of ipomeamarone in tissue very close to the infected region was not solely due to the shift of acetate utilization to furanoterpene synthesis in the infected tissue (219) but to the migration of an intermediate(s) from the noninfected tissue adjacent to the site of infection.

Increased glucose oxidation via the pentose pathway in addition to providing carbon precursors for biosynthesis, also increases the level of NADPH, the availability of which could be a brake in the synthesis of chlorogenic acid, ipomeamarone, and isocoumarin. The causal relationship between the accumulation of phenols and fluorescent compounds around lesions and the activation of glucose-6-P dehydrogenase has been emphasized with viral diseases (114). Increased utilization of the reducing power of NADPH would increase the rate of turnover of this coenzyme, possibly increasing the oxidation of glucose via the pentose pathway. Similarly, increased utilization of intermediates of the pentose pathway might increase participation of the latter. The system is similar to that suggested by Bell (211) in his work with viral diseases of plants. An increase in oxidative phosphorylation would not necessarily accompany the production of NADPH or its oxidation. The energy of NADPH is not readily subject to electron transport-chain-coupled phosphorylation and is directed into organic molecules. Oxygen uptake could increase as NADPH is oxidized by a quinone reductase. A quinone reductase system linked to phenoloxidases or peroxidases does not, however, appear to be coupled with oxidative phosphorylation. A quinone reductase might explain the suggested uncoupling effect observed following wounding or infection (214, 220, 221). Uncoupling does not seem to be responsible for the respiratory increase in safflower infected with rust (177) since host growth as well as mycelial development and sporulation was positively correlated with the increase in respiration. Marked uncoupling resulting in reduced ATP production would not be consistent with the increased synthetic activity associated with infection unless the uncoupling followed the period of synthesis as the microorganism grew in the host. Of course, increased activity of the pentose pathway does not imply reduced activity of the Embden Meyerhof pathway or TCA cycle. Though the availability of NADPH could be a primary brake controlling the synthesis of compounds by the shikimic or acetate pathways, the microorganism also releases brakes within both pathways. Thus, *H. carbonum* stimulates the accumulation in carrot root of high chlorogenic acid but low isocoumarin, *C. fimbriata* stimulates marked accumulation of both, and *Erwinia carotovora* stimulates the production of neither (74, 222). The host determines synthesis of species-specific post-infectional compounds, i.e., pisatin is synthesized in peas but not carrots. Alternates to the brake hypothesis for increased biosynthesis include: provision of specific precursors or enzymes by either host, pathogen, or their interaction, and the mobilization of intermediates to sites of active metabolism (223, 224). These sites may be initiated by the mixing of enzyme and substrate in previously compartmentalized or inactive systems.

What is the initial trigger for the profound shifts in metabolism? It is tempting to propose a mechanism based on enzyme induction and repression to explain these phenomena (225–227). Thus, repressor molecules, formed by regulator genes, may block structural genes and prevent the synthesis of a messenger RNA. The trapping of repressor molecules has been offered as a mechanism to explain the action of hormones. The hormone traps a repressor and the corresponding gene starts to provide messenger RNA. The messenger RNA then directs the synthesis of the corresponding proteins. Many hormones are simple organic molecules, hence the entrapment of repressor in a host-pathogen interaction may be a result of simple microbial or host metabolites or metabolites arising as a result of the interaction. The detection of proteins and enzymes in diseased host tissue which are not present in the healthy host or pathogen, may be explained by this phenomenon as might be the synthesis of post-infectional compounds. This concept is supported by the observation that healthy plants, possessing the pathways for synthesis, do not synthesize pisatin, phaseollin, or isocoumarin until wounded or infected. The fact that mechanical wounding or chemical toxicants can stimulate the synthesis of post-infectional compounds in the host argues against the requirement of a unique combination of host and microbe, but does not invalidate the importance of the added contribution of such a combination. The entrapment of repressor may be due to a host substance produced because of the mixing of previously compartmentalized enzyme and substrate. Zucker (228) reported the induction of phenylalanine deaminase and chlorogenic acid synthesis in potato tubers by wounding and light. Actual synthesis of the enzyme appeared to be induced and repression of synthesis controlled by the product of the reaction, cinnamic acid. Post-infectional compounds often accumulate to higher levels in infected than in wounded tissues. Appropriate concentrations of chemicals can, however, induce the production of compounds at levels comparable to those reached following infection (229).

The increased size of nuclei and other cytoplasmic components in cells of cereals infected with rust was suggested early by Allen (230). The nucleoli in such enlarged nuclei stained very strongly for RNA (231). No change in DNA was reported in leaves of a susceptible variety of wheat infected with rust until the invaded cells collapsed, but RNA content doubled in the enlarged host nuclei (232). In a recent work, Bhattachayara et al. (233) supported these earlier findings. They reported no appreciable change in DNA content of infected host nuclei until 10 to 12 days after a susceptible variety of wheat was inoculated with *Puccinia graminis tritici*. At this time, the nuclei had lost 29 per cent of their DNA. After 15 days, 51 per cent had been lost. Nuclear RNA increased as early as two days after inoculation, reached a maximum six days after inoculation and then declined slowly. Histones in infected nuclei decreased 35 per cent, total proteins increased by 30 per cent, and acidic proteins increased by 59 per cent as early as two days after inoculation. Six days after inoculation, histones had decreased by 50 per cent, total proteins increased by 69 per cent, and acidic protein by 123 per cent. Infection with the rust fungus caused an early increase in the ratio of DNA to histone and to an increase in nuclear RNA and total protein in the nuclei of host cells located within the limits of rust pustules. Since histones may play a key role in nuclear function and their removal activates the synthesis of RNA (234, 235), the decrease in histone and increase in RNA and acidic protein in infected nuclei suggest than an early event in the infection process is the activation of specific genes in the nuclei of affected host cells. The subsequent alteration of metabolic pathways in the host may determine the development of the pathogen and hence the susceptibility or resistance of the host (180,

233). This may offer an explanation for obligate parasitism and disease resistance or susceptibility to obligate and facultative parasites. The synthesis of proteins and enzymes could also arise by a direct transfer of nucleic acid between microbe and host or host and microbe, though it is difficult to understand how this could occur with an intercellular parasite.

SUMMARY

To limit disease resistance of plants to a single mechanism would be as rational as limiting disease resistance in animals to the presence of skin, white blood cells, or antibodies. The cuticle and other physical and chemical barriers to penetration, the presence of preformed inhibitors, the production of inhibitors, and the ability to establish a compatible metabolism between host and pathogen may all be important for the resistance of some plants under some conditions. Under particular conditions, and these would be of rare occurrence in nature, none of the above may be effective. All mechanisms for resistance or susceptibility are genetically controlled; however, the presence of the genetic code for resistance does not assure its expression or effectiveness in a particular host-pathogen interaction. The production of a toxin by a microorganism may overcome an otherwise effective resistance mechanism. Unsuitable environment and the dependence upon the release of a metabolic brake or trapping of repressor may metabolically prevent the expression of the genetic code, and thereby prevent the expression of resistance.

Three distinct mechanisms for the disease resistance of plants were discussed in this review. Physical or chemical barriers, including preformed inhibitors of microbial growth, detoxication of enzymes or toxins, and the lack of necessary growth factors, all represent a nondynamic mechanism. This mechanism has a minimum of specificity and provides general protection for plants. A second mechanism for resistance, based on physiological stress, includes the production, liberation, or mobilization of compounds following infection or injury. It has a degree of specificity since different microorganisms as well as different modes of injury can induce different degrees of response. The third mechanism includes the unmasking of host DNA by a specific microorganism. This gives rise to specific RNA and hence metabolic function. This would be a highly specific mechanism for susceptibility or resistance. This author is impressed by the similarities rather than the differences between metabolic processes in plants and animals, including those for disease resistance or susceptibility.

In his thought-provoking review of the physiology of disease resistance in plants, Walker (236) states " . . . we must be as much concerned with processes as with products, and in view of the potential effect of environment on the expression of resistance the more precise the control of the experimental environment the better. Furthermore, the relation of one process to another is probably just as important as any one process." Walker concludes, "In further elucidation of the nature of disease resistance of plants the investigation of the comparative physiology of susceptible and resistant plants and of the races of pathogen will be the major line of attack. This requires new men, new weapons, new points of view, and alert use of methods evolving rapidly in plant physiology and enzymology."

This author adds as a warning to those who have endured this review to the bitter end, that new and more numerous reviewers will also be required to keep abreast of the literature in this field.

LITERATURE CITED

1. Stakman, E. C., and Harrar, J. G., *Principles of Plant Pathology*, 519. (Ronald Press, New York, 1957)
2. Wingard, S. A., Plant Diseases. *U.S. Dept. Agr., Agr. Handbook*, 165 (1953)
3. Melhus, I. E., and Kent, G. C., *Elements of Plant Pathology*, 38. (Macmillan, New York, 1939)
4. Menke, G. H., Patel, P. N., and Walker, J. C., *Z. Pflanzenkrankh. Pflanzenschutz*, **71**, 128 (1964)
5. Walker, J. C., *Plant Pathology*, 1. (McGraw-Hill, New York, 1950)
6. Herndon, B. A., Kuč, J., and Williams, E. B. (Accepted for publication, *Phytopathology*, 1965)
7. Brown, W., and Harvey, C. C., *Ann. Botany, London*, **41**, 643 (1927)
8. Scott, F. M., Bystrom, B. G., and Bowler, B., *Science*, **140**, 63 (1963)
9. Goodman, R. N., in *Antibiotics in Agriculture*, 165. (Woodbine, N., Ed., Butterworths, London, 1962)
10. Juniper, B. E., *J. Linnean Soc. (Botany)*, **56**, 413 (1960)
11. Ahmad, K. J., *Can. J. Botany*, **42**, 793 (1964)
12. Baker, E. A., and Martin, J. T., *Nature*, **199**, 1268 (1963)
13. Baker, E. A., Batt, R. F., and Martin, J. T., *Ann. Appl. Biol.*, **53**, 59 (1964)
14. Fernandes, A., Baker, E. A., and Martin, J. T., *Ann. Appl. Biol.*, **53**, 43 (1964)
15. Waldron, J. D., Gowers, D. S., Chibnall, A. C., and Piper, S. H., *Biochem. J.*, **78**, 435 (1961)
16. Mazliak, P., *Phytochemistry*, **1**, 79 (1962)
17. Davenport, J. B., *Australian J. Chem.*, **13**, 411 (1960)
18. Siegal, S. M., *The Plant Cell Wall*. (Wareing, P. F., and Galston, A. W., Eds., Macmillan, New York, 1962)
19. Roelofsen, P. A., *Encyclopedia of Plant Anatomy, Part 4. The Plant Cell Wall*, 257. (Zimmerman, W., and Ozenda, P. G., Eds., Gebrüder Borntaeger, Berlin-Nikolasse, 1959)
20. Scott, F. M., *Botan. Gaz.*, **111**, 378 (1950)
21. Yamada, Y., Wittwer, H., and Bukovac, M. J., *Plant Physiol.*, **39**, 28 (1964)
22. Sitte, P., and Rennier, R., *Planta*, **60**, 19 (1963)
23. Hall, D. M., and Donaldson, L. A., *Nature*, **194**, 1196 (1962)
24. Franke, W., Ectodesmata and entry of pesticides into leaves. Contribution to Intern. Pesticides Congr., 5th, London, 1963.
25. Roberts, E. A., Southwick, M. D., and Palmiter, D. H., *Plant Physiol.*, **23**, 557 (1948)
26. Schieferstein, R. H., and Loomis, W. E., *Plant Physiol.*, **31**, 240 (1956)
27. Churchwood, J. G., *Ann. Appl. Biol.*, **27**, 58 (1940)
28. Kerr, A., and Flentje, N. T., *Nature*, **179**, 204 (1957)
29. Flentje, N. T., in *Plant Pathology, Problems and Progress 1908–1958*, 76. (Holton, C. S., Ed., Univ. of Wisconsin Press, Madison, Wis., 1959)
30. Long, W. G., Sweet, D. V., and Tukey, H. B., *Science*, **123**, 1039 (1956)
31. Lewis, S., and Goodman, R. N., *Phytopathology*, **55**, 719 (1965)
32. Yamada, Y., Martin, J. T., Bukovac, M. J., and Wittwer, S. W., *Plant Physiol.*, **39**, 978 (1964)
33. Rich, S., in Stomata and water relations in plants, *Conn. Agr. Expt. Sta., New Haven, Bull.* **664**, 102 (1963)
34. Goodman, R. N., and Addy, S. K., *Phytopathol. Z.*, **46**, 1 (1963)
35. Biehn, W., *Studies on the resistance mechanisms of Malus to Venturia inaequalis (Cke) Wint. and Helminthosporium carbonum Ull.; and of glycine max to Helminthosporium carbonum*. (Master of Science thesis, Purdue Univ., Lafayette, Ind., 1965)
36. Biehn, W., Williams, E. B., and Kuč, J. (Manuscript submitted to *Phytopathology*, 1965)
37. Grijseels, A. J., *Studies on the defense mechanisms in selections of malus to Venturia inaequalis*. (Master of Science thesis, Purdue Univ., Lafayette, Ind., 1963)
38. Crafts, A. S., and Foy, C. L., *Residue Rev.*, **1**, 112 (1962)
39. Uritani, I., in Perspectives of biochemical plant pathology, *Conn. Agr. Exp. Sta., New Haven, Bull.* **663**, 4 (1963)
40. Kuč, J. (Unpublished data)
41. Wilson, A. R., *Ann. Appl. Biol.*, **51**, 171 (1963)
42. Wallace, J., Kuč, J., and Williams,

E. B., *Phytopathology*, **52**, 1004 (1962)

43. Rubin, B. A., and Artsikhovskaya, Y. V., *Biochemistry and Physiology of Plant Immunity*, 153. (Griffiths, E., Ed., Macmillan, New York, 1963)

44. Ross, A. F., *The chemical composition of cell wall fractions isolated from maturing apple fruit as related to disease resistance*. (Master of Science thesis, Purdue Univ., Lafayette, Ind., 1965)

45. Martin, J. T., *J. Sci. Food Agr.*, **11**, 635 (1960)

46. Martin, J. T., *Ann. Rev. Phytopathol.*, **2**, 81 (1964)

47. Dickinson, S., in *Plant Physiology*, **2**, 203 (Horsfall, J. G., and Dimond, A. E., Eds., Academic Press, New York, 1960)

48. Angell, H. R., Walker, J. C., and Link, K. P., *Phytopathology*, **20**, 431 (1930)

49. Topps, J. H., and Wain, R. L., *Nature*, **179**, 652 (1957)

50. Johnstone, H. W., and Sproston, T., *Phytopathology*, **55**, 225 (1965)

51. Heinen, W., *Acta Botan. Neerl.*, **12**, 51 (1963)

52. Heinen, W., *ibid.*, **25**, 281 (1963)

53. Skoss, J. D., *Botan. Gaz.*, **117**, 55 (1955)

54. Rahe, J, and Kuć, J. (Unpublished data)

55. Mahadevan, A., Kuć, J., and Williams, E. B., *Phytopathology*, **55**, 1000 (1965)

56. Siegel, A., and Zaitlin, M., *Ann. Rev. Phytopathol.*, **2**, 179 (1964)

57. Roberts, M. F., and Martin, J. T., *Ann. Appl. Biol.*, **51**, 411 (1963)

58. Akai, S., Yasumori, H., and Terasawa, H., *Shokubutsu Byogai Kenkyu*, **6**, 97 (1959)

59. Müller, K. O., and Börger, H., *Landwirtsch. Jahrb. (Berlin)*, **87**, 609 (1939)

60. Müller, K. O., Klinkowski, M., and Meyer, G., *Naturwissenschaften*, **27**, 765 (1939)

61. Müller, K. O., and Börger, H., *Arb. Biol. Reichsanstalt Land- u. Forstwirtsch. (Berlin)*, **23**, 189 (1940)

62. Meyer, G., *Arb. Biol. Reichsanstalt Land- u. Forstwirtsch. (Berlin)*, **23**, 97 (1940)

63. Müller, K. O., *Phytopathol. Z.*, **27**, 237 (1956)

64. Müller, K. O., *Australian J. Biol. Sci.*, **11**, 275 (1958)

65. Müller, K. O., in *Plant Physiology*, **1**, 469 (Horsefall, J. G., and Dimond,

A. E., Eds., Academic Press, New York, 1961)

66. Kuć, J., Ullstrup, A. J., and Quackenbush, F. W., *Science*, **122**, 1186 (1955)

67. Kuć, J., Henze, R. E., Ullstrup, A. J., and Quackenbush, F. W., *J. Am. Chem. Soc.*, **78**, 3123 (1956)

68. Kuć, J., *Phytopathology*, **47**, 676 (1957)

69. Kuć, J., *Proc. Intern. Symp. Crop. Production (Ghent)*, **26**, 997 (1961)

70. Kuć, J., in Perspectives of biochemical plant pathology, *Conn. Agr. Expt. Sta., New Haven, Bull 663*, 20 (1963)

71. Kuć, J., Phenolic compounds and disease resistance in plants. *Proc. Symp. Plant Phenolics Group N. Am.*, 63. (Runeckles, V. C., Ed., Plant Phenolics Group, N. Am., 1964)

72. Condon, P., and Kuć, J., *Phytopathology*, **50**, 267 (1960)

73. Condon, P., and Kuć, J., *Phytopathology*, **52**, 182 (1962)

74. Condon, P., Kuć, J., and Draudt, H. N., *Phytopathology*, **53**, 1244 (1963)

75. Gaumann, E., and Kern, H., *Phytopathol. Z.*, **36**, 1 (1959)

76. Gaumann, E., and Kern, H., *ibid.*, 347 (1959)

77. Gaumann, E., and Hohl, H. R., *Phytopathol. Z.*, **38**, 93 (1960)

78. Gaumann, E., Neusch, J., and Rimparr, R. H., *Phytopathol. Z.*, **38**, 274 (1960)

79. Gaumann, E., *Compt. Rend.*, **257**, 2372 (1963)

80. Uritani, I., and Akazawa, T., in *Plant Pathology*, **1**, 349. (Horsfall, J. G., and Dimond, A. E., Eds., Academic Press, New York, 1961)

81. Minamikawa, T., Akazawa, T., and Uritani, I., *Plant Physiol.*, **38**, 493 (1963)

82. Cruickshank, I. A. M., *Australian J. Biol. Sci.*, **15**, 147 (1962)

83. Cruickshank, I. A. M., *J. Australian Inst. Agr. Sci.*, **29**, 23 (1963)

84. Cruickshank, I. A. M., *Ann. Rev. Phytopathol.*, **1**, 351 (1963)

85. Cruickshank, I. A. M., and Perrin, D. R., *Nature*, **187**, 799 (1960)

86. Cruickshank, I. A. M., and Perrin, D. R., *Australian J. Biol. Sci.*, **16**, 111 (1963)

87. Cruickshank, I. A. M., and Perrin, D. R., *Life. Sci.*, **2**, 680 (1963)

88. Cruickshank, I. A. M., and Perrin, D. R., in *Biochemistry of Phenolic Compounds*, 511. (Harborne, J. B.,

Ed., Academic Press, London, 1964)

89. Cruickshank, I. A. M., and Perrin, D. R., *Australian J. Biol. Sci.*, **18**, 817 (1965)

90. Cruickshank, I. A. M., and Perrin, D. R., *ibid.*, 829 (1965)

91. Perrin, D. R., and Bottomley, W., *J. Am. Chem. Soc.*, **84**, 1919 (1962)

92. Perrin, D. R., *Tetrahedron Letters*, No. 1, 29 (1964)

93. Klarman, W. L., and Gerdemann, J. W., *Phytopathology*, **53**, 1317 (1963)

94. Klement, Z. L., and Lovrekovich, L., *Phytopathol. Z.*, **45**, 81 (1962)

95. Uehara, K., *Ann. Phytopathol. Soc. Japan*, **XXIX**, No. 1, 1 (1964)

96. Uehara, K., *ibid.*, No. 3, 103 (1964)

97. Craft, C. C., and Audia, W. V., *Botan. Gaz.*, **123**, 211 (1962)

98. Allen, E. H., and Kuć, J., *Phytopathology* (Abstr.), **54**, 886 (1964)

99. Allen, E. H., *Steroid glycoalkaloids in the disease resistance of white potato tubers.* (Doctoral thesis, Purdue Univ., Lafayette, Ind., 1965)

100. Kirkham, D. S., and Flood, A. E., *Nature*, **178**, 422 (1956)

101. Figari, A., *Turrialba*, **15**, 103 (1965)

102. Hampton, R. E., *Phytopathology*, **52**, 413 (1962)

103. Gaumann, E., *Phytopathol. Z.*, **49**, 211 (1963/1964)

104. Sakai, R., and Tomiyama, K., *Ann. Phytopathol. Soc. Japan*, **XXIX**, No. 3, 120 (1964)

105. Ludwig, R. A., Spencer, E. Y., and Unwin, C. H., *Can. J. Botany*, **38**, 21 (1960)

106. Noveroske, R. L., Kuć, J., Williams, E. B., *Phytopathology*, **54**, 92 (1964)

107. Noveroske, R. L., Williams, E. B., and Kuć, J., *ibid.*, 98 (1964)

108. Hildebrand, D. C., and Schroth, M., *Phytopathology*, **54**, 59 (1964)

109. Tomiyama, K., *Ann. Rev. Phytopathol.*, **1**, 295 (1963)

110. Talboys, P. W., *Nature*, **202**, 361 (1964)

111. Nishimura, S., and Scheffer, R. P., *Phytopathology*, **55**, 629 (1965)

112. Klement, Z., Farkas, G. L., and Lovrekovich, L., *Phytopathology*, **54**, 474 (1964)

113. Spurr, H. W., Hildebrandt, A. C., and Riker, A. J., *Phytopathology*, **55**, 1004 (1965)

114. Farkas, G. L., and Solymosy, F., *Phytopathol. Z.*, **53**, 85 (1965)

115. Kalyanasundaram, R., *J. Madras Univ.*, **33B**, 137 (1963)

116. Farkas, G. L., and Kiraly, Z., *Phytopathol. Z.*, **44**, 8 (1962)

117. Dekhuijzen, H. M., *Neth. J. Plant Pathol.*, **70**, 1 (1964)

118. Kaars-Sijpesteijn, A., and Kalslander, J., *Outlook Agr.*, **2**, 119 (1964)

119. Wallace, J., Kuć, J., and Draudt, H. N., *Phytopathology*, **52**, 1023 (1962)

120. Kuć, J., *Phytopathology*, **52**, 961 (1962)

121. Thomas, C. A., and Orellana, R. G., *Science*, **139**, 334 (1964)

122. Thomas, C. A., and Orellana, R. G., *Phytopathology*, **50**, 359 (1964)

123. Bateman, D. F., *Phytopathology*, **54**, 438 (1964)

124. Bateman, D. F., and Beer, S. V., *Phytopathology*, **55**, 204 (1965)

125. Bateman, D. F., and Lumsden, R. D., *Phytopathology*, **55**, 734 (1965)

126. Edgington, L. V., and Walker, J. C., *Phytopathology*, **48**, 324 (1958)

127. Corden, M. E., and Edgington, L. V., *Phytopathology*, **50**, 625 (1960)

128. Davis, D., and Dimond, A. E., *Phytopathology*, **43**, 137 (1953)

129. Corden, M. E., and Dimond, A. E., *Phytopathology*, **49**, 68 (1959)

130. Corden, M. E., *Phytopathology*, **55**, 222 (1965)

131. Dimond, A. E., in Physiology of fungi and fungus diseases, *West Va. Univ. Agr. Expt. Sta. Bull.*, **488 T**, 91 (1963)

132. Byrde, R. J. W., Fielding, A. H., and Williams, A. H., in *Phenolics in Plants in Health and Disease*, 95. (Pergamon, Oxford, 1960)

133. Byrde, R. J. W., in Perspectives in biochemical plant pathology, *Conn. Agr. Expt. Sta. Bull. 663*, 31 (1963)

134. Williams, A. H., in *Enzyme Chemistry of Phenolic Compounds*, 87. (Pridham, J. B., Ed., Pergamon, Oxford, 1963)

135. Hulme, A. C., and Jones, J. D., in *Enzyme Chemistry of Phenolic Compounds*, 97. (Pridham, J. B., Ed., Pergamon, Oxford, 1963)

136. Cole, J. S., *Ann. Botany London*, **20**, 15 (1956)

137. Cole, M., and Wood, R. K. S., *Ann. Botany London*, **25**, 435 (1961)

138. Hulme, A. C., Jones, J. D., and Wooltorton, S. C., *Phytochemistry*, **3**, 173 (1964)

139. Lyr, H., *Phytopathol. Z.*, **52**, 229 (1965)

140. Kuć, J., Williams, E. B., Maconkin, M. A., Ginzel, J., Ross, A. F., and

Freedman, L. (Manuscript prepared for publication in *Phytopathology*, 1965)

141. Goldstein, J., and Swain, T., *Phytochemistry*, **2**, 371 (1963)
142. Kiraly, Z., and Farkas, G. L., *Phytopathology*, **52**, 657 (1962)
143. Deese, D. C., and Stahmann, M. A., *Phytopathol. Z.*, **46**, 53 (1963)
144. Romanko, R. R., *Phytopathology*, **49**, 32 (1959)
145. Wheeler, H., and Luke, H. H., *Ann. Rev. Microbiol.*, **17**, 223 (1963)
146. Pringle, R. B., and Scheffer, R. P., *Ann. Rev. Phytopathol.*, **2**, 133 (1964)
147. Scheffer, R. P., and Pringle, R. B., *Phytopathology*, **53**, 465 (1963)
148. Krupka, L. R., *Phytopathology*, **49**, 587 (1959)
149. Grim, R. B., and Wheeler, H., *Phytopathology*, **53**, 436 (1963)
150. Wheeler, H., Amador, E. J., and Black, H. S., *Phytopathology*, **55**, 813 (1965)
151. Scheffer, R. P., and Pringle, R. B., *Phytopathology*, **54**, 832 (1964)
152. Wheeler, H., and Doupnik, N., *Phytopathology* (Abstr.), **55**, 1055 (1965)
153. Keyworth, W. G., *Ann. Appl. Biol.*, **52**, 257 (1963)
154. Keyworth, W. G., *Ann. Appl. Biol.*, **54**, 99 (1964)
155. Sanawal, B. D., *Phytopathol. Z.*, **25**, 333 (1956)
156. Kleupfel, D., *Phytopathol. Z.*, **29**, 349 (1957)
157. Sadasivan, T. S., *Recent Advances in Botany*, **2**, 1021. (Univ. of Toronto Press, Toronto, 1959)
158. Kalyansundaram, R., *Studies on an antagonist of the phytotoxin fusaric acid*. (Thesis for the degree of Doctor of Natural Science, Swiss Fed. Inst. Tech., Zurich, Switzerland, 1960)
159. Scheffer, R. P., and Pringle, R. B., *Nature*, **191**, 912 (1961)
160. Leukel, R. W., *J. Agr. Res.*, **72**, 201 (1948)
161. Scheffer, R. P., and Ullstrup, A. J., *Phytopathology*, **55**, 1037 (1965)
162. Kern, H., and Naef-Roth, S., *Phytopathol. Z.*, **53**, 45 (1965)
163. Davis, D., *Phytopathology*, **55**, 1054 (1965)
164. Viswanth-Reddy, M., *Phytopathol. Z.*, **53**, 14 (1965)
165. Hancock, J. G., and Millar, R. L., *Phytopathology*, **55**, 356 (1965)
166. Sadasivan, T. S., and Subramanian, D., *J. Indian Botan. Soc., Comm. Vol.*, **42A**, 199 (1964)

167. Wood, R. K. S. in *Plant Pathology Problems and Progress 1908-1958*, 1st ed., 100 (Holton, C. S., Ed., Univ. of Wisconsin Press, Madison, Wisc., 1959)
168. Husain, A., and Kelman, A., in *Plant Pathology*, **1**, 143 (Horsfall, J. G., and Dimond, A. E., Eds., Academic Press, New York, 1959)
169. Garber, E. D., *Proc. Natl. Acad. Sci. U.S.*, **40**, 1112 (1954)
170. Garber, E. D., *Am. Naturalist*, **40**, 183 (1956)
171. Lukezic, F. L., and DeVay, J. E., *Phytopathology*, **54**, 697 (1964)
172. Boone, D. M., Kline, D. M., and Keitt, G. W., *Am. J. Botany*, **44**, 791 (1957)
173. Kline, D. M., Boone, D. M., and Keitt, G. W., *Am. J. Botany*, **44**, 797 (1957)
174. Williams, B. J., and Boone, D. M., *Phytopathology*, **52**, 757 (1962)
175. Allen, P. J., *Phytopathology*, **43**, 221 (1953)
176. Samborski, D. J., and Shaw, M., *Can. J. Botany*, **34**, 601 (1956)
177. Daly, J. M., and Sayre, R. M., *Phytopathology*, **47**, 1963 (1957)
178. Millerd, A., and Scott, K. J., *Ann. Rev. Plant Physiol.*, **13**, 559 (1962)
179. Bushnell, W. R., and Allen, P. J., *Plant Physiol.*, **37**, 751 (1962)
180. Shaw, M., *Ann. Rev. Phytopathol.*, **1**, 259 (1963)
181. Trower, L. B., *Phytopathol. Z.*, **52**, 319 (1965)
182. Swamy, R. N., *Phytopathol. Z.*, **50**, 227 (1964)
183. Tomiyama, K., Takakuwa, M., Takase, N., and Sakai, R., *Phytopathol. Z.*, **37**, 113 (1959)
184. Tomiyama, K., Takakuwa, M., and Takase, N., *Ann. Phytopathol. Soc. Soc. Japan*, **23** (3) 237 (1958)
185. Tomiyama, K., and Stahmann, M. A., *Plant Physiol.*, **39**, 483 (1964)
186. Krzywanski, L., and Borys, M., *Phytopathol. Z.*, **51**, 262 (1964)
187. Lakshmanan, M., *Phytopathol. Z.*, **36**, 406 (1959)
188. Diener, T. O., *Ann. Rev. Phytopathol.*, **1**, 209 (1963)
189. Rubin, B. A., and Aksenova, V. A., *Biokhimia* (Engl. transl.), **22**, 191 (1957)
190. Held, A., Kedar, N., and Birk. Y., *Phytopathology*, **55**, 970 (1965)
191. Akazawa, T., Umemura, Y., and Uritani, I., *Bull. Agr. Chem. Soc. Japan*, **21**, 192 (1957)

192. Heitefuss, R., Buchanan-Davidson, D. J., Stahmann, M. A., and Walker, J. C., *Phytopathology*, **50**, 198 (1960)

193. Uritani, I., and Stahmann, M. A., *Plant Physiol.*, **36**, 770 (1961)

194. Uritani, I., and Stahmann, M. A., *Agr. Biol. Chem. Tokyo*, **25**, 479 (1961)

195. Staples, R. C., and Stahmann, M. A., *Science*, **140**, 1320 (1963)

196. Staples, R. C., and Stahmann, M. A., *Phytopathology*, **54**, 760 (1964)

197. Rudolph, K., *Phytopathology*, **54**, 904 (1964)

198. Rudolph, K., and Stahmann, M. A., *Z. Pflanzenkrankh. Pflanzenschutz*, **71**, 107 (1964)

199. Weber, D. J., and Stahmann, M. A., *Science*, **146**, 929 (1964)

200. Schnathorst, W. C., and DeVay, J. E., *Phytopathology* (Abstr.), **53**, 1142 (1963)

201. Kawashima, N., and Uritani, I., *Agr. Biol. Chem. Tokyo*, **27**, 409 (1963)

202. Scott, K. J., *Phytopathology*, **55**, 438 (1965)

203. Fric, F., and Majernik, O., *Phytopathol. Z.*, **50**, 17 (1964)

204. Malca, I., Huffaker, R. C., and Zscheile, F. P., *Phytopathology*, **55**, 442 (1965)

205. Malca, I., Huffaker, R. C., and Zscheile, F. P., *Phytopathology*, **54**, 663 (1964)

206. Malca, I., and Zscheile, F. P., *Phytopathology*, **54**, 1281 (1964)

207. Strobel, G. A., and Sharp, E. L., *Phytopathology*, **55**, 413 (1965)

208. Farkas, G. L., and Lovrekovich, L., *Phytopathology*, **55**, 519 (1965)

209. Yu, L. M., and Hampton, R. E., *Phytochemistry*, **3**, 499 (1964)

210. Yu, L. M., and Hampton, R. E., *ibid.*, 269 (1964)

211. Bell, A. A., *Phytopathology*, **54**, 914 (1964)

212. Farkas, G. L., Dezsi, L., Horvath, M., Kisban, K., and Udvardy, J., *Phytopathol. Z.*, **49**, 343 (1963)

213. Udvardy, J., Horvath, M., Kisban, K., Dezsi, L., and Farkas, G. L., *Experientia*, **20**, 214 (1964)

214. Akazawa, T., and Uritani, I., *Plant Physiol.*, **37**, 662 (1962)

215. Ap-Rees, T., and Beevers, H., *Plant Physiol.*, **35**, 839 (1960)

216. Minamikawa, T., and Uritani, I., *Arch. Biochem. Biophys.*, **108**, 573 (1964)

217. Imaseki, H., and Uritani, I., *Plant and Cell Physiol.*, **5**, 133 (1964)

218. Imaseki, H., Takei, S., and Uritani, I., *Ibid.*, 119 (1964)

219. Akazawa, T., Uritani, I., and Akazawa Y., *Arch. Biochem. Biophys.*, **99**, 52 (1962)

220. Rubin, B. A., and Ozeretskovskaya, O. L., *Biochemistry USSR* (Engl. transl.), **28**, 61 (1963)

221. Shaw, M., and Samborski, D. J., *Can. J. Botany*, **35**, 389 (1957)

222. Sandstedt, K., and Kuć, J. (Unpublished data)

223. Beevers, H., *Respiratory Metabolism in Plants* (Brown, E. H., Ed., Row-Petterson, Evanston, Ill., 1961)

224. Thrower, L. B., *Phytopathol. Z.*, **52**, 269 (1965)

225. Jacob, F., and Monod, J., *J. Mol. Biol.* **3**, 318 (1961)

226. Monod, J., Jacob, F., and Gros, F., in *The structure and biosynthesis of macromolecules*, 104, *Biochem. Soc. Symp.*, *Cambridge Univ.*, *New York*, *1961*, 21 (1962)

227. Karlson, P., *Perspectives Biol. Med.*, **6**, 203 (1962–63)

228. Zucker, M., *Plant Physiol.*, **40**, 779 (1965)

229. Perrin, D. R., and Cruickshank, I. A. M., *Australian J. Biol. Sci.*, **18**, 803 (1965)

230. Allen, R. F., *J. Agr. Res.*, **23**, 131 (1923)

231. Person, C., *Can. J. Genet. Cytol.*, **2**, 103 (1960)

232. Whitney, H. S., Shaw, M., and Naylor, J. M., *Can. J. Botany*, **40**, 1533 (1962)

233. Bhattachayara, R. K., Naylor, J. M., and Shaw, M., *Science*, **150**, 1605 (1965)

234. Huang, R. C., and Bonner, J., *Proc. Natl. Acad. Sci. U.S.*, **48**, 1216 (1962)

235. Goodwin, B. C., and Sizer, I. W., *Science*, **148**, 242 (1965)

236. Walker, J. C., in *Physiology of fungi and fungus diseases*, 1, *West Va. Agr. Expt. Sta. Bull 488T* (1963)

MICROBIAL TRANSFORMATION AND TRANSFECTION[1]

By John Spizizen, B. E. Reilly, and A. H. Evans

*Department of Microbiology, Scripps Clinic and Research Foundation,
La Jolla, California*

Contents

COMPETENCE.. 372
    Genetic Control of Competence................................. 373
    The State of Competence....................................... 374
    Formation of Competence State................................. 375
        Physiological state of culture.......................... 375
        Evidence for wall changes accompanying competence...... 377
    Evidence for a DNA Receptor or Competence "Factor"............ 378
    Characteristics of Biologically Active DNA.................... 379
        Molecular size... 379
        Strandedness... 381
DNA INTEGRATION IN TRANSFORMATION: FATE OF TRANSFORM-
    ING DNA.. 382
    Integration of One or Two Strands: The Problem of
    Heterozygotes.. 385
LINKAGE GROUPS AND MAPPING OF GENOME BY TRANSFORMA-
    TION.. 386
RNA TRANSFORMATION... 389
TRANSFECTION.. 390

This review is not intended to encompass this ever burgeoning field. Excellent reviews of the subject of bacterial transformation have been presented by Schaeffer (1) and Ravin (2). Other reviews by Hotchkiss (3), Ephrussi-Taylor (4, 5), Zamenhof (6), and Thomas (7) are less recent. Important information relating to current studies on recombination and genetic maps as revealed by transformation could best be presented in a separate review.

The range of genetic analysis in microbial systems has been greatly extended by transformation, although still confined to certain species in the following genera: *Diplococcus, Streptococcus, Hemophilus, Neisseria, Bacillus, Rhizobium*, etc. Genetic homology, a requirement for genetic recombinations, as determined by transformation, has important implications for taxonomy. Thus, intergeneric transformation of *Streptococcus* and *Diplococcus* (8), as well as *Streptococcus* and a strain of *Staphylococcus* (9), has revealed kinships. Interspecific transformation has been documented for *Hemophilus* species (10), *Neisseria* species (11), *Rhizobium* species (12), and *Bacillus* species (13). The relationship of physical homology of the component DNA of different strains to genetic homology has been reviewed by Marmur et al. (14).

[1] The survey of the literature pertaining to this review was concluded April 1, 1966.

The transfer of genetic information by deoxyribonucleate permits bio-physical analyses of DNA in biologically active forms. The mechanics of transformation, however, place certain restrictions on the analysis of bio-logical activity of isolated DNA. Thus, the DNA must be above a minimal molecular weight and be double-stranded. Further amplification of these analyses to degraded forms of DNA might conceivably be effected by melting and reannealing techniques. This may ultimately lead to direct isolation of pieces of genome which would permit the analyses of nucleotide sequences of individual genes. In this context, the analysis of the action of mutagens on DNA would be significant.

To permit DNA uptake, the recipient cells must be in a state of "com-petence." The nature of the competence period, which occurs only under special growth conditions and is often short-lived, has not yet been well de-fined. The use of competent cells for studies of bacteriophage DNA has pro-vided a new tool for genetic study of viral systems and the competence pro-cess.

Certain principles and problems have become evident from recent and current progress in this field. Are both strands of transforming DNA recom-bined with the recipient genome? Is there a specific orientation of the DNA molecule during uptake and penetration? Are the uptake and integration processes related to each other and to replication? What is the nature of the recombination process? The use of transformation systems should permit an analysis of the fate of transforming DNA and of viral DNA, recombinational mechanisms, and the kinetics of replication of different portions of the genome (15).

COMPETENCE

Genetic transformation (i.e., genetic transfer mediated by free DNA) is possible only because there appears in certain cell populations a state of "competence." Implicit in the process of transformation are the stages of DNA uptake and penetration of the cell, association and recombination with the recipient genome, and subsequent phenotypic expression and replication of the transferred genetic information. However, it is with the initial phase of DNA transfer that the designation "competence" is usually associated: but which processes are involved cannot be specified. Thus, uptake of nonhomol-ogous DNA (i.e., from genetically unrelated species) occurs with competent cultures in the absence of genetic recombination and expression. That genetic integration is not the defective process in certain noncompetent strains is in-dicated by the observation that transduction of genetic markers in these strains occurs as readily as in competent cells (16, 17). Bacteriophage DNA is also accepted by competent cells and in those instances in which phage replication can occur, result in DNA replication and phage production. Al-though DNA transfection probably does not involve association with the re-cipient genome, the possibility is not excluded that specific uptake sites may occur in relation to replication points of the recipient genome, possibly in the membrane of the cells.

GENETIC CONTROL OF COMPETENCE

The classical studies of Avery, McLeod & McCarty (18) identified the essential requirement of specific strains for transformation. A rough strain of *Diplococcus*, R36A, was found to undergo competence, but many derivative strains were inactive. Transformation occurred at a reduced frequency in capsulated strains of *Diplococcus* (19) and *Bacillus licheniformis* (20). With *B. licheniformis* (18), rough variants from colonial outgrowths often yielded highly competent strains.

When individual clones of *Bacillus subtilis* were tested for competence, the frequency of transformation obtained was quite variable. In an extreme instance, Young & Spizizen (21) isolated a stable noncompetent mutant of *B. subtilis*, 168, that had concomitantly lost the ability to bind DNA at any stage of growth studied. Venema (personal communication) found spontaneous morphological mutants of *B. subtilis* that transformed at either lower or higher frequency than the original strain.

When the mutant of Young & Spizizen (21) was grown under conditions normally used to develop competence, about 4 cells in 10^7 cells could be transformed. Ten clones that had been transformed were grown to competence and transformed for another marker. The average frequency of transformation was identical to that obtained with the original mutant strain. Several clones were serially transformed four times. The ability to be transformed remained at the low level of the mutant (22). In a survey for competence in *B. subtilis*, as evidenced by transfection, several strains were shown to be infected at the same low level of the 168 mutant (22).

Thus, in the *B. subtilis* transformation system, strains exist that routinely transform at a high level and can give rise to mutants which develop competence at a low level. Although the physiological state of some cells in the mutant population permits transformation, these cells appear at random and their progeny seem to be typical of the general population in their capacity to develop competence.

In *B. subtilis*, Spizizen suggested that the competence state might be associated with certain phases of the process leading to sporulation, and certain asporogenous mutants were found whose potential for developing competence was impaired. α-Picolinic acid, an inhibitor of sporulation in *Bacillus* (23), was found to inhibit the formation of competence at levels that did not influence the growth rate in minimal medium (unpublished observations). Among a set of asporogenous mutants obtained by ultraviolet irradiation, were strains in which the development of competence was partially or completely impaired (24). These cells were unable to take up DNA or to be transfected by bacteriophage DNA (25). The competence defect could be repaired by transformation and the progeny clones developed competence at the high level of the parent competent strain. In fact, in some asporogenous strains, the genetic locus for competence was separated from the one controlling spore formation, although these loci are linked to each other and to genes controlling the formation of a protease and an antibiotic. Other classes of asporogenic mutants were found in which competence had been retained at the level of the wild-type strain.

The notion that competence may be related to some process in sporulation has been questioned by Schaeffer (1), since many asporogenous mutants of *B. subtilis* isolated in his laboratory remain competent. It seems evident that the occurrence of competence in asporogenous mutants relates to the stage in the cycle of sporulation at which the block occurs. The work of Young & Spizizen (21) and of Young (26) suggest that wall and membrane changes occur at early stages of presporulation. If asporogenous mutants are blocked at a stage in the sporulation cycle that occurs after the transient competence phase has passed, then the uptake of DNA and transformation would occur.

Although a genetic basis for competence has been established in *B. subtilis* it is not known whether the locus studied defines the total genetic control of competence. A class of amino acid-requiring mutants has been found [(24) and unpublished data], which is partially or completely defective in sporulation. Many of these mutants, particularly those requiring glutamate, are defective in competence. Some defective sporulating strains with an altered growth rate were produced by acriflavine (Spizizen, unpublished findings). These strains had impaired competence. However, other acriflavin-induced asporogenous mutants were fully competent (M. Rogolsky, unpublished results in this laboratory). These findings again suggest that, in *B. subtilis*, the development of competence may also be related to a function associated with the process of sporulation. Using radio-autographic techniques, Young (in press) has presented evidence suggesting that DNA becomes irreversibly attached to the cell surface mainly in association with structures suggestive of fore spores at one end of the cell.

A reasonable hypothesis to account for the development of competence in *B. subtilis* suggests that certain gene products are formed in cells during the process of presporulation or sporulation which can act in such cell populations to produce competence for transformation. The eventual product of the gene known to control the production of high level competence may be a competence factor of the type to be discussed later in this review.

The State of Competence

The kinetics of DNA uptake by competent cells have been defined by Lerman & Tolmach (27); Fox (28); Young & Spizizen (21); Barnhart & Herriott (29), and Stuy & Stern (30). The data indicate that homologous DNA binding leading to insusceptibility to deoxyribonuclease is often almost precisely correlated with genetic transfer. Instances of lack of correlation have been noted (21, 31). A reversible binding of DNA preceding or concomitant with the irreversible event appears to be particularly significant in *Hemophilus influenzae* (29, 32). The use of P^{32}-labeled DNA can, however, lead to ambiguous results because of contamination with phosphorus-containing polymers such as teichoic acid. Teichoic acid was found by Young (personal communication) to contaminate DNA isolated by the usual procedures. It does not penetrate competent cells but bands broadly in the region of DNA in a cesium chloride gradient after ultracentrifugation. Hence, some of the kinetic data obtained with P^{32} labeling require reinterpretation.

The data concerning the kinetic analysis of DNA uptake suggest that irreversible attachment and "penetration" of DNA cannot readily be dissociated. Young & Spizizen (21) showed that inhibitors of oxidative phosphorylation such as 2, 4-dinitrophenol and cyanide prevent irreversible DNA uptake by competent *B. subtilis* cells, presumably because of inability to penetrate. The requirement for an energy source such as glucose was also demonstrated. This argues for a metabolically primed active transport mechanism for DNA intake. Similar findings with metabolic inhibitors have been made in *H. influenzae* (29, 30). Certain divalent cations appear to be essential for DNA uptake. In *B. subtilis*, it appears that at least one of the following ions is necessary for uptake: Sr, Ba, Ca, and Mg (33). The requirement for Ca ions for uptake in *Diplococcus* (34), Ca and Mg ions in *Hemophilus* (35), Ca ions in *Neisseria* (36), and Mn, Ca, or Mg in *B. licheniformis* (37) has also been demonstrated.

FORMATION OF COMPETENCE STATE

Physiological state of culture.—Although competence is characteristic of specific strains, it cannot be manifested except under certain growth conditions and at special periods. It is generally unstable, and the conditions for its production vary with the species used. The extent of competence, i.e., the proportion of cells capable of DNA uptake, is not easily determined.

The most definitive demonstration that competence appears at a specific stage of cell growth was made by Hotchkiss (38). Synchronous growth of *Diplococcus* achieved by temperature shifts resulted in peaks or waves of competence, suggesting that competence arises at a specific phase of cell growth.

Studies with *Bacillus subtilis*, 168 strain, have shown that competence appears optimally in a minimal medium toward the end of exponential growth (39). Complex media were found to yield populations of low competence (21). The essential requirements, in addition to glucose-salts for the development of competence, appear to include the auxotrophic requirements and additional small quantities of amino acids required for growth and chelation of cupric ions.

The relationship between growth conditions and the development of competence has been further elucidated by Spencer & Herriott (40) in the *H. influenzae* system. A system for the development of high competence was found when cells, previously grown in a complex medium, were incubated in a defined medium which was itself limited in its ability to permit cell divisions. The essential components for the formation of competence were L-aspartic acid, L-glutamic acid, L-cystine, L-arginine, or L-citrulline and fumarate in addition to salts, including Mg and Ca. Protein synthesis appeared to be essential during competence development in this medium, since chloramphenicol inhibited, as did deletion of any of the amino acids. Although the addition of the following compounds, nicotinamide adenine dinucleotide, thiamine, calcium pantothenate, uracil and hypoxanthine was required for cell divisions, the presence of these components dramatically inhibited competence development.

A similar procedure for "step-down" development of competence was employed for *B. licheniformis* (37). After growth in a nutrient broth with salts and glycerol to a late stationary phase, the culture was transferred to a minimal-glucose medium and competence developed in 3 to 4 hours at which time cell divisions no longer occurred.

A number of inhibitors of competence formation during the growth phase have been found in the different systems examined. Thus, in addition to chloramphenicol (34), L-valine was found to inhibit competence formation but had no effect once competence was present in *Hemophilus* (40). The inhibition of L-valine was reversed by L-isoleucine or L-leucine, and these effects were found also to influence growth in complete minimal medium. Inhibition of competence formation by Cu at extremely low concentrations $(10^{-5}M)$ in *B. subtilis* (34) was also noted, but in this instance no measurable effect was observed on cell divisions. A similar effect has been noted with certain inhibitors of sporulation such as α-picolinic acid (Spizizen, unpublished results). It is thus obvious in these sytems that certain phases of biosynthesis during cell growth (especially protein synthesis) are essential for competence formation, but that the competence state appears under conditions when the cells have reached a "resting" state. The requirements for protein synthesis may be attributed to the necessity for formation of a competence receptor or autolytic enzyme, or both (see below).

Further support for the "nongrowth" condition of competent cells comes from the work of Nester (41) who showed that competent *B. subtilis* cells are more resistant to killing by penicillin than are noncompetent cells. In fact, more rapid and extensive killing of the population of cells from poorly competent cultures occurred than among cells from a competent culture. The effect of penicillin in decreasing the number of competent cells suggests that various stages of competence may exist. Moreover, it was found that the addition of chloramphenicol to a competent culture (or tryptophan starvation with a tryptophan-auxotroph) resulted in extensive loss of competence. Thus, protein synthesis appears to be required for maintenance of competence. It has been demonstrated that the competent cells of *B. subtilis* maintain competence for periods of 3 to 4 hours by transfer to the same cells of a second marker at different times up to 4 hours after the first marker was introduced.

The possibility that competent cells of *B. subtilis*, 168, are relatively defective in photoreactivating ability has been suggested by the experiments of Kelner (42). In these experiments, competent cells which have been in contact with transforming DNA for 26 minutes followed by deoxyribonuclease, were irradiated with ultraviolet light, followed by visible light. Under conditions giving a tenfold increase of the total viable cells over cells kept in the dark after exposure to ultraviolet light, the transformants were increased only by 1.5. This suggests that competent *B. subtilis* cells are in a special physiological state. Experiments reported by Okubo & Romig (160) with irradiated *B. subtilis* phage DNA also indicates that competent cells are impaired in repair mechanisms. They found that infectious SPO2 phage DNA was more sensitive to ultraviolet irradiation than SPO2 phage particles, and in the presence of acriflavine, which inhibits dark repair, the sensitivity of the phage approached that of its DNA. In addition, ultraviolet irradiation reduced indole transformants to 1 per cent of the unirradiated control as compared with 50 per cent survival of the total viable cells.

An inhibition of thymidine incorporation into synchronously growing pneumococci immediately prior to competence formation was noted by Ephrussi-Taylor & Freed (43), which confirms the notion that depression of DNA synthesis may be characteristic of the competence state.

In other systems, the physiological condition of culture growths which predispose the cells to competence appears to be somewhat different from those in the instances cited above. Thus, in *Rhizobium* (44) and *Neisseria* (36) under the conditions employed, competence developed in early exponential growth.

Evidence for wall changes accompanying competence.—The possibility that an altered wall structure resulting from unbalanced growth conditions forms the chemical basis for competence in *B. subtilis*, was suggested by Spizizen (45). Thus, the addition of certain wall precursors, such as L-alanine and L-glutamate, to the medium used for development of competence, reduced the level of competence attained. Since extensive wall changes accompany the transition of vegetative cells to spores, it was of some interest to find that certain asporogenous mutants of *B. subtilis*, 168 strain, were blocked in their ability to develop competence (21, 46). Transformable strains were shown to contain a higher content of N-acetyl galactosamine associated with the teichoic acid of walls than those of poorly transformable strains (26). These changes could decrease the net negative charge on the wall. It has been suggested by Jensen & Haas (47, 48), that *B. subtilis* cells in the competence state show changes in surface charge. Studies by Barnhart & Herriott (29) indicate marked dependence of both the reversible and irreversible phases of DNA uptake by compent *H. influenzae* on ionic environment. Further studies may elucidate the structural basis for the ability of the cell wall to permit attachment of DNA molecules. The role of the autolytic enzyme found in association with walls and showing higher activity in competent cells (66, 67), is not clear but it may contribute to the production of certain wall changes leading to competence. The possibility was suggested by Thomas (49) that a partial protoplast formed during competence would allow for DNA penetration.

Ephrati-Elizur (50) showed that actinomycin resistance mutation in *B. subtilis*, 168 strain, was usually correlated with loss of ability to develop competence. It has been suggested that actinomycin resistance is due to antibiotic impermeability (51), thus implicating wall or membrane changes.

Altered biosynthesis of pneumococcal walls associated with the competence state has been suggested by Ephrussi-Taylor &Freed (43), who showed that, although a number of amino acids are normally incorporated into cell material during the synchronous formation of competence, there is a reproducible lag of 8 minutes in the incorporation of lysine, a wall constituent. Thus protein synthesis appears to occur at a normal level, but the synthesis of the wall peptide might be inhibited. The degradation of wall peptide by an autolytic enzyme might also explain the results.

The formation of a specific antigen in *Diplococcus*, characteristic and essential for DNA uptake, has been suggested by Nava, Galis & Beiser (52), Tomasz & Beiser (53), and Pakula & Hauschild (54). Formaldehyde-treated competent pneumococcal cells were employed as antigen, and antibodies that specifically inhibited the transformation of streptomycin, erythromycin, and micrococcin markers were produced in rabbits. Globulin fractions of rabbit antisera were employed to avoid nonspecific serum components which inhibit transformations. The amount of antibody was found to be extremely low as compared to antibodies against other cellular components. The antibody was found to inhibit transformation in α-hemolytic streptococci, strain D, closely related to pneumococcus, but had no effect on *H. influenzae* or *B. subtilis* competence (53).

These studies suggest that specific receptor sites might be elaborated for the uptake of DNA, a notion early suggested by Hotchkiss (38) and Fox & Hotchkiss (34).

Evidence for a DNA Receptor or Competence "Factor"

Pakula and co-workers (54–56), have presented evidence for an extracellular factor produced by competent cells of *Streptococcus* Group H, strain Challis, which, when added to a noncompetent *Streptococcus* Group H, strain Wicky, made the latter competent for streptomycin resistance transformation. Irreversible C^{14}-labeled DNA uptake by Wicky cells was increased in the presence of the factor, although nontransformable cells without factor attached at least one half of the labeled DNA. The factor appears to be nondialyzable, and is inactivated at temperatures above 100° C (60 min at 115° C). Slade (personal communication) has obtained similar results. Culture filtrates from Group A streptococci (nontransformable) produced a threefold increase in transformants with Challis' streptococci. Perry & Slade (57) had shown that P^{32}-labeled DNA was taken up by nontransformable Group A streptococci to the same extent as transformable strains. This suggested to Slade (personal communication) that the lack of transformation in Group A cells resulted from processes other than attachment. DNA, reextracted after adsorption to Group A cells, was still biologically active, hence DNase degradation did not appear to account for nontransformability.

Tomasz & Hotchkiss (58) and Tomasz (59) have also presented evidence for a competence "activator" in *Diplococcus*. By means of a U-tube experiment in which a "millipore" membrane separated two cultures, one competent and the other noncompetent, it was found that the latter became quite competent for transformation after 60 minutes at 30° C. The active material was eluted from cell debris of competent cells and was found to be of a high molecular weight since it was not retained on Sephadex G25 although small retention occurred on Sephadex G75. The activity was maximal at pH 7.7, was enhanced by mercaptoethanol, and was inactivated by proteolytic enzymes, and thus appears to contain protein. Maleate $(0.5M)$ was found to inhibit the activator effect on transformability, but DNA attachment was apparently not affected. The competence activator was found to be active with α-hemolytic streptococcus, strain D, a close relative. Antibodies against competent cells neutralized the capacity of the competence-activator to convert noncompetent cells to competence (52). An explanation for the transient nature of the competence in this organism was suggested by the finding of an inhibitor produced by cells after competence has developed, or by cells growing under conditions not leading to competence. The inhibitor is nondialyzable, stable to 15 minutes at 90° C, appears to be without effect on cells already competent, and thus distinguishable from deoxyribonuclease. The data are not consistent with the hypothesis that the inhibitor is a proteolytic enzyme.

Charpak & Dedonder (60) demonstrated that supernatants of competent *B. subtilis*, 168, cells or phosphate-extracted acetone powders of *B. subtilis* when added to a noncompetent *B. subtilis*, niger strain, permitted transformation for a methionine marker. The activity was destroyed by heating for 5 minutes at 100° C or by added trypsin and chymotrypsin. A competence factor was also suggested for *Bacillus cereus*, strain 569, which was produced during the development of competence in a minimal growth medium (61). A crude concentrate added to cells which had reached competence, but lost it by a washing procedure, restored competence. No confirmation of a transformation system in this species has been recorded, however, and it is conceivable that the organism was improperly identified.

Although the work on competence "factors" needs amplification, it is probable that one aspect of competence may involve the attachment of DNA to a specific protein. The details of the mechanism of DNA penetration, a metabolically dependent phenomenon, still remain to be probed.

CHARACTERISTICS OF BIOLOGICALLY ACTIVE DNA

The ability of DNA to penetrate competent cells is dependent upon at least two physical properties, namely, molecular size and double-strandedness.

Molecular size.—Lerman & Tolmach (27) first observed, with a low concentration of deoxyribonuclease (10^{-3} μg/ml), that labeled pneumococcal DNA lost transforming and uptake abilities. One-hit reduction in both activities occurred, albeit at different rates. The use of a P^{32} label may have obscured closer correlations, since DNA preparations may have other phosphorus-containing compounds. Litt et al. (62) investigated the transforming activities and molecular weights of sonicated pneumococcal DNA in the presence of S-(2-aminoethyl) isothiuronium bromide hydrogen bromide. The latter compound prevented secondary reactions leading to inactivation. Loss of biological activity of three markers occurred as a function of breaks in the molecules attending sonication. The logarithms of the decay of relative transforming activities was directly proportional to the reciprocal of molecular weights as determined by sedimentation, and thus to the fraction of bonds broken. A critical molecular weight of 1.0 million for biological activity was thus obtained. The recovery of biological activity lost by sonication was demonstrated by reannealing pneumococcal DNA with undegraded DNA (63).

Rosenberg et al. (64) investigated the effects of mechanical shear performed by a spray method on the transforming activities of pneumococcal DNA. Molecular weights and residual transforming activities of sheared samples were determined. Four markers showed differences in the curves relating biological activity to molecular weight, using the same DNA preparation. All markers, however, show a sharp drop in activity with shear, as does the uptake by competent cells, suggesting that the major loss of transforming ability is due to lack of uptake of the DNA. The kinetic data were interpreted to indicate that two types of absorption site occur on the pneumococcal cell. The main site appears to permit the attachment of DNA molecules of more than 2.2×10^6 molecular weight.

Szybalski & Opara-Kubinska (65) present evidence that the B. subtilis-transforming DNA has little or no activity below 10^7 molecular weight. These workers consider that previous data are unreliable since DNA was not adequately sheared and fractionated.

Although the minimal molecular weight required for biological activity (by virtue of uptake capability) has been determined with pneumococcal DNA, the maximal limits are unknown. Transfection experiments indicate that B. subtilis bacteriophage DNA molecules of molecular weight 120×10^6 readily penetrate (68, 150, 151).

Molecular size has been implicated in the efficiency of cotransfer of unlinked markers in B. subtilis. Direct demonstration of the effects on DNA of hydrodynamic shear was obtained with the use of different flow rates through a 27-gauge needle: flow rates of 2 ml/min reduced the cotransfer of indole and methionine markers to 27 per cent of the unsheared control. Low levels of deoxyribonuclease (10^{-3} µg/ml) also reduced the cotransfer frequency of these markers.

Strauss (70, 71) has presented data with B. subtilis which suggests that the entry of transforming DNA occurs in a longitudinal manner, since the lag period for irreversible uptake of markers appeared to be a linear function of the distance between the markers. Comparison was made of DNA isolated by the Marmur (72) procedure with that isolated by the method of Berns & Thomas (73). The latter procedure produces DNA of higher molecular weight and with this DNA preparation the "unlinked" markers try_2^+ and his_9^+ appeared to enter by a single fragment. The markers appeared to be associated with separate fragments when DNA prepared by the Marmur procedure was employed.

Strandedness.—Lerman & Tolmach (74) demonstrated a decrease in uptake of pneumococcal DNA as a result of heating, although transforming activity for a number of markers was decreased to a greater extent at some temperatures. Young & Spizizen (21) also demonstrated a loss of uptake ability by competent *B. subtilis* cells when transforming DNA was heat-inactivated, as did Barnhart & Herriott (29) with *H. influenzae.*

The studies of Roger & Hotchkiss (75) indicated that different critical inactivation temperatures were characteristic for a number of unlinked markers. Linked markers inactivated at the same critical temperature. The other characteristic of "critical heat inactivation" was the residual activity of approximately 10 per cent for all markers. The conclusion reached was that heating at high temperature disrupted the hydrogen-bonded structure of the double helix of individual DNA molecules. Unlinked markers could be associated, therefore, with different molecules, although the possibility of intramolecular heterogeneity was also suggested. Geiduschek (76) and Guild (77) provided evidence for heterogeneity within DNA molecules. They concluded that distribution of guanine-cytosine pairs in the molecule could account for the critical inactivation temperatures.

The residual activity associated with heated preparations (rapidly cooled) was notably constant for different markers (75). It appeared to be insensitive to ionic strength, hence was not the product of reannealing of denatured strands. It was suggested that this fraction contained molecules in which the single strands were only partially separated, but that sufficient hydrogen-bonding portions of the molecules was present to hold the strands together. Studies of this residual activity have been pursued in many laboratories (78–83). Ginoza & Zimm (79) have shown that the heat-resistant fraction is independent of DNA concentration during denaturation and thus probably is not the product of renaturation. Guild (80) and Rownd et al. (81) showed that the residual activity is in a DNA fraction which bands in a CsCl density gradient as if it were denatured. With *B. subtilis*, Rownd et al. (84) subsequently showed that residual activity was associated with a density range in a CsCl gradient characteristic of native and partially denatured molecules. Chevallier & Bernardi (83) by fractionation on hydroxy-apatite of heated *H. influenzae* DNA showed that residual activity could be eluted at a higher molarity than the fully denatured biologically inactive portion. The degree of reaction with formaldehyde was greater with the denatured fraction than with comparable amounts of the active fraction. It was concluded that the residual activity was associated with partially denatured molecules.

Barnhart (82) came to similar conclusions in a detailed study of the residual activity of heated *H. influenzae* DNA. He found that the activity was resistant to Lehman's exonuclease I which digests denatured DNA, but was very sensitive to digestion by snake venom diesterase. Since the latter enzyme releases 5' mononucleotides from 5' phosphate end groups, it suggests that the residual activity is associated with a molecule possessing free 5' phosphates. The resistance to formamide, a mild denaturing agent, as compared with native DNA indicated that it had a double-stranded structure unlike native DNA. It resembled native DNA in its reactivity with formaldehyde at high temperatures, suggesting that hydrogen bonding was important for biological activity. Thus, the properties of the material associated with residual activity suggest partial denaturation of the DNA molecules. It would be of interest to determine the precise relationship between molecules with varying degrees of bonding and helical conformation and the biological activities of a number of markers as related to uptake by competent cells.

DNA INTEGRATION IN TRANSFORMATION: FATE OF TRANSFORMING DNA

The fate of transforming DNA has been investigated in *Diplococcus* (85–90), in *Hemophilus* (91, 92), and *B. subtilis* (31, 93–97). These studies were designed to determine the manner in which DNA associates, integrates, and recombines with the resident genome and if both strands of the DNA duplex are required for the transfer of genetic information.

Fox & Hotchkiss (85) initiated studies on the fate of transforming pneumococcal DNA carrying biological and isotopic labels. Following fixation and incubation at 37° C for 5 minutes, transforming DNA was isolated and passed to new recipients. The ratio of new marker to label was identical after a second passage. In addition, after longer periods of incubation, the introduced marker activity increased at the same rate as culture growth. The ratio of biological activities of newly introduced DNA to resident DNA was constant from 5 minutes and this ratio approximated the frequency of transformation. When DNA was extracted from cells following very short exposures to transforming DNA, an eclipse of biological activity was discovered (86). An eclipse is also known in viral infections. Within 5 minutes at 37° C, however, biological activity was recovered. At 30° C this recovery was delayed. A linkage group of the sulfonamide locus was recovered in approximately twice the time period required for recovery of a single marker. Similar results have been obtained with *B. subtilis* transformation (94, 98). Recovery of biological activity was found to occur in the absence of detectable growth and was unaffected by 5-fluorodeoxyuridine at concentrations thirty times higher than required for growth inhibition. Incorporation of P^{32} into DNA was also negligible during this period. Further studies with DNA heavily labeled with P^{32} (87) following P^{32} disintegration, indicated the retention of physical integrity of the introduced DNA both in the eclipse and on integration with the recipient genome. The data suggest that a minimum of 900 nucleotide pairs are contained in the acquired segment of the transforming DNA.

Lacks (89), in an effort to define the eclipse, examined DNA isolated in very early times after DNA uptake by competent pneumococcal cells and concluded that about one half of the DNA is converted to a single-stranded stage, the remainder being degraded to dialyzable oligonucleotides. Extensive degradation of transforming DNA following irreversible uptake has also been observed in *B. subtilis* (101) (Young, personal communication). Methylated albumin-kieselguhr columns were employed by Lacks (89) to fractionate deproteinized extracts of deoxycholate-lysed cells after uptake of labeled DNA by competent cells. At the earliest time sampled, following uptake, the radioactivity of the transforming DNA is found to be equally distributed between a low molecular weight fraction and a fraction eluted only at pH 10. The latter fraction was found to sediment in CsCl as single-stranded DNA with a higher density than double-stranded DNA. With time, up to ten minutes, the amount of the single-stranded moiety as measured by radioactivity is decreased. At the same time, there is an increase in the peak represented by double-stranded DNA. The appearance of radioactivity in the native DNA occurs at the time when the eclipse of the donor marker (streptomycin resistance) disappears. It was concluded that the eclipsed biological activity is due to single-stranding of the transforming DNA, since single-stranded DNA is incapable of being taken up by competent cells in a biological assay. The single-strand formed following uptake might be bound to protein (99) or form a three-stranded structure, as suggested for messenger RNA by Zubay (100).

Fox & Allen (90) also found a small amount of a denatured form of transforming DNA and demonstrated the formation of a hybrid molecule of transforming DNA and recipient DNA held together by covalent links. The biological activity and radioactivity of the donor DNA was found from earliest times (1 minute) to be associated with material banding in a position very close to that of recipient DNA. Thus, all the donor biological activity recoverable and 36 per cent of the radioactivity of donor DNA was found in this fraction. The remainder of the radioactivity was present as denatured and degraded DNA. At 15 minutes, about 90 per cent of the donor biological activity was found in the recipient DNA region with 81 per cent of the radioactivity and there was a decrease of P^{32} in the acid-soluble fraction. A detailed examination of the fraction of donor DNA associated with recipient DNA was made, using sonication and denaturation procedures. Sonication produced molecules which were heterogeneous in density, and little radioactivity appeared in the native heavy DNA fraction. Denaturation shifted a small amount of P^{32}-DNA to the fraction of heavy denatured DNA but the bulk of the label was still associated with light denatured recipient DNA. Sonication followed by heat denaturation produced fragments in which most of the P^{32} was in heavy denatured DNA. Thus, hybrid material containing fully heavy (donor) and light (recipient components) was demonstrated. The presence of P^{32} label in light denatured DNA produced by these manipulations was assumed to be due to new synthesis from degradation of the transforming DNA. The occurrence of all isolated donor biological activity in the hybrid thus suggests that only one strand of the donor DNA couples with the DNA of the recipient genome. The other strand might then be degraded by exonucleases, thus accounting for degradation products of donor DNA. The question then raised is whether a unique strand of donor DNA is incorporated or whether either strand can be used.

Pene & Romig (93) investigated the fate of transforming DNA in *B. subtilis* and concluded that no single-stranded form was present after uptake. Using N^{14}, P^{32}-labeled donor DNA and N^{15}-unlabeled recipient cells, they found two radioactive peaks in the CsCl density gradient. One peak represented donor DNA and the other a complex of donor and recipient. They were able to show that the latter peak was not due to nonspecific aggregation and, by using labeled DNA from *B. cereus* (which does not recombine to form genetic recombinants), that the acquired label was not the result of degradation and incorporation into recipient DNA.

More detailed studies of the fate of transforming DNA in *B. subtilis* have been made by Bodmer & Ganesan (31) and Bodmer (96). DNA labeled with N^{15}, H^2, and H^3 was employed with the competent cells labeled with P^{32}. Fractionation of the DNA isolated from cells in contact with transforming DNA for 10 to 30 minutes revealed donor atoms in fractions corresponding to native donor, native recipient, hybrid, and denatured donor DNA. Donor and recombinant biological activities were associated with all fractions except the denatured. The association of donor DNA with recipient DNA was resistant to shearing or denaturation. The data are not inconsistent with single-stranded integration. Calculations indicated 8.4×10^3 nucleotide pairs of donor DNA were inserted in an integrated region.

Venema, Pritchard & Schroder (95) have presented evidence that in *B. subtilis* transformation the complex of donor and recipient DNAs first formed may not represent complete chemical integration. Donor DNA, isolated at early times from transformed cultures, appeared to be less sensitive to thermal denaturation (and less reannealable) than recipient DNA. At later times this difference vanished. It was thus suggested that an early phase of incomplete integration of donor DNA with recipient genome occurs immediately following the eclipse, possibly as a result of a single strand of donor DNA being complexed with a homologous segment of recipient. Such a triple-stranded structure was suggested by Zubay (100). It would be of interest to determine whether such a structure displays the property of relative heat resistance. The decreased renaturability might be the result of incompletely integrated, smaller donor segments. It would also be of some interest to determine whether "complete" integration occurs only as a result of replication of the resident genome.

The very elegant studies of Bodmer (96) in which the integration of transforming DNA was shown to occur in the virtually complete absence of DNA synthesis, may thus relate to the initial stages of integration. The subsequent growth of transformed *B. subtilis*, thymine-requiring, in the presence of 5-bromouracil indicated that donor DNA was integrated in a region in which reinitiation of DNA synthesis appeared. It was concluded that integration may occur at a stationary replicating point of the genome, presumably in association with the bacterial membrane.

The problem of integration in relation to replication may relate to the phenomenon of the delay in expression of introduced markers in *B. subtilis* observed by Anagnostopoulos and Spizizen (unpublished observations) and by Nester & Stocker (102). The former investigators observed a 2- to 3-hour delay in the expression of the markers: a repressive alkaline phosphatase, an inducible sucrase, and a constitutive theonine deaminase, introduced by transforming DNA in *B. subtilis*. Nester & Stocker showed that the enzyme tryptophan synthetase was not synthesized by transformed cells of a deficient population for 3 to 4 hours after DNA uptake, even though re-extraction of DNA from cells indicated that recombination of markers $try_2 his_2$, had occurred in 30 minutes. By contrast, expression of the amylomaltase gene in *Diplococcus* appears to be more rapid (103), presumably since DNA integration is completed in a shorter interval.

Studies with *Hemophilus* transformation (91, 92) argue against a single-stranded stage of donor DNA in these organisms. In fact, extensive degradation of DNA occurred soon after uptake. Undegraded DNA, however, which participates in integrative events, appeared to retain its double-stranded form, and no eclipse was observed. Voll & Goodgal (92) observed differential inactivation of markers following uptake and this was correlated with the efficiency of transformation of the markers.

The extensive degradation of transforming DNA following irreversible attachment (DNase-insensitive stage) has been observed in all transformation systems. In *B. subtilis* (101) (Young, unpublished results) this is particularly marked. This may be due to DNA attachment to multiple sites on the membrane, but penetration and subsequent association with resident genome may require special limited sites. The manner in which cells are made competent may be of importance in the discrimination of productive from nonproductive attachment.

INTEGRATION OF ONE OR TWO STRANDS: THE PROBLEM OF HETEROZYGOTES

Studies on the fate of transforming DNA in *Diplococcus* and *B. subtilis* have suggested the possible transient formation of single-stranded molecules and more definitely have shown that only one strand participates in integration with the resident genome. A number of melting and annealing experiments that indicate the involvement of one strand in the integration process have been performed recently (94, 104, 105). Venema (personal communication) has also demonstrated, by using DNA bifilarly labeled with 5-bromouracil as donor, that after completed integration the ultraviolet sensitivity of the isolated DNA material was that of DNA unifilarly labeled with 5-bromouracil. Venema et al. (94) used a mixture of DNA-containing linked markers $ind^- tyr^+$, $ind^+ tyr^-$, $ind^+ tyr^+$ in the proportion of 100:1:0.3, respectively. The mixture was heated to melting and reannealed. The single strands of $ind^+ tyr^-$ and $ind^+ tyr^+$ would be expected to reanneal with the predominant $ind^- tyr^+$ single strands. If both strands were used for integration then the number of $ind^+ tyr^-$ and $ind^+ tyr^+$ transformants would be twice that of the mixture before reannealing. If either strand was involved, no change would be observed. The latter was found experimentally. A model for hybrid transforming unit or heterozygote was proposed by Herriott (105). In this model, two strands each containing markers in a linkage group are partly paired to a common strand. Thus, a reannealing mixture of three singly marked DNAs formed triply marked recombinants.

The possibility that one of the strands is unique in transcribing the genetic message has been suggested by Guild & Robison (106). In their experiments, pneumococcal DNA denatured at pH 12 was found to consist of a slightly more dense fraction and a lighter fraction in a CsCl density gradient. The expression time (of novobiocin resistance trait) for the light fractions (after renaturation) was found to be less than for the denser fractions, suggesting that reading of messages was associated with the light strand. The denser strand expressed in a period required for a cell duplication, suggesting that it was replicated before the reading of messenger RNA could be made.

LINKAGE GROUPS AND MAPPING OF GENOME
BY TRANSFORMATION

Linked transformations, which indicate that a single DNA molecule can carry information for a number of genes, was first observed in *Diplococcus* with the streptomycin and mannitol markers (107). Subsequently it was found that the cathomycin and streptomycin resistance traits in *Hemophilus* were transferred as a linked pair (108). Transformation of markers controlling the synthesis of capsular material in *Diplococcus* revealed linkage of a number of genes controlling a biosynthetic pathway (109).

Interest in linkage of genes involved in related biochemical functions was aroused by the "operon" concept postulated by Jacob & Monod (110). A cluster of genes was found in *B. subtilis* bearing the code for the enzymes of the tryptophan biosynthetic pathway (111). By two- and three-point crosses, it was determined that the genes were ordered as the biochemical sequence, with one exception. Linked to the tryptophan locus in *B. subtilis* are genes for the biosynthesis of a number of aromatic amino acids (112) as well as of histidine (113, 114). Thus, a transforming DNA molecule was found to contain at least 13 genetic loci (112). Other loci for histidine and certain aromatic amino acids syntheses appear to be unlinked. Three unlinked loci for arginine biosynthesis have been demonstrated in *B. subtilis* by transformation (115).

In an extensive study of genes directing the synthesis of branched amino acids (isoleucine, valine, leucine) in *B. subtilis*, Anagnostopoulos et al. (116, 117) showed that two separate linkage groups were present in transforming DNA molecules. Two- and three-point crosses revealed that genes for threonine deaminase and dihydroxy acid dehydrase were linked with a methionine locus. The reductoisomerase locus was found to be linked to leucine genes. Confirmation of gene orders was achieved by transduction with the PBS-1 phage of Takahashi (118). Cotransduction of certain markers, showing little linkage by transformation, was demonstrated to occur with higher frequencies. In a number of instances where no linkage could be observed with transformation, cotransduction was found to occur. Thus, extension of the map was achieved with transduction, possibly as a result of the transfer of larger portions of the genome than in transformation. In addition, the recombinational frequencies (but not the order) were different with the two methods of genomic transfer. Recombination frequencies in transduction were considerably lower than those in the corresponding regions with transformation. It was suggested that this may be due to different sizes of the pairing pieces, as occurs when mapping by transduction and conjugation are compared in *Escherichia coli* K-12.

Kelly & Pritchard (69) have confirmed in part the extended map of the *B. subtilis* chromosome observed with transduction tests by employing DNA isolated under extremely mild conditions. They demonstrated cotransfer of markers normally found to be unlinked when the usual methods for DNA isolation are employed. These linkages were destroyed when their DNA preparations were diluted, or subjected to hydrodynamic shear, or treated with low concentrations of deoxyribonuclease. The effect of dilution could be prevented by employing carrier DNA (100 μg per ml) in the diluent. The linkage was undisturbed by treatment of DNA with proteolytic enzymes, lipase, phospholipase, or ribonuclease. Nevertheless, the possibility of break-points held together by proteins or other cementing compounds has not been rigorously excluded. A linear map could be constructed from their data, which suggests that the linkage relationships were associated with single molecular species. These findings provide a significant new probe for mapping of the *B. subtilis* chromosome. Thus, linkage relationships of genes could be uncovered by employing highly polymerized transforming DNA treated *in vitro* by mutagens, as has been so successfully employed for closely linked genes (111). Using kinetic methods, Strauss (70, 71) proposed a mapping procedure which also employs high molecular weight DNA.

A novel approach to mapping of the *B. subtilis* chromosome was suggested by the studies of Yoshikawa & Sueoka (119–121). Based on the notion
that a polarity in the replication of the chromosome exists in growing cells,
the relative frequencies of markers were determined. With strain 23 (related
to strain 168) it was found that the ratio of the adenine to methionine
markers approached the value 2 when transforming DNA was isolated from
exponentially growing cells. The ratio of 1 was found for this pair of markers
when stationary phase cells were used for DNA isolation. Relative to the
methionine marker, other markers gave values below 2 when exponential
phase cells were examined. In this manner, a relative order of genes was determined with adenine and methionine at the extreme ends. From the exponential phase, the adenine marker gave the highest frequency of transformation, and methionine and isoleucine the lowest, suggesting that the adenine gene represented the origin of the replicating unit. The ratio of isoleucine to methionine markers was nearly 1 in all DNA preparations from
different stages of growth, suggesting linkage, which was confirmed by direct
cotransfer experiments.

Confirmation of this type of oriented replication in *B. subtilis*, strain 23,
was obtained by employing heavy-labeled (D_2O–N^{15}) transforming DNA
from exponential and stationary growths. (Cells grown in heavy medium
with P^{32} were transferred to light P^{32} medium and samples were removed at
various intervals which represented fractions of generation times as determined by turbidity.) Cell lysates were fractionated by CsCl centrifugation
and profiles of P^{32} and transforming activities were determined. The data on
the rates of conversion of parental into hybrid DNA molecules, so determined, confirmed the sequence of marker replication. When stationary cells
were used as inoculum for the growth series, about 20 per cent of the terminal
markers, methionine and isoleucine, were found in the hybrid material, suggesting that some chromosomes were not completely replicated in the stationary phase.

Sequential replication of markers was, however, not observed with strain
168. The chromosomes in the stationary phase of growth appeared to be in
various stages of replication but to a lesser extent than in exponential phase,
as compared with marker ratios from spore DNA. The same polarity was
found in the 168 strain as in the 23 strain, when spore DNA was used as
standard. Thus, chromosomes of the spore appear to be in a completed form
of replication. Studies with germinated spores indicated synchrony of chromosome replication, with polarity, as shown for the 23 strain in the vegetative growth phases. Predictions on the basis of a model of dichotomous replication were borne out by a study of the kinetics of replication in the spore
germinating system.

Problems related to factors influencing integration which must be con-
sidered in evaluating map distances have been discussed in recent work in
Diplococcus by Rotheim & Ravin (122), Sicard & Ephrussi-Taylor (123), and
Lacks (124).

RNA TRANSFORMATION

The direct infectivity of viral RNA has been demonstrated in a number of systems. Recently, Evans (125) has reported the isolation from *Diplococcus pneumoniae* of RNA-containing fractions which are capable of converting a suitable population of sensitive recipient cells to a level of drug resistance resembling that of the donor strain from which the RNA fraction had been derived. The biological activity of the particles was found to be quite drastically reduced if the preparations were treated with either DNase or RNase. This dual sensitivity of the preparation to both nucleases strongly suggests that the active fraction in this instance is a polynucleotide complex consisting of both DNA and RNA. Such naturally occurring DNA-RNA complexes have been reported in other organisms (126) and, although not demonstrated in bacteria, might be inferred for the latter (45). However, it was shown that the RNA component of the pneumococcal fractions is in itself capable of biological activity. This was accomplished by treating pneumococcal extracts of this DNA-RNA complex with catalytic concentrations of DNase sufficient to degrade the DNA component and destroy the biological activity of the preparation. The residual RNA molecules were subsequently annealed to heat-denatured DNA which did not bear the sulfonamide resistance marker contained on the RNA. It was found that such artificially produced DNA-RNA hybrids were capable of conferring sulfonamide resistance upon sensitive recipient cells. Furthermore, the artificial hybrid preparations were also inactivated by treatment with either of the nucleases. These experiments not only demonstrate the genetic potential of bacterial RNA but also indicate that the uptake of RNA by competent cells, like that of DNA, is highly dependent on the physical configuration of the molecules. Maintenance of a particular kind of structural integrity (possibly double-strandedness) seems important for the detection of transforming activity. Evidence has also been obtained that biologically active fractions can be synthesized enzymatically (127).

A number of features distinguish biologically active RNA complexes from transforming DNA. These include: (*a*) sensitivity of the complex to both nucleases; (*b*) higher concentrations of this material (approximately twenty times that of purified DNA) are required to saturate competent cells; and (*c*) the nature of the host response to this material. It was expected that those cells converted to sulfonamide resistance by virtue of the action of RNA would maintain the property for a limited number of generations since messenger RNA was considered unstable and capable of sponsoring the formation of a relatively low concentration of protein molecules. Some of the transformant clones did lose the sulfonamide resistance property which they initially exhibited after undergoing four or five divisions. However, a surprisingly high proportion of the resistant clones were able to maintain the resistance property (at a level resembling that of the donor cells) for at least fifty divisions before losing it. This relative persistence of the acquired trait through many generations strongly suggests that the introduced fraction is capable of being replicated by cellular polymerases to a limited extent and in some as yet unknown manner. Furthermore, an analysis of the segregation behavior of many of the transformant clones was made, using a particularly appropriate genetic marker system. In this system the donor cells were resistant to *para*-nitrobenzoic acid, an analogue of sulfanilamide, as well as the natural metabolite *para*-aminobenzoic acid, and sensitive to sulfanilamide. The recipient cells (conversely) were resistant to sulfanilamide but not to *p*-nitrobenzoic acid.

The phenotypic transformants obtained by treating such recipient cells with the DNA-RNA complex isolated from donor cells were found to be semistable heterozygotes in which both parental and donor properties could be detected. The appearance of these semistable heterozygotes strongly suggests that the introduced hybrid fractions are capable of residing in the cells in a loosely integrated state, possibly cytoplasmic. However, the donor genetic marker, which is carried in this case on both DNA and RNA (but in the artificial hybrids on the RNA component only), is capable of being expressed as a specific enzyme, namely folic acid synthetase. The state of coexistence achieved between the resident genome and the hybrid fraction is ultimately disturbed and the acquired particles either become fully integrated into the resident genome with attendant formation of a permanently resistant transformed clone, or the hybrid complex and the resistance property are completely lost, resulting in clones having only the recipient phenotype. The precise characterization of the events involved awaits the outcome of experiments now in progress. This apparent ability of the DNA-RNA complex to exist in the cells in two stages strongly suggests their resemblance to certain episomal elements. It seems reasonable to suppose that further studies on the structure and fate of these biologically active fractions should provide us with important information on several aspects of cell-polynucleotide interactions and more specifically on the role of RNA in determining the phenotypic properties of cells.

An unconfirmed report of RNA transformation of a penicillin-resistance trait (inducible penicillinase formation) in *B. subtilis* IRC, has been presented (128). As little as 10^{-8} μg per ml of RNA was found to give transformants for this trait.

TRANSFECTION

The discovery of competence in *B. subtilis* strain 168 resulted in a renewed interest in the bacteriophages of *B. subtilis*. A number of transducing phages have recently been isolated and characterized (129–139) and transformation and transduction compared in *B. subtilis* (117, 137–140). Applied in concert, these techniques have generated a powerful new tool for use in the classification of *B. subtilis* and closely related species (140).

In a novel approach, Takagi & Ikeda (138) extracted DNA from purified transducing phages and were able to assay the bacterial DNA contained in these phages by means of transformation. By similar methods, the analysis of DNA extracted from *B. subtilis* phages SP10 (141) and PBS1 (142), has provided insight into the mechanism of general transduction in *Bacillus*. In addition, the elegant studies of Barat, Anagnostopoulos & Schneider (117) indicate that high molecular weight host DNA extracted by phage PBS1 can greatly facilitate the mapping of the *B. subtilis* genome.

The scope of the study of transfection (143), defined as "infection of cells by the isolated nucleic acid from a virus resulting in the production of a complete virus" has recently been enlarged by the infection of cell populations competent for transformation by viral DNA. Kaiser & Hogness (144) first demonstrated transfection by infecting intact *E. coli* K-12 cells. Infection resulted from the inter-reaction of DNA isolated from a defective λ phage and cells infected by a related "helper" phage. This system has subsequently been analyzed in great detail and continues to provide new insight into the viral-cell nucleic acid interaction in bacterial cells. The evaluation of the results of these investigations and their conceptual impact in the area of molecular genetics should certainly be considered in detail in a separate review. Tokunaga & Sellers (145) have infected *Mycobacterium smegmatis* with DNA of mycobacteriophages and the properties of this system are currently being delineated (Tokunaga & Sillers, in press). A third type of transfection, infection by DNA in cell populations that had developed competence for bacterial transformation was first investigated by Romig (146). Subsequent research with *B. subtilis* transfection has indicated that polyoma virus (147) or vaccinia virus (148) can be formed in *B. subtilis* cells infected by the corresponding viral DNA. Confirmation of these results by independent investigations will certainly suggest novel problems that can be examined by this type of transfection.

Transfection by bacteriophage DNA can be envisioned as a simplified model of bacterial transformation. A single viral DNA molecule would enter the bacterial cell by a mechanism similar to that which introduces bacterial DNA in transformation and initiate the formation of an infectious center. Simplification follows from the implication that recombination and other events that occur in the growth of the transformed bacterial clone would not necessarily occur in transfection. However, each transfection system examined has characteristic features and the recognition of these features is fundamental to an evaluation of this model system.

The primary complicating factor is the particular mode of infection of the virus chosen for study. Each virus contains a DNA capable of programming such an infection, and the spectrum of chemical and physical DNA structures that have evolved with bacteriophages is amazing. Complications also arise from simple technical considerations. The choice of bacterial species, the strain and the conditions employed to initiate the development of competence in the bacterial strains is quite variable. Finally, there are some aspects of transfection that could be quite foreign to transformation. For example, to initiate infection, a complete molecule of extremely high molecular weight might have to enter the bacterial cell. It is not certain that this must occur in transformation. If infection by fragments occurred in transfection, then a type of recombination would be a prerequisite for either transformation or transfection and in this sense, transfection could hardly be considered a simple model of transformation.

Harm & Rupert (149) studied transfection of the Rd strain of *Hemophilus influenzae*, using the DNA of a clear mutant of a temperate phage. The infectious agent was destroyed by pancreatic DNase but not by *E. coli* phosphodiesterase. Infectivity inactivated by ultraviolet irradiation was restored by the yeast photoreactivating enzyme. A relationship to transformation was suggested by several observations. The simultaneous addition of host and viral DNA substantially reduced transfection. Susceptibility to infection and competence for bacterial transformation decreased concomitantly when competent cells were maintained at 37° C. Finally, transfection showed saturation infection at high DNA concentration and, as in transformation, a linear dependence on the concentration of DNA added. However, although a single cycle of viral replication occurred, DNA uptake and the initiation of infection were not complete by 50 minutes in the competent population.

Using phenol extracts of the *B. subtilis* phage SP3, Romig (146) isolated an infectious agent sensitive to DNase but resistant to RNase, trypsin, and antiserum prepared against SP3. In the *B. subtilis* population, the appearance of susceptible cells correlated with the time of development of competence for bacterial transformation. Unfortunately, infected cells could not be assayed; infection was detected after cycles of phage replication. Only a tenuous relationship between transfection and transformation was established in this system because probably less than a single infection occurred for each 10^5 competent cells present, and less than one in 10^8 phage equivalents of DNA was infectious.

The DNA of bacteriophage SP50 was used by Földes & Trautner (143). The infection was DNase-sensitive and occurred only when *B. subtilis* had developed competence for bacterial transformation. The simultaneous addition of host and viral DNA resulted in the reduction of the number of cells infected, suggesting a competition for DNA uptake analogous to that observed in transformation. But, again, infected cells were relatively unstable. Ninety per cent of the infectious centers were lost when infected cells were pipetted 25 minutes after the addition of SP50 DNA. Some infectious centers retained sensitivity to DNase addition 3 hours after exposure to viral DNA. Unlike transformation, the dilution of viral DNA indicated a nonlinear dependence of infection on DNA concentration.

Infectious DNA has been isolated from phages SP8 (147), SP82, (150), SPO-1 (151), and Φ25 (25). The morphological, biological, and chemical properties of these phages suggest a close relationship (22). The central features of this transfection system are the unique chemical and physical properties of these DNA molecules.

Phage SP8 was isolated and characterized by Romig & Brodetsky (152, 153). The guanine-cytosine content of hydrolysates of SP8 DNA was similar to host DNA, about 43 ± 1 per cent (154). However, no significant amount of base sequence homology was found between host and viral DNA (155, 156). In SP8 DNA, thymine was replaced by the pyrimidine bases 5-hydroxymethyluracil (154).

Sedimentation coefficients obtained with SP8 DNA indicate a molecular weight roughly equivalent to that of coliphage T2, about 120×10^6 (68). Similar values were obtained for DNA isolated from SP82, SPO-1, and Φ25 (22, 150, 151). The data reported by Green with SP82 is consistent with the conclusion that the entire genome of SP82 is contained in a single molecule. When compared with *B. subtilis* DNA, having a very similar guanine-cytosine content, each viral DNA was found to have an unexpected high sensitivity to heat denaturation reflected in a low T_m and a buoyant density of about 1.743 gm/cc in CsCl. Following heat denaturation, a bimodal distribution of ultraviolet absorbing material formed in the CsCl density gradient.

In this transfection system, infection occurred only in competent cell populations; it was sensitive to DNase and all results were consistent with the conclusion that neither RNA nor protein, especially the tail structure of the mature virus particle had any role in the infection process (22, 150, 151). However, it must be noted that less than one phage equivalent of DNA per 10^4–10^6 added to the cells could form an infectious center. Thus, the chemical and physical structure of the infectious particle is not necessarily reflected in the gross properties of the viral DNA solutions.

In *B. subtilis* transformation, Levine & Strauss (157) demonstrated a linear appearance of transformants for 6 minutes when competent cells and DNA were separated by washing and there was no time lag in the appearance of transformants. With similar methods, Barnhart (82), using λ transfection, and Green (150), with SP82 DNA, showed that there was no apparent lag in DNA adsorption. When transformation was terminated by DNase, however, a lag period of 1 to 1.5 minutes was observed and transformants appeared at an increasing rate (157). Very similar kinetics of infection were observed with Φ25, SP82, and SPO-1 DNA infection. Infectious centers appeared at an exponential rate and several minutes had elapsed before the first infectious centers formed. Green estimated that about 13 minutes was required to establish an infection, and that within 17 minutes after the appearance of the first DNase-resistant infection, 50 per cent of the infections were DNase-insensitive. Although this is a relatively slow process compared to transformation, Strauss found that when multiple transformation was scored following the addition of DNase, the lag period was found to increase and to be a function of the genetic or map distance between the markers chosen for study

(70). In addition, with infection by DNA of a phage Φ29, not related to Φ25 and known to have a lower molecular weight, the kinetics of uptake were similar to those obtained for multiple transformation.

When the method devised by Goodgal (158) was used to plot the time course of infection, a linear uptake of Φ25 DNA was indicated. With this plot the formation of the last 90 per cent of the infections is emphasized, not the early events which, in fact, represent a very low fraction of the total infection. These results were quite similar to those obtained by Kent & Hotchkiss in a study of the kinetics of linked marker transformation with *Diplococcus* (159).

In summary, the kinetics of transformation and transfection are quite similar. The differences that exist could reflect the fact that the viral DNA of the SP8 group has a very high molecular weight.

The investigations of Green (150), Okubo et al. (151), and Reilly & Spizizen (25), indicate that cells which are susceptible to infection or competent for transformation occur at about the same frequency in the competent cell population. With Φ25 DNA, 1 to 2 per cent of the viable cells can be infected. The critical question is, does infection or transformation occur in the same subpopulation of cells? During the phase of growth in which competence appears there is a parallel increase and then decrease in transformability or susceptibility to infection. In mutant strains unable to develop competence or that transform at a low level, phage DNA infection occurs at the same level. When these mutants regain the ability to develop a high level of competence by transformation they also regain the ability to become susceptible to transfection. Therefore, it appears that the genetic basis for the ability to be transformed or transfected is similar (25). But this does not exclude the possibility that, during growth, two physiologically distinct subpopulations appear. Nester (41) was able to demonstrate that competent cells could interact with DNA for several hours. When competent cells, unable to adsorb Φ25, were mixed with host DNA and then infected by viral DNA, bacterial transformation was reduced by more than 80 per cent. At the time of viral DNA addition, the initial transformation event was DNase-insensitive. This suggests that cells that have taken up DNA and would have subsequently been scored as transformants could be infected by viral DNA. Comparable results were obtained with DNA of the unrelated phage Φ29 and with cells unable to adsorb the virus (22, 25).

In a competent population of about 3×10^8 *B. subtilis* cells, about 1 or 2 per cent of the cells can be transformed for a given marker and about 0.1 μg of bacterial DNA is sufficient to saturate the population of cells. At lower concentrations of DNA, there is a linear relationship of transformation of the amount of DNA added. By contrast, although saturation of the population by viral DNA occurs at high DNA concentration, transfection by Φ25, SP82, or SPO-1 DNA showed a disproportionate loss of infectivity upon dilution.

Okubo et al. (151) observed a significantly higher frequency of recombination in cells infected by DNA than by mature virus. When the burst of phage liberated from single cells which had been infected by dilute DNA preparations were examined, a large number of bursts consisted solely of recombinant phage. The authors suggest that the infected cells resulted from the interaction of fragmented molecules and that at high SPO-1 DNA dilutions most infectious center formation is a result of such an interaction. Okubo & Romig (160) have isolated recombination-defective mutants of *B. subtilis* when analyzed by transformation. The capacity of SPO-1 DNA to infect these cells is also markedly reduced. Transfection by an unrelated phage SPO-2 occurs at the same level in the mutant or wild-type competent cells. This supports the hypothesis that recombination plays a role in SPO-1 DNA transfection.

With SP82 transfection, Green (150) has inferred from the concentration dependence of infectivity that three or four molecules must interact to infect a cell. By using a mutant virus, he was able to rescue markers introduced by viral DNA and to show a linear recovery of the diluted marker DNA, and to show that uptake of the marked DNA piece occurred at a rate more rapid than transfection. It cannot be determined if the marker rescued by the phage entered the cell as a DNA fragment or as a molecule containing the entire genome. By using DNA isolated from two marked SP82 strains, Green could demonstrate infection resulting from the interaction of two DNA molecules of separate origin.

Although Reilly & Spizizen (25) observed a nonlinear response of infectivity to DNA concentration with Φ25 DNA and the DNA of a nonrelated phage Φ1, the kinetics of transfection suggested infection by a single DNA molecule. They infer that the loss of activity upon dilution could have resulted from hydrodynamic shear degradation of the DNA at some stage or operation in the transfection process. Kelly & Pritchard (69) have observed an unstable linkage between genetic markers in *B. subtilis* transformation that could be preserved by the presence of high molecular weight carrier DNA when present at high concentration.

Without regard to mechanism, these results could seem to indicate some substantial difference between transfection and transformation. However, with DNA extracted from Φ29, the relationship of infection to DNA dilution and the kinetics of infection were not significantly different from those relationships observed in *B. subtilis* transformation (25). With SPO-2 DNA, transfection has recently been shown to be linearly related to DNA concentration (160).

In short, the evidence indicates that in *B. subtilis* the initial stages of transformation and some types of transfection are identical. A similar conclusion was reached by Harm & Rupert (149) with *H. influenzae*. In this sense, transfection in some instances can be regarded as a simple model of transformation. The results of Green (150), Okubo et al. (151), and Okubo & Romig (160), implicating recombination in the viral DNA infection, may prove to be to a very significant by-product of the attempt to relate transfection to transformation.

In general, with each *B. subtilis* transfection system, the viral nucleic acid is characterized by a low absolute efficiency of infection. Young & Spizizen (33) observed irreversible uptake of 1 to 4 per cent of added DNA even when the concentration of added DNA was sufficient to transform all of the competent cells present. More recently, Bodmer & Ganesan (31) have reported similar results with *B. subtilis* transformation. These observations may have some relevance to the finding of low efficiency of infection by phage DNA. The potential utility of transfection as an assay system for homogenous DNA preparations for use in integrated chemical, physical, and biological studies of the properties of DNA seems to be limited principally by this efficiency problem. Whether or not this is the result of trivial technical problems remains to be determined.

LITERATURE CITED

1. Schaeffer, P., in Heredity, *The Bacteria*, **V**, 87–153. (Gunsalus, I. C., and Stanier, R. Y., Eds., Academic Press, New York, 1964)
2. Ravin, A. W., *Advan. Genet.*, **10**, 61–163 (1961)
3. Hotchkiss, R. D., in *The Nucleic Acids*, **II**, 435–73. (Chargaff, E., and Davidson, J. N., Eds., Academic Press, New York, 1955)
4. Ephrussi-Taylor, H., *Advan. Virus Res.*, **3**, 1275 (1955)
5. Ephrussi-Taylor, H., in *Growth in Living Systems*, 39. (Zarrow, M. X., Ed., Basic Books, New York, 1961)
6. Zamenhof, S., *Prog. Biophys. Biophys. Chem.*, **6**, 85 (1956)
7. Thomas, R., in *Mécanismes d'autoreproduction*, 235–50. (Thomas, A. J., Ed., Masson et Cie, Paris, 1957)
8. Bracco, R. M., Krauss, M. R., Roe, A. S., and Macleod, C. M., *J. Exptl. Med.*, **106**, 247 (1957)
9. Pakula, R., *Acta Microbiol. Polon.*, **10**, 249 (1961)
10. Schaeffer, P., and Ritz, E., *Compt. Rend.*, **240**, 1491–93 (1955)
11. Catlin, B. W., *Science*, **131**, 608–10 (1960)
12. Balassa, R., *Naturwissenschaften*, **42**, 422 (1955)
13. Marmur, J., Seaman, E., and Levine, J., *J. Bacteriol.*, **85**, 461 (1963)
14. Marmur, J., Falkow, S., and Mandel, M., *Ann. Rev. Microbiol.*, **17**, 329–72 (1963)
15. Sueoka, N., and Yoshikawa, H., *Cold Spring Harbor Symp. Quant. Biol.*, **28**, 47–54 (1963)
16. Young, F. E., *A study of competence in the B. subtilis transformation system*. (Doctoral thesis, Western Reserve University, Cleveland, Ohio, 1962)
17. Takahashi, I., *Biochem. Biophys. Res. Commun.*, **5**, 171–75 (1961)
18. Avery, O. T., MacLeod, C. M., and McCarty, M., *J. Exptl. Med.*, **79**, 137–58 (1944)
19. Ravin, A. W., *Ann. N.Y. Acad. Sci.*, **68**, 338–45 (1957)
20. Leonard, C. G., and Mattheis, M. J., *J. Bacteriol.*, **90**, 558–59 (1965)
21. Young, F. E., and Spizizen, J., *J. Bacteriol.*, **81**, 823–29 (1961)
22. Reilly, B. E., *A study of the bacteriophages of Bacillus subtilis and their infectious nucleic acids*. (Doctorial thesis, Western Reserve University, Cleveland, Ohio, 1965)
23. Gollakota, K. G., and Halvorson, H. O., *J. Bacteriol.*, **79**, 1–8 (1960)
24. Spizizen, J., in *Spores*, **III**, 125–37. (Campbell, L. L., and Halvorson, H. O., Eds., *Am. Soc. Microbiol.*, 1965)
25. Reilly, B. E., and Spizizen, J., *J. Bacteriol.*, **89**, 782–90 (1965)
26. Young, F. E., *Nature*, **207**, 104–5 (1965)
27. Lerman, L., and Tolmach, L., *Biochim. Biophys. Acta*, **26**, 68–82 (1957)
28. Fox, M. S., *Biochim. Biophys. Acta*, **26**, 83–85 (1957)
29. Barnhart, B. J., and Herriott, R. M., *Biochim. Biophys. Acta*, **76**, 25–39 (1963)
30. Stuy, J. H., and Stern, D., *J. Gen. Microbiol.*, **35**, 391–400 (1964)
31. Bodmer, W. F., and Ganesan, A. T., *Genetics*, **50**, 717–38 (1964)
32. Goodgal, L., and Herriott, R. M., in *The Chemical Basis of Heredity*, 336. (McElroy, W. D., and Glass, B., Eds., Johns Hopkins Press, 1957)
33. Young, F. E., and Spizizen, J., *J. Bacteriol.*, **86**, 392–400 (1963)
34. Fox, M. S., and Hotchkiss, R. D., *Nature*, **179**, 1322–25 (1957)
35. Leidy, G., Jaffee, I., and Alexander, H. E., *Proc. Soc. Exptl. Biol. Med.*, **111**, 725–31 (1962)
36. Lie, S., *Acta Pathol. Microbiol. Scand.*, **64**, 119–29 (1965)
37. Leonard, C. G., Mattheis, D. K., Mattheis, M. J., and Housewright, R. D., *J. Bacteriol.*, **88**, 200–25 (1964)
38. Hotchkiss, R. D., *Proc. Natl. Acad. Sci. U.S.*, **40**, 49–55 (1954)
39. Anagnostopoulos, C., and Spizizen, J., *J. Bacteriol.*, **81**, 741–46 (1961)
40. Spencer, H. T., and Herriott, R. M., *J. Bacteriol.*, **90**, 911–20 (1965)
41. Nester, E. W., *J. Bacteriol.*, **87**, 867–75 (1964)
42. Kelner, A., *J. Bacteriol.*, **87**, 1295–1303 (1964)
43. Ephrussi-Taylor, H., and Freed, B. A., *J. Bacteriol.*, **87**, 1211–15 (1964)
44. Zelazna, I., *Acta Microbiol. Polon.*, **13**, 291–98 (1964)
45. Spizizen, J., *Federation Proc.*, **18**, 957–65 (1958)

46. Spizizen, J., in *Spores*, **II**, 142–48. (Halvorson, H. O., Ed., Burgess Publ. Co., Minneapolis, Minn., 1961)

47. Jensen, R. A., and Haas, F. L., *J. Bacteriol.*, **86**, 73–78 (1963)

48. Jensen, R. A., and Haas, F. L., *J. Bacteriol.*, **86**, 79–86 (1963)

49. Thomas, R., *Biochim. Biophys. Acta*, **18**, 467–81 (1955)

50. Ephrati-Elizur, E., *Biochem. Biophys. Res. Commun.*, **18**, 103–7 (1965)

51. Ceferri, O., Polsinelli, M., Carson, G., and Albertini, A., Federation European Biochem. Soc., 1st Meeting, 77 (1964)

52. Nava, G., Galis, A., and Beiser, S. M., *Nature*, **197**, 903–4 (1963)

53. Tomasz, A., and Beiser, S. M., *J. Bacteriol.*, **90**, 1226–32 (1965)

54. Pakula, R., and Hauschild, A. H. W., *Can. J. Microbiol.*, **11**, 823–27 (1965)

55. Pakula, R., and Walczak, W., *J. Gen. Microbiol.*, **31**, 125–33 (1963)

56. Pakula, R., *Can. J. Microbiol.*, **11**, 811–22 (1965)

57. Perry, D., and Slade, H. D., *J. Bacteriol.*, **83**, 443–49 (1962)

58. Tomasz, A., and Hotchkiss, R. D., *Proc. Natl. Acad. Sci. U.S.*, **51**, 480–87 (1964)

59. Tomasz, A., *Nature*, **208**, 155–59 (1965)

60. Charpak, M., and Dedonder, R., *Compt. Rend.*, **260**, 5638–41 (1965)

61. Felkner, I. C., and Wyss, O., *Biochem. Biophys., Res. Commun.*, **16**, 94–98 (1964)

62. Litt, M., Marmur, J., Ephrussi-Taylor, H., and Doty, P., *Proc. Natl. Acad. Sci. U.S.*, **44**, 144–52 (1958)

63. Doty, S., *Harvey Lectures*, **55**, 103–39 (1959–60)

64. Rosenberg, B. H., Sirotnak, F. M., and Cavalieri, L. F., *Proc. Natl. Acad. Sci. U.S.*, **45**, 144–56 (1959)

65. Szybalski, W., and Opara-Kubinska, Z., *Symp. Biol. Hung.*, **6**, (1965)

66. Young, F. E., and Spizizen, J., *J. Biol. Chem.*, **238**, 3126–30 (1963)

67. Young, F. E., Tipper, D. J., and Strominger, J. L., *J. Biol. Chem.*, **239**, 3600–2 (1964)

68. Davison, P. F., Freifelder, D., and Holloway, B. H., *J. Mol. Biol.*, **8**, 1–10 (1964)

69. Kelly, M. S., and Pritchard, R. H., *J. Bacteriol.*, **89**, 1314–21 (1965)

70. Strauss, N., *J. Bacteriol.*, **89**, 288–93 (1965)

71. Strauss, N., *J. Bacteriol.* (In press, 1966)

72. Marmur, J., *J. Mol. Biol.*, **3**, 208–18 (1961)

73. Berns, K. I., and Thomas, C. A., Jr., *J. Mol. Biol.*, **11**, 476–90 (1965)

74. Lerman, L. S., and Tolmach, L. J., *Biochim. Biophys. Acta*, **33**, 371–87 (1959)

75. Roger, M., and Hotchkiss, R. D., *Proc. Natl. Acad. Sci., U.S.*, **47**, 653–69 (1961)

76. Geiduschek, E. P., *J. Mol. Biol.*, **4**, 467–87 (1962)

77. Guild, W. R., *J. Mol. Biol.*, **6**, 214–29 (1963)

78. Marmur, J., and Lane, D., *Proc. Natl. Sci. U.S.*, **46**, 453–61 (1960)

79. Ginoza, W., and Zimm, B. H., *Proc. Natl. Acad. Sci. U.S.*, **47**, 639–52 (1961)

80. Guild, W. R., *Proc. Natl. Acad. Sci. U.S.*, **47**, 1560–64 (1961)

81. Rownd, R., Lanyi, J., and Doty, P., *Biochim. Biophys. Acta*, **53**, 225–27 (1961)

82. Barnhart, B. J., *J. Bacteriol.*, **89**, 1271–79 (1965)

83. Chevallier, M. R., and Bernardi, G., *J. Mol. Biol.*, **11**, 658–60 (1965)

84. Rownd, R., Green, D. G., and Doty, P., Nucleic Acids, **II**, TB 7. (Biophys. Soc. Abstr., 7th Ann. Meeting, 1963)

85. Fox, M. S., and Hotchkiss, R. D., *Nature*, **187**, 1002–4 (1960)

86. Fox, M. S., *Nature*, **187**, 1004–6 (1960)

87. Fox, M. S., *Nature*, **187**, 1006–12 (1960)

88. Fox, M. S., *Proc. Natl. Acad. Sci. U.S.*, **48**, 1043–48 (1962)

89. Lacks, S., *J. Mol. Biol.*, **5**, 119–31 (1962)

90. Fox, M. S., and Allen, M. K., *Proc. Natl. Acad. Sci. U.S.*, **52**, 412–19 (1964)

91. Stuy, J. H., *J. Mol. Biol.*, **13**, 554–70 (1965)

92. Voll, M. J., and Goodgal, S. H., *J. Bacteriol.*, **90**, 873–83 (1965)

93. Pene, J. J., and Romig, W. R., *J. Mol. Biol.*, **9**, 236–45 (1964)

94. Venema, G., Pritchard, R. H., and Schroder, T. V., *J. Bacteriol.*, **89**, 1250–55 (1965)

95. Venema, G., Pritchard, R. H., and Schroder, T. V., *J. Bacteriol.*, **90**, 343–46 (1965)

96. Bodmer, W. F., *J. Mol. Biol.*, **14**, 534–57 (1965)

97. Szybalski, W., *J. Chim. Phys.*, **58**, 1098–99 (1961)
98. Joys, T. M. (Unpublished observations in this laboratory)
99. Ephrussi-Taylor, H., *Compt. Rend.*, **154**, 1951–52 (1960)
100. Zubay, G., *Proc. Natl. Acad. Sci. U.S.*, **48**, 456–61 (1962)
101. Miller, I. L., and Landman, O. E., in Symposium on the Mutational Process. (Czechoslovak Acad. Sci., Prague, 1965)
102. Nester, E. W., and Stocker, B. A. D., *J. Bacteriol.*, **86**, 785–96 (1963)
103. Lacks, S., and Hotchkiss, R., *Biochim. Biophys. Acta*, **45**, 155–63 (1960)
104. Suzuki, H., Yamagami, H., and Rebeyrotte, N., *J. Mol. Biol.*, **5**, 577–79 (1962)
105. Herriott, R. M., *Genetics*, **52**, 1235–46 (1965)
106. Guild, W. R., and Robison, M., *Proc. Natl. Acad. Sci. U.S.*, **50**, 106–12 (1963)
107. Hotchkiss, R. D., and Marmur, J., *Proc. Natl. Acad. Sci.*, *U.S.*, **40**, 55 (1954)
108. Goodgal, S. H., and Herriott, R. M., *Genetics*, **42**, 372 (1957)
109. Austrian, R., Bernheimer, H. R., Smith, E. E. B., and Mills, G. T., *Cold Spring Harbor Symp. Quant. Biol.*, **23**, 99 (1958)
110. Jacob, F., and Monod, J., *Cold Spring Harbor Symp. Quant. Biol.*, **26**, 193–211 (1961)
111. Anagnostopoulos, C., and Crawford, I. P., *Proc. Natl. Acad. Sci. U.S.*, **47**, 378–90 (1961)
112. Nester, E. W., Schafer, M., and Lederberg, J., *Genetics*, **48**, 529–51 (1963)
113. Nester, E. W., and Lederberg, J., *Proc. Natl. Acad. Sci. U.S.*, **47**, 52–55 (1961)
114. Ephrati-Elizur, E., Srinivasan, P. R., and Zamenhof, S., *Proc. Natl. Acad. Sci. U.S.*, **47**, 56–63 (1961)
115. Mahler, I., Newmann, J., and Marmur, J., *Biochim. Biophys. Acta*, **72**, 69–79 (1963)
116. Anagnostopoulos, C., Barat, M., and Schneider, A. M., *Compt. Rend.*, **258**, 749–52 (1964)
117. Barat, M., Anagnostopoulos, C., and Schneider, A. M., *J. Bacteriol.*, **90**, 357–69 (1964)
118. Takahashi, I., *Biochem. Biophys. Res. Commun.*, **5**, 171–75 (1961)
119. Yoshikawa, H., and Sueoka, N., *Proc.*

120. Yoshikawa, H., O'Sullivan, A., and Sueoka, N., *Proc. Natl. Acad. Sci. U.S.*, **52**, 973–80 (1964)
121. Oishi, M., Yoshikawa, H., and Sueoka, N., *Nature*, **204**, 1069–73 (1964)
122. Rotheim, M. B., and Ravin, A. W., *Proc. Natl. Acad. Sci. U.S.* (In press, 1966)
123. Sicard, A. M., and Ephrussi-Taylor, H., *Genetics*, **52**, 1207–27 (1965)
124. Lacks, S., *Genetics*, **53**, 207–35 (1966)
125. Evans, A. H., *Proc. Natl. Acad. Sci. U.S.*, **52**, 1442 (1964)
126. Schulman, H. M., and Bonner, D. A., *Proc. Natl. Acad. Sci. U.S.*, **48**, 53–63 (1963)
127. Hurwitz, J., Evans, A., Babinet, C., and Skalka, A., in Synthesis and Structure of Macromolecules, *Cold Spring Harbor Symp. Quant. Biol.*, **28**, 59–65 (1963)
128. Shen Shan Chiung, Hung Mang-Ming, Cai Rui-Chu, Chen Wai-Chu, and Chang Wen-Lin, *Sci. Sinica, Peking*, **XI**, 233–40 (1962)
129. Thorne, C. B., *J. Bacteriol.*, **83**, 106–11 (1962)
130. Takahashi, I., *J. Bacteriol.*, **89**, 294–98 (1965)
131. Ivanovics, G., and Csiszar, K., *Naturwissenschaften*, **49**, 309–10 (1962)
132. Takagi, J., *J. Gen. Appl. Microbiol.*, **8**, 214–22 (1962)
133. Takahashi, I., *J. Gen. Microbiol.*, **31**, 211–17 (1963)
134. Taylor, M. J., and Thorne, C. B., *J. Bacteriol.*, **86**, 452–61 (1963)
135. Csiszar, K., and Ivanovics, G., *Acta Microbiol., Acad. Aci. Hung.*, **12**, 73–89 (1964)
136. Ivanovics, G., and Csiszar, K., *Acta Microbiol. Acad. Sci. Hung.*, **9**, 209–18 (1962)
137. Ephrati-Elizur, E., and Fox, M. S., *Nature*, **192**, 433–34 (1961)
138. Takagi, J., and Ikeda, Y., *Biochem. Biophys. Res. Commun.*, **7**, 482–85 (1962)
139. Iijima, T., and Ikeda, Y., *J. Gen. Appl. Microbiol.*, **9**, 97 (1963)
140. Aoki, H., Saito, H., and Ikeda, Y., *J. Gen Appl. Microbiol.*, **9**, 307 (1963)
141. Okubo, S., Stodolsky, M., Bott, K. F., and Strauss, B., *Proc. Natl. Acad. Sci. U.S.*, **50**, 679–86 (1963)
142. Mahler, I., Cahoon, M., and Marmur, J., *J. Bacteriol.*, **87**, 1423–28 (1964)
143. Földes, J., and Trautner, T. A., *Z. Vererbungsl.*, **95**, 57–65 (1964)

Natl. Acad. Sci. U.S., **49**, 559–66 (1963)

144. Kaiser, A. D., and Hogness, D. S., *J. Mol. Biol.*, **2**, 392–415 (1960)
145. Tokunaga, T., and Sellers, M., *J. Exptl. Med.*, **119**, 139–49 (1964)
146. Romig, W. R., *Virology*, **16**, 452–59 (1962)
147. Bayreuther, K. E., and Romig, W. R., *Science*, **146**, 778–79 (1964)
148. Abel, P., and Trautner, T. A., *Z. Vererbungsl.*, **95**, 66 (1964)
149. Harm, W., and Rupert, C. S., *Z. Vererbungsl.*, **94**, 336–48 (1963)
150. Green, D. M., *J. Mol. Biol.*, **10**, 438–51 (1964)
151. Okubo, S., Strauss, B., and Stodolsky, M., *Virology*, **24**, 552–62 (1964)
152. Romig, W. R., and Brodetsky, A. M., *J. Bacteriol.*, **82**, 135–41 (1961)
153. Brodetsky, A. M., and Romig, W. R., *J. Bacteriol.*, **90**, 1655–63 (1965)
154. Kallen, R. G., Simon, M., and Marmur, J., *J. Mol. Biol.*, **5**, 248–50 (1962)
155. Marmur, J., Greenspan, C. M., Palecek, E., Kahan, F. M., Levine, J., and Mandel, M., *Cold Spring Harbor Symp. Quant. Biol.*, **28**, 191–99 (1963)
156. Marmur, J., and Greenspan, C. M., *Science*, **142**, 387–88 (1963)
157. Levine, J., and Strauss, N., *J. Bacteriol.*, **89**, 281–87 (1963)
158. Goodgal, S. H., *J. Gen. Physiol.*, **45**, 205–28 (1961)
159. Kent, J. L., and Hotchkiss, R. D., *J. Mol. Biol.*, **9**, 308–22 (1964)
160. Okubo, S., and Romig, W. R., *J. Mol. Biol.* (In press, 1966)

SUPPRESSION[1,2]

By Luigi Gorini and Jonathan R. Beckwith

Department of Bacteriology and Immunology, Harvard Medical School, Boston, Massachusetts

Contents

INTRODUCTION.. 401
INDIRECT SUPPRESSION... 404
INTRAGENIC SUPPRESSION.. 405
INFORMATIONAL SUPPRESSION....................................... 407
  Suppressors Possibly Affecting mRNA.............................. 407
  Suppression at the Translation Level............................. 408
  The Nature of Amber and Ochre Mutants........................... 409
  The Nature of Amber and Ochre Suppressors...................... 411
    Genetics of suppressor mutations.................................. 411
    The mechanism of suppressor action............................... 412
PHENOTYPIC INFORMATIONAL SUPPRESSION.................... 414
  Other Examples of Suppression Induced by Streptomycin and by Other Agents with Similar Action.. 415
  Type of Mutations Corrected by Streptomycin.................... 416
  Relation Between Streptomycin-Induced Suppression and Mutations of the Classical Streptomycin Locus........................... 416
THE ROLE OF RIBOSOMAL MUTATIONS IN INFORMATIONAL SUPPRESSION... 417
UNCHARACTERIZED SUPPRESSOR MUTATIONS.................. 418
  Unstable Suppressors.. 418
  Other Suppressors... 419
CONCLUSIONS... 419

INTRODUCTION

The term "suppression" originated from classical genetics some four decades ago (1). It designated the reversal of a mutant phenotype via mutation at a locus distinct from that of the original mutation. Operationally, any "back mutation" is classified as a suppressor mutation, whenever, by genetic crosses, the nonidentity of the sites of the original and reverse mutations can be demonstrated. Since, by definition, reversion by a suppressor mutation

[1] The survey of the literature pertaining to this review was concluded in February 1965.

[2] The following abbreviations are used: CRM (cross-reacting material); CSD (conditional streptomycin-dependent); Sm (streptomycin); *Sm* (streptomycin locus); *Sm*[Dep] (streptomycin-dependent); *Sm*[r] (streptomycin-resistant); *Sm*[s] (streptomycin-insensitive); SSu (streptomycin-suppressible); HFT (high frequency transducing); Att-80 (attachment site for Φ'80); Gal (galactose fermentation); Lac (lactose fermentation); Mel (melibiose fermentation); Arg (arginine); Cys (cysteine); His (histidine); Leu (leucine); Pro (proline); Pur (purine); Thy (thymine); TL (threonine and leucine); Try (tryptophan).

leaves the original mutation intact, the original mutant type should be recovered among the progeny of a cross between wild type and revertant.

Among the first experiments attempting to analyze the biochemical mechanism underlying a suppression were those reported by Beadle & Ephrussi in 1936 (2). These authors demonstrated that a recessive, allele-specific suppressor of vermillion eye color (the result of a homozygous mutant "v" genotype) in *Drosophila* acted by partially restoring the ability of the mutant organism to produce V^+ substance (kynurenine), which is required for the development of wild-type eye color. Experiments of this type provide biochemical evidence that suppression is a restoration of a function possessed by the wild-type organism. However, the use of a single term "suppression" to encompass all of these restorations due to mutations at a secondary site is misleading, since it implies a unity of mechanism which certainly does not exist. In fact, a great variety of different topological and functional relationships have been found between suppressors and the alleles they suppress.

From the genetic point of view, the second mutation may be located within the same cistron in which the first one occurred, within the same chromosome or even in a different chromosome. Moreover, a suppressor may be strictly allele-specific, that is, it suppresses only mutations which arise at a particular codon within a cistron, or it may be able to suppress equally well several (or all) mutations occurring at different codons within the same cistron or mutations of the same codon occurring in different, unrelated cistrons.

From the point of view of their mode of action, suppressors may be distinguished in the following way:

1. The second mutation may be in a gene whose mutated product opens an alternate pathway. For instance, as a result of a second mutation an enzyme activity may appear which permits the synthesis of an intermediate whose synthesis, through the usual pathway, was barred by the first mutation.

2. The second mutation may be in a gene whose mutated product may substitute directly the function of the product of the first gene. For instance, a second enzyme (or protein) may mutate to a broader specificity (or function) encompassing that of the missing first enzyme (or protein).

3. The second mutation provides cytoplasmic conditions which affect the structure of the finished product of the first mutated gene. For instance, the condition may stabilize an enzyme which, as a result of a structural change, is unstable in the wild-type cytoplasmic surrounding.

4. The second mutation introduces a second alteration within the same peptide chain (a second amino acid substitution) which reintegrates, completely or partially, the protein function, with reappearance of the wild type or of a quasi wild-type phenotype.

5. The second mutation reintroduces the correct code-meaning, by frame shift, within the same cistron in which the codon reading-frame was altered by addition or deletion of a base pair.

Strictly speaking, all "back mutations" within the same cistron, not concerning the base pair which mutated firstly, are suppressor mutations of types 4 or 5.

6. The second mutation concerns one of the factors controlling the mechanism of transfer of genetic information from DNA to protein.

There is a basic difference between suppressions arising from the first three and the last three mechanisms. The first group of suppressor mutations clearly act indirectly to circumvent, rather than directly to repair the primary genetic lesion. The suppressions could be designated as "indirect suppressions." They will be mentioned only briefly in this review since they actually belong to the field of classical intermediary metabolism. It seems advisable, in fact, to discuss in detail the second group of suppressions by which a new field of research has been opened and in which the suppressor mutation results in a direct correction of the product of the gene altered by the primary mutation.

The group of direct suppressors includes two quite different classes. Those outlined in points 4 and 5, which may be designated as "intragenic suppressors," are characterized by the fact that, barring the extreme case of intracodon suppression, the primary and the suppressor mutations are both transcribed into the gene product. This results in two amino acid substitutions, or possibly more in the case of point 5, in the suppressed mutant protein with respect to the wild-type protein.

Finally, suppressions of the type described in point 6 are due to meaning alterations of a codon and therefore are not themselves transcribed in the suppressed mutant protein as a second amino acid substitution. By definition, these suppressors are always intergenic and may be designated as "informational suppressors." Given the two conceivable ways by which the mechanism of transmission of information from DNA to protein may be modified, two aspects of informational suppression will be discussed: (a) Alteration of macromolecules involved in the transmission (transcription or translation) process. This alteration can be only genetic, by mutation, and therefore inheritable. (b) Alteration in cytoplasmic conditions which interfere with the standard process of transmission. This may be genetic, by mutation, or from the outside, by changing external conditions, in which case it is not inherited and may be designated as "phenotypic informational-suppression."

The only recent review of suppression is the discussion included by Yanofsky & St. Lawrence in their article on Gene Action (3). Background information on the code, the translation, and transcription processes can be obtained from several excellent reviews in Volumes 1 and 2 of *Progress in Nucleic Acid Research* (4).[3]

[3] The Cold Spring Harbor Symposium on Quantitative Biology, Volume 31 (1966), "The Genetic Code," contains several papers on the subject of suppression (note added in proof).

INDIRECT SUPPRESSION

As indicated in the introduction, only a few examples of indirect suppression are presented here. The criterion of their choice is to provide the analysis of the most indicative situations leading to indirect suppression one may encounter in studying reverse mutations.

Several mutational blocks in the synthesis of a given metabolite may be similarly suppressed by a single external mutation. It has been possible to demonstrate in several instances that the second mutation opens a new metabolic path leading to the same end product. This is the case for a suppressor of several acetate⁻ mutants of *Neurospora crassa* (5, 6) and for a suppressor of several cysteine⁻ mutants in *Salmonella typhimurium* (7). These suppressors restore activity to all mutations affecting the enzymes which are bypassed by the new pathway. Their efficiency depends on the readiness with which the metabolite is supplied through the new path.

In other cases, the primary mutation may lead to an unbalanced competition between two precursors, causing the accumulation of an inhibitor or the deprival of an essential metabolite. A second mutation may bring about a deficient activity of an enzyme placed in a key position of metabolism in such a way that it corrects the imbalance. It was shown, for instance, that the growth of a *Neurospora* mutant is inhibited by exogenous addition of threonine, and that this inhibition is reversed by methionine. It is assumed that an unknown product of threonine metabolism inhibits methionine synthesis in this mutant. The suppression of this phenotype is brought about by a second mutation introducing a block which diverts threonine metabolism (8). Another somewhat similar situation has been recently clarified (9). It has been found that a pyrimidineless mutant of *Neurospora* (*pyr-3a*), blocked before aspartate transcarbamylase, the enzyme utilizing carbamyl phosphate for pyrimidine biosynthesis, is suppressed if a second mutation (*arg-12*ˢ) is introduced into the genome. The *arg-12*ˢ mutation has the effect of lowering drastically the level of ornithine transcarbamylase, the enzyme utilizing carbamyl phosphate for arginine biosynthesis (10, 11). In a completely symmetrical fashion, an arginineless mutant (*arg-2*), blocked before ornithine transcarbamylase, was found suppressed if another mutation (*pyr-3d*) was introduced. The *pyr-3d* mutation eliminates aspartate transcarbamylase activity (12). This complicated pattern of suppression is explained by supposing, in *Neurospora*, two pools of carbamyl phosphate independently synthesized, carbamyl phosphate_pyr and carbamyl phosphate_arg. A mutation preventing the synthesis of the former pool will be suppressed by a mutation diverting the latter to the pyrimidine pathway, and vice versa.

The following is an example of suppression by substituting for the nonfunctional product of a mutated gene that of another gene capable of assuming the missing function. *Saccharomyces cerevisiae* synthesizes two cytochromes *c*, iso-1 and iso-2, produced by unlinked genes. In the wild-type organism, however, the aerobic metabolism is insured by iso-1, which constitutes 95 per cent of the total amount of cytochrome c, whereas the function of iso-2 appears to be that of controlling iso-1 synthesis (13). A mutant of iso-1, cy-1-1, possesses a very low level of cytochrome c because its iso-1 component is absent, its respiration is grossly impaired, and it is unable to grow on lactate. Most of the reversions selected for the ability to grow on lactate possess a high level of cytochrome c, which, however, is exclusively composed of iso-2. Thus, the mutation cy-1-1 is still present in these reversions, but iso-2 has taken over the respiratory function (14, 15).

A suppressor may activate, via the cytoplasm, the inactive enzyme produced by a mutant gene. For example, a specific allele (td 24) of the tryptophan-synthetase locus in *Neurospora* yields an enzyme which is inhibited by zinc, so that extracts of td 24 are active only when purified by procedures known to dissociate metal-protein complexes. A specific, unlinked suppressor for td 24 is known and it may operate by preventing zinc from complexing with the altered enzyme (16).

Finally, it should be pointed out that the nature of the first mutation should be carefully analyzed before postulating a suppression. In fact, the absence of an enzyme is not always caused by a defect in the corresponding structural gene. The existence of control mechanisms indeed makes life more complicated. For instance, an *Escherichia coli* mutant is unable to produce β-galactosidase even upon addition of inducer; however, in diploid association with a β-galactosidase$^+$ wild-type genotype, the mutant-defective genotype is dominant. This peculiar situation is due to the fact that the mutant genotype is β-galactosidase-uninducible rather than β-galactosidase$^-$. In fact, the presence of a specific allele (i^s) of the regulatory gene, probably leading to production of a repressor which cannot recognize the inducer, makes this mutant unable to produce β-galactosidase under any condition. A second mutation (o^c) at the operator locus renders i^s ineffective so that the double mutant $i^s o^c$ produces β-galactosidase constitutively (17). This mimics suppression of a defective β-galactosidase gene and may be confused with it.

INTRAGENIC SUPPRESSION

A mutation which leads to the change of one amino acid in a polypeptide chain may be reversed by another mutation which causes the replacement of a second amino acid at a different site in that chain. There is one well-characterized example of this type of suppression (18). A mutation of the gene for the tryptophan-synthetase A protein causes the substitution of a glutamic acid for a glycine residue. A second mutation, at a site 36 amino acids distant, which causes a replacement of a tyrosine by a cysteine residue, restores A protein activity. The second mutation (the suppressor mutation) by itself, also renders the A protein inactive. In some way, the substitution of the second amino acid compensates for the deleterious effects of the mutation on the protein structure and function. We can only speculate on the mechanism by which two amino acid substitutions interact, but it is possible that such well-defined cases may add to the knowledge of the relationship between primary and tertiary structure of a protein. However, such a mechanism of suppression may be applicable only to some of the mis-sense mutations causing amino acid changes.

A superficially equivalent type of intragenic suppression is that observed with acridine-induced mutants in the bacteriophage T4 (19). Again, two genetically separable alterations in a gene, which lead to mutant phenotype individually, exhibit gene-product activity when combined in a double mutant. Mutagenesis with acridines appears to cause single-base additions (+) or deletions (−) in the nucleotide sequence of a gene. The result of such mutations is to shift the reading of the triplet codon sequence of the mRNA copy of the gene, so that, from the point of the mutation on, a completely new set of codons is read by the translation machinery. Thus, the resultant protein product should contain an entirely new sequence of amino acids distal to the site of the genetic lesion. However, combination of such a mutation (+ or −) with another nearby acridine mutation of opposite sign (− or +), can restore the correct codon reading sequence. If the new amino acid sequence introduced between the sites of the two mutations (within the frame shift) is not harmful to protein-function, a wild type or semiwild-type phenotype will be restored.

The nature of acridine-type mutants was deduced from purely genetic studies on the characteristics of such mutants in the T4 *rII* region. Recently, one of the major predictions of this theory of acridine mutations, that a gene containing a frame shift produces a protein with a sequence of amino acids different from the wild type, has been confirmed (20). Two acridine-induced mutations in the gene for the T4 lysozyme were combined to make a double mutant which exhibited lysozyme activity. A column analysis of the wild type and suppressed mutant proteins showed a one-peptide difference. The amino acid sequence of the wild type and double mutant protein was determined, showing that the two proteins differed in a sequence of five amino acids. From the differences in the two amino acid sequences, and from knowledge of the code, the codon sequence within the frame shift and the sites of the base addition and deletion could be determined.

A major criterion for distinguishing the two types of intragenic suppression is the extent of change of amino acid composition in the suppressed protein. The suppression of acridine-type mutants in most cases would lead to a change in sequence of more than two amino acids in the suppressed mutant product; in contrast, suppressions of the other type lead to the alteration of only two amino acids. Of course, in the extreme cases the acridine-type suppression might lead to a change of only one or two amino acids and would be difficult under these conditions to distinguish from the other type of suppression. The study of reversions using specific mutagens can be employed to distinguish these two types.

INFORMATIONAL SUPPRESSION

Until 1960, the only types of intergenic suppressions that were understood were indirect suppressions. However, the understanding in chemical terms of the process by which genetic information is transmitted within the cell from DNA to proteins, was growing very rapidly. In that year, Yanofsky & St. Lawrence (3) postulated that suppression may act at the level of the translation process involving mutations in the amino acid specificity of tRNA or of activating enzymes. This proposal was based on the study of suppression of mutants in *Neurospora* and *E. coli* forming cross-reacting material (CRM) instead of active trytophan-synthetase (21). This provided evidence that suppression brings about the appearance of a small amount of the missing enzyme activity (22), and that this is really due to the production of active enzyme protein (23). Subsequent fingerprint analysis of the tryptophan-synthetase A protein confirmed that the specificity of a suppressor is at the codon level. The A protein produced by mutant A36 contains an arginine residue instead of glycine in a given position on the peptide chain (24), whereas that produced by suppressed A36 is a mixture of A36 protein with a small amount of wild-type protein containing again a glycine residue in the same position (25). Moreover, the A36 suppressor failed to suppress mutant A46 which produces an A protein containing a glutamic acid residue instead of glycine at the same position.

The suggestion of Yanofsky & St. Lawrence drew attention to a new concept previously not considered; i.e., the molecular mechanisms by which the fidelity of transmission of the genetic script to protein structure is insured, may be violated. The study of informational suppression was open. The informational suppressors include all of those intergenic suppressors which act on the transmission of information from the mutant gene to the altered protein product of that gene. The result of this suppression is the production of a protein with an amino acid sequence different from that of the mutant product. The suppression of a mutation in a DNA base pair might occur in several ways: (*a*) by an alteration at the gene level; (*b*) by an effect on the transcription process; (*c*) by acting on the messenger RNA copy of the gene; or (*d*) by alterations in the translation machinery. Although no reports of suppressor mutations of types 1, 2, and 3 have been published, many of the uncharacterized suppressors which do exist in the literature may fall into one of these groups. Therefore, we present some hypothetical mechanisms for these types, in which the suppressor mutation results in an altered mRNA product of the mutated gene.

SUPPRESSORS POSSIBLY AFFECTING mRNA

A suppressor mutation which leads to an altered pattern of methylation of nucleic acids could result in the methylation of the base pair at the mutant site in the gene. Such a change may lead to occasional errors in transcription resulting in the substitution of the correct base in the mRNA gene copy. An analogous change, the methylation of the mutant site in the mRNA, could cause mispairing of a transfer RNA with this site so that an acceptable amino acid is introduced at the mutant site in the protein. Another possibility is that a suppressor mutation leads to the increased synthesis of a naturally occurring base analogue or to the appearance of a new base analogue. A base analogue may then cause errors in DNA-mRNA transcription similar to those in DNA replication caused by mutagenic agents such as 5-bromouracil and 2-aminopurine, or may be incorporated into mRNA and cause errors in the translation process. An example of the manner by which internally synthesized base analogues might suppress may be seen in the suppression of mutants of the T4 rII (26) and alkaline phosphatase (27, 28) genes by the uracil analogue, 5-fluorouracil. This substance is incorporated in place of uracil during mRNA synthesis and most probably causes mistakes in the translation process. In addition, mutations in the RNA polymerase might lead to an increased error frequency in transcription similar to the mutator gene effects of a DNA polymerase mutant of T4. It has indeed been found that a mutation leading to a temperature-sensitive T4 DNA polymerase also results in a much higher spontaneous mutation frequency for the bacteriophage (29). Finally, changes in the RNA polymerase might also compensate for the effect of mutations which prevent completion of gene transcription.

Suppression at the Translation Level

At present, the study of suppressors acting at the translation level has been by far the most successful. Suppression of this sort may occur either through a mutation which affects the macromolecular components (activating enzymes, tRNA and ribosome) of the translation machinery or through the action of small molecules suspected to interfere in the translation process. The present knowledge of the translation process based on the adaptor theory (30) requires that among the macromolecular class of suppressors the ribosomal type should be far less specific than the tRNA or activating enzyme type, which should be codon-specific. Therefore, a knowledge of the nature of the mutation which is being suppressed is essential in understanding the suppression itself.

A mutation by base change may lead to "mis-sense," i.e., a substitution of a codon designating one amino acid for another, or to "nonsense," i.e., the substitution of a codon not designating any amino acid. The "nonsense" codon may not necessarily be devoid of some other function such as code punctuation. Although suppressors of both classes of mutations are found, suppressors of nonsense mutations have been more extensively studied. Features distinguishing suppression of these two classes of mutations are:
(a) There are only a few (probably two) triplets out of 64 for which no amino acid assignment has been found (the evidence being based on the E. coli genetic code) (31, 32). Accordingly, the number of suppressors of nonsense mutations should be limited as compared to that of suppressors of mis-sense mutations. (b) Furthermore, since a mutation to mis-sense is, in fact, the changing of a sense codon to another codon which is sense wherever else it is

read in the genome, suppression of this codon leads to translation of sense into mis-sense in many other positions. Therefore, an effective mis-sense suppressor will probably be lethal to the cell and only weak mis-sense suppressors are expected and found. Suppression of a nonsense mutation, however, may lead to no harmful effects to the cell, if that nonsense codon is not a natural component of the bacterial codon complement. As it will be discussed later, this may be true of one of the two nonsense mutant classes which can be suppressed to 63 per cent of the normal reading without any effects on cell growth. In consequence its suppressors are the best known and characterized. (c) The result of a mis-sense mutation is an amino acid replacement at the protein site corresponding to the gene site where the mutation occurred, whereas the effect of a nonsense mutation, as it will be discussed later, is to stop peptide chain elongation at that site. Accordingly, as a result of suppression of a mis-sense mutant, two proteins differing in their amino acid composition should be found, whereas as a result of suppression of a nonsense mutant the two products are finished molecules of a given protein and unfinished peptides of the same protein.

THE NATURE OF AMBER AND OCHRE MUTANTS

The best characterized and most intensively studied of the suppressor mutations which affect the translation process are the suppressors of the two classes of mutants, "amber" and "ochre." The relationship between amber and ochre mutants and their suppressors is shown in Figure 1. A class of mutants, later termed amber mutants (33), was first characterized in λ (33a), in T4 rII genes (26) and in the alkaline phosphatase gene of E. coli (27), and ochre mutants were found in the lac and rII genes (34). Both amber and ochre mutants are defined as nonsense by their effects upon the expression of an rII mutant, the deletion r1589. This deletion, which spans part of both the A and B cistrons of the rII region, abolishes A activity but leaves at least some B activity intact in spite of the deletion of the beginning of the B gene. Presumably, the mutant produces a protein which is part A and part B. Amber mutants of the A cistron when combined with r1589 result in the abolition of the B activity. Benzer & Champe proposed that these mutants caused the interruption of protein synthesis at the site of the mutation as a result of the failure of the translation machinery to read the altered triplet (26). The altered site was thus presumed to have a codon which did not correspond to any amino acid. Subsequently, it was shown that ochre mutants

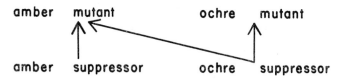

FIG. 1. The relationship between nonsense mutants and their suppressors. An arrow indicates that the suppressor is active on the mutation.

had the same effect, when combined with r1589 (34). In contrast, other mutants of the A cistron of the base substitution type had no effect on B activity when combined with r1589.

The prediction that amber mutations result in the cessation of polypeptide chain propagation was confirmed by demonstrating that amber mutants of the coat protein of bacteriophage T4 produce only fragments of that protein and, in addition, that the length of the fragment depends on the distance of the amber mutation from the end of the gene corresponding to the N-terminal end of the protein (35). These results do not, however, prove that the mutation acts directly at the translation level, since the protein fragments might have resulted from the production of mRNA fragments. However, genetic evidence has been presented indicating that these mutations act at the level of translation rather than transcription; the expression of both amber and ochre mutants is prevented when the phase of translation of the genetic message is altered (36). It is indeed very difficult to see how the frame shifts could suppress a mutation which affects the transcription process. In addition, the existence of amber mutants of the RNA phage suggests that the mutants affect the transmission of information from RNA to protein (37).

It was further demonstrated that amber mutations in the T4 coat protein result in quantitative synthesis and release of the N-terminal portion of a protein terminating with the amino acid immediately preceding that coded for in the altered codon (38). Thus, it is confirmed that the amber mutation is a signal for chain termination. Similar studies have not been carried out with ochre mutants because of the difficulty in isolating ochre mutants of the coat protein (see later). But, since, in all other respects studied, the two classes of mutations have identical effects, it seems likely that ochre mutations also lead to chain termination.

The distinction between amber and ochre mutants is based first of all on the different suppression patterns of the two classes (Fig. 1). The failure of amber suppressors to restore activity to ochre mutants cannot be explained by supposing that the amber suppressors allow translation at the mutant site, but an inactive protein is produced. First, whereas amber suppressors suppress the polarity effect of z amber mutants of the *lac* operon, a suppression independent of the functioning of the z gene product, they do not suppress the polarity effect of z ochre mutants. Secondly, the amber suppressors restore B activity to A amber mutants of the *rII* region combined with the deletion r1589, but not to ochre mutants combined with r1589 (34).

Furthermore, it has been determined that two different triplets correspond to an ochre and an amber codon. It was demonstrated, using hydroxylamine and base analogues, that ochre mutants can be converted to amber mutants by an A-T to G-C transition. In addition, it was deduced that the ochre triplet contains only A and U while the amber triplet differs from the ochre triplet, either a G replacing an A or a C replacing a U (39). An analysis of the amino acid substitutions in back mutations of amber mutants of T4 (coat protein) and of alkaline phosphatase, taken in conjunction with a knowledge of the code, led to the conclusion that the amber triplet is UAG and thus the ochre triplet UAA (39, 40). In agreement with these conclusions, the most recent codon assignments (31, 32) indicate that these two triplets are among the few which do not appear to code for any amino acid.

THE NATURE OF AMBER AND OCHRE SUPPRESSORS

Genetics of suppressor mutations.—The existence of genetically separable loci for both amber and ochre suppressors in *E. coli* has been demonstrated in several laboratories. A list of the suppressors which have been found so far is presented in Table I and their location on the *E. coli* genetic map is shown in Figure 2. An ochre suppressor, suB, is very closely linked to the amber suppressor, suII, suggesting that the two may map in the same locus (41). Also, suC may map with one of the amber suppressors in the try region. Three of the amber suppressors listed in Table I, suYMel, suI, and suII, were detected in stock strains (YMEL, CR-63, and CR-34 (C-600), respectively) of *E. coli*, without any known prior selection for suppression for an amber mutant, although it may be that they arose through accidental selection. In conclusion it appears that there are four to six (at least) known amber suppressor loci and at least five different ochre suppressor loci.

It has been found that three ochre suppressors (suB, suC, and suL) and three amber suppressors (suII, suYMel, and su1D) are dominant over their wild-type alleles, indicating that suppressor mutations do not cause the loss of a gene activity. The dominance was demonstrated with the use of the F_1-*gal* episome carrying suB or suII (41), λ HFT particle carrying suL

TABLE I

CHARACTERISTICS OF SUPPRESSOR MUTATIONS

Type of mutations which are suppressed	Sup-pressors	Mapping data	Bibliographic data
amber	SuI	cotransducible with *his* by P1	(41)
amber	SuII	cotransducible with *gal* by P1	(41)
amber	SuIII	probably same as Su3	(34)
amber	Su1	probably same as SuI	(42)
amber	Su2	probably same as SuII	(42)
amber	Su3	closely linked to *try*	(42)
amber	Su4	not precisely mapped	(42)
amber	SuYMel	cotransducible with *try* by P1	(43)
amber	Su1D	cotransducible with *try* by P1	(44)
ochre	SuB	cotransducible with *gal* by P1	(41)
ochre	SuC	cotransducible with *try* by P1	(41)
ochre	SuL	cotransducible with *gal* by P1 and λ	(45)
ochre	SuM	cotransducible with *argF* by P1	(45)
ochre	SuN	maps near *purC*	(45)
ochre	SuO	cotransducible with *try* by P1	(45)
mis-sense	Su of a *try⁻*	cotransducible with *B1* locus by P1	(25, 94)

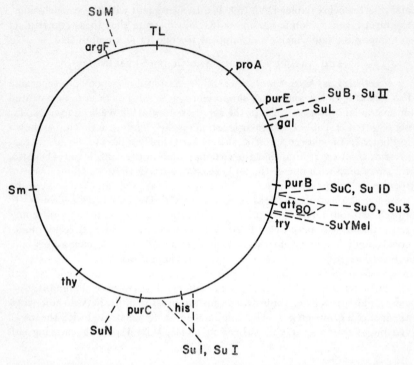

Fig. 2. A map of amber and ochre suppressors. Abbreviations: *Sm* for streptomycin, *arg* for arginine; *TL* for threonine and leucine; *pro* for proline; *pur* for purine, *gal* for galactose; *att*$_{80}$ for attachment site for Ø80; *try* for tryptophan; *his* for histidine; *thy* for thymine. Bracketing indicates that the genes in question have not been ordered.

(45), and Φ80HFT particles carrying either suC (46), suYMEL, or su1D (44).

The mechanism of suppressor action.—Since amber triplets (and probably ochre) are signals for chain termination, the suppressors of these mutations should allow propagation of the polypeptide chain beyond the site of the mutation by causing insertion of an amino acid at the site of the amber (or ochre) triplet. The first suggestion that suppression results in the insertion of an amino acid different from the wild type came from the finding that the T4-deoxycytidylic hydroxymethylase of a suppressed amber mutant of the gene for this enzyme exhibits an altered thermostability (47). Subsequent studies on suppression of amber mutants of the bacteriophage f-2 coat protein (48), of alkaline phosphatase (49), and of the T4 coat protein (38) revealed which amino acids are inserted at the site of the mutation. These studies showed changes from a glutamine or tryptophan in the wild-type protein to a serine in amber mutants suppressed by su1 or suI. It was also found that glutamine was substituted by su2 and suII, and tyrosine by su3 and suIII (50, 51). The insertion of different amino acids is reflected in the different specificities of amber suppressors. Three amber suppressor mutations have been distinguished on the basis of the spectrum of suppression of a large group of amber mutants (34).

Amber suppressors also vary in their efficiencies of suppression. Suppression of amber mutants of the T4 coat protein by suI results in the production of 63 per cent of the normal amount of coat protein and 37 per cent of the fragment found in the unsuppressed amber mutant (51). SuII suppressed to 30 per cent and suIII to 51 per cent of the normal amounts. The production of alkaline phosphatase CRM is restored to different amounts in various amber mutants of that gene suppressed by three different suppressors (42). Thus, it appears that amber suppressors, in general, suppress to relatively high levels of activity.

In contrast, ochre suppressors restore only low levels of activity to both amber and ochre mutants. SuB, suC, suD, and suE allow 1 to 5 per cent synthesis of β-galactosidase in a *lac* ochre mutant (34) and restore the same levels of synthesis to T4 coat protein ambers (52). As a result, ochre suppressors generally will suppress mutants only in genes controlling an enzymatic component as opposed to genes controlling a structural component of T4 (52). It has thus been impossible so far to isolate ochre mutants of the coat protein and, therefore, the direct demonstration of the chain-terminating effects of ochre mutants has not been obtained. In addition, because of the low level suppression, it is difficult to determine the amino acids inserted by the action of these suppressors. However, four ochre suppressor mutations, suB, suC, suD, and suE, are distinguishable by their suppression patterns of a large group of ochre and amber mutants, suggesting that four different amino acids are inserted (34).

The nature of the chain-terminating mutants and of their suppression indicates that the suppressor mutation affects the translation apparatus. However, the proof of the nature of the suppressor effects depends upon the characterization of the cytoplasmic component responsible for the restoration of the translation process. Recent evidence on the nature of a suppressor locus has been obtained from studies of the *in vitro* synthesis of coat protein of RNA phage employing phage RNA from an amber mutant in this gene (53, 54). Extracts from bacteria carrying the suppressor mutation, suI, allow synthesis of the coat protein with insertion of serine at the mutant site. By fractionation of the bacterial extract, it was shown that a serine-specific tRNA was the altered component of the suppressor strain responsible for suppression. A serine-specific tRNA present in these cells can "read" the amber triplet. It has yet to be determined whether the altered tRNA corresponds to a serine tRNA that is normally present or whether it is another tRNA which has changed so that it can be activated by a serine-activating enzyme. In addition, it is not known whether the suppressor mutation directly alters the tRNA structure by a mutation in the structural gene, or if it alters the tRNA structure indirectly through, for instance, an effect upon the methylating enzymes. At any rate, these results provide direct proof that at least one amber suppressor exerts its effects directly at the level of translation of mRNA information into protein. Thus, the presence of a suppressor results in the appearance of a new or altered function. This conclusion is in complete agreement with the dominance of su$^+$ mutations found in the genetic studies.

The similarity of effects of different amber suppressors, i.e. (a) their specificity of suppression of only one triplet, UAG; (b) the insertion of specific amino acids; and (c) the high levels of suppression, suggests that they may all act by the same mechanism, the alteration of a tRNA. The ochre suppressors are only somewhat less specific in that they allow the reading of two closely related triplets, UAA and UAG. The finding that at least one pair of amber and ochre suppressors may map in the same locus indicates that the ochre suppressors may also affect tRNA. So far no suppressors have been characterized which correspond to mutations of activating enzymes. Suppression through the ribosome will be discussed in a later section.

As has already been said in the introductory remarks to this section, it appears unlikely that UAG, the amber triplet, is used as the normal chain-terminating signal, since amber suppressors which suppress to very high levels have no effect upon the growth rates of bacteria in which they occur (39, 42). If, for instance, su1 were suppressing chain-termination of all proteins 63 per cent of the time, that cell could not survive without serious effects on cell growth. The more likely candidate for the normal chain termination signal is the ochre triplet, UAA. Ochre suppressors are far less effective than amber suppressors[4] and, furthermore, most ochre suppressors do slow the growth rate of the cell in which they are carried (45, 55, 56). It is possible, in fact, that in strains carrying ochre suppressors, some polypeptide chain synthesis is continued beyond the normal point of chain termination.

So far only one mis-sense suppressor has been described and mapped. It has been found that a try$^-$ mis-sense suppressor is cotransducible with the B1 locus (25). Attempts to determine the altered cellular component have been as yet unsuccessful and, in fact, it cannot be said whether or not the effect of the suppression is directly at the translation level.

PHENOTYPIC INFORMATIONAL SUPPRESSION

It has been found (57) that 1 to 5 per cent of the auxotrophic mutants obtained from *E. coli* after a mutagenic treatment (ultraviolet irradiation, nitrosoguanidine, ethylmethanesulfonate) are able to grow in the absence of their specific growth factor, provided that streptomycin (Sm) is present in the growth medium. They were designated as conditionally Sm-dependent (CSD) mutants. These mutants, isolated from a Sm-resistant (Sm^r) parent, were auxotrophs for a number of different amino acids with unrelated biosynthetic pathways; thus, their common denominator could not be found in an identical defective enzyme influenced by Sm and common to all of them. The first CSD mutant was isolated fortuitously after the imposition of a

---

[4] However, Gallucci, E., and Garen, A. [*J. Mol. Biol.*, **15**, 193 (1966)] have recently described a strong ($\simeq$16 per cent) ochre suppressor, Su5, mapping near Su3 (note added in proof).

Sm^r mutation in a Sm-sensitive (Sm^s) arginine requirer bearing a defective ornithine transcarbamylase, the enzyme converting ornithine to citrulline. It was observed that only a fraction of the Sm^r clones independently isolated were CSD, the others being arg^- under all conditions. It was already known that mutations at the classical Sm locus correspond to structural changes in the ribosome (58), more precisely in the 30S ribosomal subunit (59, 60). Therefore, Gorini & Kataja (57) proposed that Sm corrects these mutants by altering the standard meaning of the genetic code and they suggested the ribosome as the site of action of Sm in performing the correction of the CSD mutants. They equated this correction to a Sm-induced phenotypic suppression. This hypothesis implied that the ribosomal structure could influence the accuracy of the reading of the code during its translation.

Experiments *in vitro* on amino acid incorporation directed by synthetic messenger confirmed this hypothesis. Misreading was observed in a system in which the 30S ribosomal subunit was derived from Sm^s cells and not from Sm^r mutants. The origin of all other components, tRNA, activating enzymes, 50S subunit, was irrelevant. For instance, in the presence of streptomycin the polyuridylate-stimulated incorporation of phenylalanine was inhibited 50 to 60 per cent and that of isoleucine, serine, and tyrosine was increased. In the case of isoleucine, the increase was from about zero to about 60 per cent of the standard phenylalanine incorporation (61). The relationship between the *in vivo* observations and these results *in vitro* became clearer when it was subsequently proven that (*a*) the original assumption that Sm resistance is necessary for the CSD phenotype was incorrect, since Sm^s mutants bearing a Sm-correctable defect were also proven to be corrected by Sm, at sublethal doses of 1 to 2 μg/ml (62); and (*b*) that Sm also induces moderate misreading with ribosomes derived from Sm^r CSD cells. (63). Subsequent work has established that Sm acts on the recognition step of the translation process, i.e., the binding of aminoacyl-sRNA to ribosomes in response to specific coding triplets (64, 65). It was also found that the polypeptide formed in the presence of Sm contains phenylalanine and isoleucine residues bound together through peptidic linkages in a random distribution, whereas that obtained in the absence of Sm was polyphenylalanine, as expected (66). It should be pointed out, however, that the *in vitro* experiments, although providing evidence for the postulated Sm-induced suppression, show that Sm not only provokes misreading but also causes a net stimulation of amino acid incorporation both with synthetic (67) and natural (68) messengers, and even with the denatured DNA (69). These observations are not understood at present. In any case it seems that only the misreading effect is pertinent to the present discussion of suppression.

OTHER EXAMPLES OF SUPPRESSION INDUCED BY STREPTOMYCIN AND BY OTHER AGENTS WITH SIMILAR ACTION

It has been found, as expected, that bacterial and viral mutant functions may both be suppressed by streptomycin. Among the other bacterial mutants suppressible by Sm, a galactose-negative *E. coli* mutant (70) and a number of histidine mutants in *Salmonella typhimurium* (71) have been described. Among the bacteriophages there are CSD mutants of T4 (72), T7 (73), MS2 RNA phage (74), and of λ (75, 67). Other antibiotics which, like streptomycin, may be classified chemically as aminoglycosides have been shown to suppress *in vivo* (62) and *in vitro* (67). We shall not discuss here the numerous different agents which have been found to cause misreading only *in vitro*.

TYPE OF MUTATIONS CORRECTED BY STREPTOMYCIN

There is extensive evidence that streptomycin suppresses nonsense mutations. A number of amber mutants in T4 and an F2 RNA-phage mutant have been found to be suppressed by the antibiotic (72, 74, 76). In addition, it has been recently reported that 100 per cent of the amber and five out of eight ochre mutants of the *Salmonella typhimurium* histidine operon (71) are suppressible by Sm. Direct evidence for suppression of mis-sense is scanty. It has been suggested that 20 per cent of mis-sense mutants in the *Salmonella His⁻* group are suppressible by Sm (71). However, there are two indirect pieces of evidence suggesting an amino acid substitution caused by Sm, thus indicating the possibility of mis-sense suppression. In a study of amino acid incorporation directed by natural messenger extracted from F2 RNA phage, it was found that under conditions in which the lack of asparagine in the incubation mixture is the factor which limits incorporation, the addition of either asparagine or of streptomycin permits incorporation to proceed. It is assumed that Sm causes the substitution of the missing asparagine by some other amino acid, presumably arginine (77). According to other results, it appears that in the presence of Sm, *E. coli* produces upon induction an inactive CRM along with a reduced amount of active β-galactosidase (78).

The codon specificity of Sm suppression can also be judged *in vitro*. The use of homopolynucleotides as messenger has shown that Sm induces misreading of only one base in a triplet and that a 5′-terminal or internal U would be misread as A or C, 5′-terminal C as A or U, and internal C as A. Streptomycin induces little or no misreading of A, but extensive misreading of I (67). However, with alternating UC, UG, AC, and AG copolymers, the Sm-induced misreading is much more specific than that predicted from the results obtained using homopolynucleotides. This indicates that a substantial number of the available coding triplets are refractory to Sm-induced misreading (79).

RELATION BETWEEN STREPTOMYCIN-INDUCED SUPPRESSION AND MUTATIONS OF THE CLASSICAL STREPTOMYCIN LOCUS

Since the classical *Sm* locus is believed to be one of the genetic loci controlling ribosomal (30S) structure, the relationship between Sm-induced suppression and this locus is important. Apparently, the CSD phenotype depends on a close relationship that appears to exist between the Sm-suppressible (SSu) mutation and the allele present at the classical *Sm* locus.

Considering only the Sm^r mutants, it is known, in fact, that those which are incompetent to permit the Sm-correction of a given SSu mutation, are, nevertheless, competent for a second superimposed SSu mutation (57, 63). At present it is not known, however, whether competence-incompetence is only a matter of level of correction or more specifically a type of correction.

A second point of importance is to establish whether or not, besides the SSu mutation and the Sm mutation, other genes (for instance, suppressors) are involved in determining a CSD phenotype. Given the difficulty in deciding whether a wild-type strain contains an undetected suppressor, this question may have a positive answer only when a suppressor is found. Some instances are known in which this situation exists. The gal^- CSD strain mentioned above is derived from a $gal^-Su^+ Sm^s$ genotype. As a result of the introduction of the Sm^r genotype (by spontaneous mutation, the Su^+ is reversed in some of the mutants which appear now as $gal^-Su^- Sm^r$, except in the presence of Sm when they appear as gal^+ (70). A similar situation occurs in strain C600 which is known to contain a suppressor which permits the growth of suppressor-sensitive mutants of λ. It has been found that in the absence of Sm, some Sm^r derivatives behave as Su^-, except in the presence of Sm when they appear Su^+ (75, 76). A similar observation has been made with T7 (73). It appears, in these cases, that a mutation of the ribosomal structure interferes with the action of a genetic suppressor, but the action of streptomycin on the mutated ribosomal structure re-establishes the relationship between ribosome and suppressor required for suppression. In other cases, as in the "oversuppressed" mutations (80, 81), in which the genetic suppressor is active in the presence of a competent Sm^r mutation, the addition of Sm has a synergistic effect.

THE ROLE OF RIBOSOMAL MUTATIONS IN INFORMATIONAL SUPPRESSION

Since the fidelity of translation appears to be secured not only by tRNA and activating enzymes but also by the ribosome, the question arises whether a structurally mutated ribosome may permit specific violations in the translation of the genetic script leading to suppression. So far, only one instance has been reported in which it is claimed that a suppression occurs because of a structurally mutated ribosome (82) but the evidence presented is not conclusive. In any case, mutations at, or presumably at, the classical Sm locus have drawn extensive attention since, undoubtedly, at least some of the determinants of ribosomal structure are located in that chromosomal region. A brief survey of two features connected with this genetic locus appears to be pertinent to this review, the reader being referred to the original papers for more information.

One is the frequently observed pleiotropism of mutations involving the Sm phenotype. They include several types: (a) Mutations conferring auxotrophy as well as resistance to Sm (83–87) in $E.\ coli$ and $Salmonella\ typhimurium$ prototrophs. (b) Mutations which confer Sm dependence along with prototrophy in $Proteus\ mirabilis$ auxotrophs (88). (c) Mutations in which Sm resistance brings about also a change in host-prophage relationship (89) or in the ability to perform host-controlled modifications of infecting bacteriophage (90). (*d*) Mutations to Sm resistance which reverse at the same time the ability to suppress a bacterial mutation (70) or a bacteriophage mutation (73, 76, 91). The list is impressive, although it is not proven as yet whether all types of pleiotropy, registered above, constitute a homogeneous group of mutations at a ribosomal structural locus. Moreover, an enlargement of the concept of suppression is necessary in postulating for all these pleiotropic mutations a common mechanism based on ambiguity introduced by structurally altered ribosomes. Violations of code translation due to ambiguous reading may result in two opposite situations, depending on the genetic surrounding in a given cell: either suppression of a mutation which actually persists in the genome or "impression" of a mutated phenotype into a wild-type genotype. The occurrence of "impressor" mutations, together with the more classical suppressor mutations, should be entertained as a possibility if a common denominator for all pleiotropic *Sm* mutations is postulated.

The second feature connected with the *Sm* locus is that the *Sm*^{r} and *Sm*-dependent (*Sm*^{Dep}) phenotypes may be suppressed by genetic suppressors. This was observed in *E. coli* in which was found that several independently isolated *Sm*^{s} revertants from *Sm*^{Dep} strains are a result of a suppressor closely linked to the *Sm* locus (92). An analogous situation was found in *Salmonella typhimurium* (87). The biochemical behavior of suppressed *Sm*^{Dep} mutants of *E. coli* has been analyzed (93). It was found that these suppressed mutants still retaining the *Sm*^{Dep} genotype are not killed but only inhibited in the presence of Sm in a way similar to the oversuppressed ones, which contain a genetic suppressor and still retain the *Sm*^{r} genotype (80). In both cases it can be shown that protein synthesis continues in the presence of *Sm* and that the inhibition is brought about by an amount of faulty proteins beyond the limits compatible with cell growth. It is conceivable, in fact, that a suppressor of a ribosomal mutation should affect nonspecifically the structure of all proteins of the cell.

It was shown *in vitro* that *Sm*^{s} wild-type ribosomes allow a low level of ambiguity (isoleucine incorporation about 1 per cent of the correct phenylalanine incorporation, using polyuridylate as a messenger) even in the absence of streptomycin (63). Under the same conditions *Sm*^{r} ribosomes are about 10 times less ambiguous. This change in level of ambiguity *in vitro* between different *Sm* alleles could account for the frequent pleiotropic effect of the *Sm* mutation if one assumes that pleiotropism is due to misreading or to the absence of it.

UNCHARACTERIZED SUPPRESSOR MUTATIONS
UNSTABLE SUPPRESSORS

An additional class of suppressors has been described which are unstable, i.e., they segregate the mutant parent with high frequency. In addition to the try⁻ mis-sense suppressor already mentioned (94) (see Table I), others have been described (95–97). It has been suggested in these cases that the suppressor is carried on an episome, and that the observed instability is due to segregation of this episome. The most convincing evidence for episomal suppressors comes from studies of an unstable suppressor of a *lac⁻* mutant. The suppressor which could not be mapped on the chromosome, was curable by acridine orange and could be stabilized by integration of the episome at various sites on the chromosome (97).

OTHER SUPPRESSORS

Suppressor mutations of a *leu⁻* mutant of *Salmonella typhimurium* have been isolated (98). It appears that the original mutant maps in the *leu* operator. The suppressor mutations lie in a region between *try* and *cys* on the chromosome and are often due to deletions extending into these loci. These suppressor mutations may be in a regulator gene.

Many other suppressors have been studied, the mechanisms of action of which are still unknown (45, 99–103).

CONCLUSIONS

The concept of suppression, although very precisely definable operationally, covers, like that of mutation, the most disparate situations. In this review we were forced to spread the discussion from problems of classical intermediary metabolism to those of synthesis of macromolecules and to that of code reading. In fact, the reversion of a mutation by the classical procedures of genetics usually yields suppressor mutations along with true revertants, without offering an unambiguous simple way to distinguish them. Frequently, the slow growth of the clone is a good indication of a suppressor mutation because the probability is high that a less efficient cell is the result of an alternate pathway, of an intragenically repaired enzyme, or of a partial reading correction due to informational suppression. In some other instances, unexpected pleiotropism is an indication of a suppressor mutation. At any rate, even after recognition by genetic crosses of a suppressor mutation, its classification may still require a thorough critical analysis of a number of genetic as well as biochemical data.

The value of the study of suppression is undoubtedly established. In the field of indirect suppression we should like to underscore the discovery of the two parallel paths of carbamyl phosphate synthesis and metabolism in *Neurospora*, indicated by the peculiar pattern of cross-suppression between pyrimidine and arginine mutants. The analysis of intragenic suppression offered the basic elements of our understanding of the mechanism whereby the genetic code is deciphered by reading frames. Informational suppression, hopefully, will continue to help in understanding certain aspects of the translation process, in particular, the nature of the *in vivo* signals of chain initiation and termination and the role of the ribosome in securing an unambiguous reading of the genetic code. It appears that fidelity of translation depends on the interaction of at least three macromolecular elements: activating enzymes, tRNAs and the ribosome. The first two are each a class of more than

20 different molecules and the third is a complex aggregate of several different RNAs and proteins. Under these circumstances it should be expected that the pattern of informational suppression may be highly complex when the interaction of mutations in more than one of these elements is considered. Synergistic or antagonistic effects may be predicted between two (or more) suppressors acting simultaneously. It has indeed been observed that the superimposition of phenotypic suppression induced by streptomycin on a genetic suppressor may result in oversuppression in a CSD mutant (80) and that at least four genetic loci interact in the suppression of different amber mutants of T4 (104). The changes in suppression characteristics, from Su^+ to Su^-, frequently observed (70, 73, 76) in Sm^r mutants derived from $Sm^s Su^+$ parents is also indicative that the phenotype may depend upon the interaction of two suppressor mutations, one at a locus (Sm) controlling ribosomal structure. In addition, two type of ribosomal mutations are found: sensitive or insensitive to the phenotypic suppression induced by streptomycin.

Finally, we consider the biological significance of translation ambiguity, if any exists in the wild-type, nonmutated cell. Genetic informational suppressors are frequently found in strains presumably wild type or at least to which a pressure has not been intentionally applied for selecting such suppressors. On the other hand, it is found that ribosomes extracted from Sm^s cells, the type naturally selected, possess, in the absence of Sm, an intrinsic level of misreading many times higher than ribosomes extracted from Sm^r mutants. One cannot help but wonder whether genetic systems that allow a certain degree of ambiguity may possess a selective advantage of some kind. Presumably, a population should, in this way, preserve mutations, hidden, but stored for future evolutionary trials. A wide range of mutability of different sites in a chromosome, could be accounted for by a variety of loci whose mutations have a better chance of being preserved through the ambiguity of the wild-type translation machinery. It seems reasonable to anticipate that the mutability should be more evenly distributed along the chromosome in a less ambiguous system, for instance, in a Sm^r mutant.

LITERATURE CITED

1. Sturtevant, A. H., Proc. Soc. Exptl. Biol. Med., 17, 70 (1920)
2. Beadle, G. W., and Ephrussi, B., Proc. Natl. Acad. Sci. U.S., 22, 536 (1936)
3. Yanofsky, C., and St. Lawrence, P., Ann. Rev. Microbiol., 14, 311 (1960)
4. Progress in Nucleic Acid Research. (Davidson, J. N., and Cohn, W. E., Eds., Academic Press, New York, 1963)
5. Lein, J., and Lein, P. S., Proc. Natl. Acad. Sci. U.S., 38, 44 (1952)
6. Strauss, B. S., and Pierog, S., J. Gen. Microbiol., 10, 221 (1954)
7. Howarth, S., Genetics, 43, 404 (1958)
8. Doudney, C. O., and Wagner, R. P., Proc. Natl. Acad. Sci. U.S., 41, 364 (1955)
9. Davis, R. H., Biochim. Biophys. Acta, 107, 54 (1965)
10. Houlahan, M. B., and Mitchell, H. K., Proc. Natl. Acad. Sci. U.S., 33, 223 (1947)
11. Davis, R. H., Science, 134, 470 (1961)
12. Reissig, J. L., J. Gen. Microbiol., 30, 327 (1963)
13. Slonimski, P. P., Acher, R., Péré, G., Sels, A., and Somlo, M., Intern. Symp. Mechanisms of Regulations of Cellular Activities in Microorganisms, Marseilles, 1963, 435. (Ed. Centre Natl. Rech. Sci., Paris, 1965)

14. Clavillier, P., Péré, G., Slonimski, P. P., and Somlo, M., *Proc. Intern. Congr. Biochem.*, *6th*, New York, IX, 51 (1964) (Abstr.)
15. Péré, G., Clavilier, L., and Slonimski, P. P., *Ann. Génêt.*, 8, 112 (1965)
16. Suskind, S. R., and Kurek, L. I., *Proc. Natl. Acad. Sci. U.S.*, 45, 193 (1959)
17. Jacob, F., and Monod, J., *Cold Spring Harbor Symp. Quant. Biol.*, 26, 193 (1961)
18. Yanofsky, C., Horn, V., and Thorpe, D., *Science*, 146, 1593 (1964)
19. Crick, F. H. C., Barnett, L., Brenner, S., and Watts-Tobin, J., *Nature*, 192, 1227 (1961)
20. Terzaghi, E., Okada, Y., Streisinger, G., Emrich, J., Inouye, M., and Tsugita, A. To be submitted to *Proc. Natl. Acad. Sci. U.S.*
21. Stadler, J., and Yanofsky, C., *Genetics*, 44, 105 (1959)
22. Yanofsky, C., and Crawford, I. P., *Proc. Natl. Acad. Sci. U.S.*, 45, 1016 (1959)
23. Crawford, I. P., and Yanofsky, C., *Proc. Natl. Acad. Sci. U.S.*, 45, 1280 (1959)
24. Helinski, D. R., and Yanofsky, C., *Proc. Natl. Acad. Sci. U.S.*, 48, 173 (1962)
25. Brody, S., and Yanofsky, C., *Proc. Natl. Acad. Sci. U.S.*, 50, 9 (1963)
26. Benzer, S., and Champe, S. P., *Proc. Natl. Acad. Sci. U.S.*, 48, 114 (1962)
27. Garen, A., and Siddiqi, O., *Proc. Natl. Acad. Sci. U.S.*, 48, 173 (1962)
28. Rosen, B., *J. Mol. Biol.*, 11, 845 (1965)
29. Speyer, J. F., *Biochem. Biophys. Res. Commun.*, 21, 6 (1965)
30. Crick, F. H. C., "A note for the RNA Tie Club," 1955
31. Brimacombe, R., Trupin, J., Nirenberg, M., Leder, P., Bernfield, M., and Jaouni, T., *Proc. Natl. Acad. Sci. U.S.*, 54, 954 (1965)
32. Söll, D., Ohtsuka, E., Jones, D. S., Lohrmann, R., Hayatsu, H., Nishimura, S., and Khorana, H. G., *Proc. Natl. Acad. Sci. U.S.*, 54, 1378 (1965)
33. Epstein, R. H., Bollé, A., Steinberg, C. M., Kellenberger, E., Boy De La Tour, E., Chevalley, R., Edgar, R. S., Susman, M., Denhardt, G. H., and Lielausis, A., *Cold Spring Harbor Symp. Quant. Biol.*, 28, 375 (1963)
33a. Campbell, A., *Virology*, 9, 293 (1959)
34. Brenner, S., and Beckwith, J. R., *J. Mol. Biol.*, 13, 629 (1965)

35. Sarabhai, A. S., Stretton, A. O. W., Brenner, S., and Bollé, A., *Nature*, 201, 13 (1964)
36. Brenner, S., and Stretton, A. O. W., *J. Mol. Biol.*. 13, 944 (1965)
37. Zinder, N. D., and Cooper, S., *Virology*, 23, 152 (1964)
38. Stretton, A. O. W., and Brenner, S., *J. Mol. Biol.*, 12, 456 (1964)
39. Brenner, S., Stretton, A. O. W., and Kaplan, S., *Nature*, 206, 994 (1965)
40. Weigert, M. G., and Garen, A., *Nature*, 206, 992 (1965)
41. Signer, E. R., Beckwith, J. R., and Brenner, S., *J. Mol. Biol.*, 14, 153 (1965)
42. Garen, A., Garen, S., and Wilhelm, R. C., *J. Mol. Biol.*, 14, 167 (1965)
43. Henning, U., Dennert, G., Szolyvay, K., and Deppe, G., *J. Mol. Biol.*, 13, 592 (1965)
44. Dennert, G., Hertel, L., Deppe, G., and Henning, U., *Z. Vererbungslehre*, 97, 243 (1965)
45. Eggertson, G., and Adelberg, E. A., *Genetics*, 52, 319 (1965)
46. Signer, E. R., *J. Mol. Biol.*, 15, 243 (1966)
47. Dirksen, M. L., Hutson, J. C., and Buchanan, J. M., *Proc. Natl. Acad. Sci. U.S.*, 50, 507 (1963)
48. Notani, G. W., Engelhardt, D. L., Konigsberg, W., and Zinder, N., *J. Mol. Biol.*, 12, 439 (1965)
49. Weigert, M. G., and Garen, A., *J. Mol. Biol.* 12, 448 (1965)
50. Weigert, M., Lanka, E., and Garen, A., *J. Mol. Biol.*, 14, 522 (1965)
51. Kaplan, S., Stretton, A. O. W., and Brenner, S., *J. Mol. Biol.*, 14, 528 (1965)
52. Brenner, S., and Stretton, A. O. W., *J. Cellular Comp. Physiol.*, 64, Suppl. 1, 43 (1964)
53. Cappecchi, M. R., and Gussin, G. N., *Science*, 149, 147 (1965)
54. Engelhardt, D. L., Webster, R. E., Wilhelm, R. C., and Zinder, N. D., *Proc. Natl. Acad. Sci. U.S.*, 54, 1791 (1965)
55. Beckwith, J. R., in *Struktur und Funktion des Genetischen Materials, Erwin-Bauer Gedächtnisvorlesungen III*, 119. (Akademie Verlag, Berlin, 1964)
56. Gartner, T. K., and Orias, E., *Proc. Natl. Acad. Sci. U.S.*, 53, 62 (1965)
57. Gorini, L., and Kataja, E., *Proc. Natl. Acad. Sci. U.S.*, 51, 487 (1964)
58. Spotts, C. R., and Stanier, R. Y., *Nature*, 192, 633 (1961)
59. Davies, J., *Proc. Natl. Acad. Sci. U.S.*, 51, 659 (1964)

60. Cox, E. C., White, J. R., and Flaks, J. G., *Proc. Natl. Acad. Sci. U.S.*, **51**, 703 (1964)

61. Davies, J., Gilbert, W., and Gorini, L., *Proc. Natl. Acad. Sci. U.S.*, **51**, 883 (1964)

62. Gorini, L., and Kataja, E., *Biochem. Biophys. Res. Commun.*, **18**, 656 (1965)

63. Anderson, W. F., Gorini, L., and Breckenridge, L., *Proc. Natl. Acad. Sci. U.S.*, **54**, 1076 (1965)

64. Pestka, S., Marshall, R., and Nirenberg, M., *Proc. Natl. Acad. Sci. U.S.*, **53**, 639, (1965)

65. Kaji, H., and Kaji, A., *Proc. Natl. Acad. Sci. U.S.*, **54**, 213 (1965)

66. Old, D., and Gorini, L., *Science*, **150**, 1290 (1965)

67. Davies, J., Gorini, L., and Davis, B. D., *Mol. Pharmacol.*, **1**, 93 (1965)

68. Van Knippenberg, P. H., van Ravenswaay, J. C., Grijm-Vos, M., Veldstra, H., and Bosch, L., *Biochim. Biophys. Acta*, **95**, 461 (1965)

69. McCarthy, B. J., and Holland, J. J., *Proc. Natl. Acad. Sci. U.S.*, **54**, 880 (1965)

70. Lederberg, E. M., Cavalli-Sforza, L., and Lederberg, J., *Proc. Natl. Acad. Sci. U.S.*, **51**, 678 (1964)

71. Whitfield, H. J., Martin, R. G., and Ames, B. N., *Federation Proc.*, **25**, 337 (1966)

72. Reale-Scafati, A. (Personal communication)

73. Orias, E., and Gartner, T. K., *Bacteriol. Proc.*, 24, (1965)

74. Valentine, R. C., and Zinder, N. D., *Science*, **144**, 1458 (1964)

75. Meselson, M. [Personal communication; cited in (57)]

76. Couturier, M., Desmet, L., and Thomas, R., *Biochem. Biophys. Res. Commun.*, **16**, 244 (1964)

77. Schwartz, J. H., *Proc. Natl. Acad. Sci. U.S.*, **53**, 1133 (1965)

78. Bissell, M., *J. Mol. Biol.*, **14**, 619 (1965)

79. Davies, J., Jones, D. S., Khorana, H. G., and Davis, B. D., *J. Mol. Biol.* (In press)

80. Gorini, L., and Kataja, E., *Proc. Natl. Acad. Sci. U.S.*, **51**, 995 (1964)

81. Witkin, E. (Personal communication)

82. Reid, P. J., Orias, E., and Gartner, T. K., *Biochem. Biophys. Res. Commun.*, **21**, 66 (1965)

83. Watanabe, T., and Watanabe, M., *J. Gen. Microbiol.*, **21**, 16, 30 (1959)

84. Watanabe, T., *J. Gen. Microbiol.*, **22**, 102 (1960)

85. Kohiyama, M., and Ikeda, Y., *Nature*, **187**, 168 (1960)

86. Demerec, M., Lahr, E. L., Balbinder, E., Miyake, T., Ishidsu, J., Mizobuchi, K., and Mahler, B., *Carnegie Inst. Wash. Yearbook*, *1959*, 426 (1960)

87. Goldschmidt, E. P., Matney, T. S., and Bausum, H. T., *Genetics*, **47**, 1475 (1962)

88. Böhme, H., *Z. Vererbungslehre*, **92**, 197 (1961); see also *Proc. Intern. Congr. Genet.*, *11th*, *1963*

89. Lederberg, J., and Lederberg, E. M., *Genetics*, **38**, 51 (1953)

90. Lederberg, S., *Virology*, **3**, 496 (1957)

91. Thomas, R., and Lambert, L., *J. Mol. Biol.*, **5**, 373 (1962)

92. Hashimoto, K., *Genetics*, **45**, 49 (1960)

93. Brownstein, B. L., and Lewandowski, L., *J. Bacteriol.* (In press)

94. Brody, S., and Yanofsky, C., *J. Bacteriol.*, **90**, 687 (1965)

95. Hill, R. F., *J. Gen. Microbiol.*, **30**, 289 (1963)

96. Dawson, G. W. P., and Smith-Keary, P. F., *Heredity*, **18**, 1 (1963)

97. Schwartz, N., *J. Bacteriol.*, **89**, 712 (1965)

98. Mukai, F. H., and Margolin, P., *Proc. Natl. Acad. Sci. U.S.*, **50**, 140 (1963)

99. McDougall, J. K., and Woodward, V. W., *Genetics*, **52**, 397 (1965)

100. Tokuno, S., Strauss, B., and Tsuda, Y., *J. Gen. Microbiol.*, **28**, 481 (1962)

101. Luig, N. H., *Genet. Res.*, **3**, 331 (1962)

102. Siddiqi, O., *Genet. Res.*, **3**, 303 (1962)

103. Yourno, J. D., and Suskind, S. R., *Genetics*, **50**, 803 (1964)

104. Hill, R., and Stent, G. S., *Biochem. Biophys. Res. Commun.*, **18**, 757 (1965)

OTHER REVIEWS OF MICROBIOLOGICAL INTEREST

1. Gitlin, D., "Current Aspects of the Structure, Function, and Genetics of the Immunoglobulins," *Ann. Rev. Med.*, **17**, 1–22 (1966)
2. Edsall, G., "Principles of Active Immunization," *Ann. Rev. Med.*, **17**, 39–48 (1966)
3. Szulman, A. E., "Chemistry, Distribution, and Function of Blood Group Substances, *Ann. Rev. Med.*, **17**, 307–22 (1966)
4. Zabriskie, J. B., "Viral-Induced Bacterial Toxin," *Ann. Rev. Med.*, **17**, 337–50 (1966)
5. Lester, W., "Unclassified Mycobacterial Diseases," *Ann. Rev. Med.*, **17**, 351–360 (1966)
6. Andrewes, C. H., "Rhinoviruses and Common Colds," *Ann. Rev. Med.*, **17**, 361–70 (1966)
7. Tamiya, H., "Synchronous Cultures of Algae," *Ann. Rev. Plant Physiol.*, **17**, 1–26 (1966)
8. Haselkorn, R., "Physical and Chemical Properties of Plant Viruses," *Ann. Rev. Plant Physiol.*, **17**, 137–54 (1966)
9. Burris, R. H., "Biological Nitrogen Fixation," *Ann. Rev. Plant Physiol.*, **17**, 155–84 (1966)
10. Atkinson, D. E., "Regulation of Enzyme Activity," *Ann. Rev. Biochem.*, **35**, 85–124 (1966)
11. Wittman, H. G., and Scholtissek, C., "Biochemistry of Viruses," *Ann. Rev. Biochem.*, **35**, 299–334 (1966)
12. Fleishman, J. B., "Immunoglobulins," *Ann. Rev. Biochem.*, **35**, 835–72 (1966)
13. Martin, H. H., "Biochemistry of Bacterial Cell Walls," *Ann. Rev. Biochem.*, **35**, 457–84 (1966)
14. Christensen, C. F., and Kaufmann, H. H., "Deterioration of Stored Grains by Fungi," *Ann. Rev. Phytopathol.*, **3**, 69–84 (1965)
15. Large, E. C., "Measuring Plant Disease," *Ann. Rev. Phytopathol.*, **4**, 9–28 (1966)
16. Grogan, R. G., and Campbell, R. N., "Fungi as Vectors and Hosts of Viruses," *Ann. Rev. Phytopathol.*, **4**, 29–52 (1966)

AUTHOR INDEX

A

Aaronson, S., 23
Abel, P., 198, 391
Abu-Niaaj, F., 323, 324
Acher, R., 152, 161, 164, 405
Ackman, R. G., 22
Acton, J., 301
Adamcova, B., 244, 249
Addy, S. K., 339
Adelberg, E. A., 411, 412, 414, 419
Adye, J. C., 80, 90, 100
Afzelius, B. A., 133, 139
Ahlström, C. G., 232
Ahmad, K. J., 339
Ajl, S. J., 8
Akai, S., 341
Akamatsu, K., 153
Akashi, S., 255
Akazawa, T., 342, 344, 355, 356, 360, 361, 362
Akazawa, Y., 361
Aksenova, V. A., 356
Albertini, A., 378
Alberts, A. W., 14, 15, 16, 17, 18, 26
Albro, P. W., 28
Alexander, E. R., 123
Alexander, H. E., 375
Alexander, J. B., 138, 141
Alexander, J. J., 120
Alexander, P., 225, 245, 249
Alferov, V. V., 78, 79
Algire, G. H., 243
Algranati, I. D., 278
Allam, A. M., 332
Allen, C. F., 34
Allen, E. G., 109, 110, 111, 112, 115
Allen, E. H., 342, 343, 346, 347
Allen, M. K., 382, 383
Allen, P. J., 183, 355
Allen, R. D., 138
Allen, R. F., 363
Allison, A., 311
Allison, A. C., 111, 231
Allison, M. J., 28, 29, 39
Amador, E. J., 351
Ames, B. N., 416
Ammann, J., 301
Anacker, R. L., 93
Anagnostopoulos, C., 375,

386, 387, 390, 391
Anderson, D. R., 109, 110, 111, 112
Anderson, E., 131, 133, 137, 138
Anderson, J. S., 267, 270, 271, 272, 280
Anderson, M. L., 183
Anderson, R. L., 86
Anderson, T. F., 47
Anderson, W. F., 415, 417, 418
André, J., 132, 139, 140, 143
Andrewes, C. H., 50, 60, 62
Andrews, R. D., 306
Angell, H. R., 341
Aoki, H., 390
Applebaum, S., 308
Ap-Rees, T., 361
Archibald, A. R., 276
Argetsinger, J., 140
Armstrong, J. A., 109, 110, 111, 112
Arnaud, M., 173
Aronson, A. I., 172, 173
Artsikhovskaya, Y. V., 340
Ashwell, G., 274, 279, 280, 281
Asselineau, J., 14, 24, 26, 28, 30, 31, 34, 39
Atanasiu, P., 198
Attia, M. A., 244, 249
Aubert, J.-P., 170, 171, 173
Audia, W. V., 342, 347
Aurelian, L., 211, 292
Austrian, R., 255, 284, 386
Avers, C. J., 163
Avery, O. T., 373
Axelrad, A. A., 244, 249
Axelrod, D., 199, 200, 292, 294, 302, 310

B

Babinet, C., 389
Bach, J. A., 174, 175
Bachmann, B. J., 86
Baddiley, J., 34, 255, 274, 275, 276, 278, 282
Bader, J. P., 114, 115
Badian, J., 90
Bagdian, G., 269
Bailey, D. W., 240, 242
Baillie, A., 174
Bak, I. J., 132, 142

Baker, E. A., 339, 340
Balassa, G., 171, 172, 175, 176, 177, 181
Balassa, R., 371
Balbinder, E., 417
Balducci, D., 296
Balducci, M., 296
Baldwin, H. H., 183
Ballio, A., 28
Ballou, C. E., 40
Baltimore, D., 301
Banks, J., 113, 117, 118, 120, 121
Baptist, J. N., 32
Barat, M., 387, 390, 391
Barban, S., 301, 306
Barcellona, S., 28
Barile, M. R., 109, 110, 111, 112
Barker, D. C., 136, 137
Barker, G. A., 255, 278
Barker, H. A., 6, 332, 333
Barnett, L., 406
Barnhart, B. J., 374, 375, 377, 381, 382, 393
Baron, S., 291-318; 292, 293, 294, 296, 297, 298, 299, 300, 301, 302, 303, 304, 306, 308, 309, 310, 311, 312, 313
Baronowsky, P. E., 18, 19, 20, 21, 24, 25
Barrett, M. K., 248
Barron, A. L., 114
Barwell, C. F., 113
Basilico, C., 200
Bateman, D. F., 349
Bath, J. D., 143
Batra, P. P., 94
Batt, R. F., 339, 340
Batty, I., 174, 180
Bauchop, T., 329
Bauer, D. J., 312
Bauer, L., 79, 102
Baum, S. G., 203, 204
Baumann, N. A., 38
Baumann-Grace, J. B., 174
Baur, E., 81, 92
Bausum, H. T., 417, 418
Bawden, F. C., 49
Bayer, M., 136
Bayreuther, K. E., 391, 392
Beadle, G. W., 401
Beale, G. H., 132
Beals, T. F., 194

Beams, H. W., 131
Beard, P. J., 5
Beasley, A., 307
Beaudreau, C. A., 258, 262, 264, 267
Bechet, J., 159, 161
Becker, Y., 109, 110, 115, 118, 122, 213, 214, 303
Beckmann, I., 258, 262, 266
Beckwith, J. R., 401-23; 409, 410, 411, 413, 414
Bedson, S. P., 108, 113, 126
Beebe, J. M., 77, 81, 83, 90
Beer, S. V., 349
Beers, R. J., 173
Beevers, H., 361, 362
Beiser, S. M., 378, 379
Beisson, J., 146, 240
Bell, A. A., 360, 362
Bell, E., 181
Bello, L. J., 207
Beloff-Chain, A., 296
Benacerraf, H., 246
Bender, H., 96, 97, 98
Benedict, A. A., 113
Benedict, R. G., 32
Benjamin, T. L., 200
Bennet, P., 26
Bennett, B., 243
Bennett, C. W., 48
Bennison, B. E., 233
Ben-Porat, T., 191, 196, 209, 210, 211
Benson, A. A., 34, 35
Benzer, S., 408, 409
Beran, K., 321
Berenblum, I., 247
Berezesky, I. K., 204
Berg, C. M., 122
Berger, J. E., 139
Bergére, J.-I., 177
Bergh, A. K., 28
Bergheden, C., 237, 239
Bergs, V., 306
Berman, D. T., 113, 122
Bernard, J., 201
Bernardi, G., 381
Bernfield, M., 408, 411
Bernheim, B. C., 109, 110, 111, 112
Bernheimer, H. P., 255, 284
Bernheimer, H. R., 386
Bernkopf, H., 109, 110, 114, 115, 118, 122
Bernlohr, R. W., 98, 171, 172, 175
Berns, K. I., 381
Bernstein, R. L., 264, 269, 283, 284

Beskid, G., 176
Beskina, S. R., 112
Bevan, E. A., 155, 156, 158
Bhatla, M. N., 323, 324, 325, 326
Bhattacharjee, J. K., 160, 161
Bhattachayara, R. K., 363, 364
Bianchi, P. A., 195
Bianco, A. R., 246
Biehn, W., 339, 341
Billeter, M. A., 301
Birk, Y., 308, 356
Bishop, D. G., 26, 27, 31, 269
Bissell, M., 416
Bister, F., 256
Bizeau, C., 160
Black, H. S., 351
Black, P. H., 198, 199, 201, 202, 204, 208, 302
Bland, J. O. W., 108
Blaylock, B. A., 332
Blecker, H. H., 34
Blicharska, J., 173, 176
Bloch, K., 14, 15, 17, 18, 19, 20, 21, 22, 23, 24, 25, 26, 29, 30, 32, 34
Blondel-Quéroix, J., 177
Bloodgood, D. E., 332
Bloomfield, D. K., 18, 19, 20, 22
Blumbergs, P., 281
Blumenthal, H. J., 173, 180
Blumson, N. L., 282
Bodian, D., 309
Bodmer, W. F., 374, 382, 384, 385, 396
Boeye, A., 203
Bogan, R. H., 329, 330, 331
Böhme, H., 417
Boiron, M., 198, 201
Boivin, A., 256
Bollé, A., 409, 410
Bolton, E. T., 101, 112, 199, 200, 202
Bomford, R., 134
Boniforti, L., 28
Bonner, D. A., 389
Bonner, J., 363
Bonner, J. T., 89
Boone, D. M., 354
Bordes, A. M., 159
Bordet, C., 18, 33
Börger, H., 342
Borman, G. S., 211
Borst, P., 301
Borys, M., 355
Bosch, L., 415
Bott, K. F., 175, 391
Bottomley, W., 342
Bouille, M., 175
Bovarnick, M. R., 115, 120

Bovee, E. C., 95, 138
Bovell, C. R., 328
Bowler, B., 339
Boyd, W. L., 77
Boy De La Tour, E., 409
Boyle, O. W., 331
Boyse, E. A., 225, 227, 228, 243, 245, 248, 249
Bozarth, R., 308
Bracco, R. M., 371
Bradley, D. E., 49, 140
Brailovsky, C., 194
Brandes, J., 49
Braun, O. H., 257
Breckenridge, L., 415, 417, 418
Breed, R. S., 76, 78, 101
Breinig, M., 304, 305
Brennan, P., 14, 17
Brenner, S., 406, 409, 410, 411, 412, 413, 414
Bressler, R., 17, 18
Brill, W. J., 332
Brimacombe, J. S., 255, 276
Brimacombe, R., 408, 411
Brock, T. D., 151
Brockerhoff, H., 22
Brockman, E. R., 77
Brodetsky, A. M., 393
Brody, S., 407, 411, 414, 418
Brokaw, C. J., 139
Brondz, B. D., 237
Brooks, J. L., 14, 15, 17
Broquist, H. P., 160
Brown, A., 109, 110, 120, 122
Brown, J. G., 281
Brown, W., 339
Brownstein, B. L., 418
Brubaker, R. R., 116, 117
Brummond, D., 255
Brundish, D. E., 34, 255, 278
Brustad, T., 154, 157
Bryant, M. P., 28, 29, 39
Bubenik, J., 244, 246, 249
Buchan, A., 292, 294
Buchanan, J. M., 196, 215, 412
Buchanan-Davidson, D. J., 356
Buckler, C. E., 293, 298, 299, 300, 302, 304, 306, 308, 309, 310, 311, 312
Bukovac, M. J., 339, 340
Bungay, H. R., III, 320
Burchard, R. P., 93
Burdon, R. H., 301
Burger, M. M., 36, 275, 278

Burke, D. C., 292, 294, 297, 299, 304
Burnet, F. M., 108, 234
Burton, A., 258
Burton, K. A., 151
Burton, R. M., 36, 278
Busch, A. W., 322, 323, 324
Bushnell, W. R., 355
Buswell, A. M., 332
Butel, J. S., 201, 202, 203
Butterfield, C. T., 324
Button, D., 276
Buzzell, J. C., Jr., 332
Byrde, R. J. W., 350
Bystrom, B. G., 339

C

Cabib, E., 278
Cachon, J., 132
Cachon-Enjumet, M., 132
Cahen, S. F., 5
Cahoon, M., 391
Cairns, J., 112, 211, 213
Cai Rui-Chu, 390
Campbell, A., 409
Campbell, L. L., 177, 180
Canfield, R. E., 172, 173
Cantell, K., 297, 305
Canti, R. G., 108
Cappecchi, M. R., 413
Carminatti, H., 278
Carp, R. I., 198, 201, 208
Carson, G., 378
Carswell, E. A., 245, 246, 249
Carter, H. E., 34, 35, 36, 258, 278
Carter, W. A., 302, 303
Casey, M. J., 203, 204, 205, 208
Cashel, M., 178, 179
Caspar, D. L. D., 48, 194
Cassell, E. A., 332
Catanzaro, R., 296
Catlin, B. W., 371
Cattaneo, J., 277
Cavalieri, L. F., 380
Cavalli-Sforza, L., 416, 417, 418, 420
Ceferri, O., 378
Chagoya, V., 191, 207, 208, 213, 214
Chalk, K. J. I., 27
Chaloupecky, V., 181
Chaloupka, J., 171
Champe, S. P., 408, 409
Chang Wen-Lin, 390
Chanock, R. M., 203, 205, 208
Chany, C., 306

Charamella, L. J., 122
Charpak, M., 379
Chase, J. M., 81, 82, 84, 85
Chatterjee, A. N., 270
Cheissin, E. M., 137
Chenault, S., 301
Cheniae, G. M., 24, 35, 37
Chen Wai-Chu, 390
Cherniak, R., 259, 262
Cherry, J. H., 181
Chevalley, R., 409
Chevallier, M. R., 381
Chibnall, A. C., 339
Child, F. M., 138, 141
Cho, G. J., 113, 114, 115
Chroboczek, H., 181
Chung, A. E., 28
Chun-Hoon, H., 115, 117
Churchwood, J. G., 339
Chyle, P., 232
Clark, D. J., 322
Clark, W. A., 81, 83
Clarke, C. H., 154, 156, 157
Clarke, D. A., 245, 246, 249
Clavilier, L., 154, 405
Cleary, J. P., 5
Cleaver, J. E., 118
Clem, L., 307
Cleveland, L. R., 133, 134, 135, 141, 142, 144
Clifford, P., 249
Clifton, C. E., 1–12; 4, 5, 6, 7, 8, 9, 326, 329, 330, 331
Cline, J. C., 293, 311
Cocito, C., 296, 297
Cohen, A., 249
Cohen, G. N., 324
Cohen, L., 249
Cohen, S. S., 193
Cohn, J., 240, 242
Coker, L., 160, 161
Cole, J. S., 350
Cole, M., 350
Collier, L. H., 109
Colón, J. I., 114, 122
Colvin, J. R., 255
Condon, P., 342, 343, 344, 362
Consigli, R. A., 208
Constable, F. L., 109
Cook, F. D., 96, 97
Cook, W. H., 275
Coon, M. J., 32
Cooper, P. D., 49
Cooper, S., 410
Corbett, M. K., 59
Corden, M. E., 350
Cormack, D. V., 154, 157
Cornelius, A., 244, 249
Correll, D. L., 79, 95

Corrivaux, D., 160, 161
Costello, W. P., 156, 158
Costilow, R. N., 173, 174
Coto, C., 210
Couturier, M., 416, 417, 418, 420
Cowie, D. B., 200
Cox, B. S., 154, 155, 158
Cox, E. C., 415
Cox, R. A., 293, 306
Craft, C. C., 342, 347
Crafts, A. S., 340, 341, 342
Crawford, E. M., 201
Crawford, I. P., 386, 387, 407
Crawford, L., 198
Crawford, L. V., 201
Crick, F. H. C., 406, 408
Crocker, T. T., 113, 117, 118, 119, 120, 121
Cruickshank, I. A. M., 342, 343, 344, 346, 363
Csiszar, K., 390
Culbert, K., 320
Cullen, J., 18
Curtis, M. R., 249
Curtiss, R., III, 122
Cutler, R. G., 184

D

Daesch, G. E., 207
Dahl, B., 171, 175
Dales, S., 193, 206, 212, 213
d'Alesandro, P. A., 136
Daly, J. M., 355, 362
Daniel, W. A., 142
Daniels, E. W., 134, 142, 144
Dankert, M., 264, 265, 266, 267
Danneel, S., 143
D'Ari, L., 260
Dark, F. A., 175, 180
Darnell, J. E., 191, 213, 303
da Silva Pereira, A., 163
Davenport, J. B., 339
Davidoff, F., 20, 23, 31, 32
Davies, D. A. L., 226, 227, 256, 257
Davies, J., 415, 416
Davies, W. H., 35
Davis, B. D., 415, 416
Davis, D., 350, 352
Davis, R. H., 404
Davison, P. F., 380, 393
Dawes, E. A., 115
Dawson, G. W. P., 419
De Deken, R. H., 160, 161
De Deken-Grenson, M., 159, 161

Dedonder, R., 379
de Duve, C., 134
Deese, D. C., 351
Defendi, V., 200, 201, 202, 208, 234
de Haller, G., 137, 141
Deichman, G. J., 245
Deinhardt, F., 194, 306
Dekhuijzen, H. M., 348
Delaney, R., 15
Delaumeny, J. M., 30, 31, 34
Delius, H., 301
Del Valle, M. R., 172, 173
De Maeyer, E., 296, 307
De Maeyer, J., 307
Demain, A. L., 160, 180
Demerec, M., 417
DeMoss, J. A., 160
Den, H., 14
Denhardt, G. H., 409
Dennert, G., 411, 412
Denys, P., Jr., 301, 309, 312
DeOme, K. B., 244, 246, 249
Deppe, G., 411, 412
de Puytorac, P., 137, 143, 144
Derache, R., 307
Deringer, M. K., 248
de Robichon-Szulmajster, H., 159, 160, 161
Desaulles, P. A., 307
Desborough, S., 153, 154, 159
DeSimone, V., 195
Desmet, L., 416, 417, 418, 420
De Somer, P., 234, 296, 297, 301, 309, 312
DeTorres, R. A., 198, 208
DeVay, J. E., 354, 356
Dezsi, L., 360
Dickinson, S., 340
Diderholm, H., 201
Diener, T. O., 356
Dietrich, C. P., 273
Dietzler, D. N., 281
diMayorca, G., 200
Dimond, A. E., 350
Dineen, J. K., 236
Dingle, J. H., 204, 206, 207
Dippell, R. V., 132, 141
Dirksen, M. L., 196, 215, 412
Disbrey, C., 140, 141
Distler, J., 34, 35, 255, 278, 279
Dixon, C., 300
Dixon, M. K., 207
Doi, R., 172, 177, 179, 180, 181
Donaldson, L. A., 339

Dondero, N. C., 325
Donikian, M. A., 306
Donnellan, J. E., 180, 181, 183, 184
Dorfman, B., 156, 158
Doty, P., 380, 381
Doudney, C. O., 404
Douglas, H. C., 152, 157, 160, 161, 163, 164
Doupnik, N., 351
Douthit, H. A., 177, 183
Dover, A. S., 111, 112
Downie, A. W., 312
Downing, A. L., 322
Dragesco, J., 137
Draudt, H. N., 342, 343, 344, 348, 350, 362
Dressler, H. R., 115, 117
Dubbs, D. R., 192, 197, 198, 208, 211, 213, 214, 215, 301, 302
Dubnau, D., 184
du Buy, H. G., 309, 310
Dugas, D. J., 143
Duguid, J. P., 328
Dulbecco, R., 48, 194, 195, 196, 197, 198, 199, 202
Dunning, W. F., 249
Dure, L., 181
Dutta, G. P., 133
Dvorkin, B., 307
Dworkin, M., 75-106; 76, 78, 79, 81, 82, 84, 85, 86, 87, 88, 89, 90, 91, 92, 93, 94, 100, 101

E

Eagle, H., 115
Easterbrook, K. B., 213
Easton, J. M., 204
Eastwood, J. M., 113, 117, 118, 119, 120, 121
Eberhagen, D., 22, 23, 24
Ebina, T., 17
Eckenfelder, W. W., 321, 328
Eddy, B. E., 202, 230, 245
Edgar, R. S., 409
Edgington, L. V., 350
Edstrom, R. D., 36, 258, 260, 262, 264, 267, 268
Edstrom, R. E., 36
Edwards, J. R., 36
Eggers, H. J., 191
Eggertson, G., 411, 412, 414, 419
Ehret, C. F., 137, 141
Ehrhard, H.-B., 7
Elbein, A. D., 255, 260, 281, 282
Elder, A. L., 322
Elliott, A. M., 132, 142
Ellis, M. E., 38

Elovson, J., 20, 24
Elsden, S., 329
Emeis, C. C., 152, 153
Emrich, J., 406
Enders, J. F., 201, 292, 306
Engelbrecht, R. S., 325, 326, 328
Engelhardt, D. L., 412, 413
Ensign, J. C., 97
Ephrati-Elizur, E., 377, 387, 390
Ephrussi, B., 162, 163, 401
Ephrussi-Taylor, H., 371, 377, 378, 380, 383, 388
Epstein, R., 184
Epstein, R. H., 409
Erikson, R. L., 301
Erlandson, R. A., 109, 110, 111, 112
Erwin, J., 20, 21, 22, 23, 24, 34
Etémadi, A. H., 33
Ettl, H., 133, 140
Evans, A., 389
Evans, A. H., 371-400; 389
Evans, C. A., 232
Evans, J. E., 184
Evenchik, Z., 179

F

Falaschi, A., 183, 269
Falcoff, E., 306, 307
Falkow, S., 371
Fanshier, L., 244, 249
Fantes, K., 304, 308
Farkas, G. L., 347, 351, 356, 360, 362
Fauconnier, B., 306, 307
Faulkin, L. J., 246
Fauré-Fremiet, E., 138
Feeley, J., 181
Feigelson, M., 307
Feigelson, P., 307
Feldherr, C. M., 132
Feldman, L. A., 201, 202
Felkner, I. C., 379
Fenwick, M. L., 301
Fernandes, A., 339, 340
Fernandes, M. V., 237
Ferrari, R. A., 35
Fielding, A. H., 350
Figari, A., 343
Fildes, C., 109
Finck, G., 83, 84
Fink, G. R., 160
Finnerty, W. R., 32
Finter, N. B., 306, 309, 310, 311, 312
Fitz-James, P., 110
Fitz-James, P. C., 170, 171, 172, 175, 176, 180, 181

Fitzpatrick, M., 299, 306
Flaks, J. G., 193, 415
Flanagan, J. F., 206, 207
Fleming, H. P., 177
Flentje, N. T., 339, 340
Flood, A. E., 343
Fluegel, W., 89, 90
Fogel, S., 154, 155, 160
Földes, J., 391, 392
Folkes, J. P., 39
Follett, R. H., 323, 324
Force, E. E., 306
Forro, J. R., 170
Forsby, N., 232
Foster, E. M., 18, 29, 39
Foster, J. W., 32, 171, 172, 177
Fox, M. S., 374, 375, 376, 378, 382, 383, 390
Foy, C. L., 340, 341, 342
Fraenkel, D., 258, 259, 263, 264, 282, 283
Frame, J. D., 329
Franke, W., 339
Franklin, R., 301
Franklin, R. M., 292, 301
Fraser, C. E. O., 113, 122
Frearson, P. M., 197
Freed, B. A., 377, 378
Freedman, L., 351
Freese, E., 174, 178, 179
Freifelder, D., 380, 393
Fric, F., 359
Fried, M., 198
Friedman, R., 293
Friedman, R. M., 293, 298, 299, 300, 301, 302, 304, 305, 309, 312
Friis, J., 158
Fugimoto, Y., 322
Fujimoto, M., 109, 110, 111, 112
Fujinaga, K., 209
Fukada, T., 109
Fukasawa, T., 257, 258, 259
Fukushima, S., 109
Fulco, A. J., 20, 21
Futrelle, C., 8

G

Galanos, C., 257, 262, 263, 264
Galasso, G. J., 120
Gale, E. F., 39
Galis, A., 378, 379
Galzy, P., 160
Ganesan, A. T., 374, 382, 384, 396
Garber, E. D., 354
Garen, A., 408, 409, 411,

412, 413, 414
Garen, S., 411, 413, 414
Garitt, A. J., 276
Garnjobst, L., 94
Garrett, M. T., Jr., 320, 321
Gartner, T. K., 414, 416, 417, 418, 420
Gasic, G., 200
Gastambide-Odier, M., 30, 31, 32, 34
Gaudy, A. F., Jr., 319-36; 323, 324, 325, 326, 327, 328, 331
Gaudy, E. T., 319-36; 325, 326
Gaumann, E., 342, 344, 347
Gauntt, C., 303
Gaylord, W. H., 109, 110
Gebhardt, L. P., 4
Geiduschek, E. P., 381
Geisberger, G., 6
Gellerman, J., 23
Gerber, P., 201, 231
Gerdemann, J. W., 342, 345
Gerloff, R. K., 112
Gerrits, J. P., 329
Gershon, D., 195
Ghalambor, M. A., 257
Gholson, R. K., 32
Ghosh, H. P., 277, 280
Ghuysen, J. M., 276
Gialletti, L., 309
Gibbons, I. R., 138, 139, 140, 144
Gibbons, N. E., 35
Gibson, S. M., 87, 90, 93, 103
Giesbrecht, P., 132
Gifford, G. E., 293, 299, 301, 306
Gilbert, J. M., 273, 281
Gilbert, W., 415
Gilden, R. V., 198, 201, 208
Gilead, Z., 208
Giles, N. H., 154, 158, 160
Gill, J. W., 135
Gillespie, D. C., 96, 97
Gilpatrick, J., 308
Ginoza, W., 381
Ginsberg, H. S., 204, 206, 207, 208, 306
Ginsburg, V., 255, 279, 280, 281, 282, 283, 284
Ginzel, J., 350, 351
Girard, M., 303
Girard, R., 269
Girardi, A. J., 202, 205, 208, 245, 249
Glaser, L., 36, 255, 275, 276, 278, 282, 283
Glasgow, L., 304, 307

Glasky, A. V., 303
Gliddon, R., 141
Glynn, J. P., 246
Goebel, W. F., 255
Goel, K. C., 326
Gogolak, F. M., 112, 113, 114
Gold, E., 211
Goldberg, B. D., 202
Goldberg, I., 214
Goldfine, H., 18, 19, 20, 21, 24, 27, 28, 38
Goldin, A., 246
Goldman, D. S., 17, 34
Goldman, M., 173, 180
Goldman, P., 14, 15, 16, 17, 18
Goldner, H., 245, 249
Goldschmidt, E. P., 417, 418
Goldstein, J., 351
Gollakota, K. G., 373
Golub, O. J., 123
Gomatos, P. J., 59
Good, P., 34
Goodgal, L., 374
Goodgal, S. H., 382, 385, 386, 394
Goodman, R. N., 339
Goodsall, R. A., 39
Goodwin, B. C., 363
Goodwin, T. W., 35
Gordon, F. B., 117, 122, 123
Gordon, I., 301
Gorer, P. A., 242
Gorin, P. A. J., 32, 36
Gorini, L., 401-23; 414, 415, 416, 417, 418, 420
Gorman, J., 151, 160, 184
Gorman, L. R., 232
Gosh, S. N., 301
Gostling, J. V. T., 108
Gottlieb, D., 183
Gould, G. W., 179, 180
Gowers, D. S., 339
Grace, J. B., 90
Gräf, W., 79, 94, 95, 102
Grandchamp, S., 162, 163
Granger, G. A., 238
Grant, G. A., 234
Grassé, P. P., 137, 141
Grayston, T., 123
Green, D. E., 14
Green, D. G., 381
Green, D. M., 380, 392, 393, 394, 395
Green, H., 198, 201, 202, 203
Green, J. H., 174
Green, M., 189-222; 191, 193, 194, 200, 204, 205, 206, 207, 208, 209, 211, 213, 214

Green, M. H., 200
Green, R. G., 108
Greenberg, A. E., 329
Greenberg, E., 277, 280
Greenberg, R. A., 175
Greenblatt, C. I., 20, 22, 23, 24
Greene, E. L., 194
Greene, J. M., 94
Greenfield, R. E., 322
Greenspan, C. M., 393
Grelet, N., 171
Grell, K. G., 131, 132, 133, 135, 143
Grenson, M., 145, 160, 161
Gresser, I., 306, 309
Grieves, R. B., 321
Griffatin, G., 307
Griffiths, M., 94
Grijm-Vos, M., 415
Grijseels, A. J., 339
Grim, R. B., 351
Grimstone, A. V., 131-50; 131, 133, 134, 135, 137, 139, 141, 142, 144
Grisso, D. L., 112, 113, 114, 115, 116, 117
Grollman, A. P., 257
Gros, F., 362
Gross, P. R., 92, 181, 307
Grossberg, S. E., 301, 309
Grosso, E., 195
Grubbs, G. E., 245
Gudima, O. S., 109, 117
Guild, W. R., 381, 386
Gunsalus, I. C., 276, 329
Gussin, G. N., 413
Gutz, H., 153, 154, 156, 158
Guy, L. R., 8

H

Haas, F. L., 377
Habel, K., 197, 199, 200, 202, 228, 230, 234, 244, 304
Haddow, A., 225, 245, 249
Hadjipetrou, L. P., 329
Haefner, K., 157
Haff, R. F., 306
Hagen, P.-O., 38
Haig, D. A., 114
Haight, R. D., 160
Haines, T. H., 23
Hall, C. E., 181
Hall, D. M., 339
Hall, E. W., 35
Hall, M. O., 38
Hallum, J., 293, 294, 296, 304, 305
Halvorson, H. O., 169-88; 151, 160, 170, 171, 172,

173, 174, 175, 177, 178, 179, 180, 181, 182, 183, 184, 323, 373
Hamachige, S., 310
Hamada, C., 209, 210, 211
Hamburg, V. P., 248
Hamparian, V. V., 50
Hampton, R. E., 343, 360
Hamre, P., 123
Hanabusa, J., 109
Hanafusa, H., 231
Hanafusa, T., 214, 231
Hanawalt, P., 184
Hancock, J. G., 353
Hanna, L., 293
Hanson, R. S., 173, 176, 323
Harm, W., 392, 395
Harpaz, I., 308
Harrar, J. G., 337
Harris, G., 164
Harris, P., 21
Harris, P. E., 122
Harris, R. V., 21, 22, 23, 24, 34
Harrison, M. E., 323
Hartwell, L. H., 195, 196, 197, 202
Harvey, C. C., 339
Hashimoto, K., 418
Haskin, M. A., 267, 270, 271
Haslbrunner, E., 163
Hassid, W. Z., 255, 279, 280
Hastings, W. J., 179
Hatfield, W. D., 332
Haughton, G., 226, 227, 228, 237, 243
Hauschild, A. H. W., 378
Hausen, P., 195
Hawthorne, D. C., 151-68; 152, 153, 154, 155, 156, 157, 158, 159, 160, 161, 163, 164
Hayashi, J. A., 36
Hayatsu, H., 408, 411
Heath, E. C., 36, 257, 258, 260, 262, 264, 267, 268, 282
Heinen, W., 341
Heitefuss, R., 356
Held, A., 356
Helgerson, R., 328
Helinski, D. R., 407
Heller, E., 292, 294
Hellmann, H., 160
Hellstrom, I., 197, 199, 228, 237, 239, 243
Hellström, K. E., 232, 237, 239, 240, 242, 243, 245, 246, 247
Helmers, E. N., 329
Helmhold, R. J., 114
Henderson, J. R., 300

Henis, Y., 81, 99
Henle, G., 194, 306
Henle, W., 297, 306, 308
Henney, H. R., 181
Henning, U., 411, 412
Henshaw, E., 303
Henze, R. E., 342, 343, 347
Heplar, J. Q., 8
Herde, P., 208, 211, 214
Hermier, J., 177
Hermodsson, S., 300
Herndon, B. A., 338, 340, 343, 346
Herriott, R. M., 374, 375, 376, 377, 381, 386
Hertel, L., 411, 412
Herzenberg, L. A., 226, 227
Heslot, H., 157
Hestrin, S., 254, 255, 276, 277, 278
Hetling, L. J., 322, 330
Heukelekian, H., 323, 327, 329, 331
Hiatt, C. W., 204
Higa, A., 180, 181, 182, 184
Higashi, N., 109, 110, 111, 112, 113, 117, 120
Higuchi, T., 264, 265, 266
Hildebrand, D. C., 346
Hildebrand, J. G., 28
Hildebrandt, A. C., 347
Hilgert, I., 232
Hill, D. L., 40
Hill, P. B., 39
Hill, R., 420
Hill, R. F., 419
Hill, R. L., 15
Hilleman, M. R., 50, 114, 197, 205, 208, 245, 249, 296, 306, 309, 312
Hino, S., 159
Hirth, L., 71
Hitchcock, C., 21, 22
Hitchcock, G., 309, 312
Hitchcock, S., 296
Hitchins, A. D., 179, 180
Ho, M., 292, 293, 294, 295, 296, 301, 304, 305, 306, 309, 310
Hoffman, E. J., 140
Hoffmann-Berling, H., 301
Hofmann, K., 18, 24, 26, 27
Hofschneider, P. H., 301
Hoggan, M. D., 203, 208
Hogness, D. S., 279, 391
Hohl, H. R., 342, 344
Hokin, L. E., 37
Hokin, M. R., 37
Holden, M., 209
Holford, R. M., 118
Holland, J. J., 301, 415

Hollande, A., 132, 137
Holliday, R., 154, 159
Hollinshead, A. C., 231
Holloway, B. H., 380, 393
Holloway, P. W., 20, 24
Holm, G., 238
Holmes, P. K., 178
Holper, J. C., 303
Holt, J. G., 80
Holton, R. W., 34
Hoover, S. R., 329
Hopkins, J. M., 141, 143
Hopps, H. E., 109, 110, 111, 112, 293
Horecker, B. L., 253-90; 256, 257, 258, 259, 260, 261, 262, 263, 264, 265, 266, 282, 283
Horikoshi, K., 181
Horn, V., 405
Horne, R. W., 50, 51
Horning, M. G., 18, 29
Horsfall, F. L., 190
Hortsmann, D. M., 50
Horvath, M., 360
Hospodka, J., 321
Hotchkiss, R. D., 371, 375, 376, 378, 381, 382, 385, 386, 394
Hottinguer, H., 162
Houlahan, M. B., 404
Houser, H. G., 278
Housewright, R. D., 375, 376
Houtsmuller, U. M. T., 39
Hovasse, R., 143
How, M. J., 255, 276
Howarth, S., 404
Hoyer, B. H., 202
Hoyle, R. J., 22
Hrishi, N., 157
Hsu, R. Y., 14, 15, 18
Hsu, T. C., 302
Huang, A. S., 292
Huang, R. C., 363
Huck, R. A., 62
Huebner, R. J., 199, 201, 203, 204, 205, 208, 209, 231
Huffaker, R. C., 359
Hughes, W. F., 244, 249
Hulanicka, D., 21, 22, 23, 24, 34
Hulme, A. C., 350
Humphreys, T., 181
Hundin, W. D., 310
Hung Mang-Ming, 390
Hunter, G. D., 39
Hunter, J. R., 175
Hurst, A., 180
Hurst, D. D., 154, 155, 160
Hurst, E. W., 111
Hurwitz, J., 389

Husain, A., 353
Huston, C. K., 28
Hutner, S. H., 94
Hutson, J. C., 412
Hwang, Y. L., 153, 154, 156, 159
Hyatt, H., 303
Hyatt, M. T., 177, 178, 180
Hysell, P., 310

I

Ievleva, E. S., 227
Igarashi, R. T., 172, 180, 181
Iijima, T., 390
Ikawa, M., 31
Ikeda, Y., 152, 160, 301, 390, 417
Ikeola, Y., 181
Imaseki, H., 361
Imshenetsky, A., 86
Imshenetsky, A. A., 78, 79, 81, 96, 98
Inge-Vechtomov, S. G., 153, 157
Inoue, T., 175, 177, 180
Inouye, M., 406
Ionesco, H., 170, 175, 176, 177
Irie, R., 183
Isaacs, A., 292, 293, 294, 296, 297, 298, 299, 301, 304, 306, 308, 309, 310, 311, 312
Iseki, S., 268
Ishidsu, J., 417
Ito, T., 154, 155
Ito, Y., 232
Ivanovics, G., 390
Iwanaga, M., 109, 112, 118, 119, 120, 121

J

Jackson, M. J., 18
Jackson, R. W., 32
Jacob, F., 47, 154, 170, 176, 177, 362, 386, 405
Jaffee, I., 375
Jahn, E., 91, 94, 95, 100
Jahn, T. L., 95, 138
Jakob, H., 164
James, A. P., 154, 155, 157, 163
James, A. T., 18, 19, 20, 21, 22, 23, 24, 26, 28, 34, 35, 38
James, T. W., 320
Jamison, R. M., 198
Jangaard, P. M., 22
Jann, B., 255, 256
Jann, G. J., 180
Jann, K., 255
Jaouni, T., 408, 411

Jarvis, F. G., 31, 36
Jasewicz, L., 329
Jauréguiberry, G., 30
Jawetz, E., 293
Jaye, M., 177
Jenkin, A. M., 113
Jenkin, H. M., 111, 112, 113
Jennings, J., 89
Jensen, F., 201
Jensen, K. E., 293, 306
Jensen, R. A., 377
Jensen, S. L., 14
Jeris, J. S., 333
Johnson, M. J., 31, 36
Johnson, M. L., 309, 310
Johnson, P., 34, 35, 36, 278
Johnston, J. R., 152, 153
Johnstone, H. W., 341
Joklik, W. K., 112, 191, 212, 213, 214, 215, 301, 303
Jokura, K., 258, 259, 283
Jones, D. S., 408, 411, 416
Jones, E. E., 160
Jones, E. P., 209
Jones, J. D., 350
Jones, L. W., 6
Jonsson, N., 232, 245
Jordan, E., 258
Jordon, L. E., 198
Joyon, L., 137
Joys, T. M., 382
Juergens, W. E., 274
Jungwirth, C., 214, 215
Juniper, B. E., 339, 341
Jurand, A., 132, 134

K

Kaars-Sijpesteijn, A., 348
Kaerner, H. G., 301
Kahan, F. M., 393
Kaiser, A. D., 391
Kaji, A., 415
Kaji, H., 415
Kajima, M., 109, 110, 111, 112
Kakar, S. N., 154, 156, 157, 160
Kalckar, H. M., 257, 264, 277, 279, 281
Kallen, R. G., 393
Kallio, R. E., 14, 32
Kalslander, J., 348
Kalyansundaram, R., 347, 352
Kamiya, N., 138
Kamiya, T., 210, 211
Kaneda, T., 29
Kaneshiro, T., 27, 31, 38
Kanfer, J., 37, 38, 39

Kaplan, A. S., 191, 196, 209, 210, 211
Kaplan, S., 410, 411, 413, 414
Karasaki, S., 194
Karassevitch, Y., 160, 161
Karlson, P., 362
Karmen, A., 18, 29
Karnovsky, M. L., 278
Kataja, E., 414, 415, 416, 417, 418, 420
Kates, M., 13-44; 14, 18, 22, 24, 26, 28, 31, 34, 35, 36, 37, 39
Katz, I., 19, 28, 29, 39
Katz, M., 202
Katzenberger, I., 99
Kauffmann, F., 256, 257, 262
Kaufman, B., 34, 35, 255, 278, 279
Kausche, G. A., 99
Kawashima, N., 357
Kawata, T., 175, 177, 180
Kaye, A. M., 195
Ke, Y., 294
Kedar, N., 356
Keeney, M., 19, 28, 29, 39
Keir, H. M., 211
Keitt, G. W., 354
Kellenberger, E., 409
Keller, J. M., 264, 269, 284
Kellock, T. D., 19
Kelly, M. S., 387, 395
Kelly, R. B., 301
Kelman, A., 353
Kelner, A., 376
Kembo, H., 183
Kempe, C. H., 312
Kennedy, E. P., 36, 37, 38, 39, 40
Kennedy, J. R., 132
Kent, G. C., 337
Kent, J. L., 394
Kerjan, P., 182
Kern, H., 342, 344, 352
Kerr, A., 339, 340
Kerridge, D., 138
Kester, A. S., 32
Ketler, A., 50
Keynan, A., 177, 179, 180, 181, 182, 184
Keyworth, W. G., 352
Khera, K. S., 201
Khorana, H. G., 408, 411, 416
Kidson, C., 307
Kiesow, L. A., 114, 115, 117
Kilbourne, E. D., 293, 307
Kimball, R. F., 135
Kimes, R., 205

Kiraly, Z., 347, 351, 356
Kirkam, W. R., 312
Kirkham, D. S., 343
Kirschstein, R. L., 234
Kisban, K., 360
Kit, S., 192, 197, 198, 208, 211, 213, 214, 215, 301, 302
Kitahara, T., 201, 202, 203
Kivi, E. I., 157
Kjellen, L., 207
Klarman, W. L., 342, 345
Klein, E., 227, 228, 230, 233, 239, 243, 244, 245, 246, 247, 248, 249
Klein, G., 223-52; 197, 199, 226, 227, 228, 230, 233, 237, 239, 243, 244, 245, 247, 248, 249
Klein, H. P., 14, 20, 76, 83, 85, 86
Kleinschmidt, W. J., 293, 311
Klement, Z. L., 342, 345, 347
Klemperer, H. S., 296
Klenk, E., 22, 23, 24
Kletter, B., 81, 99
Kleupfel, D., 352
Klieneberger-Nobel, E., 90
Kline, D. M., 354
Klinkowski, M., 342
Kluchareva, T. E., 245
Klug, A., 48, 139
Kluss, B. C., 132
Knipprath, W., 22, 23, 24
Knivett, V. A., 18
Knox, E., 269
Knox, K. W., 269
Kobayashi, Y., 181, 182, 184
Kobuya, G., 17
Koch, M. A., 201, 202
Kodicek, E., 27
Koepfli, J. B., 31
Koerner, J. F., 196, 215
Kofler, L., 77
Kohiyama, M., 417
Kohler, K., 206
Kohno, M., 293
Kohno, S., 293
Koldovsky, P., 244, 246, 249
Komnick, H., 143
Komolrit, K., 325, 326
Kondo, M., 173
Konigsberg, W., 412
Konishi, K., 109
Kono, Y., 293, 294, 295, 296, 305, 306, 309, 310
Koof, H. P., 22, 23, 24
Kools, J. W., 174
Koprowski, H., 201, 237
Koprowski, M., 198

Korn, E. D., 20, 22, 23, 24, 31, 32
Kornberg, A., 36, 183, 269
Kornfeld, R., 283
Kornfeld, S., 283
Kornfield, J., 181, 183
Koskimies, O., 237
Kotelko, K., 269
Kowa, Y., 14, 17
Krähenbühl, C., 307
Krask, B., 177
Krauss, M. R., 371
Kreckova, P., 171
Krieg, N. R., 320
Krischstein, R. L., 309, 310, 311
Krishnan, P., 326, 331
Kröger, E., 256, 262
Krueger, A. P., 4
Krüger, L., 256, 262
Krupka, L. R., 351
Krzemieniewska, H., 77, 78, 82, 86, 90, 91
Krzemieniewska, K., 78
Krzemieniewski, S., 77, 78, 82, 86, 91
Krzywanski, L., 355
Kubo, T., 175
Kubota, V., 109
Kuć, J., 337-70; 338, 339, 340, 341, 342, 343, 344, 345, 346, 347, 348, 350, 351, 362
Kühlwein, H., 78, 79, 83, 88, 89, 95, 99, 102
Kuhn, N. J., 37
Kundig, F. D., 34, 35, 255, 278, 279
Kunnes, R. S., 37
Kurahashi, K., 258, 259, 269
Kurek, L. I., 405
Kuriki, Y., 259
Kushner, D. J., 18, 28, 31, 35, 36
Kusuirina, L. A., 81, 96, 98
Kusunose, E., 14, 17, 32
Kusunose, M., 14, 17, 32

L

LaBerge, M., 151, 183, 184
Lacks, S., 382, 383, 385, 388
Lacroute, F., 156, 159, 160, 161, 163
Lacy, S., Sr., 200, 205
Lahr, E. L., 417
Laidlow, P. P., 108
Lakshmanan, M., 355
Lambert, L., 418
Lampson, G. P., 296, 306, 309, 312

Landman, O. E., 383, 385
Landquist, J. K., 111
Lane, D., 381
Lane, W. T., 199, 204, 205, 208, 209
Lang, N. J., 140
Langridge, R., 180, 181, 182
Lanka, E., 413
Lanni, F., 60
Lanyi, J., 381
Larke, R., 309
Larson, V. M., 208, 245, 249
Lascelles, J., 38, 328
Laskowski, W., 152, 157, 159, 164
Latham, H., 303
Latour, N. E., 34
Latour, N. G., 278
Law, J. H., 27, 30, 31, 38
Law, L. W., 234
Lawrence, N. L., 174
Lawrence, W. C., 206
Leadbetter, E. R., 88, 94, 101
Leatherwood, J. M., 281
Leder, P., 408, 411
Lederberg, E. M., 416, 417, 418, 420
Lederberg, J., 7, 387, 416, 417, 418, 420
Lederberg, S., 418
Lee, B. K., 159
Lee, Y. C., 40
Leedale, G. F., 133, 137, 142
Lees, A. M., 20, 22, 23, 24
Lee-Whiting, B., 154, 155
Leidy, G., 375
Lein, J., 404
Lein, P. S., 404
Leitzmann, C., 171, 172
Lejneva, O. M., 227
Leloir, L. F., 277, 279
Lennarz, W. J., 14, 15, 17, 18, 19, 20, 21, 24, 25, 26, 28, 29, 30, 34, 35, 39, 269, 278
Leonard, C. G., 373, 375, 376
Lerman, L. S., 374, 379, 381
Leukel, R. W., 352
Leupold, U., 152, 153, 154, 155, 156, 158, 160
Lev, M., 89
Levin, E., 21, 34
Levine, A. J., 207
Levine, J., 371, 393
Levine, S., 298, 300
Levinson, H. S., 177, 178, 180, 181, 184
Levinthal, C., 181, 182, 184

Levinthal, J. D., 208
Levinthal, M., 160
Levintow, L., 191, 214
Levy, A. H., 297
Levy, H. B., 291-318; 292, 293, 294, 296, 297, 298, 299, 300, 301, 302, 303, 304, 310
Levy, R., 20
Lewandowski, L., 418
Lewin, R. A., 79, 95, 101, 140
Lewis, D., 154, 155
Lewis, M. R., 4
Lewis, S., 339
Lie, S., 375, 377
Lielausis, A., 409
Light, R. J., 14, 15, 17, 18, 19, 20, 21, 24, 25, 26
Lilly, F., 243
Lin, F. H., 163
Lin, H. S., 111, 122, 123
Lindegren, C. C., 151, 152, 153, 154, 156, 159, 160
Lindegren, G., 153, 154, 156, 159, 160, 161
Lindenmann, J., 292, 297, 299, 311
Linder, O. E. A., 233
Lingens, F., 160
Link, K. P., 341
Lipkin, D., 275
Litt, M., 380
Litwin, J., 109, 110
Liu, C., 310
Liu, O. C., 306
Liu, T.-Y., 27
Lochmann, E. R., 164
Lockart, R., 303
Lockart, R. Z., Jr., 298, 304
Lodish, H., 302
Loebeck, M. E., 76, 81, 83, 85, 86
Loebenstein, G., 308
Logan, W. A., 6
Loh, P. C., 213
Lohrmann, R., 408, 411
Long, W. G., 339
Loomis, W. E., 339
Loosli, C. G., 123
Loprieno, N., 156, 157
Lousteau, R. J., 34, 278
Lovrekovich, L., 342, 345, 347, 360
Lüderitz, O., 256, 257, 258, 259, 262, 263, 264, 268, 269, 284
Ludwig, R. A., 345
Luig, N. H., 419
Luke, H. H., 351
Lukezic, F. L., 354
Lukina, N. V., 109, 117
Lumsden, R. D., 349
Lundgren, D. G., 175, 176

Luria, S. E., 227, 264
Luzzati, M. M., 154
Lwoff, A., 45-74; 46, 47, 48, 50, 51, 107, 126
Lynen, F., 14, 15, 16, 17, 18, 26, 37
Lyr, H., 350, 351

M

Maas, W. K., 324
McArthur, C. S., 28
McAuslan, B. R., 196, 208, 211, 214, 215, 301
MacBride, W. D., 208
McCarthy, B. J., 101, 112, 200, 202, 415
McCarty, M., 274, 373
McCarty, P. L., 330, 331, 332, 333
McCloskey, J. A., 30
McCloskey, R. V., 309, 310, 311, 312
McCormick, N. G., 177, 178, 179
McCurdy, H. D., Jr., 77, 88, 89
McDonald, J. C., 81, 84, 85
McDougall, J. K., 419
McFall, E., 324
Macfarlane, M. G., 28, 34, 39
Machin, K. E., 141
McKenna, E. J., 14
McKerlie, M. L., 297
McKinley, T. W., 233
McKinney, R. E., 321, 329, 330, 332
Mackler, B., 163, 164
MacLennan, A. P., 257
Macleod, C. M., 371
MacLeod, C. M., 373
MacLeod, R., 50
McManus, M. A., 143
McMurray, R. E., 322
MacNutt, M. M., 157
Maconkin, M. A., 350, 351
Macpherson, I., 231
McVittie, A., 89, 90, 92, 140
McWhorter, T. R., 323, 327, 331
Madison, R. W., 4
Magee, W. E., 214
Maggio, R., 181
Magni, G. E., 156, 158
Mahadevan, A., 341, 351
Mahdy, M. S., 304
Mahler, B., 417
Mahler, H. R., 163, 164
Mahler, I., 387, 391
Mainx, F., 146
Majernik, O., 359
Majerus, P. W., 15, 16, 17, 18, 26

Mäkelä, P. H., 258, 264, 267, 268, 281, 284
Makino, T., 269
Malaney, G. W., 323
Malca, I., 359
Malek, I., 321
Malmgren, R. A., 233
Mandel, M., 101, 371, 393
Mandel, P., 119
Manganelli, R., 329
Manire, G. P., 111, 112, 120
Manney, T. R., 154, 158, 160
Manson, L. A., 226, 227
Manton, I., 133, 137, 140, 142, 143, 144
Maramorosch, K., 59
Marcovich, H., 156, 163
Marcus, A., 181
Margolin, P., 419
Margolith, P., 81, 96, 99
Marinetti, G. V., 34
Marino, R. J., 8
Marion, C. V., 323
Markham, R., 50, 275
Markovitz, A., 255, 279, 282, 284
Marmur, J., 86, 184, 371, 380, 381, 386, 387, 391, 393
Marquardt, H., 157
Marr, A. G., 27, 31, 38, 322
Marsh, J. B., 19, 20
Marshall, J. M., 132
Marshall, R., 415
Martin, D. B., 18, 29
Martin, H., 270, 273, 274
Martin, J. T., 339, 340, 341
Martin, R. G., 416
Mashiah, P., 109, 110, 118, 122
Mason, D. J., 76, 78, 80, 84, 91, 100
Massaro, E. J., 18
Masters, M., 184
Mathew, S., 77
Matney, T. S., 417, 418
Matsudaira, Y., 154, 155
Matsuhashi, M., 267, 270, 271, 273, 281
Matsuhashi, S., 281
Matsumura, S., 25, 26
Matsushiro, A., 172
Mattern, C. F. T., 142
Mattheis, D. K., 375, 376
Mattheis, M. J., 373, 375, 376
Mattoon, J. R., 160
Mayall, B. H., 177
Mayer, H., 277

Mayer, M. M., 242
Mayer, R. M., 36, 258, 262, 264, 267, 281, 284
Mayer, V., 300
Mayer-Pietschmann, K., 95
Mayor, H. D., 198
Mazliak, P., 339
Mead, J. F., 14, 18, 22, 23
Meadow, P. M., 270
Medawar, P. B., 226
Mecs, E., 293
Meeuse, B. J. D., 137
Megnet, R., 154, 156, 158, 159, 160
Megraw, R. E., 173
Melhus, I. E., 337
Melnick, J. L., 63, 198, 201, 202, 203, 208
Melo, A., 283
Melvin, P., 111
Mendelsohn, W., 4
Mendelson, V., 307
Menke, G. H., 338, 340
Mercer, C., 308
Mercer, E. I., 35
Merigan, T. C., 293, 294, 295, 297, 299, 300, 306, 309
Meselson, M., 416, 417
Mesrobeanu, J., 256
Mesrobeanu, L., 256
Messik, F., 92
Meyer, F., 19, 22, 24
Meyer, G., 342
Michel, G., 18, 33
Michel, M. R., 195, 197, 202
Middlekauf, J. E., 159
Miholits, E. M., 331
Milbury, W. F., 321
Milhaud, G., 171
Millar, R. L., 353
Miller, I. L., 383, 385
Miller, J. F. A. P., 234
Miller, O. L., 135
Millerd, A., 355
Millet, J., 170, 171, 173
Mills, G. T., 255, 284, 386
Mills, R., 308
Milyutin, V. N., 109, 117
Mims, C. A., 309, 310, 311
Minamikawa, T., 342, 344, 361
Ming, S. C., 239
Minoda, R., 109
Minowada, J., 195, 197
Mishizuka, Y., 234
Mishustin, E. N., 78, 86
Mitchell, H. K., 404
Mitsui, Y., 109, 110, 111, 112

Miura, M., 109
Miwatoni, T., 172
Miyake, T., 417
Mizobuchi, K., 417
Moat, A. G., 156
Möller, E., 237, 238, 242, 246
Möller, G., 226, 227, 238, 240, 242, 246
Molteni, P., 195
Monod, J., 320, 321, 324, 362, 386, 405
Monro, R. E., 171, 172
Monroy, A., 181
Montagnier, L., 198, 301
Moon, H. D., 237
Moore, D. E., 117, 118
Moore, R. W., 113
Moorehead, P. S., 201
Morgan, C., 209
Morgan, H. R., 114, 115
Morichi, T., 183
Morowitz, H. J., 180, 181, 182
Morrison, J. M., 292
Morrow, G., 5
Morse, P. M., 157
Mortimer, R. K., 151-68; 152, 153, 154, 155, 156, 157, 158, 159, 160, 163
Moscona, A., 237
Moser, H., 320
Mosevich, T. N., 137
Moulder, J. W., 107-30; 109, 110, 111, 112, 113, 114, 115, 116, 117, 118, 119, 120, 121, 122, 123, 126, 127
Mousset, M., 159
Moustacchi, E., 156, 159, 163
Mudd, S. G., 31
Mugard, H., 137
Mühlpfordt, H., 135, 136
Mukai, F. H., 419
Mulder, E. G., 319
Müller, I., 157
Müller, K. O., 342
Müller, M., 134
Munakata, M., 17
Munakata, T., 17
Munch-Petersen, A., 282
Munk, V., 209
Murphy, E. B., 292, 311
Murray, E. G. D., 76, 78, 101
Murray, R. G. E., 101
Murrell, W. G., 170, 171, 172, 175
Myers, W. F., 115, 117
Myrick, N., 323, 324

N

Nachmias, V. T., 143
Naef-Roth, S., 352
Nagai, H., 163

Nagai, J., 21
Nagai, S., 163
Nags, E. H., 178, 180, 181, 184
Naide, Y., 258, 264, 267, 268, 281, 284
Nakakuki, K., 234
Nakano, J. H., 6
Nakata, D., 172
Nakata, H. M., 171
Nasim, A., 156
Nath, V., 133
Nathanson, N., 309
Nathenson, S. G., 275
Nava, G., 378, 379
Naylor, J. M., 363, 364
Neal, A. L., 293
Nelson, N. M., 152
Nemes, M. M., 296, 306, 309, 312
Nesbitt, J. A., III, 269
Nester, E. W., 376, 385, 387, 394
Neufeld, E. F., 255, 279, 280, 283
Neufeld, E. H., 35
Neuhaus, F. C., 270, 272
Neumann, M. G., 100
Neusch, J., 342, 344
Newkirk, J. F., 180
Newmann, J., 387
Newsholme, E. A., 328
Newton, B. A., 111, 120, 138
Nichols, B. W., 21, 22, 26, 34, 35, 38
Niederpruem, D. J., 80, 86
Nielsen, B. I., 113, 117, 118, 120, 121
Nieman, C., 31
Nigrelli, R. F., 94
Nikaido, H., 257, 258, 260, 262, 264, 266, 267, 268, 281, 283, 284
Nikaido, K., 258, 262, 264, 266, 267
Nilhausen, K., 202
Nilson, E. H., 322
Nirenberg, M., 408, 411, 415
Nishimura, A., 109
Nishimura, S., 346, 408, 411
Nissen, P., 35
Nolte, E. M., 81
Nomura, Y., 109, 111
Nonoyama, M., 301
Norén, B., 77, 78, 81, 82, 83, 84, 85, 95, 96, 97, 98, 99
Norris, A. T., 18, 19, 20, 21, 24, 25, 26
Norris, J. R., 174
Notake, K., 109
Notani, G. W., 412

Novelli, G. D., 98, 175
Noveroske, R. L., 345
Novick, A., 320
Novosel, D. L., 111, 114, 122, 123
Noyes, W. F., 198
Nozima, T., 301, 302
Nugteren, D. H., 24
Nye, J. F., 38

O

Oates, K., 133, 140
O'Brien, E., 113
O'Brien, P. J., 283
O'Brien, R. T., 180
Ochoa, S., 301
O'Connor, D. J., 328
O'Connor, R., 177, 179
O'Conor, G. T., 204
Odaka, T., 206
Oeser, H., 152, 160
Oetker, H., 81, 84, 88, 98
Officer, J. E., 109, 110, 111, 120, 122
Ogata, S., 109
Ogur, M., 160, 161, 163
Ogur, S., 160, 161, 163
Ohno, S., 301, 302
Ohtaka, Y., 181
Ohtsuka, E., 408, 411
Oishi, M., 180, 182, 183, 184, 388
Okada, H., 160
Okada, Y., 406
Okazaki, R. O., 284
Okazaki, T., 284
Okita, S., 175
Okubo, S., 377, 380, 391, 392, 393, 394, 395
Okuda, R., 33
Old, D., 415
Old, L. J., 225, 227, 228, 243, 245, 246, 249
O'Leary, W. M., 18, 24, 25, 26, 27
Omura, H., 211
O'Neill, C., 308
O'Neill, G., 257
Onore, M., 34
Opara-Kubinska, Z., 380
Oppenoorth, W. F. F., 164
Ordal, E. J., 79, 86, 93, 94, 95, 319
Ordal, Z. J., 177
Orellana, R. G., 349, 350
Orford, H. E., 329
Orias, E., 414, 416, 417, 418, 420
Ørskov, F., 255
Ørskov, I., 255
Orth, G., 198
Osborn, M. J., 183, 256,

257, 258, 259, 260, 261, 262, 263, 264, 265, 266, 282, 283
Oshima, Y., 156, 160
Ossowski, L., 115
Osterbach, D. H. O., 281
O'Sullivan, A., 182, 183, 388
Ouchi, S., 160
Overath, P., 14, 15, 17
Owen, M. E., 157
Owens, R. E., 293
Oxford, A. E., 81, 96, 99
Oxman, M. M., 302
Ozeretskovskaya, O. L., 362

P

Padron, A., 306
Page, L. A., 107, 124
Pakula, R., 371, 378
Palameta, B., 35
Palecek, E., 393
Palm, J., 226, 227
Palmer, F. E., 319
Palmiter, D. H., 339
Panos, C., 8
Paoletti, C., 198, 201
Pardee, A. B., 184
Pareira, H. G., 231
Park, J. T., 270, 273
Park, S. W., 179
Parke, M., 133, 140
Parks, L. W., 157, 159, 160
Parry, J. M., 154
Parsons, J. A., 135
Pasternak, G., 227, 230
Pate, J. L., 79, 95
Patel, P. N., 338, 340
Paucker, K., 297, 305, 306
Paul, F. J., 204
Payne, F. E., 194, 213
Pazur, J. H., 280
Pearlman, M., 261
Pease, D. C., 139
Pecker, M., 34
Pelc, S. R., 113, 117, 118, 120, 121
Pelroy, G., 161
Pena, A., 307
Pene, J. J., 382, 384
Penman, S., 192, 213, 303
Pepinsky, J. B., 329
Pepper, R. E., 173
Péré, G., 152, 161, 164, 405
Perkins, H. R., 111
Perlmann, H., 237
Perlmann, P., 237, 238
Perrin, D. R., 342, 343, 346, 363
Perrin, J., 115

Perry, D., 378
Perry, J. J., 172
Person, C., 363
Pestka, S., 415
Peters, E. A., 234
Peters, J. M., 111
Peters, N., Jr., 156
Peterson, J. E., 81, 84, 85
Peterson, W., 208
Petralli, J. K., 309
Pett, D., 208, 211, 214
Pfeffer, C. R., 163
Phillips, M. M., 152, 153
Pickett, M. J., 6, 7
Piekarski, L. J., 214, 301, 302
Pierard, A., 17, 34, 160, 161
Pieringer, R. A., 37
Pierog, S., 404
Pigg, C. J., 160
Pina, M., 191, 200, 204, 205, 207, 208, 209, 213, 214
Pineau, E., 171
Pinoy, P. E., 86, 89
Piper, S. H., 339
Pipes, W. O., Jr., 321, 331
Pitelka, D. R., 131, 136, 138, 141
Pittman, D., 156, 163
Placak, O. R., 329
Plaut, W., 135, 136
Pochiari, F., 296
Podolyan, V. Ya., 109, 117
Pohland, F. G., 332
Poindexter, J., 102
Pokorny, B. A., 307
Polasa, H., 206
Polh, S., 27
Pollard, M., 109, 113, 117, 118, 119
Polli, E., 195
Pollikoff, R., 306
Polsinelli, M., 378
Pons, M., 301
Pontén, J., 201
Ponten, J. A., 201
Pope, J. H., 201, 208
Porges, N., 329
Porter, J. W., 14, 15, 18
Porterfield, J. S., 306
Postic, B., 295, 310
Powell, J. F., 175, 179
Powelson, D., 76, 78, 80, 84, 91, 100
Powelson, D. M., 80, 90, 100
Prakasam, T. B. S., 325
Prehn, R. T., 225, 228, 229, 233, 243, 244
Preiss, B., 32
Preiss, J., 277, 278, 280,

282
Prescott, D. M., 132, 135
Preston, R. E., 194
Pricer, W. E., Jr., 36
Pringle, R. B., 351, 352
Pringsheim, E. G., 137
Prinzie, A., 301, 309, 312
Pritchard, R. H., 382, 384, 386, 387, 395
Pugh, E. L., 15
Pugh, E. S., 15
Pugh, W. E., 203
Purdy, W. C., 324
Pyne, C. K., 136

Q

Quackenbush, F. W., 342, 343, 347
Quan, A. L., 117, 122, 123
Quehl, A., 88
Quinn, G., 192, 194, 195, 196, 197

R

Rabson, A. S., 204, 234
Rada, B., 297, 300, 304
Raffel, S., 8
Ragetli, H., 308
Rahe, J., 341
Raistrick, H., 256
Ramanathan, M., 321, 322
Rampton, V. W., 140
Ramsey, S., 91
Rancourt, M. W., 163
Randall, Sir John, 140, 141, 143
Ranganathan, B., 163
Rao, B. S., 327, 328, 331
Rao, C. V. R., 326
Rao, S. S., 322, 330
Raodin, R. G., 201
Raper, K. B., 99
Rapin, A. M. C., 257, 264, 277
Rapp, F., 198, 201, 202, 203, 208
Rapp, R., 201
Ratledge, C., 14, 17
Raut, C., 163
Ravin, A. W., 371, 373, 388
Raynaud, M., 256
Rayns, D. G., 133, 140
Reale-Scafati, A., 416
Rebeyrotte, N., 386
Rebiere, J. P., 198, 201
Recondo, E., 277
Reed, S. E., 109, 110, 111, 112
Reeder, R., 181

Reeves, R. E., 34, 278
Reich, E., 292
Reich, R. R., 206
Reichenbach, H., 79, 88, 95
Reid, P. J., 417
Reilly, B., 171, 175
Reilly, B. E., 371-400; 373, 392, 393, 394, 395
Reilly, C., 162, 163
Reinicke, V., 307
Reissig, J. L., 404
Rennier, R., 339
Revel, M., 303
Ribbons, D. W., 115
Rich, M., 227
Rich, S., 339
Richards, C. M., 177
Riemann, H., 177, 179
Riker, A. J., 347
Rilling, H. C., 94
Rimparr, R. H., 342, 344
Rinaldi, A. M., 181
Ris, H., 136
Risse, H. J., 257, 262, 263, 264
Ritter, D. B., 112
Ritz, E., 371
Roane, P., 211
Robbins, P. W., 256, 264, 265, 266, 267, 269, 283, 284
Roberts, C., 151, 152
Roberts, E. A., 339
Roberts, M. F., 341
Robinow, C. F., 170, 177
Robison, M., 386
Rode, L. J., 177
Rodriquez, J., 194
Roe, A. S., 371
Roelofsen, P. A., 339
Roger, M., 381
Rogers, H. J., 276
Rogolsky, M., 177
Röhlich, P., 134
Roizman, B., 211, 292
Rollins, E. L., 281
Roman, H., 152, 153, 154, 155, 159, 160, 162
Romanko, R. R., 351
Romig, W. R., 377, 382, 384, 391, 392, 393, 395
Roosa, R. A., 234
Rose, H. M., 209
Rose, J. A., 206
Roseman, S., 34, 35, 255, 278, 279
Rosen, B., 408
Rosen, S. M., 256, 257, 258, 260, 261, 262, 263, 264, 282, 283
Rosenau, W., 237
Rosenbaum, J. L., 140
Rosenberg, A., 34
Rosenberg, B. H., 380

Roshanmanesh, A., 156, 160, 161
Ross, A., 308
Ross, A. F., 308, 340, 350, 351
Ross, J., 208, 211, 214
Ross, M. R., 112, 113, 114
Rossner, W., 79
Rotem, Z., 293, 304, 306
Roth, L. E., 132, 134, 141, 142, 143, 144
Rotheim, M. B., 388
Rothfield, L., 36, 256, 257, 258, 259, 260, 261, 262, 263, 264, 265, 266
Rousta, M., 211
Rowe, A. J., 138
Rowe, W. P., 199, 201, 202, 203, 204, 205, 208, 209
Rownd, R., 381
Roze, V., 274
Rubin, B. A., 203, 340, 356, 362
Rubin, H., 231, 244, 249
Ruchhoft, C. C., 329
Rucker, R. R., 94
Rudolph, K., 356, 357
Rudzinska, M. A., 134, 136, 137, 143
Rupert, C. S., 392, 395
Rusch, H. P., 183
Ruschmann, E., 257, 262, 263, 264
Ruschmann, G. K., 195, 197, 202
Russell, W. C., 211
Ruthmann, A., 132, 133, 143
Ryhage, R., 27
Rytel, M., 293
Ryter, A., 172, 175, 176, 177

S

Sabin, A. B., 201, 202
Sachs, L., 195
Sadasivan, T. S., 352, 353
Sadler, W., 89, 91, 92
Sadoff, H. L., 174, 175
Sagan, L., 136
Sager, R., 136, 145, 146
St. John, R., 163
St. Lawrence, P., 403, 407
St. Vincent, L., 312
Saito, H., 152, 390
Saito, K., 28
Sakai, R., 344, 355
Sakai, T., 268
Saksela, E., 201
Salle, A. J., 180
Saltmarsh-Andrew, M.,

264, 265, 266
Salton, M. R. J., 111, 112, 256
Salzman, N. P., 212, 213, 214, 302
Samborski, D. J., 355, 362
Samijima, T., 111
Sanawal, B. D., 352
Sanders, K., 301
Sanderson, A. R., 274
Sands, S. M., 152, 153
Sandstedt, K., 362
Sarabhai, A. S., 410
Sarachek, A., 163
Sastry, P. S., 31, 37, 39
Satir, B., 140
Sauer, F., 15
Sauer, G., 209
Sauerbier, W., 183
Sawyer, C. M., 332
Sawyer, C. N., 320, 321, 329, 332
Saxén, L., 231
Sayre, R. M., 355, 362
Sayter, H. S., 181
Schachter, J., 113, 122, 125
Schaeffer, P., 170, 171, 175, 176, 177, 371, 374
Schafer, M., 387
Scharff, M. D., 214
Schatz, G., 163
Schechter, E. M., 113, 117, 118, 119, 120, 121
Scheffer, R. P., 346, 351, 352
Schell, K., 204, 205, 208
Scherbaum, O. H., 137, 138
Scheuerbrandt, G., 18, 19, 20, 21, 24, 29, 30
Schieferstein, R. H., 339
Schlecht, S., 257, 262, 263, 264
Schlenk, H., 23
Schlesinger, M. J., 308
Schlosshardt, J., 257, 262, 263, 264
Schmidt, F., 257, 262, 263, 264
Schnathorst, W. C., 356
Schneider, A. M., 387, 390, 391
Schneider, L., 120, 134
Schonne, E., 296, 297, 301, 309, 312
Schrevel, J., 142
Schroder, T. V., 382, 384, 386
Schroepfer, G. J., Jr., 19
Schroth, M., 346
Schulman, H. M., 389
Schulte-Holthausen, H., 257, 262, 263, 264

Schultz, E. W., 4
Schultze, K. L., 322
Schuster, F., 141
Schwaier, R., 156, 157
Schwartz, D. P., 19
Schwartz, J. H., 416
Schwartz, N., 419
Schwarz, V., 274
Scott, F. M., 339
Scott, K. J., 355, 358, 361
Seaman, E., 371
Seaman, G. R., 140
Sebring, E. D., 212, 213, 214, 302
Sela, I., 308
Sellers, M., 391
Sellers, R. F., 299, 306
Sels, A., 152, 161, 164, 405
Senez, J. C., 328, 329, 331
Senior, N., 111
Seno, T., 159
Servizi, J. A., 329, 330, 331
Seshachar, B. S., 132
Setlow, R. B., 183
Sharon, N., 117, 118, 119, 277, 278
Sharp, E. L., 359
Shatkin, A. A., 112
Shatkin, A. J., 212, 213, 214, 292, 302
Shaw, D. R. D., 282
Shaw, M., 355, 361, 362, 363, 364
Shaw, N., 34, 255, 278
Shein, H. M., 201
Sheinin, R., 192, 194, 195, 196, 197, 198
Shen, L., 277, 278, 280
Shen Shan-Chiung, 390
Sherman, F., 154, 159, 160, 162, 163, 164
Sherr, S. I., 38
Shibuya, I., 35
Shiff, E. E., 177
Shigenaka, Y., 141, 142, 143
Shindala, A., 320
Shinmyo, A., 156
Shope, R. E., 231, 293
Shult, E. E., 153, 154, 156, 159
Shuster, C. W., 329
Sibley, W. A., 309
Sicard, A. M., 388
Siddiqi, O., 408, 409, 419
Siddiqui, W. A., 136, 137
Siegal, S. M., 339
Siegel, A., 341
Siegel, B. V., 8, 329, 330
Siegenthaler, P.-A., 177
Sierra, G., 180
Sigal, I. H., 277

Sigal, N. J., 277
Sigel, M., 307
Signer, E. R., 411, 412
Silk, J. A., 111
Silvester, N. R., 138, 140, 141
Simkovic, D., 232
Simmons, R. J., 173, 174
Simon, L., 303
Simon, M., 393
Simpson, W. L., 163
Singer, S. H., 310
Singh, B. N., 77, 78, 81, 96, 98
Sinsheimer, R. L., 301
Sire, J., 159
Sirotnak, F. M., 380
Sisler, H. D., 59
Sistrom, W. R., 94
Sitte, P., 339
Sizer, I. W., 363
Sjögren, H. O., 197, 199, 225, 228, 229, 230, 232, 243, 244, 245, 248
Skalka, A., 389
Skerman, V. B. D., 76
Skoss, J. D., 341
Slade, H. D., 378
Sleigh, M. A., 138
Slepecky, R. A., 171, 177
Slettenmark, B., 227, 243
Slonimski, P. P., 152, 154, 159, 161, 162, 163, 164, 405
Sly, W., 159
Smadel, J. E., 293
Smart, K. M., 307
Smith, E. E. B., 255, 284, 386
Smith, I., 184
Smith, K. C., 183
Smith, K. O., 205
Smith, L., 328
Smith, N. R., 76, 78, 101
Smith, S., 146
Smith-Keary, P. F., 419
Snellbaker, L. F., 296, 297, 301
Socolofsky, M. D., 100
Söll, D., 408, 411
Solnetzewa, L. I., 81, 83, 86, 98
Solymosy, F., 347, 360, 362
Somlo, M., 152, 161, 164, 405
Sonnabend, J. A., 297, 298, 301
Sonneborn, T. M., 145, 146, 240
Sora, S., 156
Soriano, S., 101
Sorsoli, W. A., 159
Southwick, M. D., 339
Speece, R. E., 326

Spence, K. D., 159, 160
Spencer, E. Y., 345
Spencer, H. T., 375, 376
Spencer, J. F. T., 31, 32, 36
Speyer, J. F., 408
Spizizen, J., 371-400; 171, 175, 176, 373, 374, 375, 377, 381, 389, 392, 394, 395, 396
Spotts, C. R., 171, 172, 415
Sproston, T., 341
Spudich, J., 183
Spurr, H. W., 347
Spyrides, G. J., 279
Srb, A. M., 156, 159
Sreenivasaya, M., 77
Srinivasan, P. R., 387
Srinivasan, V. R., 171, 173, 323
Stacey, G. J., 111
Stacey, M., 255, 276
Stadler, J., 407
Stadtman, T. C., 332
Stahmann, M. A., 351, 355, 356, 357, 358
Stakman, E. C., 337
Stanacev, N. Z., 31
Stancek, D., 300
Stanier, R. Y., 46, 76, 82, 83, 86, 90, 91, 94, 100, 124, 127, 415
Staples, R. C., 356, 357
Starr, M. P., 76, 98
Starr, T. J., 86, 109, 113, 118, 119
Staub, A. M., 256, 257, 259, 262, 264, 266, 268, 269, 284
Steed, P., 101
Steinberg, C. M., 409
Steinberg, W., 169-88; 179, 180, 181, 182, 183, 184
Steinert, M., 136
Stenkvist, B., 201
Stent, G. S., 420
Stern, D., 374, 375
Stevens, A. R., 132
Stevens, C. L., 281
Stevenson, D., 301
Stewart, B. J., 175
Stewart, R. C., 306
Stierlin, H., 256, 257, 262
Still, J. L., 26, 27, 31
Stinebaugh, S. E., 198
Stinebring, W. R., 292, 293, 294, 295, 296, 298, 299, 300, 304, 305, 309, 310
Stjernswärd, J., 233, 245, 249
Stocker, B. A. D., 258, 262, 264, 266, 268, 284, 385
Stockert, E., 227, 246
Stodolsky, M., 380, 391, 392,

393, 394, 395
Stoffel, W., 20
Stoker, M., 198
Stoker, M. G. P., 48
Stollar, V., 195
Stolp, H., 98
Stone, G. E., 135
Stone, J. D., 114
Storck, R., 181
Stouthamer, A. H., 329, 330
Strange, R. E., 175, 179, 180
Strauss, B., 380, 391, 392, 393, 394, 395, 419
Strauss, B. S., 404
Strauss, N., 380, 387, 393, 394
Streisinger, G., 406
Streissle, G., 59
Stretton, A. O. W., 410, 411, 412, 413, 414
Strobel, G. A., 359
Strominger, J. L., 262, 263, 267, 270, 271, 272, 273, 274, 275, 276, 281, 282, 284, 377
Struve, W. G., 270, 272
Stück, B., 248
Stumpf, P. K., 14, 15, 17, 21
Sturtevant, A. H., 401
Stuy, J. H., 180, 183, 374, 375, 382, 385
Subbaiah, T. V., 258, 262, 266, 284
Subrahmanyan, T., 309, 311
Subramanian, D., 353
Sueoka, N., 180, 182, 183, 184, 372, 388
Summers, D., 192
Sundararajan, T. A., 257, 264
Surdin, Y., 159, 160, 161
Suskind, S. R., 405, 419
Susman, M., 409
Sussman, A. S., 170
Sussman, M., 183
Sutherland, I. W., 258, 262, 263
Sutton, R. N. P., 306
Suzuki, A., 109
Suzuki, H., 386
Svet-Moldavsky, G. J., 248
Svihla, G., 136, 137
Svoboda, J., 232
Swain, T., 351
Swamy, R. N., 355
Swanson, W. H., 8
Sweet, B. H., 197
Sweet, D. V., 339
Szilagyi, J. F., 38
Szilard, L., 320
Szolyvay, K., 411

Szulmajster, J., 170, 171, 172, 173, 175, 176, 182
Szybalski, W., 380, 382

T

Taguchi, F., 201, 208
Tajima, M., 109, 111
Takabe, T., 183
Takagi, A., 175, 177, 180
Takagi, J., 390
Takahashi, I., 176, 372, 387, 390
Takahashi, T., 152, 153, 154, 156, 160
Takakuma, M., 355
Takano, K., 293, 306
Takase, N., 355
Takeda, Y., 173
Takei, S., 361
Takemoto, K. K., 303
Takeshita, M., 36, 261
Talamo, B., 278
Talboys, P. W., 346
Tamaki, H., 153
Tamm, I., 59, 191
Tamura, A., 109, 111, 112, 113, 114, 118, 119, 120, 121
Tanami, Y., 109, 113, 118, 119
Tapley, W. W. C., 256
Tartar, V., 145, 146
Taruo, P., 151, 184
Tatum, E. L., 7, 292
Taylor, A., 269
Taylor, G., 205, 208
Taylor, J., 297, 301
Taylor, M. J., 390
Taylor, R. M., 300
Terasawa, H., 341
Terui, G., 160
Terzaghi, E., 406
Teulings, F. A. G., 329
Tevethia, S. S., 202
Thaxter, R., 75, 77, 90, 91, 99
Theriault, E. J., 322, 324
Thiery, J., 139
Thimann, K. V., 78
Thomas, C. A., 348, 349, 350
Thomas, C. A., Jr., 381
Thomas, D. C., 206, 207
Thomas, M., 201
Thomas, R., 371, 377, 416, 417, 418, 420
Thompson, C. C., 164
Thorne, C. B., 176, 390
Thorpe, D., 405
Thrower, L. B., 362
Tinelli, R., 264, 266
Ting, R. C., 234
Tipper, D. J., 272, 273, 274, 276, 377

Titoli, F., 309
Todaro, G. J., 198, 201, 202, 203, 204, 302, 311
Toivonen, S., 231
Tokoyasu, K., 137, 138
Tokunaga, T., 391
Tokuno, S., 419
Tolmach, L. J., 374, 379, 381
Tomasz, A., 378
Tomcsik, J., 174, 175
Tomiyama, K., 344, 346, 355
Tomlinson, H. D., 330
Topps, J. H., 341
Torlone, V., 309
Törö, I., 134
Tournier, P., 45-74; 48, 50, 51
Trager, W., 134, 136
Traube, E. S., 292, 293, 295, 310
Trautner, T. A., 391, 392
Treadwell, P. E., 180
Tremolieres, J., 307
Trentin, J. J., 205, 208
Tribby, I. I. E., 114, 117, 118, 120, 121, 122, 123
Trower, L. B., 355, 361
Trupin, J., 408, 411
Tsoi, A., 160
Tsuda, Y., 419
Tsugita, A., 406
Tucker, J. B., 143
Tukey, H. B., 339
Tulloch, A. P., 31, 32, 36
Tuppy, H., 163, 164
Turner, H. C., 199, 201, 208, 209, 231
Tyrell, D. A. J., 305, 306
Tytell, A. A., 296, 306, 309, 312

U

Uchida, T., 256, 264, 269, 284
Uchiyama, H., 180
Udvardy, J., 360
Uehara, K., 342, 345
Uetake, H., 269
Ugoleva, N. A., 112
Ullstrup, A. J., 342, 343, 347, 352
Umemura, Y., 356
Unwin, C. H., 345
Uritani, I., 340, 342, 344, 355, 356, 357, 360, 361, 362
Usui, M., 234

V

Vagelos, P. R., 14, 15, 16, 17, 18, 26, 29

Vahle, C., 78, 81, 88
Vainio, T., 231, 237
Valentine, R. C., 109, 416
van Deenen, L. L. M., 39
Vandeputte, M., 234
Van der Want, J., 308
van Gils, H. W., 328
Van Knippenberg, P. H., 415
van Niel, C. B., 46
van Ravenswaay, J. C., 415
Van Rossum, W., 305, 309
van Veen, W. L., 319
Vary, J. C., 169-88; 177, 178, 180
Vasquez, C., 194
Veldstra, H., 415
Vender, J., 116
Venema, G., 382, 384, 386
Vickerman, K., 135, 136
Vilcek, J., 297, 300, 304
Vinter, V., 171, 172, 175, 177, 180
Viswanth-Reddy, M., 353
Vivier, E., 132, 142, 143
Voelz, H., 78, 79, 90, 91, 92, 100
Vogel, H. J., 135
Vogt, M., 195, 196, 197, 198, 199, 202
Volcani, B. E., 22, 34, 35, 39
Volk, W. A., 281
Voll, M. J., 382, 385
von Borstel, R. C., 156
Von Praagh, T., 308
Vorbeck, M. L., 34

W

Waddington, C. H., 146
Wagner, R. P., 156, 157, 160, 404
Wagner, R. R., 291, 292, 294, 297, 299, 300, 301, 306
Wahren, B., 227, 244, 249
Wain, R. L., 341
Wake, R. G., 182, 183
Wakil, S. J., 14, 15, 17, 18, 20, 22, 24
Walczak, W., 378
Waldron, J. D., 339
Walker, J. C., 338, 340, 341, 350, 356, 364
Walker, P. D., 174, 180
Wallace, J., 340, 348, 350
Wallach, D., 226
Wallen, L. L., 32
Walter, H., 120
Warr, J. R., 140

Warren, J., 293, 306
Warth, A. D., 172, 175
Washington, D. R., 322, 330
Wassef, M., 31, 36
Wasson, G., 14, 15, 18
Watanabe, M., 417
Watanabe, T., 417
Waters, L., 181
Watson, B. F., 86
Watson, D. H., 211
Watson, J. D., 190
Watson, M. R., 138, 141
Watson, R. O., 112
Watts-Tobin, J., 406
Wax, R., 184
Weaver, J. M., 243
Webb, J. P. W., 19
Webb, S. J., 28
Weber, D. J., 356, 358
Weber, E. J., 34, 35, 36, 278
Webster, R. E., 413
Wegner, G. H., 18, 29, 39
Weibull, C., 95
Weidel, W., 257, 274
Weigert, M. G., 411, 412, 413
Weil, R., 195, 197, 202
Weinberg, E., 180, 181, 182, 184
Weiner, I. M., 258, 263, 264, 265, 266, 282, 283
Weintraub, M., 308
Weiser, R. S., 232, 238
Weismyer, H., 258
Weiss, D. W., 244, 246, 249
Weiss, E., 108, 109, 111, 114, 115, 116, 117, 120
Weiss, S. W., 214
Weissman, C., 301
Weissman, S. M., 206
Werner, B., 238
Werner, M. M., 157
Wesslen, T., 201
Westphal, O., 255, 256, 257, 258, 259, 262, 263, 264, 268, 269, 284
Westwood, M. A., 306, 309, 312
Wetter, C., 49
Wheat, R., 257, 262, 263, 264
Wheat, R. W., 281
Wheatland, A. B., 322
Wheeler, H., 351
Wheelock, E. F., 293, 309
Wheelock, F., 295
White, A., 307
White, J. R., 415
Whitfield, H. J., 416
Whitney, H. S., 363
Wiame, J. M., 159, 160, 161

Wiberg, J. S., 196, 215
Wickerham, L. J., 151
Wiener, A., 208
Wigzell, H., 226
Wilbur, J., 309
Wilcox, R. L., 330
Wilcox, W. C., 206
Wildner, G., 164
Wildy, P., 48, 50, 211
Wilhelm, R. C., 411, 413, 414
Wilkie, D., 154, 155, 159, 162, 163
Wilkinson, J. F., 328
Wilkinson, R. G., 258, 264, 268, 284
Will, S., 163, 164
Williams, A. H., 350
Williams, B. J., 354
Williams, E. B., 338, 339, 340, 341, 343, 345, 346, 348, 350, 351
Williams, M. G., 194
Williams, P. J. LeB., 38
Wilson, A. R., 340
Wilson, D. B., 237, 279
Wilson, F., 163
Wilson, I. S., 322, 323
Winder, F. G., 14, 17
Winderman, S., 160
Windisch, S., 152, 153, 160
Wingard, S. A., 337
Winge, O., 151, 152
Winget, C., 300
Winn, H. J., 243
Winocour, E., 195, 199, 200
Winogradsky, S., 95
Wise, E. M., Jr., 273
Witkin, E., 417
Wittwer, H., 339
Wittwer, S. W., 339, 340
Woese, C. R., 170, 178, 180, 181, 182
Wohlfarth-Bottermann, K. E., 143
Wolf, J., 174
Wolfe, R. S., 97, 319, 332
Wolff, E., 237
Wolin, E. A., 332
Wolin, M. J., 332
Wollman, E. L., 177
Wolman, S. R., 201
Wolpert, L., 143
Wolstenholme, D. R., 135
Wood, B. J. B., 21, 22, 26, 34, 35, 38
Wood, E., 282
Wood, J. M., 332
Wood, R. K. S., 350, 353
Woods, D. D., 6
Woods, N. A., 76, 94, 99
Woodward, V. W., 419
Wooltorton, S. C., 350

Work, E., 269
Wright, A., 264, 265, 266, 267, 269, 284
Wright, B. E., 183
Wyss, O., 100, 379

Y

Yabe, Y., 205, 208
Yagi, T., 35
Yamada, Y., 339, 340
Yamagami, H., 386
Yamamoto, S., 175
Yamamura, Y., 14, 17
Yamasaki, T., 154, 155
Yanagashima, N., 163
Yanagita, T., 183
Yang, S. P., 159
Yano, N., 183
Yanofsky, C., 403, 405, 407, 411, 414, 418
Yarwood, C., 308
Yasumori, H., 341
Yengoyan, L. S., 31
Yoneda, M., 173
Yoshida, A., 174
Yoshida, T., 153, 159
Yoshikawa, H., 180, 182, 183, 184, 372, 388
Yotsuyanagai, Y., 162
Young, F. E., 372, 373, 374, 375, 377, 381, 396
Young, I. E., 171, 172, 180
Young, M. R., 132
Young, R. D., 245
Youngner, J. S., 292, 293, 294, 295, 296, 298, 299, 300, 305, 309, 310
Youngner, S. S., 304, 305
Yourno, J. D., 419
Yu, L. M., 360
Yuan, C., 22
Yusa, A., 137

Z

Zahler, S. A., 89, 90, 92, 112
Zaitlin, M., 341
Zakay-Roness, Z., 114
Zakharov, I. A., 153
Zalkin, H., 27, 38
Zamenhof, S., 371, 387
Zeece, S., 93
Zelazna, I., 377
Zeleznick, L. D., 257, 258, 261, 262, 263, 264, 282, 283
Zevenhuizen, L. P. T. M., 277
Zilber, L. A., 227
Zill, L. P., 35
Zimm, B. H., 381
Zimmermann, F., 156, 157

Zimmermann, F. K., 156,
157
Zinder, M., 302

Zinder, N. D., 410, 412,
413, 416
Zscheile, F. P., 359

Zubay, G., 383, 384
Zucker, M., 363
Zwickey, R. E., 205, 208

SUBJECT INDEX

A

Absence of stable mRNA in
spores, 180
Acetyl-CoA carboxylase
in fatty acid biosynthesis,
14
N-Acetylglucosamine acid
incorporation of, 270
N-Acetylmuramic acid
incorporation of, 270
Acid sensitivity
viral classification criteria,
50
Acridine mutations
intragenic suppression,
406
Action
mechanisms of suppressor,
412
mode of suppression,
402
of penicillin, 273
Action of cycloserine on
glycopeptide, 274
Action of interferon, 296
Activated sludge
review and kinetics of,
320
Activity
enzyme in plant resistance,
355
Acyl carrier protein
in saturated fatty acid biosynthesis, 15
Addition of side chain sugars
teichoic acids, 275
Adenovirus, 204
enzyme induction, 207
helper virus, 203
macromolecular synthesis,
207
replication, 206
SV40 hybrid, 203
SV40 tumor antigen, 203
T antigen, 208
transformation, 208
Aerobic pathway
in unsaturated fatty acid
biosynthesis, 18

Age
sequential substrate removal, 325
Agents with action similar to
streptomycin, 415
L-Alanine-induced trigger
germination, 179
Allogeneic inhibition
tumor antigens, 237
Amber mutants
nature of, 409
Amber suppressors
nature of, 411
Anaerobic digestion
waste water, 332
Anaerobic pathway
in unsaturated fatty acid
biosynthesis, 24
Animal virus
classification, 191
DNA, biosynthetic modification
induced by, 189-222
neoplasia, 190
groups
diversity of, 190
Antibiotic activity
myxobacteria, 95
Antibiotic production
myxobacteria, 99
Antibodies
humoral, 242
Antigen
histocompatability, 226
localization, 226
mechanisms determining,
229
nature of tumor-specific
transplantation, 227
neoplastic cells, 223
O lipopolysaccharide, 256,
257
psittacosis group, 113
spore-specific, 174
SV40 tumor, 201
SV40 tumor in adenovirus,
203
T adenovirus, 208
transplantation in SV40 transformed cells, 202

tumor, 223-52
tumor viruses, 230
virus-free transformed cells,
199
virus-transformed cells,
198
Antigenicity
viral classification, 58
Antigenic loss
escape from immunological
surveillance, 247
Antigenic side chains
biosynthesis in E. coli,
267
biosynthesis in Salmonellae,
264
Antigenic strength
tumor, 224
Antigenic tumor cells
important host defense mechanisms, 233-43
Antiviral action mechanisms
interferon, 300
Antiviral effect of interferon
in
heterologous cells, 305
Antiviral state induction
interferon-exposed cells,
297
Assimilation
oxidative, 326
ATP production
growth rate, 329
Auxotrophic mutants
suppression, 414
Axostyles
in protozoa, 142

B

Back mutation
suppression, 401
Bacteria
developmental changes during the formation and
breaking of the dormant
state in, 169-88
relation of the psittacosis
group to, 107-30
sporogen, 171

Bacterial lipopolysaccharide
  biosynthesis
  characterization, 256
  control mechanisms, 269
  core portion biosynthesis,
    259
  core structure, 260
  Gram-negative, 256-69
  isolation, 256
  O antigen, 256, 257
  phospholipid role in core
    biosynthesis, 260
  structure, biochemistry of
    phage conversion,
    268
Bacterial outgrowth, 180
Bacterial polysaccharides
  biosynthesis of, 253-90
  capsular, 255
  cellulose, 254
  lipid A structure, 258
  of "rough" and "smooth"
    strains, 256
Bacterial spore mutants,
    176
Bacteriophage
  myxobacteria, 93
Basal bodies
  structure in protozoa, 140
Biochemical origin
  semirough strains, 268
Biochemical oxygen demand
    (BOD)
  definition, 326
  exertion of, 322
  waste water, 321
Biochemistry
  cilia, 139
  phage conversion of lipopoly-
    saccharide structure,
    268
Biologically active DNA
  characteristics, 379
Biological solids and oxygen
    uptake
  relation between in waste
    treatment, 327
Biological solids production
    and substrate concentra-
    tion
  relation between in waste
    treatment, 328
Biological solids and purifica-
    tion rate
  relation between in waste
    treatment, 328
Biology of the myxobacteria,
    75-106
Biosynthesis
  antigenic side chains in E.
    coli, 267
  antigenic side chains in
    Salmonellae, 264
  of bacterial polysaccharides,
    253-90
  of complex lipids, 34-40
  of fatty acids

cyclopropane acids, 26
  in microorganisms, 14
  methyl-branched acids,
    28
  multimethyl-branched
    acids, 30
  of glycolipids, 34-36
  of glycosides of hydroxy fatty
    acids, 36
  of glycosyl diglycerides,
    34
  of lipids in microorganisms,
    13-44
  of lypopolysaccharides,
    36
  control mechanisms in,
    269
  core, phospholipid role in,
    260
  core portion of, 259
  macromolecular
    of poxviruses, 213
  phosphatides, 36-40
  of phosphatidic acid, 36
  of phosphatidyl ethanolamine,
    37
  of phosphatidyl glycerol,
    39
  of phosphatidyl inositol,
    39
  of phosphatidyl serine, 37
  of plasmalogens, 39
  of polar fatty acids, 31-
    34
  n-hydroxy acids, 31
  mycolic acids, 32
  of polymers of glucosyl-
    glycerophosphate
    and galactosyl-glycerophos-
    phate, 275
  of polyribitolphosphate and
    polyglycerophosphate,
    275
  of polyunsaturated fatty
    acids, 22
  of saturated fatty acids
    acetyl-CoA carboxylase
    in, 14
  acyl carrier protein in,
    15
  in microorganisms, 14
  of unsaturated fatty acids,
    18-26
  aerobic pathway, 18
  anaerobic pathway, 24
Biosynthetic capacity
  development during out-
    growth, 181
Biosynthetic modifications
  induced by DNA animal vi-
    ruses, 189-222
Biosynthetic pathways
  plant resistance, 360
Breaking and formation of
    the dormant state in bac-
    teria
  developmental changes dur-

ing, 169-88

C

Capsid
  definition, 47
  subdivision of virus families,
    57
Capsomere
  definition, 47
Capsomeres
  subdivision of virus families,
    57
Capsular
  bacterial polysaccharide,
    255
Carcinogens
  chemical, 233
  tumor antigens, 229
Cell division
  mechanisms of psittacosis
    group, 110
Cells, heterologous
  antiviral effect of interferon
    in, 305
Cellular competence
  transformation, 372
Cellular DNA synthesis
  polyoma-induced, 195
Cellular localization
  antigens, 226
Cellulose
  bacterial, 254
Cell-virus interaction
  subdivision of virus families,
    58
Cell walls
  psittacosis group, 111
Centrioles
  protozoa, 144
Changes
  developmental during the
    formation and breaking
    of the dormant state in
    bacteria, 169-88
Changes in spore-forming
    machinery, 173
Characteristics
  biologically active DNA,
    379
  papovaviruses, 194
Characterization
  bacterial lipopolysaccharide,
    256
  yeast mutants, 158
Chemical carcinogens, 233
Chemical composition
  psittacosis group, 110
Chemical oxygen demand
    (COD)
  definition, 326
  test
    waste water, 326
Chemotaxis
  myxobacteria, 89
Chiasma
  yeast, 153

Chlamydiae
see Psittacosis group
Chromatid
yeast, 153
Chromatid bodies
protozoa, 136
Chromosome maps
yeast, 153
Chromosomes
protozoan, 132
Cilia
biochemistry of, 139
protozoa, 138
Ciliary corpuscles
in protozoa, 141
Ciliary movement
in protozoa, 140
Circulating interferon
control of viremia by,
309
formation and elimination,
310
protection of target organs
by, 309
Classification
animal viruses, 191
criteria in psittacosis group,
122
viral
criteria, 49
evolution of principles,
48-51
Lwoff-Horne-Tournier
system, 51-55
nomenclature, 62
nomina conservanda, 67-
71
RNA structure, 59
systematics, 62
of viruses, 45-74
antigenicity, 58
Competence
cellular, 372
"factor," evidence for,
378
genetic control of, 373
state of, 374
formation of, 375
Competent state
formation of
physiological state of culture, 375
wall changes accompanying,
377
Complex lipids
biosynthesis of, 34-40
Components
synthesis of spore-specific,
173
Conditions
interferon induction, 292
Constants for design and
operation
waste treatment, 327
Control
genetics of sporogenesis,
175

by host cell genome
interferon induction,
291
mechanisms
in lipopolysaccharide biosynthesis, 269
of viremia by circulating
interferon, 309
Conversion
gene
yeast, 154
Core portion
lipopolysaccharide biosynthesis, 259
Core structure
lipopolysaccharide, 260
Corpuscles, ciliary, 141
Critical heat "inactivation"
DNA, 381
Culture
physiological state, competence, 375
Cultures, pure
in experimental virology,
192
Curves
of growth in psittacosis
group, 109
Cuticle
in plant resistance, 339
in plants, definition of,
339
Cycle
developmental in psittacosis
group, 108
Cycles, life
in yeast, 151
Cyclopropane acids
in fatty acid biosynthesis,
26
Cytocidal infection
polyoma virus, 194
SV40, 197
Cytoplasmic microorganisms
protozoa, 134
Cytoplasmic organelles
containing DNA in protozoa,
135
problems connected with the
formation of, 144

D

DNA
biologically active
strandedness, 381
characteristics for biologically active, 379
"critical heat inactivation,"
381
cytoplasmic organelles containing, 135
host cell and interferon induction, 291
integration
transformation in, 382
metabolism

of psittacosis group,
117
receptor, evidence for,
378
replication
relationship to transcription during outgrowth,
183
synthesis
bacterial outgrowth in,
183
cellular, polyoma-induced,
195
transfection, 390
transforming, fate of, 383
DNA animal viruses
biosynthetic modifications
induced by, 189-222
Design and operation of waste
treatment
constants of, 327
Detoxication
plant resistance, 348
Development of biosynthetic
capacity
outgrowth, 181
Developmental cycle
psittacosis group, 108
Diameter
viral classification criteria,
50
Dictyosomes
see Golgi apparatus
Differential membrane permeability
in plant resistance, 339
Digestion
in protozoa, 133
Discontinuous relationship
waste water kinetics,
321
Disease resistance in plants
definition of, 337
Diseases in plants
definition of, 338
Diseases, viral
therapy and prophylaxis,
311
Diversity of animal virus
groups, 190
Dormant state, in bacteria
developmental changes during the formation and
breaking of, 169-88
Drug susceptibility
in psittacosis group, 122

E

Ecology
of myxobacteria, 77
Effect of host cell metabolism
psittacosis group, 120
Effect of steroid hormones
on interferon action, 307
on interferon production,
307

Effects of interferon on uninfected cells, 296
Ejectile organelles
in protozoa, 137
Ejectosomes
protozoa, 137
in protozoan Golgi apparatus, 133
Elimination and formation of circulating interferon, 310
Endogenous metabolism
psittacosis group, 115
Endosymbionts
in protozoa, 135
Energy metabolism
psittacosis group, 115
Enhancement, immunological, 246
Enrichment, yeast mutant, 155
Enzyme
activity
in plant resistance, 355
in experimental virology, 193
-gene relationships
in yeast, 160
induction
in adenoviruses, 207
in poxviruses, 214
polyoma-induced, 196
spore-specific, 174
subdivision of virus families, 58
synthesis
outgrowth, 182
Escape from nonimmunologisurveillance, 247
Ether sensitivity
viral classification criteria, 50
Etiology
of neoplasms
TSTA, 248
Evolution
of principles of viral classification, 48-51
viral, 54
Exertion of biochemical oxygen demand, 322
role of protozoa, 323
Experimental virology
see Virology
Explosive organelles
in protozoa, 137

F

Fate of transforming DNA, 382
Fatty acid biosynthesis
cyclopropane acids, 26
methyl-branched acids, 28
in microorganisms, 14
multimethyl-branched

acids, 30
of polyunsaturated, 22
of saturated, 14-18
of unsaturated, 18-26
aerobic pathway, 18
anaerobic pathway, 24
Feedback inhibition
sequential substrate removal, 325
Field resistance in plants
definition, 337
Flagella
protozoa, 138
Food vacuoles
protozoa, 133
Formation
of competent state, 375
of cross-linked structure
glycopeptide, 273
of cytoplasmic organelles
problems connected with, 144
and elimination of circulating interferon, 310
Fruiting body
myxobacteria, 87
Fruiting body formation
effects of nutritional milieu on myxobacteria, 88
Function
of membrane-bound lipid intermediates, 270
and structure in protozoa, 131-50
Future
of microbiology, 1-12

G

Galactosyl-glycerophosphate
biosynthesis of polymers, 275
Gene action
regulation, 161
yeast, 160
Gene conversion
yeast, 154
Gene-enzyme relationships
yeast, 160
General nature of initiator system, 179
Genetic control
of competence, 373
sporogenesis, 175
Genetic material
subdivision of virus families, 57
Genetics
of suppressor mutations, 411
yeast, 151-68
Genome
control of interferon induction by host cell, 291
mapping by transformation, 386

Genus
viral classification, 57
Germination
L-alanine-induced trigger, 179
initation of, 177
multiplicity of trigger mechanisms, 177
Poisson distribution, 178
Woese hypothesis, 178
Glucosyl-glycerophosphate
biosynthesis of polymers, 275
Glycolipids
biosynthesis of, 34-36
Glycopeptide, 270
formation of cross-linked structure and action of penicillin, 273
function of membrane-bound lipid intermediates, 270
incorporation of N-acetyl-muramic acid and N-acetylglucosamine, 270
linkage of teichoic acids to, 276
mechanism of action of cycloserine, 274
Glycosides of hydroxy fatty acids
biosynthesis of, 36
Glycosyl diglycerides
biosynthesis of, 34
Golgi apparatus
ejectosomes, 133
plasmic rodlets, 133
protozoa, 133
Gram-negative lipopolysaccharides, 256-69
Growth curves
psittacosis group, 109
Growth rate
waste water, 321
Growth requirements
psittacosis group, 109

H

Haptonema
in protozoa movement, 142
Helper virus
adenovirus, 203
Hemagglutinin
psittacosis group, 114
Herpes simplex virus
replication, 211
Herpesvirus, 209
replication of herpes simplex virus, 211
replication of pseudorabies, 209
Heterogeneous populations
of waste water, 319
Heterologous cells
antiviral effect of inter-

feron, 305
Heterozygotes
transformation, 385
Histocompatibility-2 antigen, 226
History of microbiology, 1-12
Hormones
steroid and interferon, 307
Host cell
physiological state in viral replication, 191
Host cell metabolism
effects of, 120
Host defense mechanisms
antigenic tumor cell rejection, 233-43
immunological surveillance, 234
Host penetration
by plant microorganisms, 338
Humoral antibodies
tumor cells, 242
Hybrid
adenovirus SV40, 203
Hybridization technique
in polyoma transformation, 199
n-Hydroxy acids
polar fatty acid biosynthesis, 31
Hypersensitivity in plants
definition of, 337
Hypothesis, Woese, 178

I

Immunity, in plants
definition of, 337
Immunological enhancement
tumor cells, 246
Immunological surveillance
escape from
antigenic loss, 247
enhancement, 246
"sneaking through," 245
tolerance, 244
failure of, 243
mechanism, 234
Incorporation
of N-acetylmuramic acid and N-acetylglucosamine, 270
KDO, 258
Indirect suppression, 404
Induced mutation
yeast, 156
Inducers
interferon, 293
Induction
antiviral state in interferon-exposed cells, 297
enzyme
adenoviruses, 207
poxviruses, 214

of interferon, 291
yeast, 155
Infection, multiplicity of
in experimental virology, 192
Infectious agents
resistance of plants to, 337-70
Informational suppression, 407
phenotypic, 414
role of ribosomal mutations in, 417
Inhibitor production
to plant microorganisms, 342
in plant resistance, 342
Inhibitors
in experimental virology, 193
plant disease
isocoumarin, 343
pisatin, 342
plant resistance
post-infectional, 344
wound mechanism in plants, 347
Initiation of germination, 177
Initiator system
general nature of, 179
Integration
one or two strands, 385
Interallelic recombination in yeast, 154
Interference in yeast, 153
Interferon, 291-318
different molecular species, 293
inducers, 293
induction of, 291
conditions needed for, 292
control by host cell genome, 291
phylogenetic occurrence of the system, 307
pretreatment with, 303
production
effect of steroid hormones on, 307
and steroid hormones, 307
transformation, 311
and viral oncogenesis, 311
and viremia, 308
Interferon action, 296
antiviral mechanisms, 300
effect of steroid hormones on, 307
nonheritable resistance
among viruses, 303
in uninfected cells, 296
Interferon, antiviral effect
in heterologous cells, 305

Interferon, antiviral state
induction in cells exposed to, 297
Interferon, circulating
control of viremia by, 309
formation and elimination, 310
protection of target organs by, 309
Intergenic suppression, 407
Intragenic suppression, 405
acridine mutations, 406
Intra-group relations
psittacosis group, 121
Isocoumarin
disease inhibitor in plants, 343
Isolation
bacterial lipopolysaccharide, 256
Isolation methods
myxobacteria, 76
Isotopes
experimental virology, 193

K

KDO (3-deoxyoctulosonate)
-heptosephosphate
backbone structure, 258
incorporation, 258
Kinetics of activated sludge, 320
Kinetics of substrate removal and growth in waste waters, 320
Kinetoplast
in protozoa, 135

L

Life cycle
myxobacteria, 87-92
yeast, 151
Linkage groups
by transformation, 386
Linkage of teichoic acids to glycopeptide and control of synthesis, 276
Lipid A
structure, 258
Lipid intermediates
function of membrane-bound, 270
Lipids
biosynthesis of complex, 34-40
biosynthesis in microorganisms, 13-44
psittacosis group, 113
Lipopolysaccharides
biosynthesis of, 36
of Gram-negative organisms, 256-69

see also Bacterial lipopolysaccharide
Localization of antigens,
226
Lwoff-Horne-Tournier System
(L. H. T. System)
critiques directed against,
59
variants, 61
viral classification, 51-55
Lysosomes
protozoa, 133
Lytic activity
myxobacteria, 96
Lytic enzyme
spore germination initiator,
179
Lytic factors
myxobacteria, 95

M

Macromolecular biosynthesis
poxviruses, 213
Macromolecular synthesis
adenoviruses, 207
Macromolecules
utilization by myxobacteria,
85
Macronucleus
protozoa, 132
Malonyl-coenzyme A pathway
for saturated fatty acids,
14
Mapping of genome
by transformation, 386
Maps
yeast chromosome, 153
Mastigonemes
in protozoan flagella, 140
Mechanism
of action of cycloserine
glycopeptide, 274
of antiviral action, 300
of cell division
psittacosis group, 110
of control in lipopolysaccharide biosynthesis,
269
determining antigens, 229
host defense in antigenic
tumor cell rejection,
233-43
immunological surveillance,
234
multiplicity of trigger,
177
of reproduction
psittacosis group, 108
of substrate removal and
growth
waste water, 324
of suppressor action, 412
of susceptibility in plants,
353
wound
in plant resistance, 347

Membrane-bound lipid intermediates
function of, 270
Membrane permeability
differential in plant resistance, 339
Metabolic control mechanisms
waste water, 324
Metabolic regulation
sporogenesis, 171
Metabolism
DNA
psittacosis group, 117
endogenous
psittacosis group, 115
energy
psittacosis group, 115
myxobacteria, 86
protein
psittacosis group, 120
RNA
psittacosis group, 119
shifts
plant resistance, 354
N-Methylation of phosphatidyl
ethanolamine, 38
Methyl-branched acids
fatty acid biosynthesis,
38
Microbial transfection, 371-
400
Microbial transformation,
371-400
Microbiology of waste water,
319-36
Microcyst
myxobacteria, 79
formation, 90
germination, 91
resistance of myxobacteria,
92
Microorganisms
fatty acid biosynthesis in,
14
lipid biosynthesis in, 13-
44
plant
host penetration by, 338
protozoan cytoplasmic,
134
Microtubules
protozoa, 138
"Mis-sense" suppression,
408
Mitochondria
in protozoa, 135
Mitotic segregation
yeast, 154
Mode of action
suppression, 402
Modifications
biosynthetic induced by DNA
animal viruses, 189-
222
Molecular size
biologically active DNA,
379

Molecular species
interferon, 293
Monad equation, 320
Morphogenesis
myxobacteria, 87-92
Morphogenetic mutants
myxobacteria, 92
Morphological mutants
yeast, 159
Morphological stages
sporogenesis, 175
Morphology
of myxobacteria, 78-80
Motility
of myxobacteria, 95
Movement, ciliary, 140
Muciferous bodies
in protozoa, 137
Multimethyl-branched acids
fatty acid biosynthesis,
30
Multiplicity of infection
experimental virology,
192
Multiplicity of trigger mechanisms
germination, 177
Mutant characterization
yeast, 158
Mutant enrichment
yeast, 155
Mutants
amber and ochre
nature of, 409
auxotrophic, 414
bacterial spore, 176
morphogenetic
myxobacteria, 92
morphological
yeast, 159
respiration-deficient
yeast, 162
yeast
petite strains, 162
segregational petites, 162
vegetative petites, 162
Mutation
induced
yeast, 156
spontaneous
yeast, 156
suppression, 401
yeast, 155
techniques, 155
Mutations
acridine-induced
intragenic suppression,
406
corrected by streptomycin,
416
of classical streptomycin
locus and streptomycin-
induced suppression re-
lations, 416
role of ribosomal in informational suppression, 417
suppressible

yeast, 157
suppressor
  genetics of, 411
  uncharacterized, 418
Mycolic acids
  polar fatty acid biosynthesis, 32
Myristic acids
  as product of saturated fatty acid synthesis, 17
Myxobacteria
  antibiotic activity, 95
  antibiotic production, 99
  bacteriophage, 93
  biology of, 75-106
  chemotaxis, 89
  definition, 76
  ecology, 77
  effect of mono- and disaccharides, 83
  effect of nutritional milieu on fruiting body formation, 88
  fruiting body, 87
  isolation methods, 76
  life cycle, 87-92
  lytic activity, 96
  lytic factor, 95
  metabolism, 86
  microcysts, 79
    formation, 90
    germination, 91
    resistance, 92
  morphogenesis, 87-92
  morphogenetic mutants, 92
  morphology, 78-80
  motility, 95
  nitrogen requirements, 81
  nutrition, 80-86
  pathogenicity, 94
  pigments, 94
  taxonomy, 99
  utilization of macromolecules, 85
  utilization of subcellular fractions, 86
  vegetative cells, 78
  vitamin requirements, 84

N

Nature
  of amber and ochre mutants, 409
  of amber and ochre suppressors, 411
  general, of the initiator system in germination, 179
  tumor-specific transplantation antigens, 227
"Nebenkörper," in protozoa, 135
Neoplasia
  animal viruses, 190

SV40, 197
Neoplasms
  etiology
    significance of TSTA, 248
  prevention
    significance of TSTA, 248
  therapy
    significance of TSTA, 248
Neoplastic cells
  antigens, 223
Nitrogen-deficient waste treatment, 326
Nitrogen requirements
  myxobacteria, 81
Nomenclature
  virus classification, 62
Nomina conservanda
  virus classification, 67-71
Nonheritable interferon resistance among viruses, 303
Nonimmunological surveillance
  escape from, 247
"Nonsense" suppression, 408
Nuclear envelope
  protozoa, 132
Nucleic acids
  change during sporogenesis, 172
  psittacosis group, 112
  viral classification criteria, 49, 53
Nucleocapsid
  definition of, 48
  viral classification criteria, 53
Nucleoli
  protozoa, 132
Nucleus
  protozoa, 132
Nutrition
  myxobacteria, 80-86
Nutritional milieu
  effects on fruiting body formation in myxobacteria, 88

O

O antigen
  biosynthesis of
    side chains in E. coli, 267
    side chains in Salmonellae, 264
    lipopolysaccharide, 256, 257
Occurrence
  tumor-specific antigen, 228
Occurrence of the interferon system
  phylogenetic, 307

Ochre mutants
  nature of, 409
Ochre suppressors
  nature of, 411
Oncogenesis
  viral and interferon, 311
Ordered protein and enzyme synthesis, 182
Organelles
  cytoplasmic
    containing DNA in protozoa, 135
  ejectile
    protozoa, 137
  explosive
    protozoa, 137
Organs, target
  protection by circulating interferon, 309
Outgrowth
  absence of stable mRNA in spores, 180
  bacterial, 180
  DNA synthesis, 183
  development of biosynthetic capacity, 181
  ordered protein and enzyme synthesis, 182
  relationship between transcription and DNA replication, 183
Oxidation
  products of partial, 326
Oxidative assimilation
  waste water, 326
Oxygen uptake and biological solids
  relation between in waste treatment, 327

P

Palmitic acid
  as product of saturated fatty acid synthesis, 17
Papovavirus
  adenovirus-SV40 hybrid, 203
  characteristics, 194
  polyoma virus
    and cytocidal infection, 194
    transformation, 198
  SV40 cytocidal infection, 197
  SV40 transformation, 200
  transformation of cells in vitro, 198
Parabasal bodies
  see Golgi apparatus
Pathogenicity
  myxobacteria, 94
Pathways
  biosynthetic
    plant resistance, 360
  of malonyl coenzyme A
    in saturated fatty acid bio-

synthesis, 14
Penetration
DNA
molecular size, 379
strandedness, 381
into host
by plant microorganisms, 338
Penicillin
action of, 273
Peplomers
subdivision of virus families, 57
Peplos
definition of, 48
subdivision of virus families, 58
Permeability
differential membrane
in plant resistance, 339
"Petites"
segregational
yeast mutants, 162
Petite strains
yeast mutants, 162
Phage
transfection, 391
Phage conversion
lipopolysaccharide structures
biochemistry of, 268
Phenotypic informational
suppression, 414
Phosphatides
biosynthesis of, 36-40
Phosphatidic acid
biosynthesis of, 36
Phosphatidyl ethanolamine
biosynthesis of, 37
N-methylation of, 38
Phosphatidyl glycerol and its
amino acid esters
biosynthesis of, 39
Phosphatidyl inositol and its
glycoside derivatives
biosynthesis of, 39
Phosphatidyl serine
biosynthesis of, 37
Phospholipid
role in lipopolysaccharide
core biosynthesis, 260
Phylogenetic occurrence of
the interferon system, 307
Physiological stages
sporogenesis, 175
Physiological state
host cell in viral replication, 191
of culture
competence, 375
Pigments
myxobacteria, 94
Pinocytosis
in protozoa, 134
Pisatin

disease inhibitor in plants, 342
Plant cuticle
definition of, 339
Plant disease inhibitor
isocoumarin, 343
pisatin, 342
Plant hypersensitivity
definition of, 337
Plant immunity
definition of, 337
Plant microorganisms
host penetration by, 338
Plant resistance
biosynthetic pathways, 360
cuticle, 339
definition of, 337
detoxication, 348
differential membrane permeability, 339
enzyme activity, 355
to infectious agents, 337-70
inhibitor production, 342
isocoumarin, 343
pisatin, 342
post-infectional inhibitors, 344
protein, 355
respiration, 355
stomata, 339
susceptibility, 352
symptoms of susceptibility, 353
wound mechanism, 347
Plant susceptibility
definition of, 352
Plasmalogens
biosynthesis of, 39
Plasmic rodlets
in Golgi apparatus, 133
Pleiotrophism
suppression, 417
Poisson distribution
spore germination, 178
Polar fatty acids
biosynthesis in microorganisms, 31-34
Pollution strength
waste water, 322
Polyglycerophosphate
biosynthesis of, 275
Polyoma-induced cellular
DNA synthesis, 195
Polyoma-induced enzymes, 196
Polyoma system
tumor antigens, 228
Polyoma transformation
hybridization technique, 199
Polyoma virus
-cytocidal infection, 194
-transformation, 198
Polyribitolphosphate
biosynthesis of, 295

Polysaccharides
bacterial biosynthesis, 253-90
see also Bacterial polysaccharides
Polyunsaturated fatty acids
biosynthesis in microorganisms, 22
Postgerminative development
see Outgrowth
Post-infectional inhibitors
in plant resistance, 344
Poxviruses, 211
enzyme induction, 214
macromolecular biosynthesis, 213
"uncoating," 212
viral replication, 212
Prevention
neoplasms
TSTA, 248
Problem of heterozygotes
transformation, 385
Procedures
tetrad and random spore
analysis, 152
Production of inhibitors
in plant resistance, 342
Production of interferon
pretreatment with, 303
Products of partial oxidation
waste water, 326
Prophylaxis and therapy of
virus diseases, 311
Protection of target organs
by circulating interferon, 309
Protein
plant resistance, 355
psittacosis group, 113
synthesis
ordered, 182
sporogenesis, 173
Protein metabolism
psittacosis group, 120
Protein-synthesizing system
bacterial outgrowth, 181
Protozoa
axostyles, 142
basal bodies, 140
centrioles, 144
chromatoid bodies, 136
chromosomes, 132
cilia, 137
ciliary corpuscles, 141
ciliary movement, 140
cytoplasmic microorganisms, 134
cytoplasmic organelles containing DNA, 135
digestion, 133
ejectile organelles, 137
ejectosomes, 133, 137
endosymbionts, 135
explosive organelles, 137
flagella, 138
food vacuoles, 133

Golgi apparatus, 133
haptonema, 142
kinetoplast, 135
lysosomes, 133
macronucleus, 132
mastigonemes, 140
microtubules, 138
mitochondria, 135
muciferous bodies, 137
"Nebenkörper," 135
nuclear envelope, 132
nucleoli, 132
nucleus, 132
pinocytosis, 134
plasmic rodlets, 133
ribosomes, 136
role in exertion of BOD,
    323
spindle fibers, 138
structure and function, 131-
    50
symbiosis, 134-35
trichocysts, 137
Pseudorabies
replication, 209
Pseudoviruses, 47
Psittacosis group
antigens, 113
cell walls, 111
classification criteria,
    122
developmental cycle, 108
DNA metabolism, 117
drug susceptibility, 122
effect of host cell metabo-
    lism, 120
endogenous metabolism,
    115
energy metabolism, 115
growth curves, 109
growth requirements, 114
hemagglutinin, 114
intra-group relations,
    121
lipids, 113
mechanism of cell division,
    110
metabolism, 114
nucleic acids, 112
protein, 113
    metabolism, 120
relation to bacteria, 123
    and viruses, 107-30
reproduction mechanism,
    108
RNA metabolism, 119
structure and chemical com-
    position, 110
taxonomic position, 121
vitamin requirement, 114
Pure cultures
experimental virology,
    192
Purification rate and biologi-
    cal solids
relation between in waste
    treatment, 328

R

Random spore analysis pro-
    cedure, 152
Recombination
interallelic
    yeast, 154
    yeast, 152
Regulation
metabolic, 171
yeast gene action, 161
Rejection
tumor
    failure of, 243
    important host defense
    mechanisms in, 233-
    43
Relation between biological
    solids
and oxygen uptake
    waste treatment, 327
and purification rate
    waste treatment, 328
Relation between biological
    solids production and
    substrate concentration
in waste treatment, 328
Relation of psittacosis group
    to bacteria and viruses,
    107-30
intragroup, 121
Relation between streptomycin-
    induced suppression,
    mutations of classical
    streptomycin locus,
    416
Relation between transcrip-
    tion and DNA replication
    during outgrowth, 183
Replication
adenoviruses, 206
herpes simplex virus, 211
poxviruses, 212
pseudorabies, 209
viral steps, 193
Reproduction mechanisms
psittacosis group, 108
Resistance
of microcyst
    myxobacteria, 92
nonheritable interferon
    among viruses, 303
plant
    definition of, 337
    detoxication, 348
    to infectious agents, 337-
    70
    inhibitor production,
    342
    metabolism shifts, 354
    susceptibility, 352
to plant diseases
    definition, 337
yeast mutants, 159
Respiration
in plant resistance, 355
Respiration-deficient mutants

yeast, 162
Ribosomal mutations
in informational suppression
    role of, 417
Ribosomal system
in spore outgrowth, 182
Ribosomes
in protozoan chromatoid
    bodies, 136
mRNA
absence of stable
    in spores, 180
suppressors possibly affect-
    ing, 407
RNA
metabolism
    psittacosis group, 119
structure
    virus classification, 59
    transformation, 389
Role
of phospholipid in biosynthe-
    sis of lipopolysaccharide
    core, 260
of protozoa in exertion of
    BOD, 323
of ribosomal mutations in
    informational suppres-
    sion, 417
"Rolling-tube filter" studies,
    322
"Rough" strain
polysaccharides, 256
semi-
    possible biochemical ori-
    gin, 268
Rous-Bryan system
tumor antigens, 231

S

Saccharides
effects of mono- and di- on
    myxobacteria, 83
Saturated fatty acids
biosynthesis
    acetyl-coA carboxylase in,
    14
    acyl carrier protein,
    15
    in microorganisms, 14
    myristic acids as a pro-
    duct of, 17
    stearic acids as a product
    of, 17
    products of synthesis, 17
    synthesis
    palmitic acid as a product
    of, 17
Schmidt-Ruppin-Rous system
tumor antigen, 232
Segregation
mitotic
    yeast, 154
Segregational petites
yeast mutants, 162
Sequential substrate removal

waste water, 324
  age, 325
  feedback inhibition, 325
  metabolic control mecha-
    nisms, 324
Shifts in metabolism
  plant resistance, 354
Shock loads
  waste water, 325
Shope papilloma-carcinoma
  system
  tumor antigen, 232
Size
  molecular of DNA, 379
Sludge
  activated, 320
"Smooth" strain
  polysaccharides, 256
"Sneaking through"
  tumor cells, 245
Soluble biological oxygen
  demand, 321
Species
  different molecular
    of interferon, 293
Specificity
  subdivision of virus families,
    58
Spindle fibers
  protozoa, 138
Spontaneous mutation
  yeast, 156
Spore
  absence of stable mRNA,
    180
  analysis
    yeast, 152
  bacterial mutants, 176
  -forming machinery
    changes in, 173
  -specific antigens, 174
  -specific components
    synthesis of, 173
  -specific enzymes, 174
Sporogen, 171
Sporogenesis
  bacterial, 170
  metabolic regulation, 171
  morphological and physiolog-
    ical stages, 175
  nucleic acid changes, 172
  protein synthesis, 173
  sporogen, 171
  transcriptional products,
    172
Stability of the family
  viral classification, 55
State of competence, 374
Steady-state systems
  waste water, 320
Stearic acids
  as products of saturated
    fatty acid synthesis,
    17
Steroid hormones and inter-
    feron, 307
Stomata

in plant resistance, 339
Strandedness
  biologically active DNA,
    381
Streptomycin
  -induced suppression and
    mutations of classical
    locus
    relation between, 416
  suppression induced by,
    415
  type of mutations corrected
    by, 416
Structural units
  subdivision of virus families,
    57
Structure
  and function in protozoa,
    131-50
  KDO-heptose phosphate
    backbone, 258
  of lipid A, 258
  lipopolysaccharide
    biochemistry of phage con-
    version, 268
    core, 262
    psittacosis group, 110
  of RNA
    virus classification, 59
Subcellular fractions
  utilization by myxobacteria,
    86
Subdivision of families
  viral classification, 57-
    58
Subdivision of virus families
  capsid, 57
  cell-virus interaction, 58
  enzymes, 58
  genetic material, 57
  peplomers, 57
  peplos, 58
  specificity, 58
  structural units and the
    capsomers, 57
  symptomatology, 58
  viral development, 58
  virulence, 58
Substrate
  concentration
    biological solids production
      in waste treatment, 328
    in waste water, 321
  removal and growth
    kinetics of, 320
    mechanisms of, 324
    sequential, 324
Sugars
  addition of side chain
    teichoic acids, 275
Suppressible mutations
  yeast, 157
Suppression, 401-22
  autotrophic mutants, 414
  definition of, 401
  indirect, 404
  induced by streptomycin and

other agents, 415
  informational, 407
    role of ribosomal muta-
      tions in, 417
  intragenic, 405, 407
    acridine mutations,
      406
  "mis-sense," 408
  mode of action, 402
  nature of amber and ochre
    mutants, 409
  nonsense, 408
  phenotypic
    informational, 414
  pleiotrophism, 417
  at translation level, 408
Suppressor
  action
    mechanisms of, 412
  mutations
    genetics of, 411
    uncharacterized, 418
    nature of amber and ochre,
      411
    possibly affecting mRNA,
      407
    unstable, 418
    yeast, 157
Surveillance mechanism
  tumor antigens, 234
Susceptibility
  drug
    in psittacosis group,
      122
  mechanisms of
    in plants, 353
  plant resistance, 352
  symptoms of
    in plants, 353
SV40
  -adenovirus hybrid, 203
  -cytocidal infection, 197
  neoplasia, 197
  transformed cells
    transplantation antigen,
      202
  tumor antigen, 201, 203
  virus
    transformation, 200
Symbiosis
  in protozoa, 134-35
Symmetry
  viral classification criteria,
    53
Symptomatology
  subdivision of virus families,
    58
Syngeneic preference
  tumor antigens, 237
Synthesis
  cellular DNA
    polyoma-induced, 195
  DNA
    bacterial outgrowth,
      183
  interferon
    see Interferon induction

macromolecular
  adenoviruses, 207
ordered protein during out-
    growth, 182
protein
  sporogenesis, 173
of spore-specific components,
    173
Systematics
  virus classification, 62

T

Target organs
  protection by circulation
    interferon, 309
Taxonomy
  myxobacteria, 99
  position
    psittacosis group, 121
  values of groups
    in viral classification,
      55
Techniques
  yeast mutation, 155
Teichoic acids, 274
  addition of side chain sugars,
    275
  biosynthesis
    of polymers of glucosyl-
      glycerophosphate and
      galactosyl-glycerophos-
      phate, 275
    of polyribitolphosphate and
      polyglycerophosphate,
      275
  linkage to glycopeptide and
    control of synthesis,
    276
Terminology
  viruses, 47-48
Tetrad and random spore
  analysis procedures,
    152
Therapy
  neoplasms
    TSTA, 248
  and prophylaxis of virus
    diseases, 311
Tolerance
  tumors, 244
Transcription
  "helper" phage, 391
  microbial, 371-400
  outgrowth, 181
  products
    sporogenesis, 172
  relation to DNA replication
    during outgrowth,
      183
  transfection
    definition, 391
Transfer efficiencies
  waste treatment, 331
Transformation
  adenoviruses, 208
  of cells in vitro

papovaviruses, 198
cellular competence, 372
competence "factor," 378
  definition, 372
DNA integration, 382
DNA receptor, 378
formation of competent
    state, 375
genetic control of compe-
    tence, 373
heterozygotes, 385
integration, 385
interferon, 311
linkage groups, 386
mapping of genome, 386
microbial, 371-400
polyoma
  hybridization technique,
    199
RNA, 389
state of competence, 374
yeast, 164
Transformed cells
  SV40-
    transplantation antigen,
      202
  virus-
    antigens, 198
  virus-free
    antigens, 199
Transforming DNA
  fate of, 382
Translation
  outgrowth, 181
Translation level
  suppression at, 408
Transplantation antigens
  SV40-transformed cells,
    202
  see Tumor-specific
Trichocysts
  protozoa, 137
Trigger
  L-alanine-induced, 179
Trigger mechanisms
  multiplicity of
    germination, 177
Tumor
  antigenic cells
    host defense mechanisms
      in rejection, 233-43
  antigenic strength, 224
  antigens, 223-52
    allogeneic inhibition,
      237
    SV40, 201
    syngeneic preference,
      237
  cells
    enhancement, 246
    humoral antibodies, 242
    "sneaking through,"
      245
    tolerance, 244
  rejection
    failure of, 243
Tumor-specific antigens

carcinogens, 229
  viruses, 230
Tumor-specific transplanta-
    tion antigen (TSTA)
  cellular localization,
    226
  mechanism determining,
    229
  nature of, 227
  occurrence of, 228
  polyoma system, 228
  Rous-Bryan system, 231
  Schmidt-Ruppin-Rous sys-
    tem, 232
  Shope papilloma-carcinoma
    system, 232
Type of mutations corrected
  by streptomycin, 416

U

Uncharacterized suppressor
  mutations, 418
Uncoating
  poxviruses, 212
Uninfected cells
  interferon effects, 296
Unsaturated fatty acids
  biosynthesis
    aerobic pathway, 18
    anaerobic pathway, 24
    in microorganisms, 18-
      26
Unstable suppressors, 418

V

Vacuoles
  food, 133
Variables and pitfalls
  in experimental virology,
    191
Vegetative cells
  myxobacteria, 78
Vegetative petites
  yeast mutant, 162
Viral classification
  criteria, 49
  evolution of principles, 48-
    51
Viral development
  subdivision of virus families,
    58
Viral evolution, 54
Viral oncogenesis
  and interferon, 311
Viral replication, 193
  physiological state of host
    cell, 191
  poxviruses, 212
Viremia
  control by circulating inter-
    feron, 309
  and interferon, 308
  protection of target organs
    by circulating interferon,
      309

Virion
  definition, 47-48
Virology
  experimental
    enzymes, 193
    inhibitors, 193
    isotopes, 193
    multiplicity of infection,
      192
    pure cultures, 192
    variables and pitfalls,
      191
Virulence
  subdivision of virus families,
    58
Virus
  animal
    classification, 191
    diversity of, 190
    neoplasia, 190
  characteristics of, 46
  DNA animal
    biosynthetic modifications
      induced by, 189-222
  nonheritable interferon re-
    sistance among, 303
  relation of psittacosis group
    to, 107-30
  terminology, 47-48
  transfection, 391
  tumor antigens, 230
Virus classification, 45-74
  antigenicity, 58
  genus, 57
  Lwoff-Horne-Tournier sys-
    tem, 51-55
  nomenclature, 62
  nomina conservanda, 67-
    71
  stability of the family,
    55
  RNA structure, 59
  systematics, 62
  taxonomic value of groups,
    55
Virus diseases
  therapy and prophylaxis,
    311

Virus-free transformed cells
  antigens, 199
Virus-transformed cells
  antigens, 198
Vitamin requirements
  myxobacteria, 84
  psittacosis group, 114

W

Wall changes
  accompanying competence,
    377
Waste water treatment
  anaerobic digestion, 332
  biological oxygen demand,
    321
  biological solids
    and oxygen uptake,
      327
    and purification rate,
      328
  dependence of growth rate
    on substrate concentra-
    tion, 321
  kinetics
    discontinuous relationship,
      321
    Monad equation, 320
  mechanisms of substrate
    removal and growth,
      324
  metabolic control mecha-
    nisms, 324
  microbiology of, 319-36
  pollution strength, 322
  products of partial oxidation,
    326
  relation between biological
    solids production and
    substrate concentration,
    328
  "rolling-tube filter" studies,
    322
  sequential substrate remov-
    al, 324
  shock loads, 325
  steady-state systems, 320

transfer efficiencies, 331
Woese hypothesis
  germination, 178
Wound mechanism
  in plant resistance, 347

Y

Yeast
  chiasma, 153
  chromatid, 153
  chromosome maps, 153
  gene action, 160
  gene conversion, 154
  gene-enzyme relationships,
    160
  genetics, 151-68
  induced mutation, 156
  induction, 155
  interallelic recombination,
    154
  interference, 153
  mitotic segregation,
    154
  morphological mutants,
    159
  mutant characterization,
    158
  mutant enrichment, 155
  mutants
    petite strains, 162
    respiration-deficient,
      162
    segregational petites,
      162
    vegetative petites, 162
  mutation, 155
    spontaneous, 156
    suppressible, 157
  techniques, 155
  recombination, 152
  resistance, 159
  suppressors, 157
  tetrad and random spore
    analysis,
    152
  transformation,
    164

CUMULATIVE INDEXES

VOLUMES 16-20

INDEX OF CONTRIBUTING AUTHORS

A

Adelberg, E. A., 16:289
Ahmadjian, V., 19:1
Ajl, S. J., 17:297
Alexander, M., 18:217
Arber, W., 19:365
Arseculeratne, S. N., 18:195

B

Barnett, H. L., 17:1
Baron, S., 20:291
Beckwith, J. R., 20:401
Benacerraf, B., 17:263
Billingham, R. E., 17:531
Bovee, E. C., 19:21
Bradley, S. G., 16:35
Brisbane, P. G., 19:351
Bryant, M. P., 18:131
Buetow, D. E., 18:167

C

Campbell, A., 17:49
Champe, S. P., 17:87
Clark, A. J., 16:289
Clifton, C. E., 20:1
Cohen, G. N., 19:105

D

Dawes, E. A., 16:241
Dekker, J., 17:243
DeLey, J., 18:17
Dworkin, M., 20:75

E

Eaton, M. D., 19:379
Eisen, H. N., 16:101
Evans, A. H., 20:371

F

Falkow, S., 17:329
Fenner, F., 18:47
Fudenberg, H. H., 19:301

G

Gaudy, A. F., Jr., 20:319
Gaudy, E. T., 20:319
Gorini, L., 20:401

Graham, A. F., 17:139
Green, M., 20:189
Grimstone, A. V., 20:131
Guillard, R. R. L., 17:373

H

Habel, K., 17:167
Halvorson, H. O., 20:169
Hawthorne, D. C., 20:151
Hirsch, J. G., 19:339
Hoffman, H., 18:111
Hoffmann, J. A., 17:199
Holton, C. S., 17:199
Holz, G. G., Jr., 16:189
Horecker, B. L., 20:253
Hungate, R. E., 18:131
Hutner, S. H., 16:189

J

Jacobs, L., 17:429
Jahn, T. L., 19:21
Jawetz, E., 18:301
Jensen, D. D., 17:495

K

Kabler, P. W., 16:127
Kallio, R. E., 19:183
Kates, M., 20:13
Kendrick, E. L., 17:199
Klein, G., 20:223
Kuć, J., 20:337

L

Ladd, J. N., 19:351
Levedahl, B. H., 18:167
Levine, N. D., 17:179
Levinthal, C., 19:267
Levy, H. B., 20:291
Lewin, J. C., 17:373
Liaaen Jensen, S., 19:163
Luke, H. H., 17:223
Luria, S. E., 16:205
Lwoff, A., 20:45

M

Maas, W. K., 18:95
McCluskey, R. T., 17:263
McFall, E., 18:95
McKenna, E. J., 19:183

Mah, R. H., 18:131
Mäkelä, O., 16:53
Mandel, M., 17:329
Maramorosch, K., 17:495
Marmur, J., 17:495
Martin, S. M., 18:1
Mortenson, L. E., 17:115
Mortimer, R. K., 20:151
Moulder, J. W., 20:107
Moyed, H. S., 18:347

N

Neidhardt, F. C., 17:61
Nelson, R. R., 17:31
Newton, B. A., 19:209
Nossal, G. J. V., 16:53

P

Panos, C., 17:297
Pardee, A. B., 16:1
Pearce, J. H., 16:101
Phaff, H. J., 17:15
Purdy, L. H., 17:199

R

Rake, A. V., 17:139
Reifel, R. M., 17:451
Reilly, B. E., 20:371
Ribbons, D. W., 16:241
Richter, A., 17:415
Riley, M., 16:1
Rosenberg, L. T., 19:285
Ross, J. D., 16:141
Rovira, A. D., 19:241

S

Sambrook, J. F., 18:47
Schlesinger, R. W., 19:267
Seaman, G. R., 17:451
Sherris, J. C., 17:565
Silvers, W. K., 17:531
Sinkovics, J. G., 16:75
Skerman, V. B. D., 19:407
Sneath, P. H. A., 18:353
Spizizen, J., 20:371
Starr, M. P., 19:79; 407
Steinberg, W., 20:169
Stolp, H., 19:79
Strickland, J. D. H., 19:127

Sussman, M., 19:59
Syverton, J. T., 16: 141
Szenberg, A., 18:253

T

Tournier, P., 20: 45
Treadwell, P. E., 16: 141

V

van Heyningen, W. E., 18: 195
Vary, J. C., 20:69

W

Wagner, R. R., 17:285
Warner, N. L., 18: 253

Wheeler, H., 17:223
Wissler, R. W., 16:265

Y

Youmans, G. P., 17:473
Young, G. A., 18:219

Z

Zinder, N. D., 19:455

INDEX OF CHAPTER TITLES

VOLUMES 16-20

PREFATORY CHAPTERS
Microbiology--Past, Present and Future   C. E. Clifton   20:1-12
GENERAL CHARACTERISTICS
Cell Wall of Yeasts   H. J. Phaff   17:15-30
Effects of Environment on the Composition of Bacterial Cells   F. C. Neidhardt   17:61-86
New Approaches to Bacterial Taxonomy   J. Marmur, S. Falkow, M. Mandel   17:329-72
Diatoms   J. C. Lewin, R. R. L. Guillard   17:373-414
Chemical Composition and Metabolism of Protozoa   G. R. Seaman, R. M. Reifel   17:451-72
Conservation of Microorganisms   S. M. Martin   18:1-16
Pseudomonas and Related Genera   J. De Ley   18:17-46
Morphogenesis of Bacterial Aggregations   H. Hoffman   18:111-30
The Rumen Bacteria and Protozoa   R. E. Hungate, M. P. Bryant, R. A. Mah   18:131-66
Biochemical Ecology of Soil Micro-organisms   M. Alexander   18:217-52
New Approaches to Bacterial Taxonomy: Use of Computers   P. H. A. Sneath   18:335-46
Lichens   V. Ahmadjian   19:1-20
Movement and Locomotion of Micro-organisms   T. L. Jahn, E. C. Bovee   19:21-58
Bacteriolysis   H. Stolp, M. P. Starr   19:79-104
Phytoplankton and Marine Primary Production   J. D. H. Strickland   19:127-62
Interactions between Plant Roots and Soil Microorganisms   A. D. Rovira   19:241-66
Pleuropneumonia-Like Organisms and Related Forms   M. D. Eaton   19:379-406
Bacterial Diversity: The Natural History of Selected Morphologically Unusual Bacteria   M. P. Starr, V. B. D. Skerman   19:407-54
The Classification of Viruses   A. Lwoff, P. Tournier   20:45-74

The Biology of the Myxobacteria   M. Dworkin   20:75-106
The Relation of the Psittacosis Group
  (Chlamydiae) to Bacteria and
  Viruses   J. W. Moulder   20:107-30
Structure and Function in Protozoa   A. V. Grimstone   20:131-50
GENETICS   LIFE CYCLES   AND VARIATIONS
Gene Expression: Its Specificity and
  Regulation   M. Riley, A. B. Pardee   16:1-34
Parasexual Phenomena in Micro-
  organisms   S. G. Bradley   16:35-52
Genetics of Bacteriophage   S. E. Luria   16:205-40
Bacterial Conjugation   A. J. Clark, E. A. Adelberg   16:289-319
Interspecific Hybridization in the
  Fungi   R. R. Nelson   17:31-48
Fine Structure Genetics and its Rela-
  tion to Function   A. Campbell   17:49-60
The Genetics of Animal Viruses   F. Fenner, J. F. Sambrook   18:47-94
Genetic Aspects of Metabolic Control   W. K. Maas, E. McFall   18:95-110
The Rumen Bacteria and Protozoa   R. E. Hungate, M. P. Bryant,
                                         R. A. Mah   18:131-66

Developmental Phenomena in Micro-
  organisms and in Higher Forms of
  Life   M. Sussman   19:59-78
Yeast Genetics   R. K. Mortimer, D. C.
                                         Hawthorne   20:151-68

Developmental Changes During the
  Formation and Breaking of the
  Dormant State in Bacteria   H. O. Halvorson, J. C. Vary,
                                         W. Steinberg   20:169-88

Microbial Transformation and Trans-
  fection   J. Spizizen, B. E. Reilly,
                                         A. H. Evans   20:371-400
Suppression   L. Gorini, J. R. Beckwith   20:401-22
GROWTH AND NUTRITION
Lipid Requirements of Micro-
  organisms   S. H. Hutner, G. G. Holz, Jr.   16:189-204
Responses of Microorganisms to
  Sterols and Steroids   D. E. Buetow, B. H. Levedahl   18:167-84
Biosynthesis and Function of Carotenoid
  Pigments in Microorganisms   S. Liaaen Jensen   19:163-82
METABOLISM
The Endogenous Metabolism of Micro-
  organisms   E. A. Dawes, D. W. Ribbons   16:241-64
Nitrogen Fixation: Role of Ferredoxin
  in Anaerobic Metabolism   L. E. Mortenson   17:115-38
Metabolism of Microorganisms as Re-
  lated to Their Pathogenicity   C. Panos, S. J. Ajl   17:297-328
Chemical Composition and Metabolism
  of Protozoa   G. R. Seaman, R. M. Reifel   17:451-72
Genetic Aspects of Metabolic Control   W. K. Maas, E. McFall   18:95-110
The Rumen Bacteria and Protozoa   R. E. Hungate, M. P. Bryant,
                                         R. A. Mah   18:131-66

Regulation of Enzyme Activity in Micro-
  organisms   G. N. Cohen   19:105-26
The Biology of Hydrocarbons   E. J. McKenna, R. E. Kallio   19:183-208
Complementation at the Molecular Level
  of Enzyme Interaction   M. J. Schlesinger, C.
                                         Levinthal   19:267-84

Biosynthesis of Lipids in Micro-
  organisms   M. Kates   20:13-44
The Biosynthesis of Bacterial Poly-
  saccharides   B. L. Horecker   20:253-90
CHEMOTHERAPY AND AGENTS OF
Biochemical Mechanisms of Drug
  Resistance   H. S. Moyed   18:347-66
Mechanisms of Antibiotic
  Action   B. A. Newton   19:209-40

ANIMAL PATHOGENS AND DISEASES

Coccidiosis — N. D. Levine — 17:179-98

Toxoplasma and Toxoplasmosis — L. Jacobs — 17:429-50

The Pathogenic "Atypical" Mycobacteria — G. P. Youmans — 17:473-94

Some Recent Advances in Diagnostic Medical Bacteriology — J. C. Sherris — 17:565-92

Exotoxins — W. E. van Heyningen, S. N. Arseculeratne — 18:195-216

Viral Infections of Domestic Animals — G. A. Young — 18:269-300

PLANT PATHOGENS AND DISEASES

The Nature of Mycoparasitism by Fungi — H. L. Barnett — 17:1-14

Dwarf Bunt of Wheat — L. H. Purdy, E. L. Kendrick, J. A. Hoffmann, C. S. Holton — 17:199-222

Microbial Toxins in Plant Disease — H. Wheeler, H. H. Luke — 17:223-42

Antibiotics in the Control of Plant Disease — J. Dekker — 17:243-62

Harmful and Beneficial Effects of Plant Viruses in Insects — K. Maramorosch, D. D. Jensen — 17:495-530

Resistance of Plants to Infectious Agents — J. Kuć — 20:337-70

INFECTION AND RESISTANCE

The Interferons: Cellular Inhibitors of Viral Infection — R. R. Wagner — 17:285-96

Metabolism of Microorganisms as Related to Their Pathogenicity — C. Panos, S. J. Ajl — 17:297-328

IMMUNE BODIES AND REACTIONS

Elaboration of Antibodies by Single Cells — G. J. V. Nossal, O. Mäkelä — 16:53-74

The Nature of Antibodies and Antigens — H. N. Eisen, J. H. Pearce — 16:101-26

Effects of Specific Antibodies on Tissue Cells — R. W. Wissler — 16:265-88

Methods of Immunologic Injury to Tissues — B. Benacerraf, R. T. McCluskey — 17:263-84

Sensitivity to Homografts of Normal Tissues and Cells — R. E. Billingham, W. K. Silvers — 17:531-64

The Immunological Function of the Bursa of Fabricius in the Chicken — N. L. Warner, A. Szenberg — 18:253-68

"Complement" — L. T. Rosenberg — 19:285-300

The Immune Globulins — H. H. Fudenberg — 19:301-38

Phagocytosis — J. G. Hirsch — 19:339-50

Tumor Antigens — G. Klein — 20:223-52

Interferon — S. Baron, H. B. Levy — 20:291-318

APPLIED MICROBIOLOGY

Purification and Sanitary Control of Water (Potable and Waste) — P. W. Kabler — 16:127-40

The Role of Microorganisms in Petroleum Exploration — P. G. Brisbane, J. N. Ladd — 19:351-64

Microbiology of Waste Waters — A. F. Gaudy, Jr., E. T. Gaudy — 20:319-36

VIRUSES

Viral Leukemias in Mice — J. G. Sinkovics — 16:75-100

Cultural Characterization of Animal Cells — J. D. Ross, P. E. Treadwell, J. T. Syverton — 16:141-88

Genetics of Bacteriophage — S. E. Luria — 16:205-40

Bacteriophage Reproduction — S. P. Champe — 17:87-114

RNA Synthesis and Turnover in Mammalian Cells Propagated in Vitro — A. F. Graham, A. V. Rake — 17:139-66

Malignant Transformation by Polyoma Virus — K. Habel — 17:167-78

The Interferons: Cellular Inhibitors of Viral Infection — R. R. Wagner — 17:285-96

Structure of Viral Nucleoproteins — A. Richter — 17:415-28

Harmful and Beneficial Effects of Plant Viruses in Insects — K. Maramorosch, D. D. Jensen — 17:495-530

The Genetics of Animal Viruses	F. Fenner, J. F. Sambrook	18:47-94
Viral Infections of Domestic Animals	G. A. Young	18:269-300
Agents of Trachoma and Inclusion Conjunctivitis	E. Jawetz	18:301-34
Host-Controlled Modification of Bacteriophage	W. Arber	19:365-78
RNA Phages	N. D. Zinder	19:455-72
The Classification of Viruses	A. Lwoff, P. Tournier	20:45-74
Biosynthetic Modification Induced by DNA Animal Viruses	M. Green	20:189-222
Interferon	S. Baron, H. B. Levy	20:291-318